International Atomic Weights

	SYM-BOL	ATOMIC NUMBER	ATOMIC WEIGHT[a]		SYM-BOL	ATOMIC NUMBER	ATOMIC WEIGHT[a]
Actinium	Ac	89	227	Mercury	Hg	80	200.61
Aluminum	Al	13	26.98	Molybdenum	Mo	42	95.95
Americium	Am	95	[243]	Neodymium	Nd	60	144.27
Antimony	Sb	51	121.76	Neon	Ne	10	20.183
Argon	Ar	18	39.944	Neptunium	Np	93	[237]
Arsenic	As	33	74.91	Nickel	Ni	28	58.69
Astatine	At	85	[210]	Niobium (Colum-			
Barium	Ba	56	137.36	bium)	Nb	41	92.91
Berkelium	Bk	97	[249]	Nitrogen	N	7	14.008
Beryllium	Be	4	9.013	Nobelium	No	102	[253]
Bismuth	Bi	83	209.00	Osmium	Os	76	190.2
Boron	B	5	10.82	Oxygen	O	8	16.000
Bromine	Br	35	79.916	Palladium	Pd	46	106.7
Cadmium	Cd	48	112.41	Phosphorus	P	15	30.975
Calcium	Ca	20	40.08	Platinum	Pt	78	195.23
Californium	Cf	98	[249]	Plutonium	Pu	94	[242]
Carbon	C	6	12.010	Polonium	Po	84	210
Cerium	Ce	58	140.13	Potassium	K	19	39.100
Cesium	Cs	55	132.91	Praseodymium	Pr	59	140.92
Chlorine	Cl	17	35.457	Promethium	Pm	61	[145]
Chromium	Cr	24	52.01	Protactinium	Pa	91	231
Cobalt	Co	27	58.94	Radium	Ra	88	226.05
Columbium (see Niobium)				Radon	Rn	86	222
Copper	Cu	29	63.54	Rhenium	Re	75	186.31
Curium	Cm	96	[245]	Rhodium	Rh	45	102.91
Dysprosium	Dy	66	162.46	Rubidium	Rb	37	85.48
Einsteinium	Es	99	[254]	Ruthenium	Ru	44	101.1
Erbium	Er	68	168.94	Samarium	Sm	62	150.43
Europium	Eu	63	152.0	Scandium	Sc	21	44.96
Fermium	Fm	100	[255]	Selenium	Se	34	78.96
Fluorine	F	9	19.00	Silicon	Si	14	28.09
Francium	Fr	87	[223]	Silver	Ag	47	107.880
Gadolinium	Gd	64	156.9	Sodium	Na	11	22.991
Gallium	Ga	31	69.72	Strontium	Sr	38	87.63
Germanium	Ge	32	72.60	Sulfur	S	16	32.066
Gold	Au	79	197.0	Tantalum	Ta	73	180.95
Hafnium	Hf	72	178.6	Technetium	Tc	43	[99]
Helium	He	2	4.003	Tellurium	Te	52	127.61
Holmium	Ho	67	164.94	Terbium	Tb	65	158.93
Hydrogen	H	1	1.0080	Thallium	Tl	81	204.39
Indium	In	49	114.76	Thorium	Th	90	232.05
Iodine	I	53	126.91	Thulium	Tm	69	169.4
Iridium	Ir	77	192.2	Tin	Sn	50	118.70
Iron	Fe	26	55.85	Titanium	Ti	22	47.90
Krypton	Kr	36	83.80	Tungsten	W	74	183.92
Lanthanum	La	57	138.92	Uranium	U	92	238.07
Lead	Pb	82	207.21	Vanadium	V	23	50.95
Lithium	Li	3	6.940	Xenon	Xe	54	131.3
Lutetium	Lu	71	174.99	Ytterbium	Yb	70	173.04
Magnesium	Mg	12	24.32	Yttrium	Y	39	88.92
Manganese	Mn	25	54.94	Zinc	Zn	30	65.38
Mendelevium	Md	101	[256]	Zirconium	Zr	40	91.22

[a] A value given in brackets denotes the mass number of the isotope of longest known half-life.

[b] Because of natural variations in relative abundance of the sulfur isotopes, its atomic weight has a range of ± 0.003.

SOIL
CHEMICAL ANALYSIS

M. L. JACKSON

Professor of Soils, University of Wisconsin
Agricultural Experiment Station, Madison, Wisconsin

PRENTICE-HALL, INC.
Englewood Cliffs, N.J.

First printing . . . . *February, 1958*
Second printing . . . . *May, 1960*

Preface

As Sir Francis Bacon wrote in his *Of Studies,* "Books must follow sciences, not science books." The maturity of any science may be measured in the growth of integrative publications—reviews, monographs, and specialized textbooks. Soil Science is an infant compared to the older disciplines of mathematics, astronomy, physics, chemistry, and medicine, but the trend toward integrative writing in the field has been firmly established. The annual review, *Advances in Agronomy,* and the monograph series, *Agronomy,* first appeared in 1949 and textbooks both general and specialized are available. The author hopes that the comprehensive treatment of procedures and fundamental principles presented in *Soil Chemical Analysis* will foster progress in the science of soil chemistry.

Methods applicable to the chemical analysis of soils are as numerous and varied as the field of chemistry itself. The *extraction* of a chemical constituent from soil is purely a procedure of soil chemistry, while the *determination* of the extracted constituent is an analytical process, limited in range of methods only by consideration of soil characteristics. Although the powerful techniques of fritted glass filtration, centrifugation, absorption and emission spectrophotometry are emphasized, some procedures are included because they can be executed with simple equipment.

The original publications of procedures and critical studies are cited throughout *Soil Chemical Analysis* and the many modifications and improvements developed by the author and his students are included. The free availability of information during the 20 years in which the materials for this book were accumulated made many improvements possible. Great pains have been taken to eliminate flaws in procedure and the author will be grateful to readers who may call his attention to those inadvertently missed.

The author wishes to extend grateful acknowledgments to Dr. M. D. Weldon of the University of Nebraska, who first introduced him to soil science; to Professor E. Truog of the University of Wisconsin, who encouraged the writing of soil chemical methods; to Dr. N. J. Volk of Purdue University, who fostered a broadened outlook of the field of soils and soil chemistry; and to Dr. I. L. Baldwin of the University of Wisconsin for his warmth and encouragement. Special thanks are extended to Dr. B. R. Bertramson of Washington State College, to Dr. J. L. White of Purdue University, and to the many other former associates who encouraged completion of this work. Appreciation is extended to Dr. W. R. Schmehl of Colorado A. & M. College, to Dr. L. D. Swindale of the New Zealand Soil Bureau, to Dr. A. W. Taylor of Rothamsted Experiment Station, and to others who kindly read and supplied criticism of portions of the manuscript.

M. L. JACKSON
Madison, Wisconsin

To the Reader

This book gives the most frequently used soil chemical analysis procedures, useful in instruction and research in soil chemistry, soil fertility, and soil genesis. Because plant growth is essentially related to these fields, procedures are given for plant inorganic constituents. More specialized procedures of these fields have had to be excluded in the interest of space economy. The student in a soil chemical analysis course will, later in research, find a continuing need of the information given. The teacher will find time-saving discussions of principles. The following are suggested weekly assignments for an undergraduate-graduate course:

Determinations

Exercise number

1. Check desk, apparatus and reagents; take soils samples in field (¶ 2–19) or if weather does not permit, prepare samples issued by instructor; in which case field sampling to be introduced as soon as weather permits; exercise on colorimetric pH indicators (¶ 3–45, 3–46).
2. Determine soil pH with glass electrode (¶ 3–22); colorimetric measurement of soil pH (¶ 13–91); thiocyanate test for acidity (¶ 13–93).
3. Exchangeable hydrogen of soils (¶ 4–50); lime requirement of soils (¶ 4–64).
4. Neutralizing equivalence of limestone (¶ 4–66).
5. Exchangeable metallic cations of soils (¶ 5–1 or 18–24).
6. Available phosphorus of soils (¶ 7–69, 7–86, 7–99).
7. Organic matter of soils (¶ 9–57).
8. Total nitrogen of soils (¶ 8–13).
9. Ammonia of soils (¶ 8–33); nitrate of soils (¶ 8–48).
10. Plant tissue analysis (¶ 12–19).
11. Soluble salts of soils and waters (¶ 10–25).
12. Rapid soil tests (¶ 13–75).
13. Plant tissue test (¶ 13–3).
14. Total phosphorus of soils (¶ 7–128).
15. Total potassium and sodium of soils (¶ 11–37, 11–177); silicate analysis of soils (¶ 11–100).
16. Check in apparatus and reagents; turn in reports; check out.

Contents

Plant Tissue Analysis—Mineral Constituents (*Cont.*)

13. RAPID CHEMICAL TESTS OF SOILS AND PLANT TISSUE 339

14. BORON DETERMINATIONS FOR SOILS AND PLANT TISSUE 370

15. IRON, MANGANESE, COPPER, ZINC, MOLYBDENUM, AND COBALT DETERMINATIONS 388

16. POLAROGRAPHIC ANALYSIS FOR SOILS AND PLANT TISSUE 416

List of Tables

xiii

Introduction

The soil is a medium of great complexity, and soil science has not progressed very far.

—RICHARDS[1]

1–1. Soil Presents a Complex Analytical System. The analysis of soils and plants presents an interesting challenge to a prospective soil scientist. In his Fisher award address, H. H. Willard[2] states,

> The number of chemical reactions, the types of apparatus used, and the varied techniques utilized by the analytical chemist today makes one who is broadly trained in this field valuable in solving problems quite outside of analytical chemistry.

This challenge is acute because a soil consists of an extraordinarily complex chemical mixture of different mineral and organic substances. The plant presents a special type of soil extraction. Soil chemical analysis deals (as determinations of soil elements or indirectly as reagents and equipment) with over 60 of the naturally occurring chemical elements (Fig. 1–1). Additional soil elements continually become of interest in plant nutrition, in relation to essentiality or toxicity, or for physiological substitution. As many as half of the remaining 32 naturally occurring elements may be involved ultimately one way or another in soil and plant analysis. Appropriate chemical analysis systems have been developed for quantitative analysis of the mineral elements present, but the determination of mineral structure requires an advanced system of mineralochemical analysis. Likewise, the organic matter in soil or plants growing on or applied as residues to soil is an analytical field in itself. But the total organic matter of soil can

---

[1] *Diagnosis and Improvement of Saline and Alkali Soils* (Riverside, Calif.: U.S. Salinity Lab., 1947), p. iii.
[2] *Anal. Chem.,* 23:1726 (1951).

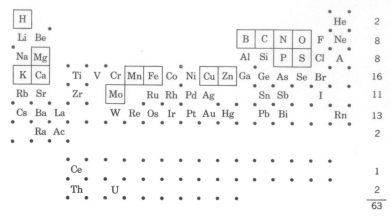

Fig. 1–1. Elements employed in soil chemistry as determinants or indirectly as reagents and equipment. Elements in boxes are essential to plants. A complete chart appears inside the back flyleaf.

readily be estimated from the total organic carbon or by reactions with strong oxidizing solutions.

1–2. Because of the complexity of the material to be analyzed, the prospective analyst should consider the mandate of former President Chamberlin[3] of the University of Wisconsin, as so aptly set forth by Rich,[4]

> To be efficient, the gathering of data must be selective, and the best guide to its collection is probably the method of *multiple working hypotheses* proposed many years ago by Chamberlin. The available information is first studied and analyzed; several working hypotheses are formulated; from each of these are deduced the consequences which should follow if that hypothesis were correct; further data are then sought and the old data reexamined for evidence which would either bear out or refute the hypothesis under scrutiny.
>
> When search for data is thus guided, there will be a minimum of blind collection of irrelevant facts and a minimum cluttering of the literature with undigested factual information. . . .

These principles of research indicate the importance of proper forethought before launching into a set of soil or plant tissue analyses.

1–3. The analyst should make a sharp distinction between the procedures of *extracting* a chemical constituent from the soil or plant (which is a phenomenon purely of soil or plant chemistry), and *determining* the constituent once extracted. The determination is a matter solely of analytical chemistry, with consequent range in possible methods, except as limited by consideration of concentration range and interfering substances that might be present. Newly developed instruments continually broaden the

---

[3] *J. Geol.,* 5:837 (1897).
[4] *Sci.,* 107:581 (1948).

field of soil or plant analysis. However, some procedures can effectively be executed with simple equipment, in the absence of more specialized equipment. For example, potassium may be determined by cobaltinitrite when a flame emission spectrophotometer is not available. Powerful techniques include absorption and emission spectrophotometry, fritted glass filtration, centrifugation, and systematic schemes of analysis of several constituents. These avoid the time-consuming steps of evaporation, paper filtration, and heating to constant weight. The analyst seeking a suitable procedure for a given determination should consult first textbooks on analysis to learn the range of choice and some of the advantages and disadvantages of different procedures. Sometimes he will need to consult abstract journals and journal articles for any recent advances on a particular determination.

ANALYTICAL REAGENTS

1–4. Reagents are supplied commercially in different grades, the purest being "analytical reagent" or "reagent grade," the second, "C.P." and the third, "technical" or "U.S.P." Each of the various grades has a distinct purpose and range of uses for which it is satisfactory. The alert chemist will find that there seems to be a suitable reagent for each specialized analytical function.

1–5. Concentrated Acids and Bases of Commerce. During manufacture, it is customary to express the strength of concentrated acids and bases of liquid form in terms of specific gravity because it is used for controlling their strength and because specified weights can be approximated volumetrically. However, in the laboratory, their strength is best expressed on the basis of chemical equivalence or normality (Table 1–1).

TABLE 1–1
Strength of "concentrated" acids and bases

Reagent	Concentration		Approximate specific gravity
	Normality	Per cent by weight	
HCl	11.6	37 to 38	1.19
H_2SO_4	35 to 36	97 to 100	1.84
HOAc	17.5	99.5	1.13
HNO_3	16	70 to 71	1.42
$HClO_4$	9 to 11.6	60 to 70	1.51 to 1.67
H_3PO_4	45	85	1.71
NH_4OH	15	28 to 29	0.90
HOH	55	100	1.00

1–6. Distilled Water. Water freed to varying extent of dissolved substances is essential for all chemical analysis. The quality varies from simple distilled water condensed in a copper or tin still to double or triple distilled water. A number of treatments are sometimes applied to the water between distillations to effect oxidation of organic substances and to suppress the passage of ions into the distillate. The substances employed for oxidation include $KMnO_4$ or Br_2. Sometimes even for minor element work, the redistillation of ordinary distilled water in a Pyrex glass still makes it sufficiently free from metallic ions for analytical purposes.

1–7. Sometimes condensation of high pressure steam coupled with some filtration of the gas produces condensate of a quality suitable to be used as distilled water. Steam condensate usually contains volatile oils and to some extent suspension of solid particles carried from the steam lines. Successful steam condensation as a substitute for distilled water was reported by Margolis.[5] A commercial high pressure steam condenser designed by Truog is described by Stark.[6]

1–8. Commercially available ionic columns are able to produce water of sufficiently low ionic content for analytical work. Commercial sources include LaMotte Chemical Products Co. (Towson, Baltimore, Md.), Wilken-Anderson Co. (Chicago, Ill.), Sargent Co. (Chicago, Ill.), and Enley Products, Inc. (254 Pearl St., New York 38, N.Y.).

1–9. Filter Paper. The several types of filter paper vary greatly in their content of total ash and in their content of major and minor elements. There is no substitute for experimental check on contamination; the question of paper purity parallels that of reagent purity. Filter paper pulp often is a useful expediter for filtrations through paper. Several types of filter paper in a range of suitable porosities have been prepared by commercial manufacturers. The leading brand names of filter paper, available from the usual chemical supply houses, are Whatman, Munktells, Schleicher and Schuell, and "E and D" (Lapine Co., Chicago, Ill.).

1–10. Chromic Acid Cleaning Solution. Chromic-sulfuric acid cleaning solution is valuable for the final cleaning of glassware. Visible materials and organic solvents should be rinsed out with water before using the cleaning solution.

1–11. The solution is made up by dissolution of 80 gm of $K_2Cr_2O_7$ or $Na_2Cr_2O_7$ in 300 ml of water (with heating). The aqueous solution is placed in a Pyrex container, and one liter of technical grade H_2SO_4 is added cautiously with stirring. Considerable red chromic oxide (Cr_2O_3) precipitates.

1–12. A cleaning solution which does not involve Cr_2O_3 crystallization is made by dissolution of 5 gm of $K_2Cr_2O_7$ in a minimum of water and addition of this solution to one liter of technical grade H_2SO_4.

1–13. Aqua Regia. The acid oxidant aqua regia is prepared by mixing

[5] *Sci.,* 115:552 (1952).
[6] *Modern Hosp.,* 43(3) (Sept. 1934).

3 volumes of concentrated HCl with 1 volume of concentrated HNO_3. Free Cl_2 is liberated.

LABORATORY APPARATUS

1–14. A. N. Whitehead states, "In science, the most important thing that has happened is the advance in instrumental design." The soil chemist is dependent on all manner of physical instruments, from analytical balance to spectrophotometer, for the chemical analysis of soils. Fortunately for efficiency in analysis, apparatus has been developed to a high degree, from the resistant glass beakers to flame emission equipment.

1–15. Analytical Balances. The beginning student should review his quantitative chemical text on the care and use of the analytical balance. He should know the "method of swings" for calculating the rest point, the method of checking for unequal balance arms, the method of calibration of weights, and the theory and practice of balance weights. These matters have been summarized concisely by MacNevin,[7] Swift,[8] and others.

1–16. Analytical balances differ in complexity from the simple balance, which requires gram weights, fractionals, and a balance beam rider, to the chainomatic balances, which require no fractionals or rider, to the keyboard balance, which requires only the heavier weights, and finally to the Gram-atic balance, which has but one pan, has no weights to be handled by the analyst, and automatically gives complete weighing to four places. The analyst should have a chainomatic balance or better. He should also have a torsion balance sensitive to 0.05 gm and a solution balance that will weigh up to 10 kgm or more.

1–17. Chemical Glassware. The technology of chemical glassware has been developed to a high state. Different glasses are available in varying compositions and physical properties to meet the requirements of nearly any of the common analyses. The analyst should review the composition of the glass in relation to the analysis to be made. He should recall that Pyrex glass is a borosilicate glass that contains arsenic; that it is suitable for most laboratory operation, but unsuitable for boron determination, and a possible source of arsenic in an arsenic determination. On the other hand, Cavalier or Corning 728 glassware is boron-free. Ordinary soft glass is relatively low in boron and frequently can be cleaned sufficiently to contain reagents for boron. It is also suited for some of the phosphorus reagents. However, soft glass is readily attacked by neutral or slightly alkaline solutions, and thus is a ready source of sodium contamination. Care in selection of the composition of the glass, coupled with adequate cleaning and testing for contamination, are essential.

---

[7] *The Analytical Balance* (Sandusky, Ohio: Handbook Publishers, Inc., 1951).

[8] *Introductory Quantitative Analysis* (Englewood Cliffs, N.J.: Prentice-Hall, Inc., 1950).

1–18. Volumetric glassware is now available with high standards of calibration and utility. Standard-taper volumetric flasks are preferred. Burets are available with calibration lines extending completely around for elimination of parallax. Notice should be paid to whether the volumetric pipette is calibrated to deliver (T.D.) or to contain (T.C.).

1–19. Filters Composed of Glass and Other Mineral Substances. Although paper filters (¶ 1–9) have been improved, purified, and toughened, for many purposes there is no substitute for the mineral, or inorganic, types of filter. The most commonly used is the fritted glass filter, manufactured in various porosities and in various sizes, fitted in the bottom of different types of crucibles and into various shapes of funnels. For semimicro work the filter tube (Fig. 5–2), which is a very small funnel with the top enclosed with porous glass and from which liquid is drawn through the stem, is indispensable. In addition to glass filters there are clay and alundum filters of various porosities. Alundum powder, "celite," and other mineral filter aids are often useful.

1–20. Centrifuge Washing in Lieu of Filtration. Alternative to the use of filters is the washing of precipitates with the centrifuge. Elimination of filtration by the use of centrifuge tubes and centrifugation is especially advantageous for removal of precipitated elements which would otherwise interfere with the determinations of ions in solution. The suspension may be simply diluted to volume in a centrifuge tube, clarified, and an aliquot then taken of the supernatant liquid for analysis (for example, ¶ 11–40).

1–21. For the analysis of the precipitate wherein ions in solution interfere, the centrifuge tube washing is not so advantageous. The filter tube is ordinarily more rapid and convenient in this case.

1–22. Cutting of Large Glass Cylinders. There are two techniques for cutting large glass cylinders that seem to be more effective than the common hot-wire procedure. In one a large glass cylinder is surrounded by

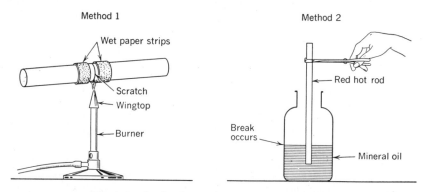

Fig. 1–2. Cutting large glass cylinders and bottles.

two wet paper strips (Fig. 1–2) placed on either side of a light scratch. Heat is applied at the scratch with the wing top burner as the tube is rotated. The cooling by the wet paper strips localizes the heat and gives a clean cut of a rather large glass tube, 2 to 10 cm in diameter.

1–23. The second method, described by Dr. C. B. Tanner of the University of Wisconsin, is mainly applicable to large cylinders, including bottles. The cylinder is filled with mineral oil to the depth at which the cut is wanted (Fig. 1–2). Then a red hot iron rod is thrust into the oil causing hot oil to flow out over the surface to produce a crack.

1–24. Mortars and Pestles. A mortar and pestle is a vital aid to the analyst. The agate mortar and pestle of a suitable size (Fig. 1–3) is com-

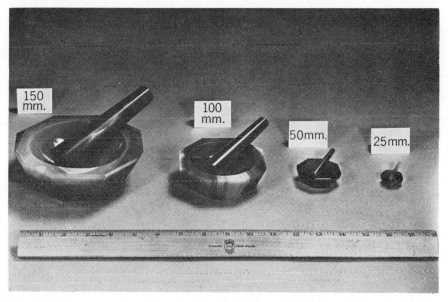

Fig. 1–3. Agate mortars and pestles of suitable size are indispensable to the analyst. (Courtesy Eldot and Co., 33 West 60th Street, New York.)

monly used. Newer materials for mortars and pestles include mullite and synthetic sapphire. The synthetic sapphire mortar has been recommended for preparations for spectrographic analysis. Mortars made of this material have been described[9] as being "hard as tungsten carbide." The porcelain mortar is generally considered to introduce too much contamination for most soil analysis work except for the preparation of bulk soil samples for passing relatively coarse screens.

1–25. Sieve Openings versus Meshes per Inch. In stating the size of sieve openings, one widespread custom is to specify the number of meshes per

---

[9] *The Laboratory,* 18(5):131 (Pittsburgh: Fisher Scientific Company, 1949).

inch, without reference to the actual size of the opening. The opening in mm can be fairly well approximated on the assumption that the opening is 0.63 of the mesh interval, whence,

$$\text{mm per opening} = \frac{16}{\text{meshes per inch}} \tag{1-1}$$

For example, a "100-mesh" screen has openings of 0.16 mm.

LABORATORY REPORT OUTLINE

1–26. The report of each laboratory is to be developed around the following outline, to be submitted on sheets 8.5 by 11 inches in size, and typewritten (or neatly and legibly written in ink if a typewriter is not available).

  I. Number and title of experiment.
 II. Objective.
III. Methods employed.
    A. Principles—Principles studied are to be outlined; all chemical equations involved are to be given.
    B. Apparatus—Any apparatus not already pictured in the directions is to be sketched.
    C. Procedure—Given by reference to directions, with careful notes on any departures from given procedure.
IV. Data—The original laboratory record is submitted in the data section.
    A. Sample calculation—A sample calculation is given in outline form, indicating each step, with letters or words for the functions. All notations are defined and all dimensions given. Finally, numerical data for one sample calculation are substituted in the equation and the result computed.
    B. Original as well as final computed results are tabulated and also shown in graphic form.
    C. Analysis of error—An estimate is to be made of significant figures and the extent of inherent error.
 V. Conclusions—The significance of the experiment is summed up. Answers are to be written for questions supplied by the instructor.
VI. Abstracts—A brief abstract of one or more articles pertaining to the experiment may be assigned by the instructor. The abstract will be submitted in typewritten form, usually 0.2 to 0.5 page in length.

LABORATORY ORDERLINESS

1–27. Cleanliness and Orderliness in the Laboratory. These are universally conceded to be requisite for high efficiency of the laboratory worker. Each student is judged by his associates and by his prospective employer on the condition in which he maintains his laboratory. The following general rules are presented as a guide:

1. Dirty glassware should be washed promptly, and stored away immediately after it has drained. *It should not be left on the drain board* for more

than the few minutes required to complete the washing job, never left there to dry.

2. All glass and other containers of solutions *will bear a label of the contents and the initials of the user.*

3. Each student will discard his samples, clean the containers and return them to the stock room.

1–28. General Laboratory Tables and Equipment. These need to be cleaned periodically. *Each user is responsible for leaving them clean.* In addition, cooperative arrangements will be made by all students for assignment of cleaning special equipment to individual students.

1–29. Everyone will profit by experience in a well-ordered laboratory where high standards of orderliness and cleanliness will be established for laboratories placed in your charge in the future. It will pay good dividends. Remember, your prospective employer cannot see at a glance the inner workings of your mind, nor the work you have done, but he can see at a glance the condition of the space assigned to you. *He can judge your ability to organize by the way you organize your equipment.*

QUESTIONS

1. Outline the functions of textbook treatment of analytical determinations.

2. Outline what should be done in making a selection among established analytical procedures.

3. Explain how each element in the third period (or another period selected) of the periodic chart is of concern in soil chemical analysis.

4. What are the normality and molarity of common acids and bases of commerce? What is the molarity of H_2O in water?

5. What are the chief impurities in distilled water made by condensation of boiler steam?

6. Discuss several ways in which soil chemical analysis (and chemical analysis in general) has been aided by improved physical instruments; give several examples.

7. Make an outline of the different kinds of filtering devices and their relative advantages and disadvantages.

8. Describe two methods for cutting large glass cylinders.

9. Outline the kinds of mortars and pestles as to substances from which made.

10. What is the approximate conversion to sieve size in mm from "meshes per inch"?

11. What are the chief advantages to the research student of keeping a neat laboratory?

2

Soil Sampling

The analysis can be no better than the sample.
—An axiom

2–1. The sampling of soils is a challenging problem, worthy of detailed consideration. The general problem of soil sampling has been summarized by the Association of Official Agricultural Chemists[1] as follows:

> In view of the variability of soils, it seems impossible to devise an entirely satisfactory method for sampling. It is obvious that the details of the procedure should be determined by the purpose for which the sample is taken.

This passage brings into focus the twin problems of soil variability (sampling "all out-of-doors") and the divergency of types of analyses to be performed on samples. Soil sampling includes taking the soil material so as to take into account the variability of soils, handling and processing the sample, and final subsampling for the actual analytical determination.

2–2. Soil sampling must take into account variations of soil according to profile depth and landscape area. These may be viewed in terms of *natural* soil type units of soil development or in *practical* units of farm, field, or plot size.

2–3. Importance of the Soil-Volume Concept. The soil body sampled should be referred to as the sampling *volume,* rather than as the sampling *area.* Farmers till the soil on a volume basis—the furrow slice. Chemical analyses are often reported on that basis (Table 2–1). Soil physicists refer to percentage of moisture and air by volume. Soil geneticists classify the soil three dimensionally (Fig. 2–1). Crop yields are produced by the entire soil volume, the roots deriving moisture and nutrients from the entire depth

---

[1] *Official and Tentative Methods of Analysis,* 6th ed. (Washington, D.C.: A.O.A.C., 1945), p. 1.

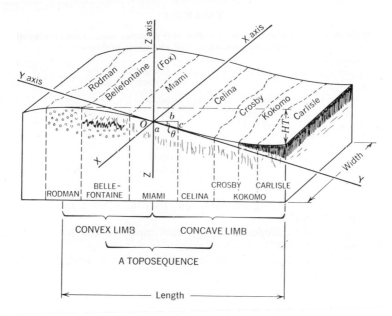

Fig. 2–1. Soil associations in a landscape viewed with reference to three coordinates in space designated the *X, Y,* and *Z* landscape axes extending from any designated point of origin, *O.* The *soil profile* is the landscape viewed as horizons developed *anisotropically* along the vertical or *Z*-axis, the soil *depth function,* with depth units *a.* The *contour* line follows, at any point, the direction of the *X*-axis, along which the soil profile displays *isotropism.* The *Y*-axis is oriented with the slope of the soil surface and perpendicular to the *relief* contour. The angle, θ, is the slope, conventionally expressed in per cent, 100 c/b. A toposequence in a given landscape may have a characteristic *length* and *height* (ht.) as a whole and of the *convex* and *concave* limbs. The soil *toposequence* (¶ 2–10) is the landscape viewed primarily in the two dimensions, along the *Y* and *Z*-axes, and is of great importance to all kinds of soil sampling. (Courtesy Dr. F. D. Hole.)

of the profile. Occurrence of gravel at a shallow depth has led to some of the locally known "Poverty Ridges" because productive soil material was too shallow. The deep loess in central Nebraska permits penetration of alfalfa roots to a depth of 8 or 12 meters and furnishes available water throughout that depth at a rate of 1 cm of water to 6 cm of soil depth. Some soils have most of their exchangeable potassium in the "plow layer"; the deep loess referred to has about 500 to 1000 pp2m in each plow-layer thickness throughout the 10 or more meters of depth.

2–4. Principal Sources of Variability of Soil Chemical Analysis. The principal sources of variability in the chemical analyses of samples from a given soil are:

TABLE 2-1

Weights of representative furrow slice soil volumes sometimes employed
in expressing results of soil chemical analyses

Soil texture	Bulk density, gm/cm³	Weight of furrow slice volume		Factor from ppm
		Per hectare (17 cm), kgm	Per acre (6.7 in.), pounds	
Silt or clay loam	1.3	2,220,000	2,000,000	2.0
Sands	1.6	2,770,000	2,500,000	2.5
Peats, mucks	0.32	550,000	500,000	0.5

1. Variability among different samples drawn from the same volume (sampling "error").

2. Variability introduced among subsamples of the same soil sample (subsampling "error").

3. Variability from one chemical determination to another on the same subsample (analytical "error").

Procedures are well established for decreasing the variability due to subsampling and variability due to analytical procedures. Thus, the main source of variability in the analytical results stems from variability of the soil samples. The standard error arising from sampling and sample treatment has been shown[2] to be 3 to 6 times greater than those arising from the subsampling and analytical procedures, even when the soil sampling procedure in the field was much more refined than is common. Samples taken at 6-inch intervals in 24 square feet of a uniform, virgin, red-brown earth soil area showed[3] coefficients of variation of 10 per cent for 6 metallic cations (rarer elements), and the highest concentration of each element was twice the lowest among the 68 samples taken.

2-5. Composite Soil Sample Equivalent to an Average. A composite soil sample gives a mean analytical value representative of the soil sampling volume from which the composite sample was drawn. (Any analytical value is a mean for the individual soil particles, hence the futility of an argument against obtaining mean-value analyses.) Analyses[4] for carbon, nitrogen, phosphorus, and for soil pH values[5] made on composite samples have been found (as would be expected) to be equivalent to the mean of analyses of individual cores. The standard deviation from the mean can be calculated from separate core analyses; however, individual cores are subject

---

[2] Cline, *Soil Sci.,* 58:275 (1944); Robinson and Lloyd, *J. Agr. Sci.,* 7:144 (1915); Waynick, *Univ. Calif.* (Berkeley), *Pubs. Agr. Sci.,* 3:243 (1918).

[3] McKenzie, *Australian J. Agri. Res.,* 6:699 (1955).

[4] Robinson and Lloyd, U.S.D.A. Cir. 139 (1939); Waynick and Sharp, *Univ. Calif.* (Berkeley), *Pubs. Agr. Sci.,* 4:120 (1919).

[5] Chapman *et al., S.S.S.A. Proc.,* 5:197 (1941).

to large variations *which are not significant to plant growth individually.* The extensive volume through which roots of one plant spread, together with the interlacing of root systems of various crop plants growing in association, severely limits the degree of dependence of the crop on chemical properties of the soil in any given soil core. Disproportionate uptake occurs, of course, from a soil volume of a few cm diameter that has a high nutrient concentration, such as a fertilizer band, but this has been shown by radiochemical tracer experiments to be less extensive than is sometimes supposed. Growth restrictions in pots and small lysimeters further testify as to the dependence of plants on rooting extensity. The root spread volume of many field crop plants is a cylindrical soil volume of 1 to 2 meters radius and of 1 to 10 meters depth. Crop plant spacing is ordinarily only 1 to 10 per cent of the land area over the root spread volume of each plant. Root contact with the side of each cubic soil volume of 1 to 2 mm on an edge can be observed in the field, illustrating the intensity and extensity of root coverage of the soil. Composite sampling of soils restricts the samples to be analyzed to those useful as a basis for soil management recommendations.

2–6. Requirements of Composite Sampling Procedure. The fundamental requirements of valid composite sampling are:

> 1. Each core should be of the same volume and represent the same *cross section* of the sampling volume.
> 2. The cores should be taken at *random* with respect to the sampling volume, usually restricted (¶ 2–35) to criss-cross the direction of cultural operations and natural trends of change such as slope.
> 3. *Enough* cores should be taken to represent the whole sampling volume adequately.
> 4. There should be no chemical *interactions* of soil material composited that are significant to the objective.
> 5. The soil unit selected for one composite sample should be *homogenous for the objective* of the analysis, for example, division of a field into several areas on the basis of observed or otherwise known heterogeneity permits analysis of a sampling volume for each field area the farmer should treat separately.

2–7. Number of Cores Required for a Composite Sample. The A.O.A.C.[6] states that the sample should include ". . . a sufficient number of [cores] to insure a composite sample that will be representative of the tract sampled." Increasing the number of cores lowers the variability of the sample characteristics. Standard statistical tables in books give the number of replications (cores) to composite in terms of the variability of the analyses of individual cores and the level of probability sought. In practice, compositing 20 to 30 cores usually narrows[7] the distribution curve down until it has the same shape as the analytical distribution curve.

---

[6] *Official and Tentative Methods,* 6th ed. (Washington, D.C.: A.O.A.C., 1945), p. 1.
[7] Reed and Rigney, *J. Am. Soc. Agron.,* 39:26 (1947).

SOIL PROFILE SAMPLING

2–8. The generalizations as to the uniformity and differences in soils are systematized by soil classification specialists and embodied in *soil type* definitions. A soil chemist should always work in close cooperation with soil classification specialists in sampling soil profiles.

2–9. Objectives. Chemical analysis of soil profiles generally are made for information on the chemical processes of soil development and long range soil fertility. The soil profiles to be sampled are selected:

1. To represent agriculturally important soils.
2. To represent soil development factors functionally.
3. To represent the sequence of mineral weathering functionally.

2–10. Selecting soil types to represent the soil development and chemical weathering factors functionally simplifies the interpretation of results and provides the maximum of useful information per determination on the processes responsible for the soil properties. It is important to recognize that the variation of one factor, such as climate or parent material, inevitably involves significant changes in other more or less "independent" factors, particularly the nature of the vegetation. Bray[8] studied profiles varying in over-all degree of development, termed a *maturity series*. It is impossible "to hold all other factors constant" while varying one. Rather, the change in the soil type is observed as a function of the change in a developmental or weathering factor, with the recognition that other factors also change as a function of the factor under study. A sequence of soil types is selected to isolate the effect of a single factor in so far as possible. Examples of such sequences[9] follow:

> 1. Soil types in *toposequence* (Fig. 2–1), such as a developmental sequence from well-drained soils to planosols on a uniform loessial parent material, or well-drained to poorly-drained soils in the tropical red and black complex.
> 2. Soil types in *climosequence,* such as soils in successive great soil groups on the same parent material; or soil types of a tropical region representing various proportions of wet and dry seasons, such as high magnesium, manganous, ferruginous, and aluminous families of Latosols (leaching and oxidation sequence); or soil types in a mountainous region representing the same parent material at various altitudes (temperature and rainfall sequence).
> 3. Soil types in *chronosequence,* such as soils representing various periods of time since glacial, loessial, or volcanic deposition.
> 4. Soil types in *biosequence,* such as grassland and forest soils developed on the same parent material.

---

[8] *Am. Soil Survey Assoc. Bul.,* 15:58 (1934).
[9] Names of sequences proposed by Jenny, *Soil Sci.,* 61:375 (1946); also, Jenny, *Factors of Soil Formation* (New York: McGraw-Hill Book Company, Inc., 1941), p. 6.

5. Soil types in *lithosequence*, with closely similar environment but developed on different parent materials (a measure of specific mineral susceptibility to weathering).

2–11. The *catena* (toposequence) was described in 1935 by Milne.[10] The interrelationships of several Nebraska soil types were sketched[11] in 1935 as a toposequence. Soil sequences controlled primarily by drainage were detailed by Bushnell.[12] Several other subdivisions of the toposequence would be possible.[13] Hole[14] assigned index values to catena members.

2–12. Deep Profile Sampling Recommended. Sampling of the profile of soil and subsoil to the full depth of geochemical weathering is recommended in so far as possible. Interesting facts of mineral weathering and soil formation are revealed by analyses of profiles to the full depth of geochemical weathering, whether the deeper horizons are considered a part of the soil profile proper or not. Knowledge thus gained of the course[15] of mineral weathering as a function of depth (the "depth function") is useful in the interpretation of soils, their formation, and potential fertility.

APPARATUS AND SUPPLIES

2–13. Apparatus needed for soil profile sampling includes spades for excavation of the soil profile pit; soil augers, a small one for examination of the soil and a large one (Fig. 2–2) for taking deeper samples; paper bags for the samples; and a dark wax crayon for labeling.

2–14. The closed-cylinder type auger[16] (Fig. 2–2a) has been found by several state experiment stations to be suitable for dry soils, including sands. Two tool steel cutting blades loosen the soil and feed it back into the closed cylinder. Its disadvantages are that moist clay soils pack hard in the cylinder and are difficult to remove, and the soil structure is not preserved for examination. The standard 8- or 10-cm post-hole auger (Fig. 2–2b) is often employed for sampling. Its disadvantages are that loose dry soils do not remain in the hopper as it is pulled from the hole, and, since it is slightly tapered, some of the upper soil layers are continually mixed with somewhat lower layers. The latter difficulty is not considered very serious by Piper,[17] in recommending the 10-cm post-hole auger for taking soil samples under Australian conditions.

---

[10] *Soil Research,* 4(3):183 (1935).

[11] Jackson *et al., S.S.S.A. Proc.,* 2:437 (1938).

[12] *Purdue Univ. Agr. Exp. Sta. Spec. Cir. No. 1* (1944); *S.S.S.A. Proc.,* 10:335 (1946).

[13] Winters, *Soil Sci.,* 67:131 (1949).

[14] *S.S.S.A. Proc.,* 17:131 (1953).

[15] Jackson *et al., J. Phys. Colloid Chem.,* 52:1237 (1948).

[16] Available commercially from R. C. Jordan, Soil Testing Equipment Manufacturers, 4616 Olivewood Ave., Riverside, Calif.

[17] *Soil and Plant Analysis* (New York: Interscience Publishers, Inc., 1944), p. 1.

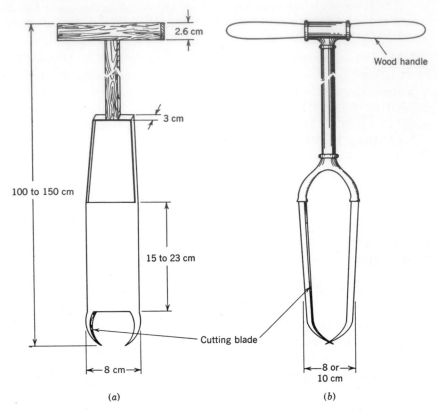

Fig. 2–2. Post-hole type soil sampling augers: (*a*), closed cylinder auger suitable for dry soils (after Cole and Retzer, *S.S.S.A. Proc.*, 1:305, 1937); (*b*), conventional post-hole auger.

PROCEDURE

2–15. Selection of the Profile-Sampling Site. The profile site for sampling is chosen on the basis of vegetation, microclimate, degree of erosion, surface drainage, proximity to trees, and any other factors which are pertinent to identification of the profile with the soil type. Road cuts are not the best sampling sites because they are likely to have an overburden and a deposition of limestone dust. To study the most extensive agriculturally important profiles may necessitate the use of some cultivated sampling sites. The degree of disturbance should be carefully noted in the profile description, and the fact of disturbance recognized in the interpretation of the analyses. If virgin and cultivated soil profiles are being compared, the virgin soil is selected as the modal soil for the type, and the cultivated soil is taken as near to it geographically as possible.

2–16. Location. The location of the site selected is carefully recorded on a detailed map, for example, on a detailed soil survey map or a county road map. The state, island, county, detailed legal location (section, town, and range) of the site, and directions for locating it from a nearby town are recorded with the description. The soil *map* represents the landscape in the dimensions along the X-axis and Y-axis (Fig. 2–1). The soil type, or phase, symbol denotes characteristics along the Z-axis.[18] Lines within the XY quadrants mark the map into *isotypic* soil areas.

2–17. Replication. Soil profile sampling obviously must take into account the *range* of variations in the soil type, which are most clearly defined if resolved into those occurring specifically along either the X- or the Y-axis. Different profiles along the X-axis tend to give the least variability and narrowest range of confidence limits. Selection along the X-axis fits the concept of selection to be "representative of the modal profile of the soil type. . . ."[19] There is also true isotypic variation within one soil type along the Y-axis; in fact, one soil type must necessarily grade into another along the toposequence. Analyses of several profiles representing a developmental sequence of soils, either modal profiles of a soil catena or a soil family, provides a measure of systematic variability, and thus enhances the replication. Composite sampling is not employed.

2–18. At least three replicate soil profiles are sampled. They are separated geographically as widely as possible, preferably by at least 50 miles (100 kilometers) to represent normal isotypic variations resulting from variations in parent materials. Analyses of at least three profiles are required before any generalizations are made for the soil type as such. Two soil types may not be proved to differ if only one profile of each is analyzed.

2–19. Excavation and Description of the Profile. The profile pit is excavated deep enough to reveal the principal features and to extend down to the parent material. The pit should be oriented so that profile is uniformly lighted. Before and during the taking of the samples, the profile horizons are carefully described as to depth, color, morphology, texture, consistency, and drainage. Detailed nomenclature and criteria for each feature are set forth in the Soil Survey Manual.[20] A system of symbols may conveniently be used to describe the various properties semi-quantitatively. For example, a system for quantitative expression of colors is employed by the U.S. Division of Soil Survey.[21] Nikiforoff[22] described a system of symbols for the other profile features. The parent material, age (from geological data), vegetation, altitude, rainfall, temperature, and other factors such as

---

[18] Different conventions were employed by Mattson and Wiklander, *Soil Sci.,* 49:154 (1940); Z corresponds to their "y" and Y to their "x."

[19] Cline, *Soil Sci.,* 59:3 (1945).

[20] *U.S.D.A. Handb.* 18 (1951).

[21] *Ibid.,* p. 194 (color chips are obtainable from Munsell Color Co., 10 E. Franklin St., Baltimore 2, Md.); also, Pendleton and Nickerson, *Soil Sci.,* 71:35 (1951).

[22] *S.S.S.A. Proc.,* 1:307 (1937).

the wet/dry ratio of seasons or frozen subsoil are recorded. The various horizons are delineated and marked with pegs. A photograph and a sketch of the profile are usually made. Collaboration between the soil chemist and the soil classification specialists is always useful and usually mandatory during the profile sampling process.

2–20. Removal of Soil Samples from the Profile. The surface accumulation of organic matter (A_o horizon) is sampled separately and its average thickness estimated. This horizon may have to be collected over an area of one or more square meters to provide an adequate sample volume, usually about 2 liters. Successive horizons are next sampled, a volume of about 1 liter of each usually being taken. The sampling volume is a cylindrical core centered on the Z-axis of the profile. The diameter of the sampling volume is varied so as to provide adequate soil material even from thin horizons. If the horizons are uniform through a thickness up to 30 cm and sharply delineated, the cylinder of soil is taken throughout the horizon thickness. The procedure of sampling every 10 cm or other arbitrary depth is avoided. For very thick horizons bounded by long transition zones, the cylinder of soil taken extends vertically only through the most typical, central, 10- or 15-cm portion of the horizon, the transition horizons being sampled separately. Less laborious procedures such as pH and organic matter determinations are carried out on all horizons. The most extensive and laborious analyses may need to be carried out only on the 4 or 5 principal horizons. This procedure has been found satisfactory in the author's laboratory and concurs with Piper's recommendation.[23] He suggests sampling into the C horizon, to a depth of 1 to 1.5 meters. Profile sampling for mineralogical studies almost always should be extended down into the parent soil material, preferably through the C and into the D horizon (¶ 2–12). Monolith sampling should be considered (¶ 2–22).

2–21. Labeling and Transporting the Profile Samples. Each horizon sample is placed in a double-walled cloth or paper bag. The bag is labeled with a blue wax crayon (pencil or red wax crayon is not satisfactory), and a file card is dropped into it, bearing the same label, written in blue wax crayon. If the samples are very wet, the bags are left open and the soil is placed to dry partially before packaging. The bags are then transported to the laboratory.

MONOLITH MOUNTING OF SOIL PROFILES

2–22. Mounted profile monoliths set in plastic for permanence and natural, moist appearance are valuable for instruction and study of profile analyses. Frequently these monoliths are taken in the same profile excavation as the profile samples taken for analysis. Methods of taking relatively

---

[23] *Op. cit.,* p. 3.

thin monoliths, in the interest of light weight and small space for display, have been described by Harper,[24] Lyford,[25] and Berger and Muckenhirn.[26] The latter authors point out the need for a thickness of 2 to 3 cm to show the natural structure of many soil types. They developed this effective procedure for cementing the soil material together in monoliths of this thickness.

APPARATUS

2–23. Needed apparatus is a flat spade, knife, spatula, hand pick, monolith sampling tool (Fig. 2–3a), cloth and wood board backing, and hydraulic jack.

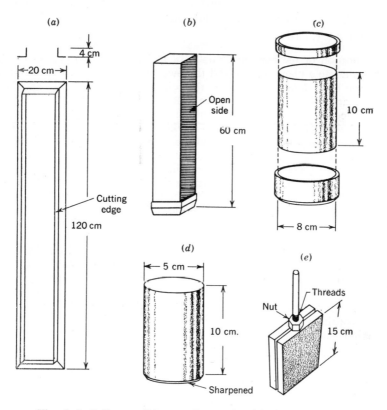

Fig. 2–3. Soil monolith sampling tools: (*a*), frame for profile sample mounting (after Berger and Muckenhirn, *S.S.S.A. Proc.,* 10:368, 1946); (*b, c, d*), types of columns to be thrust into the soil from above; (*e*), turf profile sampler.

[24] *Okla. Agr. Exp. Sta. Bul. 201* (1932).
[25] *S.S.S.A. Proc.,* 4:355 (1940).
[26] *S.S.S.A. Proc.,* 10:368 (1946).

2–24. Two reagents are employed, which are mixed together in the proper proportions just before using:

Solution A: 12% vinylite resin in acetone.
Solution B: 12% vinylite resin in methyl isobutyl ketone.

The vinylite resin employed is vinyl acetate-vinyl chloride copolymer, grade VYHH in powder form (Bakelite Corporation, 230 North Michigan Ave., Chicago 1, Ill.).

PROCEDURE

2–25. The Berger and Muckenhirn procedure[27] for removal of the monolith from the soil varies somewhat according to soil texture and compactness. For fine textured soils,

> a portion of the exposure, about 18 inches [30 or 40 cm] in width, is smoothed to a plane surface and the metal frame is pressed or driven into the soil bank until it is flush with the soil. The back is then fastened to the frame and the soil dug away around the sides. The soil in the frame is then separated from the exposure by cutting between the bank and frame with a large knife, starting at the top and working down. While cutting is in progress, slight pressure [is] exerted on the frame, pushing it toward the bank to prevent slumping of the soil. If the soil tends to slump out of the frame, a metal or plywood strip, just over 8 inches [20 cm] wide [is] inserted behind the frame, from the top down, as the cutting progresses. After severance from the bank, the frame with the soil profile in it is tilted back and the exposed face smoothed level with the edge of the frame.
> The exposed face of the soil profile is then painted with vinylite solution A. A board 9 × 50 inches [23 × 125 cm] is also moistened with the solution and, with moistened side down, placed and centered on the exposed face of the profile. The board and frame are then held tightly together and turned over so the profile rests on the board. The back is removed from the frame and the soil is forced out by lifting the frame gently, while pressing downward on the soil with a board small enough to fit inside the cutting edges of the frame. Before the frame is entirely lifted away from the profile, the latter is enclosed by placing . . . wood strips around the sides. After the frame has been removed, these strips are nailed to the board underneath and the profile is ready for transportation to the laboratory.

2–26. For coarse textured soils, the exposed soil profile is first allowed to dry to a low moisture content. Then

> a liter or more of a solution consisting of two-thirds of solution A and one-third of solution B is poured or painted over an area 8 inches [20 cm] wide and 48 inches [120 cm] in [depth] . . . A piece of gauze cloth about 16 × 60 inches [40 × 150 cm] is then pressed against the treated soil surface and wetted with additional solution. The gauze provides some support

---

[27] *S.S.S.A. Proc.*, 10:368 (1946).

and makes the profile easier to handle in the laboratory. After the solvent has evaporated and the plastic has hardened, the metal frame [is] pressed into sandy soils around the area treated with plastic and gauze and the soil removed as described above for fine-textured soils. Generally, however, and especially with gravelly soils, a board about 9 × 50 inches [23 × 125 cm] is placed against the profile and the loose ends of the cloth are tacked to the board to prevent slumping of the soil layer during removal.

A profile about 2 inches [5 cm] thick is then separated from the soil bank by cutting from the top downward with a knife or trowel. A plywood board or sheet of metal is slipped behind the profile as cutting proceeds, although slight pressure must be maintained throughout against the board to which the gauze was tacked. When cutting is completed or nearly so, the profile, held between the boards, is removed from the bank.

After the tacks are taken out, the surplus cloth is folded over the exposed face of the profile and sewn together so as to hold the soil in place during transportation to the laboratory. Later, before cementing the profile to the board backing, the excess cloth is trimmed to the dimensions . . . of the finished profile.

2–27. To complete the mount for display, wood strips are temporarily tacked on a 23 × 125 × 2 cm (9 × 50 × 0.75 inch) wood board to form a box 20 × 120 × 2.5 cm. Vinylite solution A is poured into the box to cover the surface outlined by the strips.

These strips are needed to maintain straight edges during subsequent trimming and plastic treatment of the profile. The soil profile is then placed inside the rectangle enclosed by the strips, pressed down firmly, and the plastic underneath allowed to harden.

The thickness of the profile is then [cut down] to about [2.5 cm] in the case of silt and clay loam soils and about [1.5 cm] in the case of sands and sandy loams. The excess soil is removed by prying and lifting with a sharp pick or knife point so as to expose the natural structure. Where the edges of the profile are irregular or broken, they are repaired with loose soil material previously trimmed from a corresponding position in the profile. This trimming and preparatory work is more easily and effectively done when the soil is fairly moist; after it has been completed, the soil is allowed to dry before being impregnated with the vinylite solution.

The vinylite solution is poured over the face of the profile until the soil is nearly saturated, requiring usually about 1 to 2 liters. For most soils, a mixture consisting of two-thirds of solution A and one-third of solution B is satisfactory; for clay soils, however, a higher proportion of solution B is preferable.

After the plastic has dried at room temperature for about 30 minutes, the wood border strips are removed, and excess solution and soil material are cleaned from the edges of the board. After standing for about 24 hours, the profiles become dry and hard and may be set upright. If the face becomes glossy in places, this glossiness may be removed by brushing the face lightly with a paint brush moistened with pure isobutyl ketone.

The simulation of natural moist appearance and color is superior in the above preparations to coatings with cellulose nitrate.[28]

----

[28] McClure and Converse, *S.S.S.A. Proc.,* 4:120 (1940).

2–28. Miniature soil profiles, 5 cm wide and 30 cm long were assembled by Berger and Muckenhirn[29] from the soil material trimmed from the full size profile. The respective material is placed to scale in a box as described for the full size profile, and set in the vinylite plastic, or embedded in "Selectron" or "Castolite" resin by a process described by Bourbeau and Berger.[30]

2–29. A wide variety of tools and methods have been designed for monolith samples (Fig. 2–3). Types (*b*) and (*c*) are thrust into the soil by pressure from a hydraulic jack anchored against a cross bar held down by two heavy screw-type augers. Type (*d*) may be thrust in by hand or by means of the jack, but is suitable only for relatively friable soils. The cylinders (*c* and *d*) provide soil sample cores suitable for preparation of thin sections by plastic embedding. Type (*e*) has been used for examination of golf greens, when a view of the profile to 15 cm is wanted without greatly disturbing the turf. Kelley *et al.*[31] describe a soil sampling machine which takes undisturbed soil cores 10 cm in diameter to a depth of 2 meters.

2–30. Hole[32] has employed relief models to visualize further the relation of the soil profile to the landscape.

SAMPLING SOIL OF ESTABLISHED EXPERIMENTAL PLOTS

2–31. The purpose of soil sampling, to measure soil properties that influence the production of crops, invariably is best accomplished by composite sampling (¶ 2–5). When the set of replicate plots is all of one soil type, phase, and subtype, each plot is composite sampled as a unit. A plot is used here to designate the smallest field area that receives a given treatment and is harvested as a unit. When more than one soil type, phase, or subtype occurs within one plot, and different proportions are present in different plots, it is difficult to obtain valid samples of soil.

2–32. Needed apparatus includes a soil-sampling tube[33] (Fig. 2–4); spade; paper bags, cardboard cartons, or sample bottles; dark wax pencil; stakes; and string. For hard, dry, or stony soils, a hand pick and soil auger are needed.

---

[29] *S.S.S.A. Proc.*, 11:484 (1947).
[30] *S.S.S.A. Proc.*, 12:409 (1948).
[31] *S.S.S.A. Proc.*, 12:85 (1948).
[32] *Agron. Jour.*, 42:520 (1950).
[33] Obtainable from the Oakfield Apparatus Company, Oakfield, Wis., or Central Scientific Company, 1700 Irving Park Road, Chicago, Ill.

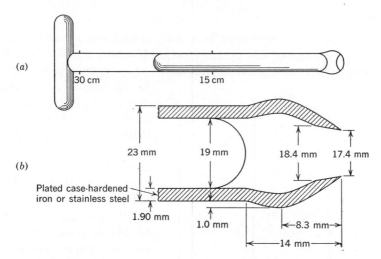

Fig. 2–4. Details of construction of cut-away soil sampling tube: (*a*), depth intervals grooved each 15 cm (6 inches), lengths of 33 and 93 cm are convenient; (*b*), details of hardened cutting edge, which should be hard enough to resist bending if thrust into gravel, but not hard enough to be brittle.

2–33. The cut-away type soil sampling tube is remarkably effective for composite sampling the plow layer and upper subsoil of moist, stone-free, friable soils. Permanent grooves on the outside of the tube indicate the soil depth sampled. The semicircular opening permits visual inspection of the horizon for conditions of structure, mottling, mild compaction (Hoffer chalk test,[34] ¶ 13–74), contamination of surface with subsoil, moisture penetration, and root distribution. These observations can be made rapidly as the composite sampling progresses. The semicircular opening permits the soil core to drop out into the paper bag or other sample container.

2–34. The King type of soil sampling tube[35] (closed cylinder with enlarged portion back of cutting edge) has long been employed. The top end is re-enforced for use with a soil tube driver that consists of a hammer guided by a steel rod that fits into the tube. Threaded sections of this type of tube permit extension to depths of 10 meters or more. This tube, when ruggedly built, is suitable for sampling to great depths in fairly dry soils. Wet soils tend to stick and clog the tube. A lighter weight cylindrical tube similar to the King tube but with handle has been designed by Hankinson-Hester.[36]

---

[34] Best used with extra-long cut-away soil sampler obtainable from Elano Corp., Xienia, Ohio, or Ken Standard Co., Evansville, Ind.

[35] Available from several supply houses, including R. C. Jordan, Soil Testing Equipment Manufacturers, 4615 Olivewood Ave., Riverside, Calif.

[36] Available from LaMotte Chemical Products Co., Baltimore 4, Md.

PROCEDURE

2–35. Each plot is delineated by a stake at each corner, and sometimes is outlined by a string. The operator proceeds across the plot in a zigzag path (Fig. 2–5, A) taking a core with the cut-away core sampler (Fig. 2–4) to plow-layer depth every 2 steps. Sampling of the 50-cm border of the plot is avoided. Criss-crossing the plot provides for chance sampling of fertilizer ordinarily applied parallel to the rows and the long direction of the plot. A composite sample of 10 to 30 cores (usually 20 to 25) is placed in a water-resistant paper bag that has been plainly labeled with a dark wax crayon. A spade is sometimes employed in lieu of a soil-sampling tube for composite sampling of plots. A spade or hand pick is best for sampling stony or hard, dry soils, but is many times more laborious than the sampling tube for moist, friable soils. A narrow, flat blade with parallel sides facilitates obtaining a soil-sample slice with uniform size of cross section. However, it is easily bent and cannot be employed for the excavation. A hand trowel aids in manipulating a parallel-sided block of soil for compositing from a slice

x=core-sampling position

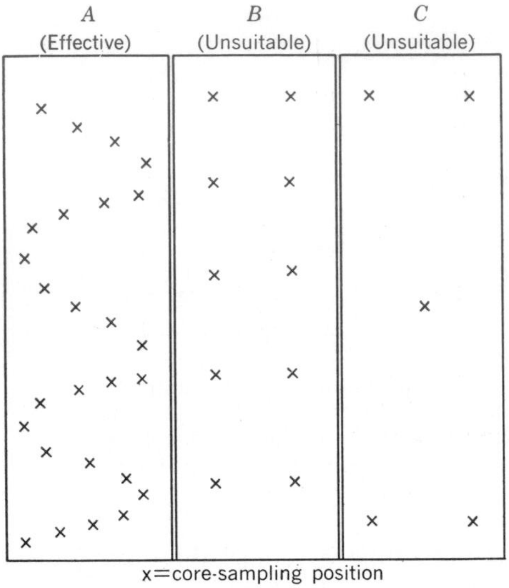

Fig. 2–5. *A,* Correct procedure, a zigzag pattern across the plot gives a proper composite of 10 to 30 cores for a single soil sample. Valid replication is provided by sampling a replicate plot similarly or resampling the same plot in a similar pattern. *B,* Unsuitable procedure, regular positioning of the cores in a plot, from which samples are likely to be biased by row applications; analysis of these cores separately as replicates is an inefficient practice. *C,* Unsuitable procedure, regular positioning of the cores with a distinct bias toward the ends of the plot; too few cores are represented to make an accurate composite sample.

taken with the tile spade. Cline[37] indicates that in an hour 20 circular holes 40 cm in depth and diameter can be excavated, and a 10-cm slice cut from the wall of each with the spade and sampled with the trowel. The time required, of course, depends on how hard the soil is. Twenty cores of a moist, friable soil can be taken and composited in 5 or 10 minutes with the soil-sampling tube.

2–36. It is convenient to leave the bags standing on the plot where taken

---

[37] *Soil Sci.,* 59:3 (1945).

until the entire series of samples has been obtained. In this way, the sample-numbering system is self-checking and no confusion as to the sampling area from which the sample was obtained can occur.

2–37. The samples are collected into suitable cardboard boxes and transported to the laboratory without drying. The particular determinations that are to be made should be considered in deciding upon the procedure from this point forward. Some determinations require field-moist samples so that the equilibrium is not disturbed by drying, and others require air-dried samples.

2–38. Replication. One composite sample is generally obtained from each of several replicated experimental plots, thus providing the most suitable sample replication of each treatment. Replicate samples may be obtained from each plot by repeated composite sampling; this procedure is necessary for testing for differences between the different replicate plots in the experiment, but is not done in routine plot sampling. A plan for replication is developed and mapped before sampling is initiated.

2–39. Sampling Soil Under a Single Plant. Soil sampling for correlation with the analysis of a single plant is restricted to a composite sample from the central portion of the root-spread volume (¶ 2–5), which is more or less a hemispherical body of soil surrounding the base of the plant. This root-spread hemisphere represents the theoretical minimum part of a plot that a single sample should represent.

SAMPLING SOILS IN SELECTION OF SOIL EXPERIMENT FIELDS

2–40. The popular directive given for selection of a soil experiment field is "select a uniform soil area." Unfortunately, this is a very difficult if not impossible requirement to fulfill completely. Except for some loessial, alluvial, and lacustrine soils under grassland vegetation, soils are generally found to be *lacking* in uniformity over areas the size of a field experiment. As nearly uniform soil as possible is located, and then soil sampling and analysis are employed to assay the extent of soil variation that exists.

2–41. The Plot-Size Sampling Volume. In a field being examined for adequate uniformity for fertility plots, the smallest unit generally employed for variability measurement is a sampling volume having the size, shape, and orientation the plot will have (Fig. 2–6). *Composite sampling* of such a plot-sized soil volume performs the same integration as the roots of a growing crop effects (¶ 2–5) within each plot. The difference between analyses of a series of such composite samples provides a basis for calculating the variance of soil properties among different plots. Once the standard deviation of analytical characteristics is established for composite samples from well distributed plot-size sampling volumes, it tends to apply for the whole experimental field whether or not the actual fertility plots fall exactly within the individual limits of the plot-size sampling volumes (Fig.

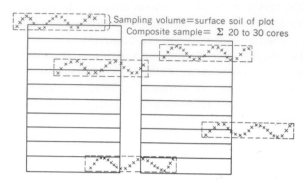

Fig. 2–6. Chemical analyses of composite samples drawn from plot-size volumes (dotted lines) permits statistical analysis of significant soil variability between future yield plots (solid lines) to be laid out later, even though the latter may not fall within the original boundaries.

2–6). The *significant* "deviation from the mean" is the deviation of various plot-size volumes from the *mean of the field*. The distribution of semimicro soil variations and the characteristics of crop growth and management, make the long, narrow plot, and therefore, a long, narrow sampling volume, the most efficient for yield measurement. No gain in estimation of the variability of the plot-size sampling volume would be made by analysis of individual cores. Individual cores taken at distances apart of plot dimensions and analyzed separately characterize the field as a whole (as would one composite), but little or no significant information is provided about the homogeneity or heterogeneity of a set of plots to be placed in the field. *Microvariations* in soil are induced by individual trees, windrows or shocks of grain, or deposits of animal excrements, but these are of little significance because rooting of the individual plant (¶ 2–5) and coverage of a single long narrow plot average the soil properties over each plot.

APPARATUS AND SUPPLIES

2–42. Needed apparatus includes sampling tube (Fig. 2–4), spade, and auger. Needed supplies include paper bags or cartons and dark wax pencil.

PROCEDURE

2–43. Preliminary Inspection. Within a prospective experimental field area having suitable topography, the soil is examined to a meter depth or more to establish whether the soil type is that wanted. This preliminary inspection is carried out in at least 5 places, well distributed in the prospective experimental field.

2–44. Preliminary Composite Sampling of Blocks. Between 10 and 30 cores (usually 20 to 25) are composited in a paper bag from the full plow-layer depth, taken at random over an area having the size, shape, and orientation of the prospective plot (Fig. 2–6). This procedure is repeated for other plot-size areas to represent parts of different replicate blocks. One sample per block is minimal, and, if tests of these with the field kit do not eliminate the field from consideration, additional samples are taken to give 2 or more samples of plot-size volumes per replicate block for more detailed analyses in the laboratory. This constitutes the preliminary sampling. Variability between blocks is calculated by analysis of variance. Between-block variability should be no larger than necessary, and should not affect differentially the treatments to be tested.

2–45. Detailed Sampling of Blocks. Additional detailed sampling of plot-size volumes is carried out after the plots are tentatively laid out, to provide an estimate of plot variability within blocks. This is the variability that causes the most difficulty in testing differences due to treatments. If it is large, the experimental site is unsuitable. Ordinarily the variability between long narrow plots is not excessive. This sampling can be used as a basis for discarding a few plots if they fall outside the desired limits of variability.

2–46. The chemical analyses employed as criteria for plot uniformity (e.g., soil pH, available phosphorus, available potassium, organic matter) are generally simple and few in number, and therefore can be applied to relatively large numbers of samples. The labor for analysis is relatively small compared to that involved in plot experiments. Thus, it is not unreasonable to analyze as many samples as plots to be included in the experiment, although fewer samples suffice for many purposes.

2–47. Subsoil Sampling. Soil fertility plots are generally laid out on cultivated fields or grassland, seldom on virgin lands. Soils that have been cropped are likely to exhibit their chemical variability most in the surface plow-layer, because variations in fertilizer treatments, return of plant residues in manures, accumulation of organic matter from roots, and depletion of organic matter through oxidation and erosion are concentrated in this layer. Also, the underlying subsoil tends to become more uniform chemically throughout any given field of one soil type through the action of roots in depleting available nutrients selectively in the originally more fertile spots. On the other hand, differences in the subsoil texture and depth lead to differences in the chemical properties of the subsoil in different portions of the field that are not made uniform by cropping.

2–48. The greatest emphasis in soil sampling for plots is given to the surface plot-layer of 15 to 20 cm (6 to 8 inches), after a preliminary inspection has been made for difference in the texture and chemical properties of the entire profile. A few samples are taken from the subsurface 20 cm immediately beneath the plow-layer, and a few samples are taken of the underlying profile by horizons. Comparative samples are taken of virgin profiles of the soil type for detailed evaluation of the chemical status of the soil of the experimental field.

SAMPLING FARM FIELDS

2–49. The size of a farm field area to be represented by one soil sample is determined by the size of the area to which a farmer is willing to give separate attention in his soil-management operations. Generally, in the smaller farms, fields of 5 or 10 acres (2 to 4 hectares) are managed as a single field unit, making this the logical unit for sampling, analysis, recommendations, and subsequent treatments. Larger field units on larger farms dictate larger soil sampling units, within the limitations of major natural soil sampling units delineated by changes in relief, depth, or texture of the soil. On the other hand, small trouble spots delineated by lack of productiveness, may be sampled separately (¶ 2–54).

APPARATUS AND SUPPLIES

2–50. Needed apparatus includes a sampling tube (Fig. 2–4) or spade. Needed supplies include paper for a map to be mounted on a smooth board, paper bags or cartons, and dark wax pencil.

PROCEDURE

2–51. Field or Farm Diagram. The farm or field to be sampled is given a general inspection, and a diagram is prepared showing the different fields, the drainage pattern, and the main kinds of soil, such as upland or bottom land. A plan of the number of samples and manner of composite sampling is entered on this map, different fields being designated by letters, A, B, C, etc., and samples from each field by the letter and a number. Details of soil and crop management are needed for a satisfactory interpretation of the analyses to be made in connection with soil testing service (¶ 13–80). Separate samples are taken to represent each distinct kind of topography (upland separate from lowland), soil texture, soil organic content (light colored separate from dark colored), fertility status (as indicated by crop growth), and management unit. Abnormal conditions not to be included in the samples are soil near buildings, gates, field margins, highways, and soil from crop hills or rows that were fertilized. Water-resistant paper bags are labeled with a dark wax pencil before sampling is begun.

2–52. The operator makes a traverse over each area to be sampled separately (Fig. 2–7), taking a core or slice of the plow-layer at intervals of

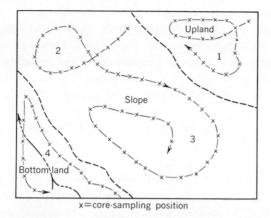

x=core-sampling position

Fig. 2–7. Farm field diagram showing layout of four soil sampling units according to typographic position and size of the field significant to management. Samples 2 and 3 are of the nature of replicate samples in the main field area. Each soil sample is a composite of from 10 to 30 soil cores.

15 to 20 steps and compositing them together in a bag. A thin slice of soil (Fig. 2–8) is taken so that the sample size is not too large. Ten to 30 well distributed cores or slices are composited for each sample. A sample that is too large is thoroughly mixed in a pail or passed through a coarse screen, and a representative portion is retained as the sample. One double handful (250 to 500 ml volume) of soil is sufficient for simpler tests. The sample

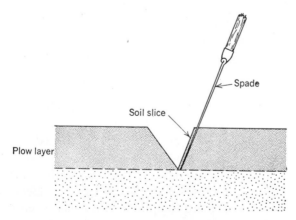

Fig. 2–8. Taking a representative thin slice of soil through the plow-layer by means of a spade. From 10 to 20 such slices are composited for one sample.

location previously marked on the bag is carefully checked and correlated with the field and area on the map.

2–53. Subsoil character. Seldom does farm field-sampling require samples from the subsoil below the plow layer. However, at the time of sampling the surface layers, an examination (and possibly sampling) is usually made of the subsoil at 1 or 2 locations. The occurrence of a highly fertile subsoil, well supplied with lime and having a high or low available water capacity is of great significance to crop growth. Such characteristics are frequently well known for the soil type and, therefore, may not necessarily be re-examined during farm sampling, simply being taken into account in the interpretation of the results of the analyses of surface samples.

2–54. Sampling Soil of a Local Problem Spot. Local soil problem spots frequently lead to requests for analysis and diagnosis; examples are local areas of high $CaCO_3$ content, local exposures of subsoil, local extremely acid (containing S and H_2SO_4) soils, local saline soil areas or alkaline soil areas, local areas underlain by hardpan, and local areas that grow chlorotic plants. A surface soil sample is taken by compositing 10 to 30 cores taken 2 or more meters apart in representative areas. Each core extends through the A_p or A_1 horizon. Subsoil samples are taken by profile horizon beneath the A_p or A_1 horizon to a depth of 1 meter by spade excavation, composited from 3 locations. If several local problem spots occur, each is sampled separately. If visible variations within one area are noted, soil representing each important kind of occurrence is composite sampled separately. One or more control samples are obtained from immediately adjacent soil profiles on which normal plant growth occurs. This precaution offers the opportunity of greatly narrowing down the analysis of soil properties responsible for the local problem.

HANDLING SOIL SAMPLES IN THE LABORATORY

2–55. Handling soil samples in the laboratory involves procedures for drying, grinding, sieving, mixing, partitioning, weighing, and storing.

APPARATUS AND SUPPLIES

2–56. Handling soil samples in the laboratory requires a drying cabinet with provision for air circulation; a drying oven, 100° to 110° C; 6-mm, 4-mm, 2-mm, and smaller sieves; sheets of rubberized cloth, wrapping paper, and glazed paper; a wooden rolling pin, rubber pestle, and agate mortar and pestle (Fig. 1–3); a riffle or large spatula for quartering; paper bags or cartons for temporary storage; screw cap jars, labels, a log book, and a storage case for standard samples; and a balance sensitive to 0.1 to 0.5 per cent of sample weight.

2–57. Drying. The soil sample is usually partially air-dried (until not sticky) at a temperature of about 25° to 35° C, and relative humidity of 20 to 60 per cent. Many determinations are not significantly affected by complete air drying for storage purposes. Analytical samples to be stored for protracted periods of time are almost invariably air-dried because of changes that occur in the chemical status of ions and organic matter of soil samples stored moist. Owing to the large and rapid changes that take place in the status of some ionic species on drying, many types of analyses must be carried out on moist samples immediately after collection. Examples are the determinations of exchangeable ferrous iron (Chapter 15) and to some extent hydrogen ion activity (Chapter 3), exchangeable potassium (Chapter 6), acid extractable phosphorus (Chapter 7), and nitrate nitrogen (Chapter 8). The common weight basis for expressing the results is the 100° to 110° C oven-dry weight of soil material (usually the "fine earth," ¶ 2–60); this may be converted to the volume basis ("plow layer," etc., ¶ 2–3).

2–58. Sieving. The bulk soil sample for chemical analysis, in its natural field moist conditions, is passed through a 6-mm (4 meshes per inch) sieve, usually by rubbing with the fingers. Passing samples other than sandy soils through the 6-mm sieve is much easier if the soil is field moist rather than air-dried. If the soil is in a very friable condition, the 6 mm material may approximate a −4-mm material without further sieving. In soil sampling in the field, the stones and large gravels are ordinarily ignored, and a few stones and gravel particles remaining on the 6-mm screen usually are discarded, since they ordinarily are less than 1 per cent of the plow layer (¶ 2–60). Sieving effects some mixing of the soil; mixing is completed next (¶ 2–65), and the soil is partitioned (¶ 2–66 or 2–67). An optimum sample volume of −6-mm material is often about 1 liter (¶ 2–63). If further decrease of sample size is needed, usually the case, the process of grinding (¶ 2–61), sieving, mixing, and partitioning are repeated. Successively smaller sieves are employed until the required laboratory sample is obtained for the particular analysis to be effected.

2–59. Soils in the right moisture condition to be mellow can be worked through a 2-mm sieve (or 10- to 20-mesh per inch) by being rubbed over the sieve surface with a rubber stopper. The common practice of passing only a portion of the gross sample through the sieve and discarding the remainder is likely to introduce positive bias in the sample by increasing the concentration of most elements of soil fertility. That practice is justified perhaps in preparing samples of primarily silty and clayey soils for rapid soil testing, the assumption being that the unsifted aggregated material is the same as that which has passed the sieve. The entire partitioned sub-sample is ordinarily made to pass a given sieve size before further partitioning.

2–60. Soil scientists have generally employed as a basis for expressing the analysis, the "fine earth," or soil material passing the 2-mm, round hole sieve. The percentage of constituents is expressed in terms of this material even if further sieving and segregation of coarse sand fractions is carried out. A moderately stony[38] field has 0.5 to 2 per cent of stones. In soils exceeding this content of stones and gravel, the "fine earth" (-2-mm) basis is biased by more than 2 per cent. For routine soil testing, the fraction coarser than 2 mm is discarded. In research work, the appearance of significant amounts (over 2 per cent) of gravel on the 2-mm sieve is a satisfactory indication that the "fine earth" basis must be corrected for agricultural soils in referring back to the plow-layer volume (¶ 2–3). For research purposes, the gravel retained on the 2-mm round hole sieve is examined for the presence of concretions or granular secondary soil particles. The primary particles and concretions are preserved intact if of interest to the research, but the tough granular secondary soil particles are further disaggregated and passed through the sieve. This is sometimes accomplished best by trituration in water. The fine particles are washed through the sieve into a large beaker. The gravel and concretions remaining on the 2-mm sieve are washed, dried, and weighed. The percentage by weight of "gravel and concretions, $+2$ mm" is calculated on the basis of the whole soil on an oven-dry basis. This fraction is bottled and labeled for further examination if significant to the analysis. Sieves finer than 2 mm are of course employed for segregating the various sand fractions used in mineralochemical analysis, but in that procedure the -2-mm sample is disaggregated chemically, rather than mechanically, prior to sieving.

2–61. Grinding. The soil aggregates are broken up by grinding lightly with a roller, rubber pestle in an agate mortar, or motorized grinder. Crushing the primary sand and gravel particles is generally avoided. Clay soils are best crushed for passing 2 mm before they reach complete air-dryness; otherwise the crushing process is difficult.

2–62. Fine grinding of the mineral grains is permissible with samples used for the determination of soil organic matter or total elemental analysis; however, such samples are not suitable for some other analytical determinations such as soil pH, exchangeable cations, easily soluble phosphorus, or mineralochemical analysis. Fine grinding is carried out in an agate mortar with agate pestle; a porcelain mortar should not be employed. Care is exercised never to strike an agate mortar a sharp blow, as it is easily chipped or broken. There is danger of breakage in heating it for drying

---

[38] Stoniness is thoroughly treated by Nikiforoff, *Soil Sci.,* 66:347 (1948).

purposes. The proper washing is with distilled water followed by drying in air or wiping with surgical gauze or filter paper.

2–63. A simple guide to required fineness is that the sieve opening should pass a spherical particle which will constitute 0.001 or less of the *minimum* subsample volume (Table 2–2). Of course, the average particle size passing the sieve will be much smaller than the maximum set by the sieve opening. The *optimum* sample volume or weight will be 3 to 4 times the minimum.

2–64. A few uncrushed sand particles may become an appreciable fraction of a small analytical sample of sandy soils. It is difficult to get a representative portion of the fine and coarse particles into each sample even by

TABLE 2–2

Relation of sieve size to minimum sample volume and weight, based on need in the sample for at least 1000 particles of sieve-opening size. The optimum sample size is on the order of 3 or 4 times the minimum

Sieve size, nominal opening		Minimum sample	
		Volume	Weight†
mm	mesh/in. (approximate)	cm³	gm
6	4	112	146
4	6	34	44
2*	10	4.2	5.3
1	20	0.52	0.68
		mm³	mgm
0.25	60	8.2	13
0.16	100	2.1	2.7
0.1	140	0.52	0.68

° Standard of reference, round holes.

† Based on bulk density of soil equals 1.3 gm/cm³; for mineral or rock grains of 2.65 gm/cm³ (no pore space) double these weights would be minimum.

careful partitioning (¶ 2–66). Peech et al.[39] have suggested a partial solution of this problem by sieving out the coarse sand with a 1-mm sieve, making the chemical analyses on the −1-mm fraction, and calculation back to the basis of the −2-mm soil by neglecting any contribution of the 1- to 2-mm fraction to the extractable constituents. The less than 2-mm fraction is simply weighed, and its percentage of the −2-mm soil is calculated. Other procedures are use of a larger sample and taking a small aliquot of solution for analysis; and fine-grinding of the −2-mm sample prior to analysis when permissible.

---

[39] U.S.D.A. Cir. 757 (1947).

2–65. Mixing. The sample is mixed by a process of rolling or turning, effected as follows: opposite corners of the cloth or paper are grasped, and one is pulled diagonally across the sample slowly so that the soil rolls over (not slides) toward the opposite corner. Then the opposite corner of the cloth or paper is pulled back over the soil to roll it back. The process is repeated by grasping the other two opposite corners. Rolling on opposite diagonals is repeated at least 5 times. Ten times may be necessary if the volume of soil is large.

2–66. Partition of the sample. The sample is partitioned with a riffle. A riffle has a series of narrow slots, arranged so that alternate slots deliver to opposite sides. The procedure is somewhat faster and more reliable than quartering (¶ 2–67).

2–67. Alternative to riffling, the sample may be partitioned by "quartering." The mixed soil material is coned in the center of the mixing sheet with

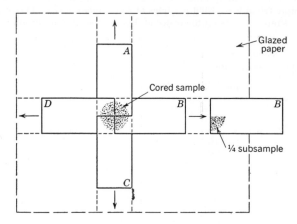

Fig. 2–9. Paper quartering technique for small samples, especially for sand and silt grains that are not to be ground. Four strips of paper are woven together and the cone formed at the center. Pulling the strips apart results in accurate quartering. (After Pettijohn, *J. Geol.,* 39:432, 1931.)

care to make it symmetrical with respect to fine and coarse soil material. The cone is flattened and divided through the center with a flat metal spatula or metal sheet, one-half being moved to the side quantitatively. Then each half is further divided into half, the four quarters being separated into separate piles or "quarters." For small samples, a paper quartering technique (Fig. 2–9) may be employed.[40] Two diagonally opposite "quarters" are discarded quantitatively. The other two are either mixed by

---

[40] Micro-subsampling is discussed by Krumbein and Pettijohn, *Manual of Sedimentary Petrography* (New York: Appleton-Century-Crofts, Inc., 1938), p. 549.

rolling if the entire half is to be retained, or resieved with a finer sieve if further partitioning of the sample is to be made.

2–68. Weighing. The analytical sample is the soil material employed as a whole in a single analytical determination. For example, the soil material placed in the funnel for extraction of exchangeable cations. Weighing out the analytical sample is fundamentally a continuation of the partition process (¶ 2–66). The minimum size of sample is best kept 1000 times (¶ 2–63) that of the sieve opening through which the sample was passed. Schollenberger and Simon[41] point out that the analytical sample of coarse-textured soil samples, which tend to segregate, should be taken by riffling or quartering down to about the desired weight, and then the entire portion should be weighed accurately.

2–69. The sample is weighed on a torsion or analytical balance having a sensitivity equal to 0.1 to 0.5 per cent of the sample weight. Thus for a 20-gm sample, a torsion balance sensitivity to 0.05 to 0.1 gm is adequate. The sample, if fine enough to be nonsegregating, is handled on a spatula, otherwise on a spoon. A smooth metal scoop and camel's hair brush are essential accessories. A counterpoise weight for the scoop is highly desirable.

2–70. Each duplicate analytical sample is taken in a different set; the 2 are not run side by side. The estimate of error obtained by duplication then encompasses variations between sets. Many analytical procedures are short compared to the time for sampling and preparation, and justify duplication. When a routine has been established to check duplication unfailingly in different sets, the analytical replication is decreased, reliance being placed on comparisons of duplicate soil samples for replication. The procedure then is to replicate only one analytical sample from the previous set in each succeeding set, or to carry a single control sample in every set. Finally, after complete reproducibility of procedure by a given analyst has been established, replication of analysis of a single sample may be discontinued. Replication is then still provided by means of replicate samples of the original soil. In routine soil testing of farm fields, variability is measured by taking samples from different small areas in a given field rather than outright replication by resampling of any one area.

2–71. Storage. Most soil samples are collected for a series of analyses to be made immediately, and then are discarded. Storage of soil samples, however, even for the period of analysis requires an orderly procedure. For soil testing, a series of cardboard cups in a tray with dimensions similar to the mass-handling testing apparatus is convenient. For longer analyses, the most satisfactory procedure is to place the samples in screw-cap jars and to array them on shelves in proper order. Great saving in time and improve-

---

[41] *Soil Sci.,* 59:13 (1945).

ment in accuracy is thus effected compared to the all-too-frequent practice of letting the soil samples accumulate in paper bags in the laboratory, where contamination may occur. A well-defined schedule for discarding samples after use should be established. Few soil samples justify storage for protracted periods.

2–72. Moist Soil Storage. Storage of moist bulk soil samples for greenhouse studies is sometimes advantageous, particularly with soils high in organic colloids, which dry irreversibly. To maintain the moist samples in tightly covered bulk storage cans, an effective procedure is to embed a beaker of water in the soil surface. The vapor pressure of water is maintained sufficiently high to preserve the natural moistness of the soil. That some chemical changes in the soil occur under these conditions must be taken into account in the experimental interpretations.

2–73. Standard Soil Samples. Standard soil samples on which an exhaustive amount of analytical work has been done, such as those involved in mineralochemical or minor element analysis, justify long-time or permanent storage. An intensive research program can be accelerated considerably by having representative reference samples at hand. A properly sieved and mixed laboratory sample, usually of 1- to 5-liter volume is appropriate for the soil chemical reference sample. The sample is placed in an air-tight glass jar with a screw cap. A permanent laboratory number is assigned, a well-designed label is carefully mounted on the jar, and a similar label is placed inside it. A water-excluding label varnish is applied over the label to insure permanence. Where great numbers of such samples are prepared, a serial number alone on the label suffices. A log book of samples is kept with copies of the information on the labels as well as additional details. The samples are stored in a locked case or room fitted with shelves for displaying them.

QUESTIONS

1. What are the two main problems of soil sampling?

2. Explain the importance of the soil volume concept, as opposed to a soil area.

3. Define the three coordinates of the landscape, depth function, toposequence, slope.

4. State the principal sources of variability in soil chemical analysis.

5. How does the root spread of plants relate to composite sampling of soil?

6. List the requirements of a valid composite-sampling procedure.

7. How many soil cores should be composited to reduce the variability of the composite sample to the variability of the analytical results?

8. Outline the considerations you would employ in sampling soil profiles for chemical analyses.

9. Of what value are soil profile monoliths?

10. How is replication ordinarily obtained when sampling established experimental plots that are replicated?

11. Outline the sampling procedure used in experimental plot site selection.

12. Outline the procedure and precautions employed in sampling a farm field. A problem spot.

13. Why must precautions be taken not to dry soil samples previous to some types of analysis?

14. What precautions should be taken about grinding soil samples?

15. State the relationship of maximum particle size to subsample size.

3

Hydrogen Activity Determination for Soils

The active mass or activity as distinguished from the total amount present.

3–1. Perhaps the most important chemical property of soil as a medium for plant growth is its pH value or "hydrogen ion activity." So familiar is this to soil scientists that the term "soil pH value" is often interpreted as an *entity* without reference to its fundamental definition as interpreted from the voltage obtained with an electrode (¶ 3–9). Moreover, the activity in soils of the twelve or more other ions that enter into plant nutrition is highly dependent upon that of the hydrogen ion. The lime requirement of soils (¶ 4–64) depends upon the adjustment of the hydrogen ion activity and the associated activities of metallic cations and anions, although it also involves adjustment of the calcium and sometimes magnesium ion activities as such. Activities of several cations other than hydrogen have been measured[1] directly by a clay membrane method analogous to hydrogen ion activity measurement with a glass electrode.

3–2. Electrical Potential Measurement with a Potentiometer. The *electrical potential* of an electrochemical cell is measured with a *potentiometer*. The line *CD* (Fig. 3–1*a*) represents a uniform resistance wire of a potentiometer. *P* and *P'* are points of contact with the terminals of the standard cell *E*. The adjustable resistance, *R*, at *SC* is varied until the drop in potential from *D* to *C* is such that the potential drop between fixed points *P* and *P'* is just equal to the standard cell voltage (1.0183 volts in this example). The reading on galvanometer *G* is zero when this condition is

---

[1] Marshall, *J. Phys. Chem.*, 43:1555 (1939); 48:67 (1944); also McLean *et al.*, *Soil Sci.*, 72:315 (1951).

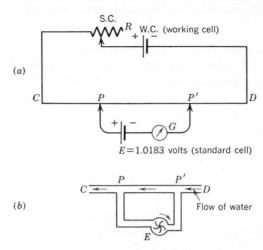

Fig. 3–1. Principle of the potentiometer: (*a*), electric circuit; (*b*), hydrologic analogy.

reached, indicating that the voltage from E exactly counterbalances any tendency for the current to flow through the circuit $P'GP$. Current from the working cell of course continues to flow through the path $DP'PC$.

3–3. The situation may be visualized by analogy to water pressure in the hydrologic system (Fig. 3–1*b*). No water will flow through the water wheel if the water wheel is turned by an external power source (analogous to the standard cell) at a rate which is just sufficient to offset the drop in pressure from P' to P. Water will continue to flow through the pipe PP'.

3–4. The space between P and P' (Fig. 3–1*a*) is divided off into a scale of 1018.3 equal units, and the voltage drop across each unit then becomes one millivolt. Since the potential of the glass or hydrogen electrode is directly proportional to the pH, the space between P and P' may be calibrated directly into a scale of pH units. It has been found that at 25°C each 59.16 millivolts (0.059 volts) corresponds to one pH unit (¶ 3–9).

3–5. The voltage of an unknown cell may be compared to the standard cell by the proportion of the two distances along the uniform resistance wire required just to balance the voltages of the two cells. Thus an unknown potential (as that from a glass electrode pH assembly) is substituted for the standard cell E and, with the setting at SC and P remaining constant, the contact point P' is moved along the slide wire CD until the galvanometer reading is again zero. (The movement of P' along the wire corresponds to the movement of the pH dial on the pH meter.) The spacing between the points P and P' when the balance against the unknown cell is obtained then represents either (a) the millivolts potential of the test cell or (b) the pH units, as read from the scales described. The details of operation of a given laboratory potentiometer should be obtained from the instructor or manufacturer.

3–6. Because some electric current is drawn from the test cell in the simple potentiometer during the time required to adjust the balance, it is not suited for the glass electrode pH meter (¶ 3–7). A vacuum tube circuit[2] is required to measure the glass electrode potential with practically no current drawn from the glass electrode.

3–7. The Glass Electrode pH Meter. The glass electrode generally used for pH measurement employs a *glass membrane* of special, chemically pure, soft (rapidly soluble, low melting point) glass.[3] For example, the composition of Corning 015 electrode glass is 72 per cent SiO_2, 6 per cent CaO,

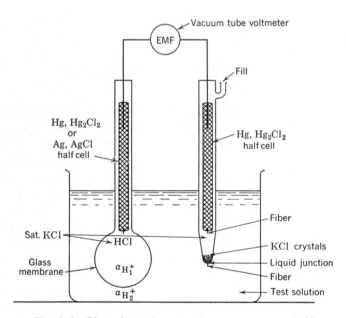

Fig. 3–2. Glass electrode system for measurement of pH.

and 22 per cent Na_2O. Across the glass membrane develops an electrical potential that is proportional to the difference in pH between the two sides, in accord with the concentration cell:[4]

$$\text{Hg, Hg}_2\text{Cl}_2\text{, KCl} \parallel \text{H}^+ (a_1) \mid \text{H}^+ (a_2) \parallel \text{KCl, Hg}_2\text{Cl}_2\text{, Hg} \qquad (3\text{--}1)$$
$$\text{(Sat.)} \qquad\qquad\qquad \text{(Sat.)}$$

[2] Daniels *et al., Experimental Physical Chemistry,* 4th ed. (New York: McGraw-Hill Book Company, Inc., 1949), p. 488.

[3] MacInnes and Dole, *J. Am. Chem. Soc.,* 52:29 (1930).

[4] Dole, *The Glass Electrode* (New York: John Wiley & Sons, Inc., 1941); Dole, *Measuring pH with the Glass Electrode,* Bul. 371 (Maywood, Ill.: Coleman Electric Co., 1937); also Haugaard, *J. Phys. Chem.,* 45:148 (1941).

in which ¦ is the glass membrane and ‖ is a liquid junction. The left calomel half-cell (often replaced by an Ag, AgCl electrode) is within the glass bulb (Fig. 3–2) and dips into the dilute acid of $a_{H_1}+$ that fills the glass bulb. The right calomel half-cell is the reference electrode that is separately placed in the outside solution of $a_{H_2}+$ that is to be measured. The voltage, E, of the glass electrode half-cell ideally is given by:

$$E = -0.05916 \log_{10} \frac{a_2}{a_1} \qquad (3\text{–}2)$$

in which 0.05916 is the function RT/nF and the ln-to-$\log_{10}$ conversion of 2.3026, $R = 8.313$, $F = 96,500$, $n = 1$ for H^+, and $T - 298°K$ (for 25°C.) An "asymmetric potential," E_{AP}, develops across the glass membrane even when solutions of the same H^+ ion activity are on the two sides. For this reason the meter must be calibrated with a standard buffer.

3–8. The glass electrode pH meter has the distinct advantages that it (a) does not expel dissolved gases such as CO_2 from the system under measurement, (b) is adaptable to thick fluids, pastes, gels, and colored solutions, (c) is not affected by oxidizing and reducing solutions in contrast to quinhydrone or hydrogen electrodes, (d) does not require H_2 gas or a catalytic surface required by the H electrode, or the addition of auxilliary material as the quinhydrone electrode, (e) has a relatively low salt error (except for Li and Na above pH 9.5), and (f) after standardization, gives an accuracy within 0.1 pH unit and with care, within 0.02 pH unit, and (g) is rapid, convenient, inexpensive, and adaptable for continuous recording.

MEASUREMENT OF SOIL pH

(Electrometrically by means of the glass electrode)

3–9. Soil pH Defined. Soil pH is conventionally defined by the equation:

$$\text{Soil pH} = \log \frac{1}{a_H+} = -\log {}_{10}a_H+ \qquad (3\text{–}3)$$

in which the activity of H^+ in the soil suspension, a_H+, is expressed as gm-ions per liter. The "effective" concentration of hydrogen ions includes all sources such as those arising by dissociation of soluble acids and those dissociated from soil particles. "Effective" is defined[5] in practical terms of the electrical potential (equation 3–2, ¶ 3–7) measured with the glass electrode applied to the soil system. Soil pH is measured almost exclusively by the glass electrode because of its advantages (¶ 3–8) over the hydrogen electrode or quinhydrone electrode.

3–10. Factors Affecting the Measurement of Soil pH. Because the soil

---

[5] Bates, *Electrometric pH Measurement* (New York: John Wiley & Sons, Inc., 1954), p. 31.

pH measure varies[6] widely with the method of preparation of a given soil, the details of the preparation procedure must be carefully specified with any soil pH data. In the preparation of the soil system the principal variables that affect the pH measurement are drying[7] of the soil sample in the preparation, the soil water content used, the content of soluble salts, the content of CO_2 as influenced by season[8] or drying, the amount of grinding given the soil, and the field variation from core to core—which is best handled by composite sampling (¶ 2–6).

3–11. Measurement of the pH soil samples directly in the field moist condition may be considered the most valid in terms of the *existing* soil-biological environment. Measurement of air-dried soil samples is the most convenient and generally used, and perhaps could be considered the standard procedure. There is reason to believe that certain soil chemical reactions are hastened by the drying process and that dried samples are therefore more nearly at equilibrium. Whether dried or field moist samples were employed for the soil pH determination should always be stated with the tabulated data.

3–12. Effect of Water Content on Soil pH Measured. In general, the more dilute the soil suspension, the higher the soil pH value found, whether the soil is acid or alkaline.[9] The rise in soil pH with dilution, from the sticky point to a soil : water ratio of 1 : 10 is usually of the order of 0.2 to 0.5 pH unit, but may be 1 or more pH units (Fig. 3–3) in certain neutral and alkaline soils.[10] A rise was observed[11] from pH 6.45 at 6.3 per cent moisture in a calcareous soil to pH 8.60 at a 1 : 5 soil : water ratio. An abrupt rise in pH occurs with alkaline soils (of pH 7.5 and above) just before the moisture saturation percentage (¶ 3–22) is reached. Thus dilution to the saturation percentage, although convenient in soil preparation and electrode insertion, involves some shift in pH for alkaline soils, though less than for greater dilutions often employed.

3–13. Junction Potential. According to some workers, an appreciable liquid junction potential, *Ej,* may occur at the liquid junction (Fig. 3–2), particularly in a very concentrated colloidal electrolyte suspension.[12] The liquid junction potential is kept low (nearly zero) and as constant as possible by the use of a saturated KCl solution (or sometimes NH_4NO_3 when

---

[6] Reed and Cummings, *Soil Sci.,* 59:97 (1945).

[7] McGeorge, *Ariz. Agr. Exp. Sta. Tech. Bul. 57* (1935) noted a rise of pH with drying calcareous soils; a rise was also observed in the author's laboratory with drying unlimed acid soils.

[8] Baver, *Soil Sci.,* 23:399 (1927).

[9] McGeorge, *Ariz. Agr. Exp. Sta. Tech. Bul. 78* (1938).

[10] Chapman *et al., S.S.S.A. Proc.,* 5:191 (1941).

[11] Huberty and Haas, *Soil Sci.,* 49:455 (1940).

[12] Jenny *et al., Sci.,* 112:164 (1950); Coleman *et al., S.S.S.A. Proc.,* 15:106 (1951). In disputation: Marshall, *S.S.S.A. Proc.,* 15:110; *Sci.,* 113:43 (1951), 115:361 (1952); and Peech and McDevit, *S.S.S.A. Proc.,* 15:112 (1951).

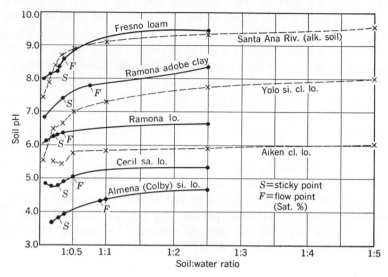

Fig. 3–3. Relation of observed soil pH values to soil : water ratio. (Solid lines from Chapman *et al., S.S.S.A. Proc.,* 5:191, 1941; dashed lines from Huberty and Haas, *Soil Sci.,* 49:455, 1940.)

K would interfere). The anion and cation of these salts have nearly equal mobilities in solution. The junction potential does not remain exactly constant even in solution systems because ions other than K and Cl are present in the junction to contribute to the transport of electrical charge. Any liquid junction potential acts additively to the potential caused by H^+ ions acting on the glass electrode. An increase in Ej with increase in soil suspension concentration would correspond to a decrease in apparently measured soil pH. To the extent that a liquid junction potential contributes to the lower pH measured in thick soil suspensions, it detracts from the arguments for measurement of the soil pH in thick suspensions in order to simulate field conditions.

APPARATUS

3–14. Needed apparatus includes a glass electrode pH meter with calomel reference electrode and salt bridge, 50-ml beakers, short stirring rods, spatula, and a distilled water wash bottle.

REAGENTS

3–15. Needed reagents are a standard buffer solution of pH 4.00 and buffers of other pH values in the range of the soil pH values expected, and saturated KCl (about 40 gm per 100 ml) for the bridge.

3–16. Standard Buffers. The standard pH 4.00 buffer for calibration is 0.05 M potassium biphthalate ($KHC_8H_4O_4$, mol. wt. 204.14). The reagent grade has a purity of 99.9 per cent or better, and is sufficiently non-hygroscopic to permit weighing without drying. A stock solution of 0.3 M is prepared by dissolving 61.2 gm of $KHC_8H_4O_4$ in one liter of hot water. Three drops of toluene are added to discourage mold growth. A dilution of 100 ml of the buffer with 500 ml of water results in a 0.05 M solution. Buffers of various pH values that meet National Bureau of Standards (Washington, D.C.) specifications can be obtained commercially (Leeds and Northrup, Philadelphia, Pa.). The "certified buffer tablets" of Coleman Electric (Maywood, Illinois) provide an accuracy of ±0.02 pH at 30°C when one is dissolved in 100 ml of distilled water. A 0.1 M KH-phthate solution of pH 3.98 has a wide tolerance of dilution without an appreciable change in pH (0.02 pH unit for 100 per cent dilution). Snell and Snell[13] state that pH 8.0 may be obtained by mixing 19.45 ml of 0.2 M Na_2HPO_4 with 0.55 ml of 0.1 M citric acid.

PROCEDURE

3–17. Preference is here given to pH determination at the moisture saturation percentage (¶ 3–22) because of the ease of routine wetting of various soils to "equipotential" moisture status. This soil moisture content is the highest likely to occur in the field. The moisture films are thick enough to give good contact with the glass electrode. Small changes in dilution cause little change in pH (¶ 3–12), so that only moderate care need be exercised in adjusting the water content of the soil for the pH measurement. This procedure has been used with facility in the routine soil testing laboratory. The use of a 1 : 1 soil : water ratio (¶ 3–25) is also common. The determination of the pH of a soil at various other moisture contents, from the sticky point to a 1 : 10 ratio, is considered (¶ 3–24) because of varying practices in different laboratories.

3–18. The Soil Sample. A composite soil sample (10 to 20 cores) is prepared, with avoidance of severe grinding,[14] and tested (¶ 3–22) at once or placed in a jar and sealed tightly to prevent contact with traces of ammonia and other laboratory fumes that would alter its pH.

3–19. Precautions in the Use of the Glass Electrode. The operational details for various instruments are obtained from the manufacturer's instructions. The glass electrode is fragile and subject to excessively rapid deterioration if not properly cared for. It is also expensive to replace. These precautions help:

---

[13] *Colorimetric Methods of Analysis,* Vol. 1 (New York: D. Van Nostrand Company, Inc., 1936), p. 677.

[14] Baver, *Soil Sci.,* 23:399 (1927), noted a 1.0 to 1.3 pH unit rise in soils of pH 4.7 as a result of grinding from 2 mm to 0.16 mm (100 meshes per inch).

1. The electrode is not allowed to remain in the test solution or suspension longer than necessary, especially if more alkaline than pH 9.

2. Immediately after testing, the electrode is washed off with a strong stream of distilled water from a wash bottle. If the system was alkaline, the electrode should be dipped for a few seconds in the acid pH buffer or dilute HCl to remove the film of $CaCO_3$ that sometimes forms.

3. For storage, after cleaning, the electrode is suspended in distilled water, and the system is protected from evaporation. Drying out of the electrode is avoided.

4. Failure of the glass electrode pH meter is indicated when, after standardization, it gives slow response to large pH changes. The glass electrode is immersed in an alkaline buffer, then in the original acid standard buffer. Readings of pH values a few tenths higher than the specified pH values of the standard after as little as 60 seconds equilibration indicates "etching" or an over-age glass membrane.

3–20. The temperature setting is adjusted, and a little KCl is passed from the junction followed by flushing with distilled water. Then the standard buffer, phthalate of pH 4.00, or another buffer of pH near that of the systems to be determined, is placed in the electrode vessel, and the glass electrode and calomel half-cell with KCl junction are immersed in the buffer. The instrument's pH dial is set at the known pH value of the standard buffer. After a suitable elapse of "warm-up" time, the instrument is balanced to eliminate the asymmetric potential. The buffer is removed, and the electrodes are carefully flushed off with water.

3–21. The pH Test. A test solution[15] or soil suspension (¶ 3–22) is now placed in the electrode vessel, and the pH dial is turned until galvanometer balance is reached. This test is repeated before each new sample is tested until stability is assured, then after each fifth determination. The pH meter is turned off when the series of readings is completed.

3–22. Water-Saturation Percentage[16] Preparation. A volume of approximately 40 ml of −2-mm or −4-mm soil is placed in a 50-ml beaker (which is about 0.7 filled with soil in lieu of weighing). Water is added to the soil in increments from a wash bottle. It is more convenient to prepare a series of several samples simultaneously. Successive increments of water are added *without stirring the soil* until water just wets the entire soil mass, then a few drops more are added slowly until the surface glistens slightly. Stirring of the soil is avoided until it is fully wetted to prevent forming of a puddled mass through which water moves only very slowly; most of the wetting is thus accomplished through the undisturbed pores. After this moisture content has been attained, the soil is stirred with a glass rod, and

---

[15] An instructive exercise on the glass electrode pH meter is to titrate 20 ml of 0.1 M H_3PO_4 with 0.1 N NaOH delivered from a buret, the pH being determined at frequent intervals as the titration proceeds.

[16] Richards, ed., *Diagnosis and Improvement of Saline and Alkali Soils,* U.S.D.A. Handb. 60 (1954), p. 17.

drops of water are added until the soil is a "thin paste" that just barely flows together to close around a hole left by the rod. The soil is now at the "moisture saturation percentage,"[17] an equipotential moisture content for soils (¶ 10–35). The surface of the water-saturated soil glistens, and air has been excluded. The soil is at the "flow point" or "liquid limit," or slightly wetter than the "upper plastic limit." The U.S. Salinity Laboratory allows the wetted soil to equilibrate for one hour before the pH measurement is made. For most practical soil testing, the pH reading may be taken right away.

3–23. The glass and calomel electrodes are inserted in the water-saturated soil, and the pH measurement is made. The glass electrode is moved about to insure removal of the water film around the electrode, and the pH reading is again taken. When the reading is constant or nearly so (the CO_2 status of some soils gradually changes with time and therefore undue delay should be avoided), the pH value is recorded. Whether field-moist or air-dried samples (¶ 3–11) were used is also recorded.

ALTERNATIVE PROCEDURES

3–24. Several alternative procedures, involving more concentrated or more dilute suspensions (¶ 3–12), are presented because each is widely employed in different laboratories, and fairly extensive pH changes occur with dilution. Stirring of water suspensions of soil is necessary[18] to keep the soil suspended during the pH measurement. Some methods involve the addition of a strong electrolyte or buffer.

3–25. Soil : Water Ratio of 1 : 1.[19] To a 20-gm sample of soil in a 50-ml beaker is added a 20-ml volume of distilled water. The suspension is stirred at regular intervals for about an hour. Then the pH is measured with the glass electrode, the suspension being stirred well just before immersing the electrode.

3–26. Soil : Water Ratio of 1 : 2.5.[20] To a 10-gm sample of soil in a 50-ml beaker is added a 25-ml volume of distilled water. The suspension is stirred at regular intervals for 20 to 30 minutes. Equilibrium can be attained in 5 minutes of continuous vigorous shaking with a reciprocating

---

[17] Scofield, U.S.D.A. Cir. 232 (1932).

[18] Bailey, *Soil Sci.,* 55:143 (1943); Miles and Reed, in *Diagnostic Techniques* (Washington, D.C.: American Potash Institute, 1948), p. 93.

[19] Biilman and Jensen, *Trans. 2nd Comm. Intern. Soc. Soil Sci.,* B:236 (1927); Purvis, *J.A.O.A.C.,* 23:219 (1940); Peech *et al., U.S.D.A. Cir.,* 757:5 (1947); Reed and Cummings, *Soil Sci.,* 59:103 (1945).

[20] Soil Reaction Committee, *Intern. Soc. Sci., Soil Res.,* 2:241 (1930). Hester, in *Diagnostic Techniques* (Washington, D.C.: American Potash Institute, 1948), p. 112, employed a 1:2 water ratio, and took 30 gm of soil in an effort to decrease the possibility of soil heterogeneity.

mechanical shaker. Then the pH is measured with the glass electrode, the suspension being stirred well just before the electrode is immersed.

3–27. Soil : Water Ratio of 1 : 5.[21] To a 20-gm soil sample in a flask, 100 ml of aerated distilled water is added and the soil is stirred for one hour. The pH value is then determined within 60 seconds after the glass electrode is immersed in the freshly shaken suspension.

3–28. Soil : Water Ratio of 1 : 10. To a 10-gm soil sample in a flask, 100 ml of distilled water is added and the soil is agitated for one hour. The pH value is then determined with the glass electrode. The pH of the 1 : 10 suspension is termed the "hydrolytic pH value" by McGeorge.[22] The hydrolytic pH value increases with degree of Na-saturation. The 1 : 10 measurement has the advantage that all Na-saturated soils have the same pH value regardless of exchange capacity (whereas the pH of Na soils are not the same at the sticky point).

3–29. Soil : Water Ratio of 1 : 2 in 0.01 M CaCl$_2$.[23] To mask the variability in salt content of soils, to maintain the soil in a flocculated condition, and to decrease the junction potential effect (¶ 3–13), the soil pH measurement is made in 0.01 M CaCl$_2$ solution. Twenty-five gm of soil is suspended in 50 ml of 0.01 N CaCl$_2$ solution and the suspension is stirred thoroughly. The pH measurement is then made in the usual way. The soil pH scale is shifted downward in this solution. Acid soils range from pH 4 to 5.0, pH 6 is the optimum pH of limed soils, and calcareous soils run pH 6.9 to 7.1 in the CaCl$_2$ solution.

3–30. Soil : Water Ratio of 1 : 2.5 with 1 N KCl Present. Because leached soils showed little change in pH with dilution, the effect of dilution was attributed[24] to the presence of small amounts of salts. To overcome large relative changes in salt content, 1 N KCl was added. The observed pH values were 1.5 units lower than those obtained in water suspension. Varying soil : water ratios were employed from 1 : 2.5 to 1 : 25, and the dilution had to be stated because the pH changed 0.6 to 1.0 unit with dilution even in the presence of 1 N KCl.

3–31. To a 10-gm soil sample in a 50-ml beaker, a 25-ml volume of 1 N KCl is added and the soil is stirred intermittently for one hour. The pH is measured with a glass electrode.

3–32. Isohydric pH Value.[25] The isohydric pH value of a soil is that of a buffer solution that shows no change in reaction on coming into contact

---

[21] Division of Soils, C.S.I.R. Australia method, according to Piper, *Soil and Plant Analysis* (New York: Interscience Publishers, Inc., 1944), p. 9.
[22] *Soil Sci.,* 59:271 (1945).
[23] Schofield and Taylor, *S.S.S.A. Proc.,* 19:164 (1955).
[24] Puri and Asghar, *Soil Sci.,* 46: 249 (1938).
[25] Puri and Sarap, *Soil Sci.,* 46:49 (1938).

with the soil and "which consequently brings about no change in the base content of the soil." A series of buffers (HOAc-KOAc in the acid range; H_3BO_3, KCl, and KOH in the alkaline range) are equilibrated with soil samples for a period of 2 hours. A 1 : 5 soil : buffer ratio is employed (no difference is found up to 1 : 20). The isohydric pH can thus be obtained by determining the pH of the series and interpolating the isohydric pH value.

3–33. Sticky Point Method.[26] Approximately 40-gm of soil is placed in a 50-ml beaker. (The beaker may be about 0.7 filled with soil in lieu of weighing.) Water is added in increments from a wash bottle, the soil being allowed to imbibe each increment before the next is added, until only about 5 or 10 ml of the soil remains unwetted. About one minute is allowed for wetting to take place, while other soils in a series are being processed. Then the soil is stirred and puddled with a spatula to make a stiff paste. The "sticky point"[27] is reached when the soil is just wet enough to stick firmly to a spatula pressed to the soil mass and pulled directly away from it. The soil remains "sticky" on the wet side of the sticky point, so this moisture content should be approached from the dry side. If the soil is too dry, additional drops of water are added, the soil is stirred, and the "sticky point" test is repeated. A definite threshold force is required to break ("click") the spatula away from the soil when the sticky point is reached. More soil may be added if the sticky point moistness is exceeded. Clay soils, which usually exhibit considerable rigidity at the sticky point moisture content, were moistened slightly more by Chapman, *et al.,* to make them soft enough to facilitate insertion of the glass electrode.

3–34. The soil paste is equilibrated for 10 minutes. Then a slit is opened in it with a spatula, the glass electrode and salt bridge are inserted and the paste is formed to cover the active portions of the electrodes completely and left 60 seconds for "conditioning" of the electrode. The pH value is then read and checked for constancy.

AVERAGE SOIL pH VALUES

3–35. The basis for the use of average soil pH values lies in the observation that:

$$\text{Soil pH, composite sample} = \frac{\text{Soil pH, cores (or subcomposites)}}{n} \qquad (3\text{–}4)$$

in which n is the number of separate pH values of cores also represented in the composite sample. The right hand expression in equation 3–4 is the average of soil pH values. Some opposition to the averaging of pH values

---

[26] Chapman *et al., S.S.S.A. Proc.,* 5:196 (1941).
[27] Keen and Coutts, *J. Agr. Sci.,* 18:740 (1928).

exists because their being $\log a_H{}^+$. Actually many useful (and frequently averaged) parameters have exponential relationships to other variables. (The average soil pH value, incidentally, is the *geometric mean* $a_H{}^+$.) The relationship expressed by equation 3–4 is supported to an accuracy of 0.02 pH unit by published data[28] and by the data of L. F. Marriott of this laboratory with limed and unlimed Plainfield sand soil samples. As would therefore be expected, averaging soil pH values gives a good estimate of the meq of exchangeable hydrogen and lime requirement of an acid soil; such estimate is *very much* better than average $a_H{}^+$. This conclusion is equivalent to the often noted fact that the portion of the pH titration curve involved in calculation of lime needs of a given soil approximates a straight line. Chapman *et al.,* placed two samples of soil, one acid and one alkaline, on two sides of the glass electrode bulb. The pH value read was the arithmetic mean of the two soil pH values. The soil pH value of a composite sample or of an individual soil core is evidently the arithmetic mean pH value of the various kinds of soil particles in a sample, such as of calcite or feldspar (alkaline) and kaolinite or allophane (normally acid).

COLORIMETRIC pH INDICATORS USEFUL IN SOIL ANALYSIS

3–36. A colorimetric pH indicator is an organic dye, the color of which is controlled by the hydrogen ion activity in solution. During analytical determinations they provide a continuous check on solution pH. They are useful in rapid testing of soil pH (¶ 13–91) in the field and laboratory. A set of the most useful and sensitive pH indicators (Table 3–1) may well be prepared at one time, and stocked in the laboratory in a convenient dropper bottle rack.

3–37. Color Range and Critical pH. The shift in pH indicator color results from a reaction of the dye with ions of the solution. Many indicator dyes form weakly colored, little dissociated acids and highly colored, strongly dissociated salts of metallic cations. Weak base forming indicators, such as methyl red, are strongly colored in acid solutions. The full color range of almost every colorimetric pH indicator is approximately the same, namely ± one pH unit from midcolor for ±90 per cent of the color change (Fig. 3–4), as determined by spectrophotometric color analysis[29] of indicator titration curves. This fact arises from the relationship of color to dissociation constant, K, of the indicator molecule. For example, a tenfold increase in $[H^+]$ (one pH unit decrease) changes the concentration ratio of [salt]/[acid] by 10/100, or roughly 90 per cent toward a complete change to acid color. The uniformity of behavior of pH indicators permits

---

[28] Chapman *et al., S.S.S.A. Proc.,* 5:191 (1941).
[29] Kolthoff, *Colorimetric and Potentiometric Determination of pH* (New York: John Wiley & Sons, Inc., 1931), p. 26.

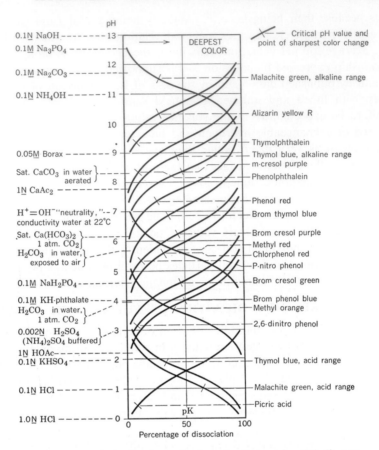

Fig. 3–4. Critical pH values of selected colorimetric pH indicators, shown on titration curves in relation to degree of dissociation and pK values. Data adapted in part from Clark, *Determination of Hydrogen Ions,* Ed. 2, Williams and Wilkins, Baltimore, Md. (1923); Snell and Snell, *Colorimetric Methods of Analysis,* Vol. 1, p. 683, Van Nostrand, New York (1936); Mellon, *Colorimetry for Chemists,* p. 33, G. F. Smith Chem. Co., Columbus, O. (1945); "Manual of Methods for Pure Culture Study of Bacteria," *Soc. Amer. Bact., Leaf.,* 9:8 (1941); and from the data of the author (1946).

the *identification* (Fig. 3–5) *of each indicator by a critical property,* the pH of most pronounced color change, termed the "critical pH value".[30] The critical pH value lies 0.1 to 0.3 pH unit from the pK value toward the weaker color for 2-color indicators and 0.6 to 1.0 pH unit toward the colorless side for the single color indicators. The pH value of a solution can be estimated visually by the increment of indicator color change from

---

[30] This is preferable to listing a pH range, which involves arbitrary assignment of numbers to the two asymptotic ends.

that at a critical pH, and thus *dependence on a color chart is eliminated* for most purposes.

REAGENTS

3–38. Aqueous Solutions of the Sulfonphthaleins (0.04 Per Cent). Aqueous solutions of the sulfonphthaleins and similarly acting dyes (No. 2, 3, 6-8, 11-14, and 18) are prepared by dissolution of 0.4 gm of the dry indicator powder (acid dye) in 5 to 15 ml (Table 3–1) of 0.1 N

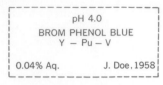

Fig. 3–5. Specimen label for colorimetric pH indicator bottle, with critical pH value (pH 4.0, midcolor, Pu = purple) used as central identification. The color changes are indicated for more acid side (Y = yellow) to the less acid side (V = violet).

NaOH by trituration in an agate mortar. An hour or more may be required. Although the process may be hastened by the addition of 10 ml 95 per cent ethanol, an aqueous solution is preferred. The low surface tension of the alcoholic solutions is generally a disadvantage, and the Na salts of sulfonphthalein type dyes are water soluble. The solution is washed into a 2-liter beaker, diluted to 1 liter, and then HCl or NaOH is added dropwise to bring the indicator to the midpoint or critical pH (¶ 3–37). The color change is more easily observed in a dilute solution, and therefore the color is judged as a drop diluted with distilled water on a spot plate.

3–39. Caution. These indicator solutions will be contaminated with Na and Cl ions. Other anions and cations should be scrupulously kept out. For work involving determination of Na or Cl especially prepared indicators are used, for example, alcoholic solutions of the acidic dyes.

3–40. Aqueous Solutions of the Nitrophenols (0.25 Per Cent). Aqueous solutions are prepared of the nitrophenols (mono, di, tri, or picric acid; Nos. 1, 4, and 10) by dissolution of 2.5 gm of the acid in 1000 ml of distilled water, warming it on the steam plate. These indicators are ordinarily left acid. However, for special work it may be desirable to adjust the pH to the critical pH value by dropwise addition of dilute NaOH.

3–41. Alcoholic Solutions of the Phthaleins (0.2 to 1 Per Cent). Alcoholic rather than water solutions of the phthaleins (phenolphthalein, thymolphthalein, Nos. 15 and 16) are required because, even with some NaOH, the phthalein indicators are extremely insoluble in water, and tend to precipitate out. The alcoholic solutions are prepared by dissolution of 2.0 to 10 gm of the dry indicator powder (acid dye) in 1000 ml of 95 per cent ethanol. For phenolphthalein, 1 per cent or 10 gm per 1000 ml is prepared. For thymolphthalein, 0.2 per cent or 2.0 gm per 1000 ml is satisfactory.

3–42. Water Solution of the Sodium Salt Dyes. The water soluble sodium salt forms of methyl orange (No. 5) and alizarin yellow R are available (No. 18); the solutions are prepared by simple solution of the salts in water at the concentrations listed (Table 3–1).

TABLE 3–1

Selected list of colorimetric pH indicators useful in soil analysis.* The following abbreviations designate colors:
B = blue; C = colorless; G = green; O = orange; P = pink; Pu = purple; R = red; V = violet;
Y = yellow. The complete set includes 17 indicators, since Nos. 16 and 19 repeat Nos. 3 and 2

Common name	Chemical name	Critical pH value†	Color change (center color is at critical pH value)	Mol. wt.	NaOH† 0.1 N (ml)	Indicator concentration to use (per cent)
1. Picric acid	2,4,6=Trinitrophenol	0.4	C-Y-Y	299	**	0.25
2. Malachite green	Phenyl di-p-dimethyl amino phenyl carbinol	1.0§	Y-YG-BG	373	10.7	0.04
3. Thymol blue	Thymol sulfonphthalein	1.9	R-O-Y	466	8.6	0.04
4. Dinitrophenol	2,6=Dinitrophenol (or 2,4)	3.1 (2.7)	C-Y-Y	184	**	0.25
5. Methyl orange	Dimethylamineazobenzene sodium sulfcnate	3.7§	R-Y-O		**	0.1
6. Brom phenol blue	Tetrabromo-phenol sulfonphthalein	4.0	Y-Pu-V	669	6.0	0.04
7. Brom cresol green	Tetrabromo-m-cresol sulfonphthalein	4.6	Y-G-B	698	5.7	0.04
8. Chlor phenol red	Dichloro-phenol sulfonphthalein	5.6§	Y-OP-V	423	9.5	0.04
9. Methyl red	Dimethylamino-azo-benzene o-carboxylic acid	5.7§	R-O-Y	269	††	0.125‡‡
10. P-nitrophenol (m-)	P-nitrophenol (m-)	5.2 (6.7)	C-Y-Y	139	**	0.25
11. Brom cresol purple	Dibromo-o-cresol sulfonphthalein	6.2	Y-Pu-V	540	7.4	0.04
12. Brom thymol blue	Dibromo-thymol sulfonphthalein	6.9	Y-G-B	624	6.4	0.04
13. Phenol red	Phenol sulfonphthalein	7.3§	Y-RO-V	354	11.3	0.04
14. m-Cresol purple	m-Cresol sulfonphthalein	8.3§	Y-O-R	382	10.5	0.04
15. Phenolphthalein	Phenolphthalein	8.3	C-P-P	318	††	1.0
16. Thymol blue	(See No. 3)	8.9	Y-Pu-BV	466	8.6	0.04
17. Thymolphthalein	Thymolphthalein	9.4	C-B-B	430	††	0.2
18. Alizarin yellow R	Nitrobenzene-azo-salicylic acid	10.3	Y-O-R	287	13.9	0.04
19. Malachite green	(See No. 2)	11.5§§	BG-BG-C	373	10.7	0.04

* These indicators were selected on the basis of laboratory experience, from the more extensive lists of Clark and Lubs, Cohen, and the Eastman Kodak Co.

† *The critical pH value* is that found with the glass electrode at the point of sharpest color change of the indicator. A knowledge of this characteristic value *decreases dependence on a color chart* for indicator interpretation. The end colors are fully developed within 1 pH unit from the critical pH value and are rather well developed within 0.6 to 0.8 pH unit of it. Thus the color shift may be subdivided mentally into 3 or 4 color segments to obtain 0.2 pH unit precision.

‡ Required to convert 0.4 gm to Na-salt.

§ Color change is not sharp; critical pH value represents midpoint of color change.

** Dissolved in water.

†† The acid form dissolved in 95 per cent ethanol.

‡‡ A brighter Pu-B-G color change is obtained with 0.8 per cent methylene blue chloride added.

§§ Decolorizes above pH 11 5, irreversibly.

3–43. Alcoholic Solutions of Methyl Red Mixed Indicators. *Methyl red-methylene blue* indicator (critical pH 5.6, G-C-Pu) is made by dissolution of 1.2 gm of methyl red and 0.8 gm methylene blue chloride in 1000 ml of 95 per cent ethanol. This mixture is especially adapted to acid base titrations in which only a small amount of CO_2 is likely to be present, as in the case of the Kjeldahl method for nitrogen.

Brom cresol green-methyl red indicator (critical pH 4.53, R-G-B) is made by dissolution of 5 gm of brom cresol green and 1.0 gm of methyl red in 1000 ml of 95 per cent ethanol and neutralization to midcolor with drops of 1 N NaOH (¶ 8–10).

3–44. Indicator Test Papers. Filter paper strips soaked in various of the indicators (*e.g.*, litmus paper) or their mixtures may be inserted in solution or in contact with a paste to test pH. A complete set is sold as "Hydrion" papers (Micro Essentials Laboratories, Brooklyn). Indicator paper strips carrying a printed color chart are available (A. Daigger Co., Chicago 10).

PROCEDURE

3–45. Choice of pH Indicator for a Specific Use. For the colorimetric determination of a soil pH, an indicator is chosen with a critical pH value as close as possible to the pH to be measured. In some systems this is unique, as for example, brom cresol purple for the pH 6.4 NH_4OH separation (¶ 11–136). From superficial consideration, pH 7 is often chosen as the end point for acid-base neutralization reactions, but further study shows that end points in specific titrations may be anywhere from pH 3 to 9, or even outside this range. Standardization of NaOH solution by neutralization of standard KH-phthalate requires titration to pH 8.3 (phenolphthalein). If CO_2 is to be produced, as in standardization of HCl against Na_2CO_3, and is to be boiled out, an indicator of critical pH 4 to 5 (brom phenol blue or methyl red) should be used, but if CO_2 is not to be boiled out, a critical pH of 3 (methyl orange or dinitrophenol) is more appropriate. Use of a critical pH of 7 to 8 is just as accurate finally after CO_2 is removed, but makes the end point laborious to find (Fig. 3–6). Boiling only once permits finding the end point with brom phenol blue, but boiling may need to be repeated 4 or more times with phenolphthalein (pH 8.3), or brom thymol blue (pH 7.0).

3–46. An Exercise on the Use of pH Indicators. The various pH indicators (Table 3–1) determine the pH value of each of a number of solutions prepared by mixing 1 gm of various salts with 100 ml of water (Table 3–2). Some of the materials are not soluble enough to go entirely into solution. The pH values are also checked by means of the glass electrode (¶ 3–21).

3–47. The pH value found in each solution is to be explained by means of ionization and hydrolysis equations.

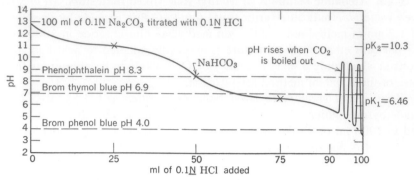

Fig. 3–6. Use of indicator with a critical pH of 4.0 or below is advantageous in a titration of a carbonate with acid.

TABLE 3–2

Determined pH values of various solutions prepared with
1 gm of solid mixed with 100 ml of water

Salt	Name of appropriate pH indicator	pH value, found by indicator	pH value, by glass electrode
1. $KHSO_4$			
2. $NaHCO_3$			
3. $NaCl$			
4. Na_2CO_3			
5. $CaCO_3$			
6. $CaSO_4 \cdot 2\ H_2O$			
7. $Ca(H_2PO_4)_2 \cdot H_2O$			
8. $Ca_2(HPO_4)_2 \cdot 4\ H_2O$			
9. $FeCl_3 \cdot 6\ H_2O$			

OXIDATION-REDUCTION INDICATORS USEFUL IN SOIL ANALYSIS

3–48. To complete the discussion of colorimetric indicators, the 3 most valuable colorimetric oxidation-reduction indicators must be included, although they are not clearly a part of hydrogen ion activity measurement. Colorimetric oxidation-reduction indicators are available to detect rapid shifts in the oxidation potential of solutions employed in analysis. The midpoint of the oxidation-reduction indicator color change is analogous to the critical pH change of the pH indicators. In the oxidation-reduction indicators, the shift in color occurs at a specific oxidation potential (Table 3–3). Either diphenylamine or "Ferroin" is employed in the chromic acid methods for organic matter (¶ 9–54, 9–67); "Ferroin" is employed for sulfato-cerate titrations (¶ 5–43, 6–49).

3–49. When solutions are highly colored, the use of colorimetric indicators is difficult. Potentiometric measurement of the endpoint is then more appropriate. A special "magic eye" potentiometric endpoint indicator has been offered (G. F. Smith Chemical Co., Columbus, Ohio).

TABLE 3–3

Three useful colorimetric oxidation-reduction indicators*

Indicator	Color change upon oxidation	Oxidation potential at color change*	Preparation of solution
1. Methylene blue	Blue to colorless	—0.53 (pH 2.86)	0.2 gm per 100 ml of H_2O
2. Diphenylamine	Colorless to violet	—0.76	1 gm in 100 ml of concentrated H_2SO_4
3. "Ferroin" (Orthophenanthroline ferrous complex)	Red to faint blue	—1.06	1.487 gm with 0.695 gm $FeSO_4$. $7 H_2O$ in 100 ml of H_2O.

* Numerical values from Smith and Richter, *Phenanthroline and Substituted Phenanthroline Indicators* (Columbus, Ohio: 1944), C. F. Smith Chemical Co., pp. 28–29.

3–50. Starch Indicator for Iodimetry. One gm of soluble starch is stirred in 5 ml of cold water in a beaker. The resulting smooth suspension is poured with constant stirring into 100 ml of boiling water containing 3 gm of boric acid preservative. This solution is cooled and transferred to a 100-ml scalded dropper bottle provided with a 2- or 3-ml calibrated dropper. The bottle is stored in a dark, cool place. A 2- or 3-ml portion of the indicator is transferred into the solution to be titrated (for example, stannous chloride, ¶ 7–19) and as the 0.1 N I_2 solution is titrated in, blue color first appears in the droplets and disappears until at the end (slight excess I_2 present) a deep blue color appears throughout the solution.

QUESTIONS

1. Why is the measurement of soil pH fundamental to the study of soil-plant relationships?

2. Identify the contents of the glass electrode and the associated components of its electrochemical cell.

3. Write the fundamental equation relating electrical potential of a cell containing a glass electrode to activities of hydrogen in solution, defining the terms.

4. State the advantages of the glass electrode for measurement of soil pH.

5. What is the effect of drying soils on the pH value measured?

6. What is the effect observed on the pH of making the soil suspension more dilute, and what is the relationship to a possible liquid junction potential?

7. Why is it necessary to use a standard pH buffer in connection with the glass electrode?

8. Explain why the average soil pH value rather than the mean activity of hydrogen is often the most valuable datum. (Consider the use of soil pH value as an estimate of liming need.)

9. Discuss the way in which colorimetric pH indicators respond to change in solution pH, employing the dissociation constant concept.

10. What is the critical pH value of an indicator and how does it aid in finding the pH of a test solution from the observed color?

11. What are the different general classes of methods of preparing pH indicator solutions?

12. Discuss the basis of choice of an indicator pH range in relation to titrations of different specific kinds of acids and hydroxides.

4

Cation Exchange
Determinations for Soils

The cation exchange reaction is the second most important in nature, surpassed in fundamental importance only by the photosynthetic process of green plants.

—MARSHALL[1]

4–1. Cation exchange in soils[2] has long been of interest to soil chemists. Cation exchange determinations for soils include the measurement of the cation exchange *capacity* of soils and soil colloids, the measurement of the *total* exchangeable metallic cations and percentage exchange saturation of soils, the measurement of the percentage of saturation with *alkali* cations and the gypsum or sulfur requirement of soils, and finally the measurement of exchangeable *hydrogen* and the lime requirement of soils. Neutralizing *equivalence* of limestone and other liming materials must also be considered in raising the percentage saturation of soils by liming. The cation exchange *status* with respect to groups of cations is the concern of the present chapter, whereas the determination of the amounts and ratios of individual metallic cation species is the subject of following chapters.

4–2. Washing Techniques. Cation exchange or removal of excess salt from a soil or colloid is effected by continuous or repeated washings. Continuous washing may be done with a percolation device such as a funnel, Gooch crucible, fritted glass crucible or leaching tube (¶ 4–10). Repeated washing may be done by repeatedly dispersing the sample in fresh portions of liquid and removing the liquid with a centrifuge (¶ 4–3) or a clay filter

---

[1] *Colloids in Agriculture* (London: Edward Arnold & Co., 1935).

[2] Kelley, *Cation Exchange in Soils* (New York: Reinhold Publishing Corporation, 1948).

(Norton Refractories, Worcester, Mass.). Washing can also be done by changing the solution about a dialysis sack.

4–3. Centrifuge Washing of a Sample. In the centrifuge washing procedure, each washing of a sample consists of the following steps:

1. The washing solution (acid, salt, water, or acetone solution) is added to the tube containing the sample in a volume ratio of at least 6 of the solution to 1 of the bulk volume of the sample cake. The procedure depends upon a cumulative dilution, which at the rate of 1 to 5 for each washing effects a dilution to less than 0.1 per cent in 5 washings.

2. The tube is stoppered and shaken by hand or mechanically until the sample is well dispersed. Samples that are resistant to dispersion by this method are triturated with a rubber ball supported on a thick glass rod, with short strokes to prevent splashing.

3. The stopper (or ball) and sides of the tube are washed down with water or the organic solvent, whichever is being used in the washing solution. In so doing, the stopper is lifted slightly to break its seal, but is left in place. Then a very fine stream of the solvent is delivered from a pressure wash bottle onto the juncture of the tube and stopper. The stopper is raised and lowered slightly and then removed, as a film of solvent sweeps down the sides of the tube. Too thick a layer of solvent over the washing solution is avoided, as it interferes with decantation later.

4. If the solvent is water or alcohol, the tube is placed for 1 to 5 minutes in a hot water bath to hasten flocculation. *Caution:* Any open flames are removed from the vicinity if an organic solvent is being employed.

5. The tube is centrifuged at 2100 to 2600 rpm (1800 rpm for tubes more than half full in the International No. 2 centrifuge) for 5 minutes to clear the suspension. The centrifuge is allowed to coast to a halt without braking, to avoid disturbing the cake.

6. The clear supernatant liquid is decanted with caution so that the tube is held in a position that permits observation of the entire clear liquid. When the meniscus strikes the cake, a little solid may be dislodged, and if so, the decantation should be stopped before the solid leaves the tube. The tube is righted abruptly, and a second pouring is never attempted without recentrifugation.

4–4. The excess salt is washed out with solvents such as water, alcohol, acetone. The washing solvent must be free of electrolyte or part of the exchangeable cation will be displaced. Alcohol, for example, should be free of organic acids. A former practice of neutralizing ethanol with NH_4OH to pH 7 (as measured by indicators or pH meter) is considered[3] undesirable because the pH measurement is not accurate in an alcoholic system (brom thymol blue turns yellow in alcohol in the absence of free acid), and *especially* because some exchangeable cation would be introduced in the washing solution. Distillation of alcohol after the addition of $Ca(OH)_2$ is a satisfactory procedure of freeing it from acids and other electrolytes.

4–5. Dispersion During Washing. As the excess of soluble electrolyte is

---

[3] Peech *et al.,* U.S.D.A. Cir. 757 (1947); Swindale and Fieldes, *Soil Sci.,* 74:287 (1952).

removed, the colloidal material tends to disperse, more so in water than in nearly anhydrous organic solvents. With monovalent ion saturations (particularly with Na) the tendency for dispersion is great even in anhydrous organic solvents. With divalent ion saturations, the tendency toward dispersion is less. Dispersion results in the colloid remaining suspended in the washing solvent after centrifugation, or passing through the filter (but not through dialysis sacks). Dispersion during washing is best prevented by one or more of the following: (a) selecting a less dispersive cation, (b) selecting the solvent, particularly using as low a concentration of water in the organic solvent as possible, (c) keeping the volume of solvent at a minimum in the third and successive washings, (d) rewashing the small fraction dispersed in small pointed tubes after reflocculation, and (e) as a last resort, removing the salts by simple dialysis in a sack, recognizing that some hydrolysis of cation occurs. Dialysis may be effected with a Cellophane or Visking sack made of commercial tubing, or with a Collodian sack.

CATION EXCHANGE CAPACITY DETERMINATION

4–6. Soil mineral and organic colloidal particles have negative valence charges that hold dissociable cations, and thus are "colloidal electrolytes" as defined in 1912.[4] The cation exchange capacity determination involves measuring the total quantity of negative charges per unit weight of the material. The amount of cation exchange capacity measured varies somewhat according to the nature of the cation employed, concentration of the salt, and the equilibrium pH (¶ 4–8). This measurement should not be thought of as highly exact, but rather as an equilibrium measurement under the conditions chosen. This fact led to the statement, "Next to lime requirement no other soil constant, perhaps, is so widely used and yet so little understood as 'base' exchange capacity."[5]

4–7. The cation exchange capacity is usually measured by leaching the soil or colloid with a 1 N salt solution buffered at a neutral or slightly alkaline pH value, and then washing out the excess salts with an electrolyte-free solvent. The buffer function, of course, may be as separate washings, followed by washings with a salt of the metallic cation employed for saturation. For example, the buffer washing may be with a NaOAc solution, and the saturating metallic cation may then be furnished from a 1 N $CaCl_2$ solution (¶ 4–20). Salts of a strongly dissociated acid are not satisfactory unless a buffer washing precedes. Thus NH_4Cl was shown[6] not to saturate acid soils completely because the reaction:

$$NH_4Cl + HX = HCl + NH_4X \qquad (4\text{–}1)$$

[4] McBain, *Sci.,* 109:291 (1949); Marshall and Krinbill, *J. Phys. Colloid Chem.,* 46:1077 (1942).

[5] Puri and Uppal, *Soil Sci.,* 47:245 (1939).

[6] Parker, *J. Am. Soc. Agron.,* 21:1030 (1929).

in which X is the soil exchange complex, is kept from completion by the activity of the HCl produced. Pretreatment was given the soil with $Ba(OH)_2$, or, better, with $Ba(OAc)_2$ to avoid the "artificial" increase[7] in exchange capacity caused by $Ba(OH)_2$ (¶ 4–52). Use of NaOAc for pretreatment (¶ 4–20) or for saturation (¶ 4–23) provides the same advantage and eliminates difficulties of precipitation of carbonate or sulfate of barium. Normal acetate salts of monovalent ions usually dissolve only traces of organic matter from soils, in solutions having pH values in the range from 7 to 8.3.

4–8. Because of the wide recommendation of liming soils to the pH range near 7, determination of cation exchange capacities at this reference pH has long been popular. Recent trends toward extraction of exchangeable hydrogen (¶ 4–50) at pH values of 8.1 to 8.3 has renewed interest in the determination of the cation exchange capacity at the same reference pH. There is some evidence that the use of a 1 N salt solution of any metallic cation that forms a strong base, strongly buffered at any pH from 4 to 9, tends to measure a constant amount[8] of exchange capacity except for specific fixation reactions (¶ 4–9). This fact is attributable to the effect of the large mass of metallic cations compared to hydrogen ions in the salt solution. Cations that form weak bases tend to give lower or higher exchange capacity. For example, a lower cation exchange capacity was determined by 1 N NH_4OAc of pH 7 than with $BaCl_2$-triethanolamine of pH 8.1 for kaolinitic soils[9] and soils with 2 : 1 types of clay.[10] With cations such as Cu, Zn, Al, and Fe, a higher cation exchange capacity was measured[11] than with cations of strong bases.

4–9. An extremely large number of "methods" for determining the cation exchange capacity of colloidal electrolytes is provided by different combinations of pretreatment, cation, salt, solvent, washing procedure, and determinative technique for the ions (¶ 4–22). Calcium[12] may be considered the standard because it is the most abundant exchangeable metallic cation in the majority of near neutral soils. Potassium[13] has the advantage

---

[7] Magistad, *J. Am. Soc. Agron.*, 21:1045 (1929).

[8] DeMumbrum and Jackson, *S.S.S.A. Proc.*, 20:334 (1956); also pointed out by Piper, *Soil and Plant Analysis* (New York: Interscience Publishers, Inc., 1944), p. 165.

[9] Mehlich, *Soil Sci.*, 60:289 (1945).

[10] Pratt and Holowaychuk, *S.S.S.A. Proc.*, 18:365 (1954).

[11] Lutz, *S.S.S.A. Proc.*, 3:7 (1939); Bower and Truog, *S.S.S.A. Proc.*, 5:86 (1941); Sieling, *J. Am. Soc. Agron.*, 33:24 (1941); Menzel and Jackson, *S.S.S.A. Proc.*, 15:122 (1951); DeMumbrum and Jackson, *Soil Sci.*, 81:353 (1956).

[12] Kappan, *Trans. 2nd Comm. Intern. Soc. Soil Sci.* (Gronigen) B:179 (1927); Truog and Drosdoff, *Trans. 3rd Intern. Congr. Soil Sci.*, 1:106 (1935); Bradfield and Allison, *Trans. Intern. Soc. Soil Sci.*, A:63 (1933); Jackson and Truog, *S.S.S.A. Proc.*, 4:137 (1940).

[13] Rendig, *S.S.S.A. Proc.*, 12:449 (1948); Swindale and Fieldes, *Soil Sci.*, 74:287 (1952).

over Ca of greater sensitivity with the flame emission spectrophotometer; also K has less tendency to cause soil dispersion than Na (¶ 4–23). Fixation by vermiculite of potassium (¶ 6–79) and ammonium (¶ 4–25) ions makes the exchange capacity lower with these ions than with nonfixing ions.

APPARATUS

4–10. Needed apparatus for rapid semimicro determinations of cation exchange capacity includes 100-ml centrifuge tubes (or smaller tubes for small samples) and International No. 2 or other suitable centrifuge (in lieu of centrifuge washing, the sample may be washed in the special small carbon funnels, Fig. 4–1, or in fritted glass or asbestos crucibles, or in an

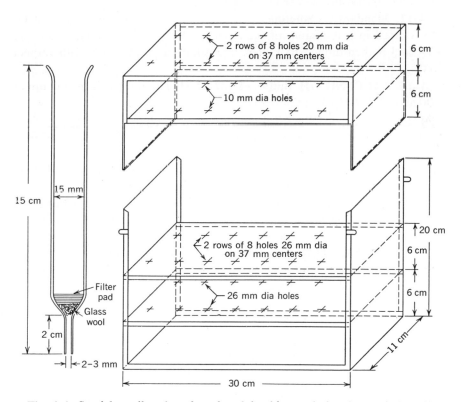

Fig. 4–1. Special small carbon funnel and leaching rack for the semimicro filter tube method of washing sample for exchange capacity. (After Swindale and Fieldes, *Soil Sci.,* 74:287, 1952; drawing courtesy of Dr. L. D. Swindale.)

ordinary funnel with filter paper), a 250-ml beaker, a 500-ml conical flask, a 25-ml pipette, and a buret for the standard Versene for Ca determination (or flame emission spectrophotometer suitable for Ca determination, ¶ 18–21).

4–11. Needed reagents are 1 N NaOAc adjusted to pH 5, 82 gm of salt and about 28 ml of glacial HOAc per liter; 30 per cent H_2O_2 (if the organic matter is to be removed); neutral 1 N NaOAc, 82 gm per liter, with pH adjusted to 7.0 with HOAc to neutralize the NaOH normally formed by hydrolysis of this salt (neutral 1 N NH_4OAc is used in addition if the flame emission spectrometer is to be employed for Ca); neutral 1 N $CaCl_2$, approximately 109 gm of $CaCl_2 \cdot 6\,H_2O$ or 73 gm of $CaCl_2 \cdot 2\,H_2O$ per liter of CO_2-free distilled water, with pH adjusted to 7.0 with $Ca(OH)_2$; 80 per cent acetone (20 per cent by volume of water); and the following special solutions for the Ca-Versene procedure.

4–12. Standard Ca Solution. A 0.5005-gm portion of pure dried $CaCO_3$ is dissolved in a minimum of 0.2 N HCl. The solution is boiled to expel CO_2 and is then diluted to 1 liter. The solution is 0.0100 N with respect to Ca.

4–13. NH_4Cl-NH_4OH Buffer of pH 10.[14] This buffer is made up of 100 ml of 1 N NH_4Cl and 500 ml of 1 N NH_4OH.

4–14. Eriochrome Black T Indicator.[15] A solution of Eriochrome black T indicator (Bersworth Chemical Co., Framingham, Mass., or Eastman, Rochester, N.Y.) is prepared by dissolution of 0.5 gm of the indicator with 4.5 gm of hydroxylamine hydrochloride in 100 ml of methanol (¶ 11–58). A 50-ml portion of 2 per cent NaCN solution is prepared.

4–15. Standard Versene Solution. A 2-gm portion of disodium Versenate (disodium dihydrogen ethylenediamine tetra-acetic acid, from Bersworth or Eastman) is dissolved in 900 ml of water. Then approximately 50 mgm of $MgCl_2 \cdot 6\,H_2O$ is added to the solution. The normality of Versene is then determined by titration of a 25-ml portion of the standard Ca solution according to the procedure (¶ 4–21).

4–16. The Sample. Enough of a sample is taken to give 0.04 to 0.2 meq of cation exchange capacity, when the determination is with Ca. This requires about 0.3 gm or less of mineral colloid and 0.5 to 5 gm of soil. (Enough of a sample for 0.002 to 0.02 meq of K in a 40-ml final volume is

---

[14] Schwarzenbach, *T. chimia*, 2:59 (1948); *Tech. Bul. 2, Sec. III* (Framingham, Mass: Bersworth Chemical Co., 1951), p. 5. Cheng and Bray, *Soil Sci.*, 72:449 (1951) used 5 ml of pH 10 buffer consisting of 67 gm of NH_4Cl, 570 ml of concentrated NH_4OH, and water to make 1 liter. Bower, *S.S.S.A. Proc.*, 19:40 (1955), to minimize the complexing of Na of the NaOAc, used pH 9.5 (10 ml of NH_4Cl-NH_4OH buffer, made up of 134 gm of NH_4Cl in 1 liter of 2.5 NH_4OH), but the end point is much less sharp.

[15] Tucker, *J. Australian Inst. Agr. Sci.*, 21:100 (1955), proposed phthalcincomplexone as a substitute.

satisfactory, ¶ 4–22. Also 0.004 to 0.04 meq of Mn may be employed, ¶ 4–29.)

4–17. Acidification of the Sample. The soil or colloid sample is placed in a 100-ml centrifuge tube and stirred in 50 ml of 1 *N* NaOAc of pH 5.0 with a policeman-tipped rod. The soil suspension is digested[16] in a near-boiling water bath for 30 minutes with intermittent stirring. The salts are removed by centrifugation of the suspension and decantation of the clear supernatant liquid (¶ 4–3). Two additional washings are given with 1 *N* NaOAc of pH 5, the 30-minute boiling water bath treatment being repeated if the sample is known to be calcareous.

4–18. Removal of Organic Matter (Optional). If the exchange capacity of only the mineral portion of the soil is wanted, the organic matter is removed by H_2O_2 treatment. The acidified sample is transferred to a 250-ml beaker with 10 ml of water (or as little as possible more). Then 5 ml of 30 per cent H_2O_2 is added, the beaker is covered with a watch glass, and the sample is heated cautiously to start the reaction. With beaker tongs, the beaker is removed from the heat and the reaction is quieted if necessary by a stream of water from a wash bottle. When the reaction is quiet at steam plate temperature, additional 5-ml increments of 30 per cent H_2O_2 are added, one at a time, and the digestion on the steam plate is continued as long as needed to bring about destruction of the organic matter. The evaporation is not carried below about 5 to 10 ml. As many as 5 to 10 increments of H_2O_2 may be needed for soils high in organic matter. The H_2O_2 treatment also removes any MnO_2 present in this acidified soil system through a rapid and specific reduction reaction bringing Mn to manganous.

4–19. Exchange Capacity of Soil Due to Organic Matter. The portion of the cation exchange capacity arising from soil organic matter is measured[17] by the determination of the exchange capacity before and after the above treatment with H_2O_2. Each 1 per cent of Walkley-Black soil carbon (¶ 9–57) was equivalent[18] to 4.9 meq of exchange capacity per 100 gm of soil (490 meq of exchange per 100 gm of organic matter). No "uncovering" by H_2O_2 of blocked[19] exchange sites was noted. Selective destruction of soil organic matter by heating at 350 to 400°C for 7 or 8 hours has also been attempted,[20] but the exchange capacity of some mineral colloids is decreased by such heating.

---

[16] 50 ml of this buffer per 5 gm of soil dissolved soil carbonates, including dolomite, present to the extent of 50% of the soil, in tests conducted at steam plate temperature in this laboratory by L. Gallardo; using the buffer is more convenient than acidifying to pH 3.5 with HCl.

[17] Robinson, *J. Agr. Res.* 34:339 (1927); Alexander and Byers, *U.S.D.A. Tech. Bul. 317* (1932); McGeorge, *Ariz. Agr. Exp. Sta. Tech. Bul. 30* (1930); Olson and Bray, *Soil Sci.,* 45:483 (1938); and Mehlich, *Soil Sci.,* 66:429 (1948).

[18] Pratt, *Soil Sci.,* 83:85 (1957).

[19] Broadbent, *Adv. Agron.,* 5:153 (1953).

[20] Mitchell, *J. Am. Soc. Agron.,* 24:256 (1932).

4–20. Exchange Saturation. The acidified soil sample (after transfer from the beaker to centrifuge or leaching tube if the H_2O_2 treatment has been employed) is washed twice (¶ 4–3) with neutral 1 N NaOAc to remove the remaining salts and to aid in making active some slowly active vermiculite-like exchange charges (¶ 4–25). Next, the sample is given 5 washings with 1 N $CaCl_2$ solution. (Four washings with N $Ca(OAc)_2$ and 1 with $CaCl_2$ is also satisfactory.) The excess salt is removed by washings (usually 5) with 80 per cent acetone (¶ 4–4) until the excess $CaCl_2$ is removed, as indicated by a negative $AgNO_3$ test for Cl in the last of the washings. Finally the Ca is replaced by means of 5 washings with a neutral 1 N NaOAc solution (1 N NH_4OAc is employed instead of NaOAc if the flame emission spectrophotometer is to be employed for the Ca determination). The Ca is then determined directly in the solution employed for displacement, by Versene titration, now to be described (or the Ca may be determined by flame emission spectrophotometry, ¶ 18–7).

4–21. Versene Titration of Ca for Exchange Capacity. The Ca solution (about 250 ml) resulting from displacement in the determination of cation exchange capacity is placed in a 500-ml conical flask. Next, 10 ml of the NH_4Cl-NH_4OH buffer solution (¶ 4–13) is added to bring the solution to pH 10 and then 10 drops of Eriochrome black T indicator solution and 1ml of 2 per cent NaCN solution are added. A blank of NaOAc is similarly prepared and is then titrated to a bright blue endpoint with standardized (about 0.01 N) Versene solution containing Mg. The test sample is titrated to the same color. The Mg present in the Versene forms a wine-red color with the indicator after the titration is begun. The color shifts to blue as the Mg is again complexed with Versene at the endpoint. The Ca complex with Versene dissociates less than the Mg complex, and therefore all of the Ca is titrated before the Mg is recomplexed by the Versene. The presence of Mg in the Versene and the use of Eriochrome black T indicator make the determination like that of Mg plus Ca (¶ 11–59), but the titer does not include the Mg because the Mg is the same form at the endpoint of the titration as in Versene reagent. The cation exchange capacity for Ca is calculated:

$$\text{meq exchange capacity per 100 gm} = \text{ml Versene} \times N \times \frac{100}{\text{sample weight in gm}} \quad (4\text{--}2)$$

ALTERNATIVE PROCEDURES

4–22. Cation exchange capacity may also be determined by other ions and with other determinative procedures. Determination with Na (¶ 4–23) or Ba (¶ 4–32) can be effected without removal of $CaCO_3$. In the determination[21] with K (¶ 4–16) in leaching tubes (Fig. 4–1), 0.1 gm of soil is leached successively with 40 ml of N KOAc, 40 ml of 95 per cent ethanol, and 40 ml of NH_4OAc in which the exchanged K is determined by flame emission spectrophotometry (¶ 18–7). Also, the soil, after Ca or Mg saturation and washing with 80 per cent ethanol, may be suspended in water and the exchangeable cation titrated with Versene.[22] The soil may be leached with K_2CO_3 and the filtrate titrated to determine[23] the alkali taken up, by comparison to a blank. Also the soil can be leached with 0.2 N KCl then with N $(NH_4)_2CO_3$, with subsequent evaporation of the second filtrate and titration of the residual K_2CO_3, thus avoiding the need to wash out the excess electrolyte.[24] The cation exchange capacity can be approximated as the sum of total exchangeable metallic cations (¶ 4–36) and exchangeable hydrogen (¶ 4–50).

4–23. Determination with Sodium.[25] Determination of cation exchange capacity by means of NaOAc solution of pH 8.2 can be effected without interference of soil $CaCO_3$ and is relatively constant from a pH of just above 7 to over 9 in 1 N NaOAc solution. The Na ion also has the advantages of being a prominent cation in some saline and alkali soils, and of not being fixed as are NH_4 and K.

4–24. A 4-gm sample of medium and fine textured soil or a 6-gm sample of coarse textured soil, of known moisture content, is transferred to a 50-ml round bottom, narrow neck centrifuge tube and 33 ml of N NaOAc solution of pH 8.2 is added. The stoppered tube is shaken for 5 minutes in a reciprocating shaker. After centrifugation, the clear supernatant liquid is decanted as completely as possible and discarded. The sample is treated with 3 additional 33-ml portions of N NaOAc solution for a total of 4 treatments. Then the sample is suspended in 33 ml of 95 per cent ethanol and shaken for 5 minutes, centrifuged, and the clear supernatant liquid discarded. The sample is washed with 2 additional 33-ml portions of ethanol. The electrical conductance of the supernatant liquid from the third washing should be less than 40 micromhos per cm. (Bower, *et al.,* show that the quantity of Na released by hydrolysis just balances the quantity of excess Na salt left in the solutions at about the third washing, and that further washing results in an erroneous lowering of the measured exchange capacity.) The adsorbed Na is replaced from the sample with three 33-ml portions of N NH_4OAc, the decantate being collected in a 100-ml volumetric flask. This solution is made to volume and mixed, and the Na is

[21] Swindale and Fieldes, *Soil Sci.,* 74:287 (1952).
[22] Perkins, *Soil Sci.,* 74:443 (1952); also suggested removal of $CaCO_3$ from soil with Versene.
[23] Schofield, *J. Agr. Sci.,* 23:255 (1933).
[24] Puri, *Soil Sci.,* 37:105 (1934).
[25] Bower *et al., Soil Sci.,* 73:251 (1952).

determined by the usual flame emission (¶ 18–21) or other procedure (¶ 5–88).

4–25. Determination with Ammonium.[26] The cation exchange capacity can be determined with ammonium following extraction of exchangeable cations (¶ 5–11). The determination with ammonium ion may not displace the last few per cent of the strongly held H^+ ions (weakly acidic) from kaolinite or halloysite, and tends to become fixed to some extent by vermiculite.[27] Neither is the determination of ammonium ion as rapid as that of metallic cations by flame emission or Versene titration. Use of 80 per cent ethanol solution of NH_4OAc for saturation and $Ca(OAc)_2$ as the replacing agent have been employed with calcareous soils. The ammonium exchange capacity was employed by Peech, *et al.* for noncalcareous soils.

4–26. The reagents required for the determination with noncalcareous soils include 95 per cent ethanol or methanol, acid-free U.S.P. grade, and acidified 10 per cent KCl (100 gm of KCl in 900 ml of water, the pH of the solution being adjusted at 2.5 with HCl, thymol blue indicator being employed with a spot plate; the solution is diluted to 1 liter).

4–27. After the ammonium acetate leaching for the removal of exchangeable cations (¶ 5–11), the upper parts of the apparatus are washed with a stream of alcohol. Then the soil is leached with 250 ml of alcohol added to the Buchner funnel in increments (500 ml through the delivery tube for the carbon funnel apparatus).[28] The last of the alcohol is drawn through by suction, but the soil is not dried lest ammonia be lost.

4–28. The soil is then leached with 450 ml of 10 per cent KCl solution of pH 2.5, and the leachate is collected in a suction flask. The leachate is washed into a 500-ml volumetric flask, made to volume, and mixed. An aliquot representing 1 to 2 meq of NH_4^+ is placed in a 800-ml Kjeldahl flask and the ammonium is distilled (¶ 8–22) and back titrated with $N/14\ H_2SO_4$. As a blank, an equal portion of the 10 per cent KCl solution is distilled.

4–29. Determination with Mn. The cation exchange capacity of small samples (10 to 80 mgm) is advantageously measured by Mn^{++}. Fortunately, as shown by Bower and Truog,[29] the cation exchange capacity measured by means of Mn^{++} is equivalent to that with Ca, which is the standard cation because it constitutes the major percentage saturation of agricultural soils. Manganese chloride or acetate solutions are invariably

26 Kelley, *J. Am. Soc. Agron.,* 21:1021 (1929); Schollenberger and Dreibelbis, *Soil Sci.,* 30:161 (1930); Chapman and Kelley, *Soil Sci.,* 30:391 (1930); Peech *et al.,* U.S.D.A. Cir. 757 (1947).

27 Bower, *Soil Sci.,* 70:375 (1950).

28 Schollenberger and Simon, *Soil Sci.,* 59:13 (1945).

29 *Ind. Eng. Chem., A.E.,* 12:411 (1940).

acid, as a result of hydrolysis, in contrast to neutral solutions obtainable with Ca. The Mn is readily determined in microchemical amounts by the classical periodate method of Willard and Greathouse[30] as adapted to spectrophotometric measurements by Mehlig.[31]

4–30. The quantity of sample (or aliquot) is taken to be equivalent to 0.004 to 0.04 meq of exchange charge (0.1 to 0.8 mgm of Mn) in 100 ml of final $HMnO_4$ solution (with smaller samples, a smaller final volume is employed). The soluble salts and $CaCO_3$ are removed (¶ 4–17); the organic matter is removed (¶4–18) if the exchange capacity of only the mineral portion is to be determined; and the exchangeable hydrogen is removed by a buffer washing (¶ 4–20). The exchange charge is then saturated with Mn^{++} by the usual washing procedures (¶ 4–2) with N $MnCl_2$ or $Mn(OAc)_2$ solution. The excess salt is removed by the usual washings with methanol or 80 per cent acetone solution in water, and the Mn^{++} is displaced by means of washings with 1 N NH_4OAc, and determined by the usual procedure (¶ 5–74). The cation exchange capacity is calculated:

$$\begin{array}{l} \text{meq of exchange} \\ \text{capacity per} \\ \text{100 gm of soil} \end{array} = \frac{\text{ppm of Mn}}{274.7} \times \frac{\begin{array}{c}\text{final } HMnO_4 \\ \text{solution volume, ml}\end{array}}{\begin{array}{c}\text{sample represented in} \\ \text{final solution, gm}\end{array}} \quad (4\text{–}3)$$

4–31. Holtzinger *et al.*,[32] replaced the Mn^{++} with N KCl, 4 33-ml washings being employed for a 4-gm soil sample. The KCl was made to 250 ml with N KCl solution. To 20 ml of this 5 drops of 2 per cent gelatin were added and the Mn was determined directly in the replacing solution with a polarograph (¶ 16–28).

4–32. Determination with Ba.[33] Barium saturation is effected during extraction of exchangeable cations from calcareous soils (¶ 5–21) with $BaCl_2$ buffered with triethanolamine. A final washing with $BaCl_2$ alone was given by Mehlich to complete the saturation for cation exchange capacity determination. Washing with $Ba(OAc)_2$ has also been employed by Mehlich, and has been combined with Ba determination in the NH_4OAc extract by flame emission[34] (¶ 18–21). Exchange capacity has been determined by conductometric titration[35] of Ba-soil with $MgSO_4$ solution.

[30] *J. Am. Chem. Soc.*, 39:2366 (1917).
[31] *Ind. Eng. Chem., A.E.*, 11:274 (1939).
[32] *Soil Sci.*, 77:137 (1954).
[33] Bobko and Arkinasi, *Z. Pflanz. Dung.*, 6A:99 (1925); Burgess and Breazeale, *Ariz. Agr. Exp. Sta. Tech. Bul. 9* (1926); Mehlich, *Soil Sci.*, 60:289 (1945); Hanna and Reed, *Soil Sci.*, 66:447 (1948); Pratt and Holowaychuk, *S.S.S.A. Proc.*, 18:365 (1954).
[34] Toth and Prince, *Soil Sci.*, 67:439 (1949).
[35] Mortland and Mellor, *S.S.S.A. Proc.*, 18:363 (1954).

TOTAL EXCHANGEABLE METALLIC CATIONS

4–33. In the equilibrium pH method,[36] total exchangeable metallic cations of soil are estimated by replacement with HOAc, the resulting pH change being carefully measured to determine the amount of H removed from the solution by reference to the standard pH titration curve of acetic acid. The reaction is made virtually complete by the great excess of HOAc, even though the metallic cations in solution are in equilibrium with the exchange charges. The total of exchangeable metallic cations has been estimated also by extraction with NH_4OAc (¶ 4–43) and with HCl (¶ 4–41).

APPARATUS

4–34. Needed are 50-ml conical extraction flasks and stoppers, a torsion balance, a 25-ml volumetric pipette, and a glass electrode pH meter.

REAGENTS

4–35. One N HOAc is made up by dilution of 57.2 ml of glacial acetic acid to 1 liter; a pH value of 2.31 should be obtained by slight adjustments of the concentration if necessary. One N NH_4OAc is made up by diluting 57.2 ml of glacial acetic acid to 800 ml and neutralizing to pH 7.00 ± 0.01 with concentrated NH_4OH and then diluting to 1 liter. Other reagents needed are standard buffers for calibrating the pH meter, with pH values known to ± 0.01 pH unit, preferably 1 in the range of pH 3 to 5 and 1 in the range of pH 6 to 7.

PROCEDURE

4–36. Total Exchangeable Metallic Cations. To 2.50 gm of soil, placed in a 50-ml conical flask, is added a 25-ml volume of 1 N HOAc. The suspension is shaken intermittently for 1 hour, and then the pH of the suspension is determined accurately to 0.01 or 0.02 unit (¶ 3–19). The pH of the clear supernatant liquid is almost exactly the same as that of the suspension in this system. The pH value of the original HOAc reagent is determined at the same time. The meq of exchangeable metallic cations is calculated from the curve (Fig. 4–2) of Brown or the following equation derived therefrom:

$$\begin{matrix} \text{meq exchangeable} \\ \text{metallic cations} \\ \text{per 100 gm of soil} \end{matrix} = (\text{pH observed} - 2.31) \times 22 \qquad (4\text{–}4)$$

which is applicable from pH 2.31 to 2.8, that is, up to 10 meq of exchangeable metallic cations per 100 gm of soil. The curve and equation are based on meq per liter, but one liter of solution corresponds to 100 gm of soil.

---

[36] Brown, *Soil Sci.*, 56:353 (1943).

For amounts of exchangeable metallic cations from 10 to 20 meq, one-half the amount of soil is taken (1.25 gm) and the meq obtained is multiplied by 2. The total exchangeable metallic cations may be employed to derive the cation exchange status (¶ 4–42).

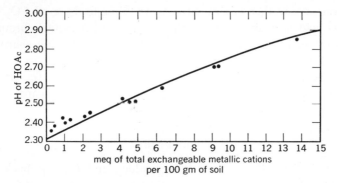

Fig. 4–2. Relation of pH of HOAc solution to total exchangeable metallic cations extracted from soil. (After Brown, *Soil Sci.,* 56:383, 1943.) The curve is for pure HOAc, while the points are soil analysis values.

ALTERNATIVE PROCEDURES

4–37. Titration of Total Exchangeable Metallic Cations.[37] The titration of metallic oxides in the residue of the NH_4OAc extract of soil gives a measure of the total exchangeable metallic cations. From the screened and well-mixed soil sample, a 10.0-gm sample is weighed out on a torsion balance and transferred to a 250-ml conical flask. Then approximately 100 ml of N NH_4OAc solution is poured into the flask, the flask is stoppered, and the suspension is shaken intermittently for 10 minutes. The suspension is then poured into the Gooch filter crucible in which the filter paper or asbestos has previously been wetted and seated firmly by suction. When the suspension has been filtered, the flask is rinsed with more of the NH_4OAc solution and the rinsings poured onto the filter. Additional increments of NH_4OAc solution are poured onto the soil until a total volume of approximately 250 ml of the extraction solution has been collected.

4–38. The NH_4OAc extract is transferred to a 400-ml beaker, and evaporated to a small volume on a steam plate in the absence of chloride fumes. Before the solution becomes gummy, it is transferred to a platinum or silica dish, and the evaporation is continued to dryness over a low flame or slowly in a muffle furnace to convert the acetates to oxides and carbon- ates. The temperature is raised gradually to a full red heat (about 700 to 800°C) for 15 to 20 minutes, and then the dish and contents are allowed

37 Bray and Willhite, *Ind. Eng. Chem., A.E.,* 1:144 (1929).

to cool slowly to room temperature, in a desiccator if necessary for protection from chloride fumes in the laboratory.

4–39. The residue is taken up in 50 ml (or other known quantity, sufficient to be an excess) of standard 0.1 N HCl delivered from a pipette. The acid is warmed gently to cause complete reaction with the metallic oxides and carbonates and then is brought just to boiling to drive off CO_2. Finally the excess acid is back titrated with standard 0.1 N NaOH, brom cresol purple being employed as the indicator. Heating to boiling sharpens the end point.

4–40. The meq of exchangeable metallic cations per 100 gm of soil equals the net ml of 0.1 N HCl consumed by the oxides and carbonates,

$$\begin{array}{l}\text{meq exchangeable}\\ \text{metallic cations} \quad = V - T \qquad\qquad (4\text{–}5)\\ \text{per 100 gm of soil}\end{array}$$

in which V is the volume of 0.1 N HCl added and T is the back titer of 0.1 N NaOH. The metallic cations usually consist dominantly of Ca and Mg with lesser amounts of K and Na. The presence of soluble chloride and sulfate salts in the soil does not interfere, although the presence of carbonates in the soil presents the usual difficulty (¶ 5–18) of increasing the quantities of metallic cations over those in truly exchangeable form.

4–41. Total Exchangeable Metallic Cations by Dilute HCl Extraction.[38] To 10 gm of acid or neutral soil (method not applicable to calcareous soils) in a 250-ml conical flask is added a 100-ml volume of standard 0.1 N HCl. The flask is stoppered and the suspension is shaken intermittently for 1 or more hours. The suspension is allowed to stand until clear. Then 25 ml is pipetted from the clear supernatant liquid and titrated with standard 0.1 N NaOH with brom cresol purple as the indicator. Warming the solution to drive off the CO_2 sharpens the end point. The calculation of total exchangeable metallic cations is by equation 4–5. Iron and aluminum extracted by the acid are reprecipitated and thus excluded from the exchangeable metallic cations, but some error occurs due to side reactions with the soil. Schofield[39] proposed the use of 0.05 N HCl in volume sufficient that only 20 per cent of it is used up.

EXCHANGEABLE METALLIC CATION STATUS

4–42. The exchangeable metallic cation status[40] of a soil refers to the

---

[38] Kappen, in *Bodenaziditat* (Berlin: J. Springer, 1929), p. 169.

[39] According to Piper, *op. cit.,* p. 189.

[40] Metallic cations with hydroxyl ions form hydroxides or bases; in older soil literature the terms "base" hence "base status" was sometimes applied to the cation instead of to the hydroxide. The hydroxide as a whole is the proton acceptor and, therefore, the base. Compare base, the proton acceptor, to acid, the proton donor (¶ 4–50).

percentage exchange saturation with metallic cations:

$$\text{Exchange status (percentage saturation)} = \frac{S}{T} \times 100 \tag{4-6}$$

in which S (after Hissink) is the total exchangeable metallic cations (¶ 4–33) as meq per 100 gm of soil and T (after Hissink) is the cation exchange capacity (¶ 4–6) as meq per 100 gm of soil. The value T is also the sum of S plus exchangeable hydrogen (¶ 4–50). A more detailed evaluation of the metallic cation status of soils includes the separate determination of the percentage saturation with each metallic cation species (¶ 5–5). The percentage exchangeable hydrogen saturation, the complement of the percentage of metallic cation saturation, once was termed percentage "unsaturation," but such usage is disfavored by the Soil Science Society of America.

4–43. The percentage metallic cation saturation of acid soils is important in soil-plant relationships, and can be raised by liming the soil (¶ 4–64). In alkaline soils, the determined exchange saturation with metallic cations (¶ 5–5) often exceeds 100 per cent of the exchange capacity as usually determined. This situation is particularly common[41] in soils high in organic matter. Calcium is released from positions not available for exchange capacity measurement by most methods. In calcareous soils, appreciable amounts of Ca and Mg tend to dissolve from the carbonate form in the extraction solution (¶ 5–18) and thus are not distinguishable from exchangeable metallic cations.

GYPSUM OR SULFUR REQUIREMENT OF SOILS

4–44. The development of physical impermeability in "alkali" soils (¶ 10–5) is correlated with the percentage Na saturation or "degree of alkalization."[42] When the percentage Na saturation exceeds 15 per cent, deterioration of the physical properties of the soil generally sets in. When a soil containing an excessively high percentage saturation with Na is shaken with a nearly saturated gypsum solution, Ca exchanges for Na and the consequent loss of Ca in the solution is an approximate measure of the gypsum requirement. The gypsum requirement is the equivalence of $CaSO_4 \cdot 2 H_2O$ or of S that should be added to "reclaim" the soil by displacing the net exchangeable Na (¶ 4–48). Use of gypsum or sulfur,[43] or acidulation[44] is the counterpart of liming soils (¶ 4–64).

---

[41] Puri and Uppal, *Soil Sci.*, 47:245 (1939).

[42] Puri, *Soils* (New York: Reinhold Publishing Corporation, 1949), p. 83.

[43] Harmer, *S.S.S.A. Proc.*, 7:378 (1943).

[44] Sherman and Harmer, *J. Am. Soc. Agron.*, 33:1081 (1941); Aldrich, *S.S.S.A. Proc.*, 13:191 (1949); Aldrich and Turrell, *Soil Sci.*, 70:83 (1950).

4–45. Needed apparatus is a 200-ml conical flask and stopper, a 100-ml pipet, and a buret and flask for Versene titration.

REAGENTS

4–46. Needed reagents are an approximately saturated gypsum solution of determined Ca concentration (5 gm of $CaSO_4 \cdot 2 H_2O$ shaken for an hour in 1 liter of water) and Versene reagents (¶ 4–11). The gypsum solution is filtered and titrated (¶ 4–21). It should have a Versene titration of at least 28 meq per liter.

PROCEDURE[45]

4–47. A 5-gm sample of air-dried soil is added to a 200-ml conical flask. Then 100 ml of the standardized gypsum solution (¶ 4–46) is added by means of a pipet. The suspension is shaken for 30 minutes and then a portion is filtered and the Ca + Mg concentration is determined in an aliquot by Versene titration (¶ 4–21). Then:

$$\text{Gypsum requirement, meq per 100 gm of soil} = 2(S - T) \quad (4\text{--}7)$$

in which S is the Versene standardization blank of the gypsum solution as meq per liter and T is the Versene titration of the filtrate as meq per liter.

4–48. Each meq of exchangeable Na or "gypsum requirement" (¶ 4–44) is approximately equivalent to 1.7 tons of gypsum or 0.3 tons of sulfur per acre-foot of soil to be reclaimed. Any gypsum already present in the soil is taken into account in the extraction. In deciding the actual size of application, the depth of soil to be reclaimed (more or less than 1 acre-foot) and the fraction of exchangeable Na to be replaced (for example, 75 per cent of it) must be considered. Also, exchangeable K does not contribute materially to the adverse effects noted for excessive Na saturation, yet this and some other methods (¶ 4–49) also include the degree of K saturation. For this reason, the determined gypsum requirement may be somewhat excessive for soils in which the saturation with K (¶ 5–5) is over a few per cent.

ALTERNATIVE PROCEDURE

4–49. Puri[46] gives a simple method of determining the total of exchangeable Na and K by extracting the soil with $(NH_4)_2CO_3$ solution, evaporating the filtrate, and titrating the two alkalies (compare ¶ 4–22).

---

[45] U.S.D.A. Handb. 60 (1954) p. 49; Schoonover, *Examination of soils for alkali* (Berkeley: U. Calif. Ext. Serv., mimeo., 1952); McGeorge and Breazeale, *Ariz. Agr. Exp. Sta. Tech. Bul.* 122 (1951).

[46] *Op. cit.,* p. 83.

EXCHANGEABLE HYDROGEN DETERMINATION

4–50. The determination of exchangeable hydrogen in soils is in fact an equilibrium determination of the proton (H^+) supplying power of the colloidal material. The stronger the proton acceptor (the weaker the acid) that is placed in equilibrium with the soil, the greater the quantity of protons removed from it. Acetate is generally used as a proton acceptor but many others are available. The quantity of protons removed in the extraction solution is reported as the quantity of "exchangeable hydrogen." This quantity in turn can be calculated into terms of "lime requirement" (¶ 4–64) of the soil.

4–51. Acid soils contain[47] a considerable quantity of active or exchangeable aluminum, in the form of Al^{+++}, $Al(OH)^{++}$ and $Al(OH)_2^+$. When a proton acceptor is equilibrated in a system containing active aluminum, hydrolysis occurs with precipitation of aluminum hydroxide and simultaneous release of a proton from water:

$$Al(OH)_2^+ + H_2O \longrightarrow Al(OH)_3 + H^+ \qquad (4\text{–}8)$$

The net effect is the release of a proton from the soil, which is equivalent to the release of an "exchangeable" hydrogen ion. Salts of a strong acid cannot be used to displace exchangeable hydrogen because they do not remove ("accept") the H^+ from the solution.

4–52. Soils also contain tightly bound hydrogen associated to varying degrees with oxygen. This hydrogen is of the nature of hydroxyls. As the strength of the proton acceptor is increased in the equilibrium system, greater and greater quantities of the hydrogen bound with varying strength is released:

$$2\,XOH + Ba(OH)_2 \longrightarrow Ba(OX)_2 + 2\,H_2O \qquad (4\text{–}9)$$

when X represents an organic or mineral colloidal electrolyte of soil. This reaction is part of the so-called[48] "build-up" of cation exchange capacity in $Ba(OH)_2$ solution.

4–53. Therefore, the quantity of "exchangeable hydrogen" released is a function of the equilibrium system in which it is measured. In general, the practice is to determine exchangeable hydrogen at an equilibrium pH of 7 to 8.3 (pH 8.3 is $1/500,000\ N$ in hydroxyl), since this range of pH values is a convenient reference point in the neutralization of acid soils in liming practice (¶ 4–8).

---

[47] Daikuhara, *Bul. Imp. Centr. Agr. Exp. Sta. Japan,* 2:18 (1914); Kappan, *op. cit.,* Paver and Marshall, *J. Soc. Chem. Ind.,* 53:750 (1934); Mukherjee, *Ind. J. Agr. Sci.,* 12:105 (1942); Chatterjee and Paul, *Ind. J. Agr. Sci.,* 12:113 (1942); Mukherjee *et al., J. Ind. Chem. Soc.,* 19:405 (1942).

[48] Magistad, *J. Am. Soc. Agron.,* 21:1045 (1929).

4–54. Needed apparatus consists of a carbon funnel with flow rate regulated with a rubber tube and screw clamp, fine glass wool, acid-washed silica sand (coarse), and a 500-ml conical flask with stopper and delivery tube for the extraction solution, a 500-ml receiving flask vented to permit escape of air, and a 600-ml beaker.

REAGENTS

4–55. Needed reagents are 1 N Ba(OAc)$_2$ extraction solution of pH 8.1, adjusted with Ba(OH)$_2$; 1 per cent phenolphthalein indicator; and 0.05 N NaOH or Ba(OH)$_2$ solution.

PROCEDURE[49]

4–56. A small sphere of fine glass wool is tamped into the bottom of the carbon filter funnel. It is then wetted with a little of the Ba(OAc)$_2$ solution and further compacted. Then a small portion of pure silica sand is spread over the glass wool. The soil sample representing 0.2 to 1 meq of exchangeable hydrogen is added to the funnel with care to prevent soil from sticking to the sides of the tube. The soil is leveled off, and additional silica sand is placed on top to a depth of about 5 mm. The flask containing 350 ml of the Ba(OAc)$_2$ extraction solution is inverted to deliver onto the soil. The leaching rate is adjusted with a screw clamp so as not to exceed 10 to 20 drops per minute.

4–57. When all the extraction solution is passed through, its volume is measured in a graduated cylinder and then it is transferred to a 600-ml beaker. Approximately 10 drops of 1 per cent phenolphthalein solution are added, and the extraction solution is then back titrated with 0.05 N NaOH or Ba(OH)$_2$ to a faint pink color. A blank titration is made on 100 ml of the extraction solution and calculated for the volume employed for extraction. The results are expressed in terms of meq of H$^+$ per 100 gm of soil:

$$\text{meq exchangeable H}^+ \text{ per 100 gm soil} = (T - B) \times N \times \frac{100}{\text{sample wt., gm}}$$

$$(4\text{--}10)$$

in which T is the ml titration, B is ml blank, and N is the normality of standard NaOH or Ba(OH)$_2$. The results are also expressed as tons of CaCO$_3$ per acre (¶ 4–64).

ALTERNATIVE PROCEDURES

4–58. Exchangeable hydrogen has been determined by the change in the pH of a 1 N NH$_4$OAc solution (¶ 4–61) or titration[50] or pH measure-

---

[49] After Parker, *J. Am. Soc. Agron.*, 21:1030 (1929), modified for extraction at pH 8.1 following Mehlich, *Soil Sci.*, 60:289 (1952).

[50] Schollenberger and Simon, *Soil Sci.*, 59:13 (1945).

ment[51] of the NH$_4$OAc extract (¶ 5–11) with a standard hydroxide solution, although the end point is indistinct. Exchangeable hydrogen may be
approximated by subtracting the sum of exchangeable metallic cations
(¶ 4–33) from the cation exchange capacity (¶ 4–16).

4–59. Mehlich[52] modified the Ba(OAc)$_2$ procedure slightly. A soil
sample having 0.5 to 1.0 meq of exchange capacity is placed in a crucible,
washed with 50 ml of 0.2 N Ba(OAc)$_2$, then with 50 ml of water. The filtrate is made to 100-ml volume and an aliquot is back titrated with
0.05 N Ba(OH)$_2$.

4–60. Instead of an acetate buffer, triethanolamine has been employed
by Mehlich[53] for buffering BaCl$_2$. In a modification, Peech *et al.*,[54] employed a solution like that described for extraction of exchangeable metallic
cations from calcareous soils (¶ 5–20), except that the BaCl$_2$ is made
0.5 N. A 10-gm soil sample is shaken with 25 ml of the buffer for 0.5 hour
and then filtered on a Gooch filter fitted with paper. The soil is completely
transferred with 25 ml more of the buffer, and then is further leached with
100 ml of 0.5 N BaCl$_2$ containing 2.5 ml of the original buffer solution per
liter. The extraction is made in not less than 1 hour. The combined filtrates
are titrated with standard 0.1 N HCl to an end point with brom cresol
green-methyl red indicator, the color being standardized against a blank
titration of similar volumes of the 2 extraction solutions.

4–61. Brown[55] determined exchangeable hydrogen of soils through
equilibration of 2.50 gm of soil in 25 ml of 1 N NH$_4$OAc (compare
¶ 4–33). The suspension was shaken intermittently for 1 hour, and then the
pH values of the suspension and original solution were carefully determined
to 0.01 or 0.02 pH units (¶ 3–19). The meq of exchangeable hydrogen
can be obtained from the curve (Fig. 4–3) or calculated from the following
equation derived from the curve:

$$\text{meq exchangeable H}^+ \text{ per 100 gm soil} = (7.00 - \text{pH observed}) \times 22 \quad (4\text{–}11)$$

which is applicable from pH 7.00 to 6.65, that is up to 10 meq of exchangeable H$^+$ per 100 gm soil. For amounts of exchangeable H$^+$ from 10 to 20
meq, one-half the amount of soil is taken (1.25 gm) and the meq obtained
is multiplied by 2.

4–62. Schofield[56] employed the Ca salt of the p-nitrophenol buffer to
extract exchangeable hydrogen. This solution is strongly buffered in the
neutral pH range. The extraction solution was titrated to pH 4.5 with dilute

[51] Maehl, *Ind. Eng. Chem., A.E.*, 12:24 (1940).
[52] *Soil Sci.*, 60:289 (1945).
[53] *S.S.S.A. Proc.*, 3:162 (1939); *Soil Sci.*, 66:429 (1948).
[54] U.S.D.A. Cir. 757 (1947).
[55] *Soil Sci.*, 56:353 (1943).
[56] *J. Agr. Sci.*, 33:252 (1933).

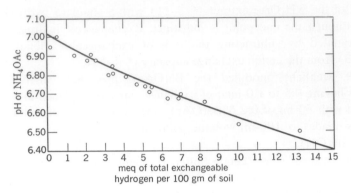

Fig. 4–3. Relation of pH of NH₄OAc solution to exchangeable hydrogen extracted from soil. (After Brown, *Soil Sci.*, 56:353, 1943.)

HCl, brom cresol green being used as an indicator, and the exchangeable hydrogen was determined by calculating it in relation to a blank.

4–63. Woodruff[57] employed a buffer mixture of acetate and p-nitrophenol that gives a linear change of pH in relation to exchangeable H in soils in the pH range 6 to 7 (compare to Fig. 4–3). The buffer consists of 8 gm of p-nitrophenol, 40 gm of $Ca(OAc)_2 \cdot H_2O$, and 0.625 gm of MgO per liter; the pH of the solution is then adjusted to 7.0 with HCl or MgO as required. Five gm of soil, 5 ml of water, and 10 ml of the buffer solution are equilibrated with stirring and allowed to stand for 30 minutes. Each change in pH of 0.1 unit going from pH 7.0 to 6.0 equals 1 meq of exchangeable H per 100 gm. If the pH drops below 6.0, indicating over 10 meq of H per 100 gm, the test is repeated with 2.5 gm of soil; each 0.1 pH unit drop equals 2 meq of exchangeable H per 100 gm. Because of the linearity of response, the pH meter dial can be directly calibrated to read as a lime-meter.

THE LIME REQUIREMENT OF SOILS

4–64. Each meq of exchangeable hydrogen (¶ 4–50) to be neutralized per 100 gm of soil requires 1000 pounds of $CaCO_3$ neutralizing equivalence (¶ 4–66) per 2 million pounds of soil. For example, 1 ton of $CaCO_3$ per acre plow layer (of 2 million pounds) would be needed to neutralize 2 meq of exchangeable hydrogen present in each 100 gm of soil (Table 5–1). The $CaCO_3$ equivalence of the exchangeable hydrogen of soils is termed the "lime requirement" of soils. Lime requirement is also judged from pH measurements (¶ 13–88) with consideration for soil texture, from solubility of iron or release of sulfide (¶ 13–93), and also through equilibration of soil

---

[57] *Soil Sci.*, 66:53 (1948); also Graham, *Mo. Agr. Exp. Sta. Cir. 345*, p. 12 (1950).

with $Ca(OH)_2$ and CO_2,[58] $CaCO_3$, $Ca(HCO_3)_2$,[59] and other methods. The lime requirement should be contrasted with the gypsum requirement (¶ 4–44).

4–65. Russell[60] states that "the vagueness of the concept of lime requirement . . . [makes it] a useful working concept that can have no exact meaning." Besides the functional nature of the "exchangeable" hydrogen, depending on the amount of $Al(OH)_2{}^+$ present (¶ 4–51), the reference pH (¶ 4–52) and so forth, the lime requirement concept is further complicated by differences between plant responses. Consideration must be given to the degree to which the exchangeable hydrogen should be neutralized. Different crops have different optimum soil pH values (¶ 13–89). Also, different soil colloids have different calcium activities at a given pH. Organic soils frequently require less liming than mineral soils to reach the point of no crop response. Some soils require lower pH levels to avoid the appearance of minor element deficiencies in plants. The actual amount of liming material to be applied is also governed by the purity and reaction rate of the liming material (¶ 4–73).

NEUTRALIZING EQUIVALENCE OF AGRICULTURAL LIMESTONE

4–66. When the percentage saturation (¶ 4–42) of a soil with metallic cations is too low, agricultural limestones are applied. Only the neutralizing equivalence of limestone, the "calcium carbonate equivalent," is considered as a first approximation in "lime requirement" (¶ 4–64). More detailed consideration takes into account the proportion of Ca and Mg in the liming material. Carbonate rocks commonly employed in finely ground form for liming soils include limestone in which the active material is calcite, $CaCO_3$, dolomitic limestone, which contains dolomite, $CaCO_3 \cdot MgCO_3$, and marl, in which the active material is calcite. Other materials used include burned limestone containing CaO, slaked lime, containing $Ca(OH)_2$ with $CaCO_3$, and limited amounts of other materials. Collectively, these materials are termed "liming materials." The titration method given here includes the determination of the $CaCO_3$ equivalence of all of these materials in accordance with the official A.O.A.C. method.

APPARATUS

4–67. Needed apparatus includes a torsion balance; a 500-ml conical flask; two burets; a steam plate; and, for the estimation of percentage of

[58] Truog, *J. Ind. Eng. Chem.*, 8:341 (1916); Bradfield and Allison, *Trans. Intern. Soc. Soil Sci.*, A:63 (1933); Truog, U.S.D.A. Yearbook, p. 563 (1938).
[59] Patel and Truog, *S.S.S.A. Proc.*, 16:41 (1952).
[60] *Soil Conditions and Plant Growth* (London: Longmans Green & Co. Ltd. 1948), p. 105.

$MgCO_3$, a 250-ml beaker, a 200-ml volumetric flask, a funnel, and a 50-ml pipet.

REAGENTS

4–68. Needed reagents are standard 1 N HCl and 1 N NaOH (the latter is standardized with potassium acid phthalate, then the titrimetric ratio is determined between the standard acid and alkali) and 1 per cent phenolphthalein indicator. To determine the percentage of $MgCO_3$, brom cresol green indicator is needed.

PROCEDURE

4–69. A 1.00-gm sample of dried and ground limestone or 0.5 gm of burned, or slaked, or other liming material, that has passed the 0.26-mm (60 meshes per inch) sieve, is weighed out into a 500-ml conical flask. Next, 25 ml of standard 1 N HCl is added. The suspension is swirled to mix thoroughly and then heated nearly to boiling, and held on a steam bath for 5 minutes (up to 45 minutes if necessary to complete the reaction). Finally, 100 ml of water is added and the solution is boiled for exactly 1 minute over a small burner, then cooled to room temperature.

4–70. Back Titration. Five drops of 1 per cent phenolphthalein indicator solution are added and the solution is then back titrated with standard 1 N NaOH to a pink color, which persists for 15 seconds as the solution is shaken. This solution is saved if Ca or Mg is to be determined for the proportionality between $CaCO_3$ and $MgCO_3$ (¶ 4–74).

4–71. The neutralizing equivalence as a percentage of $CaCO_3$ is computed as follows:

$$\% \ CaCO_3 \ \text{equivalence} = (V - T) \times N \times \frac{CaCO_3}{2000} \times \frac{100}{s}$$

$$= \text{net ml} \times \frac{5}{s} \qquad (4\text{--}12)$$

in which V is the ml of HCl initially added, T is the ml of NaOH back titre, N is normality, and s is the sample weight in gm, usually unity.

4–72. Any iron oxide that is dissolved from the original material is reprecipitated from the alkali titration so that it does not enter into the neutralizing equivalence of the sample. For compounds that have a lower molecular weight than $CaCO_3$, the neutralizing equivalence may exceed 100 per cent. For example, $MgCO_3$ has a $CaCO_3$ equivalence of 117 per cent, whereas CaO has a $CaCO_3$ equivalence of 179 per cent. The titration method includes carbonates, oxides, and hydroxides, and easily decomposable silicates of alkaline earths.

4–73. Use of $CaCO_3$ Equivalence. The quantity of a liming material to be recommended depends on the $CaCO_3$ requirement of the soil (¶ 4–64) and the percentage $CaCO_3$ equivalence of the liming material:

$$\frac{\text{Quantity liming}}{\text{material recommended}} = \frac{\text{Quantity } CaCO_3 \text{ needed} \times 100}{\% \ CaCO_3 \text{ equivalence, liming material}}$$

$$(4\text{–}13)$$

The quantity of liming material to be recommended may be increased over this estimate in proportion to the estimated percentage of the $CaCO_3$ equivalence of the material which will not soon become effective, owing to large particle size or other factors.

4–74. Estimation of Magnesium Carbonate. Estimation of the $MgCO_3$ equivalence of agricultural liming materials is often important. To do this, the solution that has been back titrated with NaOH (¶ 4–70) is acidified to a pH of 4.5 as indicated by the brom cresol green indicator, and the acidic solution is then transferred with a funnel to a 200-ml volumetric flask. The conical flask is rinsed and the rinsing is added to the volumetric flask. Finally the solution is made to volume and mixed well. The undissolved portion is allowed to settle to the bottom of the flask, and a 50-ml aliquot is pipetted from the clear supernatant liquid into a 250-ml beaker. Then Ca in this solution is determined (¶ 5–24).

4–75. The Ca so determined is calculated as the percentage of $CaCO_3$ in the original sample, the fact that only a 0.25 aliquot was taken of the original sample being taken into account in the calculation. Then:

$$\begin{array}{l}\% \ MgCO_3 \\ \text{equivalence}\end{array} = (\% \ CaCO_3 \text{ equivalence} - \% \ CaCO_3 \text{ determined}) \times \frac{84.32}{100.1}$$

$$(4\text{–}14)$$

For a more accurate determination of the $MgCO_3$ content, the Mg is determined quantitatively (¶ 5–45) as well as the Ca.

ALTERNATIVE PROCEDURES

4–76. The neutralizing equivalence of the carbonate form of the liming material may be obtained by measuring the amount of CO_2 evolved, collected and weighed in soda-lime,[61] or titrated (¶ 10–121), or measured by volume (¶ 4–77).

4–77. The gas law corrections in gasometric[62] determination of $CaCO_3$ equivalence can be eliminated by determining a standard $CaCO_3$ sample at the same time and under the same conditions as the limestone equivalence is determined. A weighed sample (approximately 1 gm) of pure

[61] *Methods of Analysis*, 7th ed. (Washington, D. C.: A.O.A.C., 1950), p. 31.
[62] Horton and Newsom, *S.S.S.A. Proc.*, 17:414 (1953) after Pierce and Haenisch, *Quantitative Analysis*, 4th ed. (New York: John Wiley & Sons, Inc., 1947).

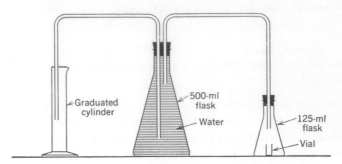

Fig. 4–4. Apparatus for gasometric determination of $CaCO_3$ equivalence of limestone by volume of CO_2 evolved. (After Horton and Newsom.)

$CaCO_3$ is placed in the 125-ml conical flask (Fig. 4–4) with a small vial containing 3 ml of concentrated HCl. The 500-ml conical flask is filled with water. All the connections are secured and the overflow tube is placed in a graduate cylinder. Then the flask containing the sample is tilted to upset the vial of HCl. The volume of water that overflows into the graduate is equivalent to the volume of CO_2 evolved. The volume of CO_2 evolved by a limestone sample to be tested is determined in the same manner. The $CaCO_3$ equivalence of the limestone is calculated:

$$CaCO_3 \text{ equivalence} = \frac{\begin{array}{c}\text{volume } CO_2 \text{ evolved} \\ \text{by 1 gm test sample}\end{array}}{\begin{array}{c}\text{volume } CO_2 \text{ evolved} \\ \text{from 1 gm pure } CaCO_3\end{array}} \times 100 \qquad (4\text{--}15)$$

The authors reported reproducible results with from 0.2 to 1 gm of $CaCO_3$ equivalence, and agreement with the titration method on pure calcite and dolomite within 1 per cent. Since any change in the atmospheric pressure results in a change in the volume of CO_2 evolved, a sample of pure $CaCO_3$ must be tested each time the method is employed.

QUESTIONS

1. Explain the principles employed in the centrifuge washing procedure for cation exchange capacity determination.

2. Explain why leaching an acid soil with an unbuffered neutral salt solution is an unsatisfactory method of effecting complete cation exchange.

3. How may the exchange capacity of the organic portion of a soil be estimated?

4. What are some important advantages of the Ca ion for the determination of exchange capacity? When may Na be employed advantageously in the determination of exchange capacity? When may K? When may Mn?

5. Why may the number of "methods" for cation exchange capacity be very large?

6. Explain why simple dialysis of soil or clay in water results in the saturation of some cation exchange charges with hydrogen.

7. Explain how the total exchangeable metallic cations of a soil can be measured by equilibration of a sample with a solution of a weak acid.

8. Describe the reactions that occur in the Bray and Willhite method for total exchangeable metallic cations of soils.

9. Define "exchangeable metallic cation status" of soils.

10. What are the principles employed in the determination of the gypsum requirement of soils?

11. What are the essential principles employed in the determination of exchangeable hydrogen of soils?

12. How is the exchangeable hydrogen analysis interpreted for the estimation of lime requirement of a soil?

13. How may the $CaCO_3$ equivalence of a liming material be estimated?

14. Explain how the dissolved iron and aluminum ions are excluded from the neutralizing equivalence of ground limestone as determined by the acid-hydroxide titration.

15. How may the percentage of $MgCO_3$ be estimated in connection with limestone analysis?

5

Exchangeable Metallic Cation Determinations for Soils

Exchangeable . . . often termed "available" constituents

5–1. The exchangeable metallic cation species of most frequent interest in soils are Ca^{++}, Mg^{++}, K^+, Mn^{++}, Na^+, all of which are readily extracted and determined in the 1 N NH_4OAc extract of soil. The principal nonmetallic exchangeable cations are NH_4^+ and H^+ (¶ 4–50). Since NH_4OAc is employed (¶ 5–7) as the extraction reagent for the exchangeable metallic cations, a separate extraction (¶ 8–33) is necessary for exchangeable NH_4^+ determination. While Al^{+++}, Fe^{+++}, Cu^{++}, Zn^{++}, and Co^{++} are extracted by NH_4OAc to some extent, their chemistry in soils is more complex than that of the more abundant exchangeable metallic cations, and their analytical determinations are given special considerations in Chapters 11 and 15.

5–2. Three factors tend to raise the quantity of NH_4OAc extracted metallic cations over the amount truly exchangeable, namely (a) the presence of soluble salts in the soil (¶ 5–3), (b) some weathering release of cations from silicate minerals during the course of prolonged extraction, controlled by standardized extraction time and technique, and (c) the dissolution of some of the carbonates of Ca and Mg (¶ 5–18). These factors tend to make the analysis for exchangeable metallic cations only approximate, yet the determination is sufficiently accurate to make it one of the most practical and valuable means of assessing soil fertility (¶ 5–6).

5–3. Exclusion of Soluble Salts. For the most accurate results on exchangeable cations, the quantities of soluble cations found in the saturation extract (¶ 10–78) are subtracted from the quantities removed in the NH_4OAc solution. Or the water soluble salts may be removed by leaching the soil with 40 per cent ethanol until the leachate is free from Cl⁻ and SO₄⁼ prior to the NH₄OAc extraction.[1] Soils high in gypsum have been preleached with water in 1 : 1 weight ratio to soil.[2] There is an equilibrium between the exchangeable and soluble cations (¶ 10–18), and this equilibrium shifts as the ratio of water to soil increases. The quantity and nature of ions in solution therefore depends upon the soil : water ratio, particularly if sulfates are present. For fertility evaluation (¶ 5–6), the soluble salts may ordinarily be lumped with the exchangeable (available) cations. For rather well leached soils that have not been recently fertilized, the content of water soluble salts may be ignored.

5–4. Report of Exchangeable Metallic Cation Species. Each exchangeable cation species of soils is reported as meq of the cation per 100 gm of soil on an oven-dry basis. The sum total of various metallic cation species as meq per 100 gm of soil, is found by summation (compare ¶ 4–33). The percentage of metallic cation saturation is then computed by equation 4–6 (¶ 4–42). If the soil is known to contain carbonates of Ca and Mg, the determination of these cations in the aqueous NH₄OAc extract may be omitted. If the soil is known to contain enough gypsum (¶ 10–113) not to be completely soluble in the saturation extract, the determination of Ca may be omitted. If the sum of exchangeable cations greatly exceeds the cation exchange capacity, indicating the presence of free carbonates or gypsum (but see ¶ 4–43), the determinations of Ca and Mg may be disregarded on completion of the analysis.

5–5. Meq Percentage of Metallic Cation Species. The amount of each exchangeable metallic cation is also calculated as percentage of the total cation exchange capacity (¶ 4–6), for example, for Na:

$$\% \text{ Na saturation} = \frac{\text{meq of Na per 100 gm of soil}}{\text{Cation exchange capacity}} \tag{5–1}$$

Also, each ion may be calculated as *meq percentage* of the total major metallic cations, for example, for Ca:

$$\text{meq \% Ca} = \frac{\text{meq of Ca per 100 gm of soil}}{\text{meq of (Ca + Mg + K + Na) per 100 gm of soil}} \tag{5–2}$$

For neutral soils, the two equations give approximately the same result (¶ 4–43). For soils which have over 15 per cent Na saturation (¶ 10–5) changing the ratio of percentage Na saturation to percentage Ca saturation is important and the needed change is designated the gypsum requirement of soil (¶ 4–44).

---

[1] Gill and Sherman, *Pac. Sci.,* 6:138 (1952).
[2] Piper, *Soil and Plant Analysis* (New York: Interscience Publishers, Inc., 1944), p. 168.

5–6. Plow-Layer Volume Basis. In soil fertility evaluation, the amounts of exchangeable metallic cations are often expressed in terms of pp2m, that is, pounds of the cation per acre plow-layer volume (¶ 2–3) of the soil. The relationship of meq to pp2m is given in Table 5–1. The quantity of $CaCO_3$ equivalent to each meq of exchangeable H in soil is also given in the table (discussed in ¶ 4–64).

TABLE 5–1

Equivalence as pp2m of 1 meq of exchangeable cation per 100 gm of soil and representative amounts in a fertile soil. If the furrow slice weighs 2 million pounds, pp2m equals pounds per acre.

Equivalent of one meq per 100 gm of soil		Representative for a fertile soil	
cation	pp2m	pp2m	meq/100 gm
Ca	401	4010	10
Mg	243	729	3
Mn	549	11	0.02
K	782	234	0.3
Na	460	92	0.2
H	20	30	1.5
$CaCO_3$	1000	—	—

EXTRACTION OF EXCHANGEABLE CATIONS WITH NH_4OAc

5–7. The exchangeable cations are determined after extraction with 1 N NH_4OAc. Prianishnikov[3] employed this reagent for the extraction of exchangeable K. The advantages[4] of this reagent are its effectiveness in wetting the soil and replacing exchangeable cations, its ease of volatility during analysis, and its suitability for use with flame emission. Although some NH_4^+ is fixed (like K) in nonexchangeable form even under moist conditions in soils containing vermiculite, accompanied by a decrease in the cation exchange capacity (¶ 4–25), the fixation of NH_4^+ from NH_4OAc apparently interferes little with the extraction of exchangeable metallic cations.[5]

APPARATUS

5–8. The apparatus needed for extraction of a soil includes a 5.5-cm Buchner funnel and 500-ml suction flask and a 250-ml conical flask. To extract soil in runoff waters, a 11-cm Buchner funnel and 1-liter suction flask are needed. Also needed are a torsion balance, a beaker of sufficient volume to hold the NH_4OAc extraction solution, a cover glass with glass

---

[3] *Landw. Vers. Sta.,* 79–80:667 (1913).
[4] Schollenberger and Simon, *Soil Sci.,* 59:13 (1945).
[5] Bower *et al., Soil Sci.,* 73:251 (1952).

hooks to support it, a glass rod with rubber policeman, a funnel, a 100-ml volumetric flask, and a steam plate.

REAGENTS

5–9. Required reagents are 1 N NH_4OAc (57 ml of glacial HOAc is diluted to 800 ml with water, then neutralized with concentrated NH_4OH to pH 7.0; the solution is then diluted to 1 liter); Whatman No. 42 filter paper, 5.5-cm and 11-cm; 6 N HNO_3, 30 per cent H_2O_2, and 6 N HCl.

PROCEDURE

5–10. The Soil Sample. Ideally, the soil sample should be in the field-moist condition so that ionic equilibria are undisturbed by drying (most important in relation to NH_4^+, K^+, Mn^{++}, and Fe^{++}). The moisture content is determined by drying a separate sample at 100°C. In practice, an air-dried soil sample is frequently extracted. The sample weight in either case is based on the "fine earth," particles passing a 2-mm sieve, and the results expressed on the oven-dry basis. Samples rich in coarse and medium sand are quartered or riffled down to the sample size (50 to 100 gm) for analysis; the entire sample thus derived is weighed for analysis. Fine textured soils, on the other hand, may be transferred with spatula or spoon while being weighed.

5–11. Extraction of Cations from Soil in a Buchner Funnel.[6] A 50-gm air-dry soil sample (or equivalent weight of field-moist soil) is weighed out into a 250-ml conical flask and 100 ml of 1 N NH_4OAc is added. The flask is stoppered and shaken for several minutes and then allowed to stand overnight. The contents of the flask is then transferred to a 5.5-cm Buchner funnel in which a moist Whatman No. 42 filter paper has been seated by gentle suction. The soil is leached with an additional 400 ml of NH_4OAc, a little at a time, so that the leaching process requires at least an hour. Two reagent blanks are run on the same volume of NH_4OAc. The NH_4OAc leachate is evaporated (¶ 5–14) or analyzed directly by flame emission (¶ 18–24). The exchangeable hydrogen may be estimated first from the pH or titration of the NH_4OAc solution (¶ 4–61). The soil in the Buchner funnel may be employed to determine the cation exchange capacity (¶ 4–25).

5–12. Extraction of Cations from Suspended Soil in Runoff. After thorough agitation of the original runoff sample, 950 ml is quickly measured in a 1-liter conical flask bearing a 950-ml mark. Then approximately 75 gm of NH_4OAc (crystals) is added (giving a 1 N NH_4OAc solution). The flask is stoppered and the solution is mixed by inversion every 5 minutes for 30 minutes (while other flasks are being prepared). While the

---

[6] Peech *et al.*, U.S.D.A. Cir. 757, p. 8 (1947).

suspension is still well-mixed, a 1-cm layer is poured into a 11-cm Buchner funnel in which a Whatman No. 42 filter paper has been moistened and sealed tightly by suction. The filtrate is received in a clean 1-liter suction flask. (If the filtrate at first comes through cloudy, seldom the case, the free liquid is suctioned through the Buchner, and the filtrate is washed back into the original flask). When all of the NH_4OAc has been suctioned through, the flask and soil are washed once with about 25 ml of 1 N NH_4OAc. The filtrate is transferred to a 1-liter beaker and the exchangeable cations are determined (¶ 5–14). Reagent blanks are run.

5–13. For rapid determination of exchangeable K only in runoff, a special extraction and determination by flame emission (¶ 18–26) is recommended.

5–14. Evaporation of NH_4OAc Extract. The beaker containing the 1 N NH_4OAc extract from the soil or suspended solids in runoff is placed on the steam plate and evaporated to dryness. Then the sides of beaker are washed down with a small amount of distilled water, and the solution is evaporated to dryness again. If the residue is dark in color, indicating organic matter remaining (usually the case), the beaker is fitted with a closely-fitting cover glass, and then to the beaker are added 2 ml of 30 per cent H_2O_2, and 2 ml of 6 N HNO_3. While tightly covered, the solution is digested on a steam plate for 20 to 30 minutes. Then the cover glass is raised on glass hooks and the solution is evaporated to dryness.

5–15. The residue is wetted with 10 ml of 6 N HCl, stirred with a policeman to bring the acid into good contact, and then the solution is diluted with 15 ml of water followed by immediate filtration through a retentive (Whatman No. 42) filter paper to remove silica. The filtrate and washings are collected in a 100-ml volumetric flask, made up to volume at room temperature, and designated *Solution A,* containing the exchangeable metallic cations. (It is analyzed by ¶ 5–24 and following.)

ALTERNATIVE PROCEDURES

5–16. A centrifuge extraction procedure[7] is rapid and convenient for semimicrochemical methods of determination, and overcomes the difficulty encountered in leaching soil samples of low permeability. A sample weight[8] of 4 gm of medium- or fine-textured soil or 6 gm of coarse-textured soil of known moisture content is weighed out and transferred to a 50-ml round-bottom narrow-neck centrifuge tube. Then 33 ml of neutral 1 N NH_4OAc solution is added, the tube is stoppered, and the suspension is shaken in a reciprocating shaker for 5 minutes. The stopper is then re-

---

[7] Bower *et al., Soil Sci.,* 73:251 (1952).
[8] Must be increased for soils of low metallic cation status to give determinable concentrations in the extract volume.

moved, and the tube is centrifuged until the supernatant liquid is clear, usually requiring 5 minutes in the International No. 2 centrifuge at a speed of 1,500 to 2,000 rpm. The supernatant liquid is decanted as soon as possible into a 100-ml volumetric flask. The sample is then extracted 2 additional times with 33 ml of NH_4OAc each time, the supernatant liquid being decanted into the same volumetric flask. The solution in the flask is made to volume and mixed, and the various cations extracted are determined by suitable semimicro procedures, such as the flame emission spectrophotometer (¶ 18–7).

5–17. Extraction of Cations from Soil in a Carbon Funnel.[9] The end of a small wad of fine Pyrex glass wool, or cotton is loosely stuffed into the stem of a carbon funnel leaching tube (Fig. 5–1) with a glass rod. Then

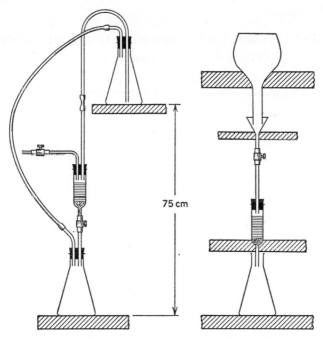

75 cm

Fig. 5–1.   Leaching apparatus for exchangeable cations. (After Schollenberger and Simon, *Soil Sci.*, 59:13, 1945.)

additional glass wool or cotton is arranged above to form a flat pad with a rubber stopper mounted on the end of a glass rod. A little water is run through to make sure that the percolation rate will not be too slow because of too tight packing of the glass wool. The glass wool is rearranged if necessary. Next, the soil sample, consisting of up to 100 gm of air-dry

9 Schollenberger and Simon, *Soil Sci.*, 59:13 (1945).

sifted soil or the equivalent weight of field-moist soil is placed in the carbon funnel in several portions, each portion being packed slightly by jabbing with a spatula, to reduce shrinkage on wetting. Then a 1-cm layer of glass wool is placed above the soil. The apparatus is next assembled (Fig. 5-1), the upper flask with 750 ml of the 1 N NH$_4$OAc being placed on a shelf, and connected with a siphon to deliver through a tight-fitting stopper into the leaching tube. Suction is applied at the collection flask to start the siphon, and then removed. Finally, the screw clamp between the extraction tube and the receiving flask is adjusted to regulate the flow rate. The time for leaching should be at least 4 hours, but no longer than overnight, if the nature of the soil permits. The leaching should now proceed without further attention (¶ 5-14). Two blanks for each set of soil extractions are run on the same volume of NH$_4$OAc, the same quantities of reagents being added throughout.

EXCHANGEABLE CATIONS OF CALCAREOUS SOILS

(Extracted with BaCl$_2$-triethanolamine)

5-18. Extracting calcareous soils with NH$_4$OAc dissolves Ca and Mg extensively from CaCO$_3$ (calcite) or CaCO$_3 \cdot$ MgCO$_3$ (dolomite), beyond their true activity for plant use. Kelley[10] concluded that exchangeable Ca and Mg determinations for calcareous soils were meaningless, and preferred to estimate their sum as the exchange capacity less exchangeable K and Na. Bower et al.,[11] also disregarded the Ca and Mg extracted in NH$_4$OAc if the soil was calcareous or gypsiferous. Peech[12] estimated exchangeable Ca in saturated soils as exchange capacity less exchangeable K, Na, and Mg. There is still a demand for an extraction method for the truly exchangeable Ca and Mg from calcareous soils. The various proposals include (a) use of 40 to 80 per cent alcoholic solutions[13] of NH$_4$OAc, (b) corrections for the solubility of CaCO$_3$ in the leachings,[14] or (c) use of alkaline solutions such as Na$_2$CO$_3$[15] or BaCl$_2$-triethanolamine extraction solution of pH 8.1 (to be described), in which BaCO$_3$ coats the surface of calcite and dolomite and makes them insoluble.

APPARATUS

5-19. Needed apparatus includes a crucible with a perforated bottom, a crucible holder mounted on a suction flask, a 100-ml volumetric flask, a 25-ml pipet, a buret, and a 150-ml beaker.

---

[10] *J. Agr. Sci.*, 24:72 (1934).

[11] *Soil Sci.*, 73:251 (1952).

[12] *Ind. Eng. Chem.*, A.E., 13:436 (1941).

[13] Magistad and Burgess, *Ariz. Agr. Exp. Sta. Tech. Bul. 20* (1928).

[14] As reviewed by Kelley, *Cation Exchange in Soils* (New York: Reinhold Publishing Corporation, 1948).

[15] Puri, *Soils* (New York: Reinhold Publishing Corporation, 1949).

5–20. Needed reagents include 0.2 N $BaCl_2$-triethanolamine of pH 8.1 (made up[16] of 25 ml of commercial triethanolamine, specific gravity 1.126 which is about 8 N, diluted to 250 ml with water and partially neutralized with HCl to adjust the pH to 8.1: this requires approximately 90 ml of 1 N HCl: this solution is diluted to 500 ml with water and then mixed with 500 ml of 0.4 N $BaCl_2$ and the resulting solution is mixed and protected from the CO_2 of the air). Also needed are filter paper discs, 0.1 N H_2SO_4, methyl orange indicator, 4 per cent $(NH_4)_2C_2O_4 \cdot H_2O$ and standard 0.025 N $KMnO_4$.

5–21. A quantity of soil or a colloidal electrolyte equivalent to 0.5 to 1 meq of exchangeable metallic cations is weighed into a perforated crucible fitted with a small, moistened filter paper disc. The sample is leached with 50 ml of 0.2 N $BaCl_2$-triethanolamine of pH 8.1 and then is washed with 50 ml of H_2O. The leachate is made to a volume of 100 ml. (To determine the exchange capacity with Ba, the soil is leached once more, with $BaCl_2$ without triethanolamine, ¶ 4–32).

5–22. Exchangeable Ca Determination. The exchangeable Ca is determined on a 25-ml aliquot of the leachate made to 100 ml (¶ 5–21). To the aliquot, 25 ml of 0.1 N H_2SO_4 and 1 drop of methyl orange indicator are added. Next 20 per cent NaOAc is added until the rose-orange color disappears. The mixture is heated to about 70°C, and two 5-ml portions of 4 per cent $(NH_4)_2C_2O_4 \cdot H_2O$ are added slowly with stirring. After digestion for about an hour, the precipitate ($BaSO_4$ and CaC_2O_4) is filtered and washed with warm water. The CaC_2O_4 is dissolved from the precipitate in 50 ml of approximately 1 per cent H_2SO_4, heated to 80°–90°C and titrated with 0.025 N $KMnO_4$.

5–23. Determination of Mg. The Mg is determined on the filtrate from the Ca determination, by means of the usual procedure (¶ 5–45).

CALCIUM DETERMINATION

(As oxalate by titration with cerate or permanganate)

5–24. The exchangeable Ca obtained in the NH_4OAc extraction (¶ 5–14) may readily be determined by means of the oxalate-cerate[18] titration pro-

---

[16] After Peech *et al.*, U.S.D.A. Cir. 757 (1947).

[17] After Mehlich, *Soil Sci.*, 60:289 (1945).

[18] Adapted from Ellis, *Ind. Eng. Chem.*, A.E., 18:426 (1938), and Katzman and Jacobi, *J. Biol. Chem.*, 118:539 (1937). Titration with permanganate is less convenient though still a standard procedure, *Methods of Analysis*, 7th ed. (Washington, D.C.: A.O.A.C., 1950), p. 33.

cedure. Also, Ca from total elemental analysis of soils (¶ 11–162), from plant tissue (¶ 12–39), from water analysis (¶ 10–85), or from other sources can be determined. Ions that may coprecipitate with Ca as the oxalate include Sr, Fe^{++}, Ti, Mn^{++}, Li, Be, Mg, and Ba. For routine Ca determinations for soils and plants, the interferences are almost invariably negligible. When the coprecipitation of Mg is known to be a factor, rarely the case, either a double precipitation (¶ 11–166) or a high dilution combined with the semimicro oxalate procedure (¶ 5–38) for Ca is an effective remedy, as is also the use of the Versene procedure (¶ 4–21 or 11–47) or the flame emission spectrophotometric procedure (¶ 18–7).

APPARATUS

5–25. Needed apparatus includes a 250-ml beaker, a buret containing $4 N NH_4OH$, a steam plate, and a fritted glass[19] crucible (medium porosity) with a holder and suction flask.

REAGENTS

5–26. Needed reagents are $6 N$ HCl; glacial HOAc; concentrated and $4 N NH_4OH$; brom cresol green indicator; 10 per cent $H_2C_2O_4$ solution; $2 N H_2SO_4$ (55 ml of concentrated H_2SO_4 slowly added to 900 ml of water, then diluted to 1 liter); 0.025 M "Ferroin" indicator (orthophenanthroline-ferrons complex, from G. F. Smith Chemical Co., Columbus, O.); and the following special reagents.

5–27. Standard Oxalate. Standard $Na_2C_2O_4$ is dried in an oven at $100°C$ and cooled. Then a 3.350-gm portion is weighed out and dissolved in approximately 600 ml of $2 N H_2SO_4$. The solution is then made to a volume of 1 liter in this solvent. This primary oxidation-reduction standard is $0.0500 N$.

5–28. Standard Cerate. Approximately 34 gm of $(NH_4)_4Ce(SO_4)_4 \cdot 2 H_2O$, ammonium tetrasulfatocerate, is dissolved in 1 liter of $2 N H_2SO_4$ to obtain a solution which is approximately 0.05 N with respect to oxidation reduction, $Ce^{4+} \longrightarrow Ce^{3+}$. (If permanganate is to be employed, a stock solution of $1 N$ $KMnO_4$ is prepared as directed in connection with the Mn determination (¶ 5–67), and an aliquot is diluted to 0.05 N and standardized.) It is preferable to standardize the oxidant solution without further dilution, rather than to attempt to dilute it to exactly 0.05 N.

5–29. Standard Ferrous Solution. A standard ferrous solution is prepared by dissolution of 30 gm of $Fe(NH_4)_2(SO_4)_2 \cdot 6 H_2O$ in 1 liter of approximately 0.5 N H_2SO_4 (exact concentration of ferrous is not impor-

---

[19] Marsden, *J. Soc. Chem. Ind.,* 60:20 (1941). Found also by this author to be eminently suitable, owing to low blank, rapidity, and convenience.

tant). This solution is approximately 0.05 N with respect to oxidation-reduction. A 10-ml aliquot of the cerate solution is titrated with the ferrous solution to the "Ferroin" end point just before each set of titrimetric determinations, and the factor, R, for the cerate equivalent of the ferrous is calculated (ml Ce/ ml Fe = R). Then, 20 ml of the standard cerate is pipetted into 10 ml of standard oxalate in a beaker and the solution temperature is brought to about 80°C and finally back to less than 50°C. The excess cerate is then back titrated with ferrous solution to the "Ferroin" end point. Then

$$N_{Ce} = \frac{\text{ml oxalate} \times 0.05}{(\text{ml cerate}) - (\text{ml ferrous} \times R)} \qquad (5-3)$$

The above procedure for standardization of the cerate is conventional for sulfatocerate oxidimetry.[20]

PROCEDURE

5-30. An aliquot of *Solution A* equivalent to 0.1 to 1 meq (2 to 20 mgm) of Ca (15 ml for silt loams, 25 ml for sands, 40 ml for runoff) is transferred with a pipet to a 250-ml beaker and diluted to about 150 ml. Then 5 ml of 6 N HCl is added to provide ample NH_4Cl to prevent co-precipitation of Mg with the CaC_2O_4. Mg, Fe, Al, and other ions remain quantitatively in solution with the acid[21] precipitation employed, in the presence[22] of excess NH_4Cl, NH_4OAc, and $(NH_4)_2C_2O_4$. Rarely, with very unusual quantities of Mg present relative to Ca, is reprecipitation necessary (¶ 11–160).

5-31. Precipitation of CaC_2O_4. To the acid solution of Ca and Mg, containing 5 ml or more of concentrated HCl in excess, 5 ml glacial HOAc and 0.5 ml of brom cresol green indicator are added. Then concentrated NH_4OH is added with stirring, until the first greenish color appears; next the solution is heated to boiling. Now 10 ml of 10 per cent oxalic acid solution is added, which makes the solution strongly acid again (full yellow color). Finally, 4 N NH_4OH is added dropwise from a buret with rapid stirring until a strong green color appears, indicating pH 4 to 4.5. Calcium oxalate precipitates slowly in the hot acid solution during the

[20] Smith, *Cerate Oxidimetry* (Columbus, Ohio: G. F. Smith Chemical Co., 1942), p. 81; Larson and Greenberg, *J. Biol. Chem.*, 123:199 (1938); Reitemeier, *Ind. Eng. Chem., A.E.*, 15:393 (1943).

[21] Chapman, *Soil Sci.*, 26:479 (1928), employed a precipitation pH of about 4.0, which suggests that brom phenol blue indicator (critical pH 4.0) may be employed instead of brom cresol green.

[22] That the use of ammonium and organic chelating agents permits a single precipitation separation of Ca from Mg is shown by Chapman, *Soil Sci.*, 26:479 (1928); Wright and Delaune, *Ind. Eng. Chem., A.E.*, 18:426 (1946); and B. Chatterjee and J. L. Huber working in the author's laboratory. See also semimicrochemical procedure (¶ 5–38).

additions of NH_4OH, with only traces of Ca left to precipitate as pH 4.5 is approached. The solution is digested on the steam plate for 1 hour, which suffices to increase the crystal size and leave a clear supernatant liquid. Prolonged digestion is avoided, because Mg is likely to begin coprecipitation.

5–32. Filtration of CaC_2O_4. The clear supernatant solution is decanted through a fritted glass crucible (medium porosity) with suction. The precipitate is suspended in the last of the liquid and poured into the filter. Then the beaker is rinsed 3 times, thoroughly, including the sides but with a minimum volume of water delivered as a fine jet, the rinsings being poured through the filter. The filter is next washed 5 times with small amounts of hot water. *The filtrate is saved for magnesium.* (In place of a fritted glass filter crucible, filter paper, a Whatman No. 42, and a fluted funnel may be used, in which case washing is continued until the washings are free from chlorides, as shown by test of 3 ml of washings with 0.5 per cent $AgNO_3$ solution, the tested solution being discarded. About 10 washings are usually required.)

5–33. Titration of CaC_2O_4. The fritted glass crucible and precipitate are placed into the original beaker. Then 75 ml of 1 N H_2SO_4 is added, as well as sufficient water to cover the crucible. The solution is warmed to 90°C and promptly titrated with 0.05 N $(NH_4)_4Ce(SO_4)_4$ (with orthophenanthroline indicator) or $KMnO_4$. The blank on fritted glass is negligible. The oxidizing solution is freshly standardized against the primary standard $Na_2C_2O_4$ and the normality of the oxidizing solution is recorded, with no attempt to adjust it to exactly 0.05 N. For work involving 0.1 meq of Ca or less, 0.015 N solutions are employed (¶ 5–38). (In case a filter paper was used, it is pierced, and the main mass of precipitate is washed into the original beaker. Then 75 ml of H_2SO_4 is poured over the paper to dissolve the precipitate in the pores of the paper. The paper is then washed several times with hot water. Finally the solution is diluted to 150 ml with hot water, heated to 90°C and titrated with 0.05 N cerate or permanganate. Near the end of the titration the paper is placed in the solution, and the titration is continued until the end point is permanent for at least 30 seconds. The blank titration obtained with filter paper alone, which usually amounts to 0.1 to 0.2 ml, is subtracted from the main titre.)

Equations:

$$CaC_2O_4 + H_2SO_4 \longrightarrow H_2C_2O_4 + CaSO_4 \qquad (5\text{–}4)$$
$$C_2O_4{}^{--} + 2\ Ce^{4+} \longrightarrow 2\ Ce^{3+} + 2\ CO_2 \qquad (5\text{–}5)$$

or, molecularly,

$$H_2C_2O_4 + 2\ (NH_4)_4Ce(SO_4)_4 \longrightarrow Ce_2(SO_4)_3 + H_2SO_4$$
$$+ 4\ (NH_4)_2SO_4 + 2\ CO_2$$
$$(5\text{–}6)$$

5–34. For soils, the results are reported as meq of Ca per 100 gm of soil:

$$\text{meq of Ca per 100 gm of soil} = (\text{ml cerate}) \times \left(\frac{\text{cerate}}{\text{normality}}\right)$$
$$\times \left(\frac{\text{aliquot}}{\text{factor}}\right) \times \frac{100}{s}$$

$$(5\text{–}7)$$

The aliquot factor is 100/ml of *Solution A* taken. One ml of 0.05 *N* cerate is equivalent to 1.0 mgm of Ca or 1.4 mgm of CaO.

5–35. For runoff, the pounds of $CaCO_3$ per acre-inch of runoff (ppai) is calculated for 40/100 aliquot of the 950 ml of runoff extracted as follows:

$$\text{pounds } CaCO_3 \text{ (ppai)} = \text{meq of Ca} \times 29.8 \qquad (5\text{–}8)$$

The factor 29.8 is derived as follows:

$$\underset{\text{(meq wt. } CaCO_3)}{\frac{100}{2000}} \times \underset{\text{(aliquot factor)}}{\left(\frac{100}{40}\right)\left(\frac{1}{950}\right)} \times 43560 \times \underset{\text{(H}_2\text{O, ppai)}}{\frac{62.4}{12}} = 29.8$$

ALTERNATIVE PROCEDURES

5–36. The oxalate of the CaC_2O_4 precipitate may be evaluated alternatively by a gravimetric procedure if over 40 mgm of Ca is available. A number of semimicro and microchemical procedures for Ca are available, including the Versene method (¶ 11–47), the picrolonate[23] method, the chloranilate[24] method, and the oxalate[25] methods. A semimicro oxalate procedure (¶ 5–38) is effective for amounts of Ca from 0.01 to 0.25 meq (0.2 mgm to 5 mgm) and is readily adaptable outside this range.

5–37. Gravimetric Procedure. In place of the titration procedure, the precipitate of calcium oxalate may also be ignited and weighed, if 2 meq (56 mgm CaO) or more of Ca is being determined. In this case the precipitate is washed free of chlorides with hot neutral 1 per cent $(NH_4)_2C_2O_4$ solution in place of hot water. The precipitate and filter paper are then ignited in a porcelain crucible and the CaO is weighed.

5–38. Semimicro Oxalate Procedure.[26] Ca is precipitated in a concen-

[23] Snell and Snell, *Colorimetric Methods of Analysis,* Vol. I (New York: D. Van Nostrand Company, Inc., 1941), p. 466; also 3rd ed., Vol. II (New York: D. Van Nostrand Company, Inc., 1949), p. 602. Alten *et al., Biochem. Z.,* 265:85 (1933); Bollinger, *Australian J. Exp. Biol. Med. Sci.,* 13:75 (1935).

[24] Tyner, *Anal. Chem.,* 20:76 (1948).

[25] Reitemeier, *Ind. Eng. Chem., A.E.,* 15:393 (1943); Peech *et al.,* U.S.D.A. Cir. 757, p. 18 (1947).

[26] Grateful acknowledgment is made to J. L. Huber and Dr. R. B. Corey for assistance to the author during the adaptation of details of this procedure, and the study of the range of its freedom from interference.

trated solution of salts, under which conditions coprecipitation with Mg is negligible up to a 20 : 1 Mg to Ca ratio with 1 mgm or less of Ca, up to a ratio of 3 : 1 for 2 mgm of Ca, and up to a ratio of 1 : 1 for 5 mgm of Ca. The method is amply sensitive to 1 mgm of Ca or less, so that a great enough dilution of the Ca solution may nearly always be made to insure freedom from Mg interference with a single precipitation. The evaluation of the oxalate may be either titrimetric, or colorimetric by means of the excess cerate color.

5–39. The reagents required are similar to those for the macro procedure except that the standard reductor and oxidant solutions are made more dilute. To make standard 0.015 N reductor solution, 1.005 gm of $Na_2C_2O_4$ is dissolved in 1 liter of 2 N H_2SO_4 in a volumetric flask. To make 0.015 N cerate, 9 gm of $(NH_4)_4Ce(SO_4) \cdot 2 H_2O$ is dissolved in 950 ml of 2 N H_2SO_4 in a 1.5-liter flask; the strength of this solution is determined in accordance with the oxidation-reduction titration procedure detailed later in this paragraph; then the solution is diluted to give exactly 0.015 N. The ferrous reference solution is prepared by dissolution of 5 gm of $Fe(NH_4)_2$ $(SO_4)_2 \cdot 6 H_2O$ in 1 liter of approximately 0.5 N H_2SO_4 (exact concentration of ferrous is not important). A 10-ml aliquot of the cerate solution is titrated with the ferrous solution to the "Ferroin" end point just before each set of titrimetric determinations, and the factor, R, for the cerate equivalent of the ferrous is calculated (ml Ce/ ml Fe $= R$). Then, 20 ml of the standard cerate is pipetted into 10 ml of standard oxalate in a beaker and the solution temperature is brought to 80°C and finally back to less than 50°C. The excess cerate is back titrated with ferrous solution. Then:

$$N_{Ce} = \frac{\text{ml oxalate} \times 0.015}{(\text{ml cerate}) - (\text{ml ferrous} \times R)} \tag{5–9}$$

The precipitate washing solution consists of an ethanol-NH_4OH solution: concentrated NH_4OH is diluted with 9 volumes of water and then this dilute solution is mixed with an equal volume of ethanol.

5–40. To the Ca solution, containing 0.2 to 5 mgm of Ca in a volume of 10 to 20 ml, are added 1 ml of 6 N HCl, 6 ml of glacial HOAc, 3 drops of brom cresol green indicator, and concentrated NH_4OH dropwise from a buret until the solution turns from yellow to faintly green. Next, 2 ml of 10 per cent $H_2C_2O_4$ solution is added and the solution is heated to boiling. Finally, 4 N NH_4OH is added from a buret until the color changes to a full green or bluish green. The CaC_2O_4 ordinarily will have begun precipitation. The beaker is placed on a steam plate for digestion of the precipitate and is allowed to remain for about 30 minutes. If no precipitate is apparent after 10 minutes of digestion, indicating only a trace of Ca present, 10 ml of 95 per cent ethanol is added and the precipitate and the solution are digested for another 20 minutes.

5–41. When the digestion is completed, a Pyrex fine porosity filter tube is placed in the beaker, arranged so that the supernatant solution can be drawn off by suction into a 300-ml conical flask (Fig. 5–2). The precipi-

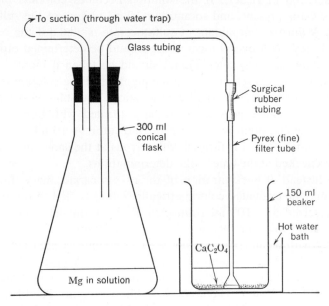

Fig. 5–2. Filtration apparatus for semimicro oxalate procedure for Ca. (Sketch courtesy J. L. Huber and Dr. R. B. Corey.)

tation beaker is kept in a hot water bath to increase the rate of filtration. The supernatant solution is drawn off almost completely and the first washing solution is added just as the last of the solution leaves the beaker, so that $(NH_4)_2C_2O_4$ will not dry on the glass. (Dried $(NH_4)_2C_2O_4$ may not redissolve completely in the washing solution and high results would be obtained.) The precipitate is carefully washed 4 times with small portions of the NH_4OH-ethanol washing solution, the filter tube being allowed to draw off all the washing solution each time.

5–42. The precipitate and filter tube contained in the original beaker, are dried on a steam hot plate. When the precipitate and filter tube are dried completely, approximately 30 ml of hot (90°C) H_2SO_4 is added to dissolve the precipitate including any adhering to the filter tube. After the precipitate has dissolved, filtered air is forced back through the stem of the filter tube to remove the adhering solution. The filter tube is then raised from the solution and about 5 drops of water are placed in it with the capillary dropper and forced back through the fritted glass surface by filtered air to complete the washing of the dissolved oxalate from the interior of the filter tube. The exterior of the tube is flushed off with distilled water. (Fritted glass crucibles are also very satisfactory for this filtration.)

5–43. A 10-ml aliquot of 0.015 N sulfatocerate solution is added to the oxalate solution in H_2SO_4. If the solution becomes colorless, more than 3 mgm of Ca is present, and so another 10-ml aliquot of the sulfatocerate is added. A third 10-ml aliquot of sulfatocerate is added if the second becomes colorless. Not over 9 mgm of Ca should be determined ordinarily in this procedure, and a smaller aliquot should be taken if more than 30 ml of the sulfatocerate is required. The temperature of the solution is raised to about 80°C to complete the oxidation reaction. The solution is then cooled to below 50°C and excess cerate is back titrated with ferrous reference solution to the end point with "Ferroin" indicator. A 10-ml portion of this standard cerate solution is titrated with ferrous at the same time and the R-value is rechecked at the time of the determinations.

5–44. Instead of back titration of the excess cerate, the yellow colored solution may be evaluated colorimetrically.[27] It is cooled to room temperature, transferred to a 100-ml volumetric flask or smaller volumetric flask. The filter and beaker are washed once with a 20-ml portion of 2 N H_2SO_4 and finally with a fine jet wash bottle. The volume is adjusted exactly to the mark with 2 N H_2SO_4 and the solution mixed. A portion is transferred to a colorimeter tube for reading which may be taken immediately with a 420 mu light maximum. The color is stable overnight. The blank for 100 per cent transmission setting is obtained with 2 N H_2SO_4. The mgm of Ca in the sample is obtained from a standard curve. The standard curve is prepared with increments of 0 to 10 ml of cerate similarly diluted. The

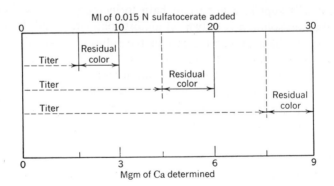

Fig. 5–3. Principle of colorimetry for semimicro oxalate procedure for Ca by residual sulfatocerate. (Sketch courtesy J. L. Huber.)

---

[27] After the procedure outlined by Weybrew *et al.*, *Anal. Chem.*, 20:759 (1948), adapted in the author's laboratory with the generous assistance of Dr. B. Chatterjee and J. L. Huber.

curve may be checked by a series of standard Ca increments.[28] The reading of Ca in the 0 to 3.0, 3.0 to 6.0, or 6.0 to 9.0 mgm of calcium range is illustrated in Fig. 5–3.

MAGNESIUM DETERMINATION

(Titration of $MgNH_4PO_4$ and $MnNH_4PO_4$ to $NH_4H_2PO_4$, then Mn colorimetrically and Mg by difference)

5–45. The exchangeable Mg obtained by the NH_4OAc extraction may be determined readily by the H_2SO_4 titration of the phosphate precipitated,[29] if 2 mgm or more is available. Alternatively, Mg can be determined by the Versene titration (¶ 11–54), by the micro 8-hydroxy quinoline procedure (¶ 5–59), or the flame emission spectrophotometer (¶ 18–24).

APPARATUS

5–46. Needed apparatus includes a 300-ml conical flask with a mechanical shaking device or a system of bubbling air through to stir the solution; a fine porosity fritted glass filter, holder, and suction flask; a 1.5 N NH_4OH wash bottle; and a 250-ml beaker.

REAGENTS

5–47. Needed reagents are concentrated NH_4OH, brom cresol purple and brom cresol green indicators, 10 per cent $(NH_4)_2HPO_4$, 1.5 N NH_4OH, 95 per cent and absolute ethanol or methanol, and standard 0.0714 N H_2SO_4 and NaOH.

PROCEDURE

5–48. Precipitation of Mg and Mn. The filtrate from the calcium determination containing over 2 mgm of Mg, is brought to pH 6.2 to 6.4 with NH_4OH (brom cresol purple indicator) and heated on the steam plate until evaporated to 150 ml. If a precipitate has formed (probably Fe $(OH)_3$), it is filtered off. It is important that the pH not exceed 6.4, or MnO_2 may precipitate.

5–49. The solution is transferred to a 300-ml conical flask and then 20 ml of 10 per cent solution of $(NH_4)_2HPO_4$ is added slowly with stirring. After thorough stirring, the solution is made strongly alkaline by slow addition, with more stirring, of 30 ml of concentrated NH_4OH. The solution is allowed to stand overnight. For small amounts of Mg, the solution *must* be agitated by a mechanical reciprocal shaker or by aspiration to insure complete precipitation.

---

[28] Equivalent curves have been shown for the dilution of cerate, and partial oxidation of it by standard $Na_2C_2O_4$ and standard increments of Ca as CaC_2O_4 in systematic studies by J. L. Huber in the author's laboratory.

[29] Dean and Truog, *Ind. Eng. Chem., A.E.,* 7:383 (1935).

5–50. Filtration. The solution is decanted through a retentive fritted glass filter arranged with a suction pump (or filtered through a Whatman No. 32 or 42 filter paper). The flask (and aspirator tube) are washed 3 or 4 times with small portions of 1.5 N NH_4OH solution. It is not necessary to remove the precipitate sticking to the flask and aspirator tube. The fritted glass filter and precipitate are then washed 3 times with the 1.5 N NH_4OH, the solution being allowed to drain from the precipitate completely between washings (10 or 12 washings are required if a filter paper is used). The removal of the last traces of free ammonia from the flask, aspirator tube, and filter are now accomplished by drying by means of two rinsings with 95 per cent ethanol followed by 1 with absolute ethanol or methanol and aspiration for a few minutes. The filtrate is retained until complete recovery of the Mg is assured and then discarded.

5–51. Note on Drying Paper Filter. Free exposure to the air at room temperature over night suffices for drying the filter paper in lieu of alcohol washing. Drying may be accomplished at a higher temperature in 2 or 3 hours, but this temperature must not exceed 45°C. Free NH_3, if left in the filter, will enter in the titration just as the $MgNH_4PO_4$ and vitiate the results.

5–52. Titration[30] of Mg and Mn Phosphates. After all free ammonia is removed from the precipitate and glassware, a carefully measured excess of standard[31] 0.0714 N H_2SO_4 (usually 15 ml will suffice) is dispensed from a buret into the original 300-ml conical flask (to which some of the now washed and dried precipitate is adhering). The acid is diluted with 10 ml of water, and this solution warmed briefly on the steam plate to dissolve the precipitate. The flask is rotated to effect contact with the surface of the flask and aspirator tube. This solution is then transferred quantitatively to a 250-ml beaker in which the fritted glass filter carrying the bulk of the precipitate has been placed. Sufficient water is added to cover the filter and 0.5 ml of 0.04 per cent brom cresol green indicator is added. Warming on a steam plate is continued for 20 minutes with occasional stirring to help dissolve the precipitate. (If a filter paper was used, the paper and standard acid are added directly to the flask.) If the color shifts from yellow to green, an additional measured amount of standard H_2SO_4 is added to maintain an excess.

5–53. The excess H_2SO_4 is then back titrated in the beaker containing the fritted glass filter (or in the flask after addition of 100 ml of water in case the filter paper has been used) with standard 0.0714 N NaOH to the first distinct blue-green color. *The titrated solution is saved for manganese.*

---

[30] Method proposed by Handy, *J. Am. Chem. Soc.,* 22:31 (1900).

[31] Use of 0.1 or 0.05 N H_2SO_4 and NaOH may be substituted if desired according to the amount of Mg present. The more dilute reagents are employed if necessary to give a net titer of at least 3 to 5 ml.

A color standard for the end point is prepared by dissolving 1 gm of KH_2PO_4 in 140 ml of water and adding 10 drops of brom cresol green indicator. The titration represents a conversion of $MgNH_4PO_4$ and $MnNH_4PO_4$ to $NH_4H_2PO_4$.

5–54. The volume of standard H_2SO_4 required may be small, and therefore both standard solutions are very carefully standardized[32] and the buret readings are estimated to within 0.01 ml. (With the use of filter paper, a blank determination must be made, and applied to the titration value to account for the appreciable amount of acid consumed by the filter paper, often as much as 0.3 ml.)

5–55. Calculation of Results. The Mg determined is calculated:

$$\text{meq of Mg per 100 gm soil} = \text{ml } H_2SO_4 \times \text{normality } H_2SO_4 \times 100/s$$
$$(5\text{–}10)$$

wherein s = weight of soil represented. Each ml of 0.0714 N is equivalent to 0.868 mgm of Mg.

$$MgNH_4PO_4 + H_2SO_4 \longrightarrow NH_4H_2PO_4 + MgSO_4 \qquad (5\text{–}11)$$
$$\text{(pH 4.6 end point)}$$

The manganese present reacts in the same way as magnesium, and if appreciable (usually not the case), the meq of Mn is subtracted from the titre.

5–56. Gravimetric Method. The $MgNH_4PO_4$ and $MnNH_4PO_4$ may be ignited to the pyrophosphate according to the following equation, after which, it is determined gravimetrically.[33]

$$2 \, MgNH_4PO_4 \xrightarrow[\text{(heat)}]{} Mg_2P_2O_7 + 2 \, NH_3 + H_2O \qquad (5\text{–}12)$$

$$\text{meq Mg per 100 gm soil} = \text{gm } Mg_2P_2O_7 \times 8.98 \times \frac{100}{s} \qquad (5\text{–}13)$$

Each mgm $Mg_2P_2O_7$ is equivalent to 0.218 mgm Mg. The gravimetric method thus is most applicable when quantities of Mg exceed 10 or 20 mgm. If the content of Mn is appreciable, it is determined separately (¶ 5–71) and the total weight obtained on ignition is corrected to Mg accordingly.

ALTERNATIVE PROCEDURES

5–57. Mg may be determined by a number of other satisfactory procedures; for semimicro quantities the alternative procedures are preferable to the titration procedure given above. The $MgNH_4PO_4$ precipitate can be evaluated by a colorimetric determination of the phosphorus (the titrimetric

[32] The standard NaOH is titrated against a weighed portion of KH-phthalate, and the acid-base ratio is determined of the solutions used.

[33] This method is employed by A.O.A.C., *Methods of Analysis,* 7th ed (Washington, D.C.: A.O.A.C., 1950), p. 22.

procedure is essentially a titration of the first hydrogen of H_3PO_4 and thus the colorimetric procedure is essentially the same in principle, but is enormously more sensitive.) The colorimetric evaluation of the precipitate has been employed.[34] The evaluation can be made with either the blue or yellow molybdophosphoric color (Chapter 7). A Beer's law relation between molybdophosphoric blue color and the Mg precipitated was obtained[35] in the range of 0.2 to 1.2 mgm of Mg, and accurate recoveries were obtained of Mg added to plant ash solutions.

5–58. The 8-hydroxy quinoline procedure is also a thoroughly satisfactory semimicro colorimetric procedure for Mg, suitable for the range of 0.1 to 1.5 mgm of Mg as this procedure is detailed below. It requires a somewhat higher manipulative skill than the titration procedure given above. Other alternative procedures for Mg include the Versene titration (¶ 4–21 and 11–54) and the flame emission spectrophotometer procedure (¶ 18–7).

5–59. Semimicro 8-hydroxy Quinoline Procedure for Mg.[36] Needed apparatus includes 60-ml pointed centrifuge tubes (Fig. 11–4) and centrifuge, an air-jet stirrer, a hot water bath and cover glass, a 50-ml pipet preferably of the 3-stopcock (Lowy) type and smaller pipets, an aspirator decanting device (Fig. 11–3), and an absorption spectrophotometer with a 660 mu light maximum.

5–60. Needed reagents are NH_4Cl, A.R.; HOAc, glacial, C.P.; concentrated and 4 N NH_4OH, and the following special reagents. For a three per cent 8-hydroxy quinoline solution, approximately 3 gm of 8-hydroxy quinoline is dissolved in 100 ml of 95 per cent ethanol. This reagent is freshly prepared before each use. For the ammonium hydroxide-ethanol wash solution, a water solution containing 10 per cent by volume of concentrated NH_4OH is mixed with an equal volume of 95 per cent ethanol. For the ferric chloride-acetic acid reagent solution, a 25-gm portion of $FeCl_3 \cdot 7 H_2O$ is dissolved in water, 25 ml of glacial HOAc is added, and the solution is diluted to 1 liter. For the standard Mg solution, a 1.521-gm portion of $MgSO_4 \cdot 7 H_2O$ is dissolved in water and diluted to approximately 900 ml. The Mg concentration in this solution is then determined gravimetrically as the hydroxy quinolate, or as the pyrophosphate (¶ 5–56), and the volume is adjusted so that 1 ml of the solution contains 0.150 mgm of Mg. To obtain the standard Mg curve, aliquots of this solution (0.5, 1, 2, 4, 6, 8, 10, and 12 ml) are placed into 60-ml pointed

[34] Reitemeier, *Ind. Eng. Chem.*, *A.E.*, 15:393 (1943).

[35] In the author's laboratory, by Dr. B. Chatterjee and J. L. Huber (1947).

[36] The details of the procedure given were adapted by Dr. R. B. Corey, working in the author's laboratory; previous reports on the method include Sideris, *Ind. Eng. Chem.*, *A.E.*, 12:232 (1940); Gerber *et al.*, *Ind. Eng. Chem.*, *A.E.*, 14:658 (1942); Weeks and Todd, *Ind. Eng. Chem.*, *A.E.*, 15:297 (1943); and Dr. A. E. Peterson in this laboratory.

centrifuge tubes and diluted to approximately 40 ml. Then 1 gm of NH_4Cl is added and precipitation of the Mg and preparation and colori-metric reading of the test solutions are carried out as described in the procedure.

5–61. The Mg is determined directly on an aliquot of *Solution A*, with-out prior removal of Ca in nearly all cases; Ca does not interfere except when very unusually high in amount relative to Mg. In case of a shortage of *Solution A*, the Mg may be determined on the filtrate from the Ca de-termination as the oxalate, but the excess ammonium salts must first be removed. To do this, 3 gm of NaOH pellets are added to the filtrate in a conical flask and the solution is boiled to expel NH_3. The solution is then made slightly acid while hot, by the addition of concentrated HCl drop-wise (indicators are already present in the solution). The Mg is then de-termined on this solution instead of *Solution A* in the following paragraph.

5–62. An aliquot of *Solution A* containing 0.1 to 1.5 mgm of Mg is placed in a graduated 60-ml pointed centrifuge tube (Fig. 11–4) and diluted to a volume of 40 ml. Approximately 1 gm of NH_4Cl is dissolved in this solution with agitation by the air-jet stirrer and then the tube is placed in a hot water bath for 5 minutes. Three drops of brom cresol purple indicator are added to the hot solution. Next, 4 N NH_4OH is added dropwise while the solution is agitated with the air-jet stirrer, until the indi-cator just turns purple. The tube is again placed in the hot water bath for 5 minutes, then cooled and diluted to exactly 60 ml. The solution is mixed and centrifuged for 5 minutes at 2000 rpm to sediment the hydroxy oxides of Fe, Al, and Ti.

5–63. An aliquot of the supernatant solution (or the standard Mg solu-tion), containing from 0.1 to 1.5 mgm of Mg, is transferred to another pointed centrifuge tube. For recovery of a maximum aliquot, a 50-ml Lowy pipet is best. To this solution are added, with constant agitation with the air-jet stirrer, 2 ml of concentrated NH_4OH and 1 ml of 3 per cent 8-hydroxy quinoline solution. The tube is placed in a water bath that is then covered with a watch glass so any precipitate that may rise on top of the solution will not dry on the sides of the tube. The water bath is heated to boiling, and then the tube is placed in a cool water bath for 2 hours, after which it is centrifuged at 2000 rpm for 5 minutes. The supernatant liquid is decanted with the device shown in Fig. 11–3. The precipitate is washed twice, each washing consisting of the addition of approximately 40 ml of the NH_4OH-ethanol washing solution, agitation with the air-jet stirrer, centrifugation, and decantation. After the last decantation, exactly 2.5 ml of glacial HOAc is added to the precipitate in the bottom of the tube, and the suspension is thoroughly mixed with the air-jet stirrer. When the precipitate has dissolved completely, the solution is diluted in the tube to exactly 50 ml and mixed well with the air-jet stirrer. This is *Solution B,* used for the determination of magnesium.

5–64. To a 50-ml volumetric flask is added 10 ml of $FeCl_3$ solution, which is then diluted to approximately 30 ml with distilled water. Exactly 10 ml of *Solution B* containing the Mg is added. (It is important that the aliquot size not vary, as the concentration of HOAc in the final solution has an appreciable effect on the color intensity.) The solution is diluted to the mark, mixed thoroughly, and a portion is transferred to a colorimeter tube. The percentage of light transmission is read with a 660 mu light maximum, and the concentration of Mg is obtained from the standard curve. The color is stable over night.

MANGANESE DETERMINATION[37]

(Colorimetric Na-paraperiodate oxidation in H_3PO_4 solution)

5–65. Manganese determination is needed in connection with numerous kinds of soil chemical analysis, but fortunately a simple determinative procedure is adequate for the many applications. A list of representative applications is given at the beginning of the procedure (¶ 5–73). Background for absorption colorimetry is supplied in Chapter 17.

APPARATUS

5–66. Needed apparatus includes a 150-ml beaker and cover glass, a glass funnel, a 100-ml volumetric flask, a steam plate, a gas burner, and an absorption spectrophotometer with 540 mu light maximum.

REAGENTS

5–67. Needed reagents are 30 per cent H_2O_2 (Mn-free), 85 per cent H_3PO_4, concentrated HNO_3, and the following special solutions:

1. $Na_3H_2IO_6$, Trisodium paraperiodate (G. F. Smith Chemical Co., Columbus, O.).

2. *Purified water diluent.* To 1 liter of distilled or redistilled water in a 2-liter Florence flask are added 100 ml of 85 per cent H_3PO_4 and 1 gm $Na_3H_2IO_6$. The mixture is heated to boiling and digested on the steam plate for 1 hour. It is then stoppered with a foil-covered stopper.

3. *Standard $KMnO_4$ solution.* A stock solution of approximately $1 N$ $KMnO_4$ is prepared by dissolving 31.6 gm of $KMnO_4$ crystals in 1 liter of distilled water. It is stored in an amber bottle. It must be purified because of the development of traces of MnO_2 as a result of traces of reducing substances in the solvent, container, etc., and through autooxidation of Mn^{++} impurity by MnO_4^- according to the equation:

$$3 Mn^{++} + 2 MnO_4^- + 2 H_2O \leftrightharpoons 5 MnO_2 + 4H^+ \qquad (5\text{–}4)$$
$$\text{(precipitate)}$$

---

[37] Based on the classical method of Willard and Greathouse, *J. Am. Chem. Soc.,* 39:2366 (1917), as adapted to photoelectric colorimetry by Mehlig, *Ind. Eng. Chem., A.E.,* 11:274 (1939). Published improvements and modifications are cited individually at appropriate places in the procedure.

in which MnO_2 is the generalized form of the precipitate. It may involve various amounts of water and mixed valences of Mn. This reaction also occurs in a $KMnO_4$ titration if insufficient excess of acid has been supplied, when considerable Mn^{++} has been formed as the product of the reaction and an excess of $KMnO_4$ is present. Purification may be hastened by boiling and filtration; long standing for the reaction and sedimentation of the precipitate at room temperature is also effective.

5–68. The standard solution of 0.05 N $KMnO_4$ (N as oxidation-reduction) is prepared by dilution of 50 ml of the purified 1 N stock solution to 1 liter. This solution is stored in an amber bottle fitted with a 2-hole stopper bearing a delivery tube bent to deliver into a buret and an air inlet tube through which air is forced to deliver the solution needed. This solution is standardized by titration of primary standard $Na_2C_2O_4$. The titration is conveniently carried out by pipetting 20 ml of 0.0500 N $Na_2C_2O_4$ solution in 2 N H_2SO_4 (¶ 5–27) into a 150-ml beaker, heating the solution to 70°C, and titration of the 0.05 N $KMnO_4$ to the appearance of a permanent faint pink color. A trace of $MnCl_2$ may be added as an accelerator to initiate the reaction. The exact normality of the $KMnO_4$ solution is calculated and the solution is labeled, a procedure that is preferable to attempting a dilution to exactly 0.0500 N $KMnO_4$.

5–69. A second dilution of 50.0 ml of the 0.05 N $KMnO_4$ to 500 ml in a volumetric flask gives a 0.005 N $KMnO_4$ solution (N as oxidation-reduction). The final colorimetric standard solution is prepared by a further 1 : 20 dilution, to 0.00025 N $KMnO_4$ as oxidation-reduction, equivalent to 0.0001 N as Mn^{++} (2.75 mgm Mn per liter). To make this dilution to a permanently colored solution, 50 ml of the 0.005 N stock is pipetted into a 1.5-liter beaker, then 100 ml of water, 100 ml of 85 per cent H_3PO_4, and 2.0 gm of sodium paraperiodate are added. The solution is heated just to boiling, 725 ml additional water is added, and the solution is digested on the steam plate for 0.5 hour. The hot solution is transferred to a 1-liter volumetric flask, diluted to volume, and mixed. When cooled to room temperature, the volume is adjusted exactly to the mark with the purified water diluent, again mixed, and stored in a cleaned amber bottle or in the flask in the dark. The color is stable for long periods, because an excess of periodate is present. Portions of the solution are read in the colorimeter as needed with a 540 mu light maximum.[38] Beer's law applies. Any light maximum from 525 to 545 mu is satisfactory if used for both standard and test sample; a 520-mu maximum has been employed but its ± 15 mm range encompasses much of the rapid rise in percentage transmission below 522 mu.

5–70. As a test of the analytical technique for developing the $HMnO_4$

---

[38] Mehlig, *Ind. Eng. Chem. A.E.,* 11:274 (1939); verified and refined by Cooper, *Anal. Chem.,* 25:411 (1953).

color that is advisable for the beginning analyst a series of aliquots (2, 4, 6, 8, 10, 12, and 14 ml) is taken of the freshly prepared and mixed 0.005 N (oxidation-reduction) $KMnO_4$ standard solution (55 ppm of Mn^{++}). The aliquots are evaporated to dryness in 150-ml beakers. These are treated as in the procedure (¶ 5–71). The percentage transmission readings are plotted on a semilog scale against concentration on a linear scale (or L-values against concentration, both on linear scales, ¶ 17–16). A straight line should pass through the point derived with the permanent $HMnO_4$ color standard (2.75 ppm Mn^{++}) prepared in the previous paragraph.

PROCEDURE

5–71. Preparation of the Mn Test Solution. Various test solutions besides that carrying exchangeable Mn^{++} may be analyzed by the manganese determination now to be described. The determination of exchangeable Mn^{++} is carried out either on the solution resulting after titration of the $MgNH_4PO_4$ and $MnNH_4PO_4$[39] or on a separate aliquot of *Solution A* (if enough is available). If filter paper instead of fritted glass is employed to filter that precipitate, the filter paper is removed by passing the solution through a second filter paper and thorough washing of the filter.

5–72. An appropriate aliquot is taken of the test solution to be analyzed, to give 0.1 to 0.8 mgm (0.004 to 0.03 meq) of Mn^{++} in the test solution to be made up to a 100-ml final volume with the $HMnO_4$ color. Increased sensitivity can be obtained by a use of a smaller final volume with the $HMnO_4$ color, proportional decreases in the volume of each solvent being added in the development of the $HMnO_4$ color (¶ 5–76).

5–73. Some examples of proper aliquot fractions for a 100-ml final volume of $HMnO_4$ color and for assumed typical concentrations and sample sizes follow:

1. For exchangeable Mn^{++}, 5 ppm in soil from 25-gm sample (¶ 5–53): 1.0 aliquot.
2. For Mn^{++} exchange capacity of soil, 10 meq/100 gm, with 1-gm sample (¶ 4–29): 0.2 aliquot.
3. For Mn^{++} exchange capacity of clay, 50 meq/100 gm, with 0.5-gm sample (¶ 4–29): 0.1 aliquot.
4. For total Mn^{++} in soil, 0.05 per cent MnO from 1-gm sample (¶ 11–173): 0.5 aliquot.
5. For total Mn^{++} in plant tissue following wet-oxidation, 50 ppm Mn from 5-gm sample (¶ 12–39): 1.0 aliquot.

5–74. The aliquot from any of these sources is evaporated to dryness, preferably in a 150-ml beaker, but in a larger beaker if the original volume

---

[39] Joint precipitation with magnesium after Dean and Truog, *Ind. Eng. Chem., A.E.,* 7:383 (1935).

of solution to be evaporated is too large. To the residue, 3 ml of concentrated HNO_3 and 2 ml of 30 per cent H_2O_2 are added; the beaker is covered and digested on the steam plate for 30 minutes. The sides of the beaker are washed down with a fine stream of water from a wash bottle. The solution is transferred to a 150-ml beaker if that size was not used for the original evaporation. It is important that this transfer not be made before the HNO_3 and H_2O_2 treatment. The cover glass on the beaker is next supported on glass hooks and the solution is evaporated to dryness to complete the oxidation of the organic matter and the removal of the H_2O_2.

5–75. Treatment with HNO_3 and H_2O_2 has been found to be highly efficacious in insuring complete removal of reducing substances without ignition in H_2SO_4. Some of the Mn tends to become insoluble as MnO_2 in HNO_3 alone, but not in the presence of both HNO_3 and H_2O_2. Interference by chloride, bromide, iodide, thiocyanate, arsenite, and organic anions such as oxalate is effectively avoided by this treatment.

5–76. Development of $HMnO_4$ Color. Ten ml of 85 per cent H_3PO_4 is added[40] to the beaker, a cover glass is placed on it, and the solution is warmed over a burner to boiling, and then cooled to about 50°C to avoid spattering when diluted with water. The cooled acid is diluted with 10 ml of water, and the solution is mixed by rotating the beaker. Approximately 0.2 gm of sodium paraperiodate is added, the beaker is covered, and the solution is heated on the steam plate until a purple color appears; then 75 ml of the purified water diluent is added and heating is continued for 40 minutes or until the purple color no longer increases. Approximately 0.1 gm additional periodate is added near the end of the period of digestion.

Equations:

$$5\ I^{7+} + 2\ Mn^{++} \longrightarrow 5\ I^{5+} + 2\ Mn^{7+} \tag{5-15}$$

or, with trisodium paraperiodate,

$$15\ Na_3H_2IO_6 + 2\ Mn_3(PO_4)_2 + 6\ H_3PO_4 \longrightarrow 15\ NaIO_3 + 6\ HMnO_4$$
$$+ 10\ Na_3PO_4 + 6\ H_2O \tag{5-16}$$

while, with potassium metaperiodate,

$$15\ KIO_4 + 2\ Mn_3(PO_4)_2 + 9\ H_2O \longrightarrow 15\ KIO_3 + 6\ HMnO_4 + 4\ H_3PO_4 \tag{5-17}$$

----

[40] Use of 85 per cent H_3PO_4 is after Willard and Greathouse, *J. Am. Chem. Soc.* 39:2366 (1917), and Peech, *Ind. Eng. Chem., A.E.,* 13:436 (1941). This acid has the advantage that the $HMnO_4$ color development is less sensitive to H_3PO_4 concentration than to that of H_2SO_4, and that Fe^{+++} is soluble and decolorized in it. The H_3PO_4 also has the advantage over the H_2SO_4 of nonprecipitation of Ca as $CaSO_4$ in case manganese is being run without prior removal of calcium, as pointed out by Sherman *et al., Soil Sci.,* 54:253 (1942).

The paraperiodate appears to be a superior reagent to the metaperiodate. The reason may lie in the requirement of acid (in an acid-rich system), and the nonrequirement of water (from a water-poor system) in the former (eq. 5–16).

5–77. The hot solution is transferred to a 100-ml volumetric flask with the purified water diluent. The flask is closed and the solution is mixed, allowed to come to room temperature, and diluted to exactly 100 ml with the purified water diluent. A portion of this solution is compared with the standard $HMnO_4$ solution, by means of a photoelectric colorimeter with 540-mu light (525 to 545 mu, as explained for the standard). Visual comparison in Nessler tubes is also possible.

5–78. Calculation of Results. The $HMnO_4$ color obeys Beer's law with 540-mu light. The normality of Mn (as divalent) in the test solution, is calculated from the percentage transmission (¶ 17–35). The exchangeable manganese is calculated to meq Mn^{++} per 100 gm soil:

$$\text{meq } Mn^{++} \text{ per 100 gm of soil} = N \times 100 \text{ ml} \times \frac{100}{s} \qquad (5\text{–}18)$$

when N represents normality in the 100 ml of test sample, and s is gm sample weight represented in the aliquot. Also parts of Mn^{++} per 2 million parts soil (pounds of Mn^{++} per acre) is calculated:

$$\text{pp2m } Mn^{++} = \text{meq } Mn^{++} \text{ per 100 gm soil} \times 549.3 \qquad (5\text{–}19)$$

In the analysis for total manganese of soil, the result is usually expressed as "% MnO":

$$\% \text{ MnO} = \text{meq } Mn^{++} \text{ per 100 gm} \times \frac{70.93}{2000} \qquad (5\text{–}20)$$
$$= \text{meq } Mn^{++} \text{ per 100 gm} \times 0.03547$$

5–79. The exchangeable manganese is calculated to "equivalent ml" of standard H_2SO_4 and this is subtracted from the Mg plus Mn titration value. Thus the magnesium is obtained by difference.

POTASSIUM DETERMINATION

5–80. The exchangeable K obtained in the NH_4OAc extraction may be determined readily by means of the cobaltinitrite procedure. To do this, an aliquot of *Solution A* that contains 0.5 to 6 mgm of K is taken for the determination of potassium (¶ 6–20). Alternatively, a rapid determination of exchangeable potassium can be made by flame emission spectrophotometry, either directly on *Solution A,* or through a rapid direct extraction of soil for K and Na (¶ 18–24).

SODIUM DETERMINATION[41]

(Precipitation as Mg uranyl acetate triple salt)

5–81. The exchangeable Na obtained in the NH_4OAc extraction may be determined readily by means of the magnesium uranyl acetate procedure to be described, or alternatively, by flame emission spectrophotometry directly on *Solution A* or through a rapid direct extraction of soil for K and Na (¶ 18–24).

5–82. The triple salt formed by Na precipitation with magnesium and uranyl acetates has the formula $NaMg(UO_2)_3(OAc)_9 \cdot 8 H_2O$. Formation of such a triple salt with other divalent cations such as Ni, Co, or Zn is known, but decreasing sensitivity has been shown[42] with increasing radius in the order listed; Mg forms the most insoluble of the triple salt precipitates. The precipitate is determined by titration with standard NaOH or alternatively by a gravimetric procedure.

APPARATUS

5–83. Needed apparatus includes 250-ml and 50-ml beakers, a 10-ml pipet, a filter (Gooch type with sintered glass, asbestos, or porous porcelain filtration substance), and a glass dropper with a rubber bulb. For the gravimetric procedure, a rubber policeman is needed.

REAGENTS

5–84. Needed reagents are standard 0.1 N NaOH and 0.1 N H_2SO_4, and the following special reagents.

5–85. Magnesium Uranyl Acetate Reagent. Approximately 32 gm of uranyl acetate, $UO_2(OAc)_2 \cdot 2 H_2O$, and 100 gm of $Mg(OAc)_2 \cdot 4 H_2O$ are dissolved in 200 ml of water, the mixture being warmed if necessary to obtain solution. The solution is cooled, and to it are added 20 ml of glacial HOAc and 475 ml of 95 per cent ethanol. The solution is diluted to 1 liter and mixed well. This solution is allowed to stand in a dark place for 48 hours and then is filtered into a Pyrex bottle. The filtered solution is stored in a dark place.

5–86. Washing Solution. A few gm of precipitated sodium magnesium uranyl acetate, made by precipitation according to the procedure, are placed in a 1-liter Pyrex bottle and then approximately 800 ml of 95 per cent ethanol is added and the mixture is shaken intermittently for several hours. Finally the suspension is allowed to settle for 24 hours. The almost clear supernatant liquid is then filtered through a Whatman No. 44 filter and the

---

[41] Precipitation method of Caley and Foulk, *J. Am. Chem. Soc.*, 51:1664 (1929), 52:1349 and 4247 (1930); Piper, *J. Agr. Sci.*, 22:676 (1932); after Peech *et al.*, U.S.D.A. Cir. 757, p. 16 (1947). Titration in accordance with Dobbins and Byrd, *J. Am. Chem. Soc.*, 53:3288 (1931).

[42] Rogers, *Sci.*, 103:420 (1946).

filtrate is transferred to a second Pyrex bottle with more of the crystalline salt. The washing solution is prepared by filtrating this second stock supply of alcohol saturated with the sodium salt just prior to use. Fresh preparations of ethanol may be made by addition to the first bottle, the solution being shaken and allowed to stand for 24 hours to precipitate organic substances prior to transfer to the second bottle, according to Piper.[43]

5–87. Na Standards. Because conditions of precipitation may result in some disparity from the theoretical composition of the precipitate, it is advisable to take standard amounts of Na as NaCl in the range from 1 to 5 mgm to determine the titer or weight in relation to the quantity of Na taken. This provides a calibration curve that is a reliable measure of the precipitate composition under the conditions employed in the determination.

PROCEDURE

5–88. An aliquot of *Solution A,* containing 1 to 5 mgm of Na is placed in a 50-ml (well weathered) Pyrex beaker and evaporated to dryness. The residue is dissolved in 6 ml of water. It is not necessary to filter this solution if it happens to be slightly turbid either for volumetric or gravimetric determination. Next, 15 ml of magnesium uranyl acetate reagent is added and the solution is stirred for about 15 seconds, after which precipitate formation normally has been started. The beaker is covered and allowed to stand for 1 hour but for no longer than 2 hours.

5–89. The solution is filtered through a Gooch type crucible (sintered glass, asbestos, or porous porcelain), and the beaker, filter, and precipitate are washed once with 2 ml of magnesium uranyl acetate reagent with the aid of a dropper and then 5 times with the 95 per cent ethanol saturated with the triple salt.

5–90. Titrimetric Procedure for Na. The precipitate in the original beaker is dissolved in a little water, and the solution is transferred to a 250-ml beaker. The crucible carrying the main mass of precipitate is placed in the 250-ml beaker and water is added to a total volume of 100 ml. Then 5 drops of 1 per cent phenolphthalein indicator is added and an excess of 0.1 N NaOH is added as indicated by the formation of a persistent pink color. The solution is heated to boiling, with further addition of NaOH if the pink color begins to fade. When the solution just reaches boiling, it is removed from the heat source and back titrated with 0.1 N H_2SO_4 just to the disappearance of the pink color.

Equation:

$$NaMg(UO_2)_3(OAc)_9 \cdot 8\ H_2O + 10\ NaOH \longrightarrow 9\ NaOAc + Na_2U_2O_7$$
$$+ MgUO_4 + 13\ H_2O$$
$$(5\text{–}21)$$

[43] Piper, *J. Agr. Sci.,* 22:676 (1932).

Each ml of 0.1 N NaOH is equivalent to 0.00023 gm of Na in the precipitate. Ten times as much NaOH is consumed as the chemical equivalent of the Na in the precipitate.

ALTERNATIVE PROCEDURES

5–91. Gravimetric Evaluation of Triple Salt Na Precipitate. The precipitate is filtered on a sintered glass, asbestos, or porcelain Gooch crucible filter. The beaker, crucible, and precipitate are washed with a sufficient number of 2-ml portions of the magnesium uranyl acetate reagent (delivered from a glass pipet) to complete the transfer of the precipitate entirely to the crucible. Usually 3 to 5 washings are required. The last of the transfer is aided by a little washing solution delivered from an extremely fine jet wash bottle. Then the filter is washed 5 times with 2-ml portions of 95 per cent ethanol saturated with sodium magnesium uranyl acetate. Finally the filter is washed twice with small portions of anhydrous ether or acetone. Air is drawn through the crucible for a few minutes to volatilize the organic solvent. The crucible is then allowed to stand 10 to 15 minutes until the odor of the organic solvent is completely gone and then is weighed. The difference in weight corresponds to the triple salt of sodium. A blank, carried out on all reagents just as in the determination, is subtracted from the above difference in weight.

weight of Na in gm = net weight of precipitate in gm × 0.01495

$$(5\text{–}22)$$

5–92. Colorimetric Evaluation of Na Triple Salt Precipitate. The evaluation of a zinc uranyl acetate precipitate of Na can be done by the development of color with sulfosalicylic acid.[44] Amounts of Na in the range of 0.010 to 0.360 mgm can be determined by means of a sensitive centrifuge washing procedure.

QUESTIONS

1. List the exchangeable cations of soils that can be determined in the NH_4OAc extract?

2. Outline some of the factors that may raise the amount of metallic cations present in this extract over the quantities that are truly exchangeable in the soil.

3. What is the equivalent in terms of pp2m of one meq of each of the following metallic cations: Ca, Mg, Mn, K, and Na?

4. Why is it advantageous to employ a field-moist soil sample for exchangeable cations such as K^+, NH_4^+, Mn^{++}, and Fe^{++}?

5. What is the purpose of allowing the sample to equilibrate with the NH_4OAc for a considerable time, as long as overnight, prior to filtration?

---

[44] Parks *et al., Ind. Eng. Chem., A.E.,* 15:528 (1943).

6. What is the purpose of having the beaker tightly covered during the H_2O_2 and HNO_3 treatment of the NH_4OAc residue?

7. What principle is employed in the prevention of precipitation of Mg with Ca as the oxalate?

8. What are the advantages of cerate over permanganate for the oxalate titration?

9. List the advantages and disadvantages of the $MgNH_4PO_4$ method for Mg?

10. State the advantages of the fritted glass filter over filter paper for recovery of the $MgNH_4PO_4$ precipitate. Why must the last traces of free NH_3 be removed prior to titration?

11. Why must the Fe and several other ions be removed prior to the determination of Mg by means of 8-hydroxy quinoline precipitation? Why may moderate amounts of Ca be present in the solution on which Mg is determined in this way?

12. Why must the last traces of organic matter be removed prior to the determination of Mn as the $HMnO_4$ purple color?

13. Why is the determination of K often considered separately from the systematic determination of all of the exchangeable metallic cations?

14. What are the chief precautions to be followed in the determinations of Na, whether by precipitation or flame emission spectrophotometry?

6

Potassium Determinations
for Soils

. . . exchange, fixation and release
—A THEME OF SOIL CHEMICAL RESEARCH[1]

6–1. The determination of potassium has been the subject of so much investigation that semimicro determination by gravimetric, titrimetric, and absorption and emission (¶ 18–7) spectrophotometric methods can now be readily accomplished. The absorption spectrophotometric determination of potassium is emphasized in this chapter, although titrimetric and gravimetric procedures are also given.

6–2. Potassium Is a Key Element in Soil Chemistry. Because the amount of exchangeable potassium is critically low for crop production in extensive soils throughout the more humid regions, this element is of key importance in soil chemistry and soil fertility.[2] Its equilibrium reactions in soils are somewhat more complex than can be predicted from the elementary principles of ionic exchange as exemplified by sodium and calcium (Chapter 5). The analytical *determination* of potassium in solution, considered first, is carefully distinguished from the extraction of exchangeable (¶ 6–67) and other (¶ 6–76) forms from soils.

6–3. Methods for Potassium Determination. Despite the prominence of

---

[1] Reitemeier, U.S.D.A. Tech. Bul. 1049 (1951).

[2] Cowie, *Potash* (London: Edward Arnold & Co., 1951); Eckstein *et al., Potash Deficiency Symptoms,* 2nd ed. (Berlin: Verlagsgesellschaft für Ackerbau, 1937; Turrentine, *Potash in North America* (New York: Reinhold Publishing Corporation, 1943).

the emission method for K (¶ 18–7), several types of simple and inexpensive potassium procedures are still important:

1. Precipitation in water as cobaltinitrite, $(K_nNa_{3-n})Co(NO_2)_6 \cdot x\, H_2O$. The term (K_nNa_{3-n}) refers to an isomorphous composition range in the crystals, in which $K_{1.6}$ to $K_{1.7}$ is the most stable and reproducible composition (¶ 6–7), and x stands for variable water of crystallization. The method requires the prior removal of ammonium and barium ions, use of a water medium of precipitation, and KCl standards for calibration. Determination is effected gravimetrically, titrimetrically for nitrite, or colorimetrically for nitrite or cobalt.

2. Precipitation as chloroplatinate, K_2PtCl_6. This method employs differential solubility in alcohol for separations and requires prior removal of ammonium. Procedures are gravimetric, or colorimetric.[3]

3. Precipitation as K-dipicrylamine, K-hexanitrodiphenylamine (¶ 13–48). This method requires the prior removal of ammonium and double precipitation to remove Na interference. The procedure is colorimetric.[4]

4. Precipitation as perchlorate, $KClO_4$. This method employs differential solubility in alcohol for separation and is often used following a preliminary separation as cobaltinitrite. It requires removal of ammonium and sulfate. The procedure is gravimetric.

5. Gravimetric determination of combined NaCl plus KCl, separate determination of chloride, and computation of K or Na by simultaneous equations (¶ 10–84).

6–4. Cobaltinitrite Method. Of the 5 methods, only the cobaltinitrite procedure is given in detail herein. Of the precipitation methods, the cobaltinitrite procedure is preferred for soils work because it is rapid, economical, adaptable to semimicro technique, and the low solubility (¶ 6–5) of the precipitate in water makes for flexibility. The only faster and more flexible method is the emission spectrophotometric method with the flame photometer (¶ 18–7). Because the cobaltinitrite of potassium (with sodium) is enormously more insoluble in water than other potassium precipitates, the cobaltinitrite has been employed[5] for preconcentration of K from salt solutions of such composition that the direct determination of K is not feasible.

6–5. The cobaltinitrites of potassium and sodium present a striking differential in the solubility in water. Were it not for the isomorphism (¶ 6–7) of Na in the K salt, the cobaltinitrite procedure would be ideal. Nonetheless, it is an effective procedure. In considering variability in the precipitate composition, in relation to other methods, one must recall that

[3] Adams and St. John, *Ind. Eng. Chem., A.E.,* 17:435 (1945).

[4] Kolthoff and Bendix, *Ind. Eng. Chem., A.E.,* 11:94 (1939); Amdur, *Ind. Eng. Chem., A.E.,* 12:731 (1940); Lawton, *S.S.S.A. Proc.,* 10:126 (1946).

[5] Washington, *Chemical Analysis of Rocks* (New York: John Wiley & Sons, Inc., 1919); Piper, *Soil and Plant Analysis* (New York: Interscience Publishers, Inc., 1944); Wright, *Soil Analysis,* 2nd ed. (London: Thomas Murby & Co., 1939).

selection of solvents and procedures for the K_2PtCl_6 and $KClO_4$ determinations are also empirically established. These must be calibrated against quantities of K taken in standardization and give an over-all accuracy in the same range as with the best cobaltinitrite procedures. Good concordance of the chloroplatinate and cobaltinitrite procedures was found in a careful experimental comparison.[6] The cobaltinitrite technique has an enormous advantage for sensitivity to small amounts of K.

6–6. Cobaltinitrite Ion. Nitrite reacts with cobaltous ion to form a cobaltic complex $Co(NO_2)_6^{---}$, the oxidation of Co^{++} to Co^{+++} being accomplished by the reduction of 1 nitrite ion. Sodium is commonly used as the cation of this complex salt for a potassium precipitating reagent, but silver[7] and zinc[8] have been employed. The complex soluble salt may be purified by recrystallization from organic solvents, and is available as a bright orange salt from chemical supply houses. In many procedures[9] it is formed during the preparation of the precipitation reagent, by mixing solutions of the nitrite and cobaltous salts and allowing time for the reaction to be completed. The necessity of precipitation of the potassium in the presence of the large excess of sodium salt (by-product) is not a disadvantage to the method; many procedures which employ the purified salt call for the addition of more sodium salts.

6–7. Isomorphism. Extensive studies have demonstrated the fact of isomorphism of Na and K in the cobaltinitrite precipitate crystal, between the *n*-value of 3 and 1.5 in the formula (¶ 6–3, 1). The upper limit of Na content appears to be approximately at a 1 : 1 ratio to K, as would be expected from the extreme solubility of the sodium cobaltinitrite salt. One Na can proxy for 1 K so long as there is a K ion immediately adjacent to cover it in the crystal. The chief factors determining the composition of the precipitate are (a) the concentration of sodium ion, including that from the precipitation reagent, and its general magnitude in relation to that of potassium (Fig. 6–1), and (b) the temperature of the solution from which it is precipitated. Coincidence will be noted in Fig. 6–1 of curves representing 10 and 2 mgm of K precipitated under the same conditions by the author and N. J. Volk, respectively, working independently. Volk's 2 curves, obtained with room temperature precipitation, illustrate the effect of a large amount (5 per cent) of Na in the system in addition to that in the precipitation reagent. Cooling the system to 3°C lowered the author's curve about as much as Volk's addition of 5 per cent extra Na at room temperature.

[6] Hibbard and Stout, *J.A.O.A.C.*, 16:137 (1933).
[7] Breth and Gaebler, *J. Biol. Chem.*, 87:81 (1930).
[8] Adams *et al., Ind. Eng. Chem., A.E.*, 7:310 (1935).
[9] An early procedure was described by Adie and Wood, *J. Chem. Soc.*, 77:1076 (1900).

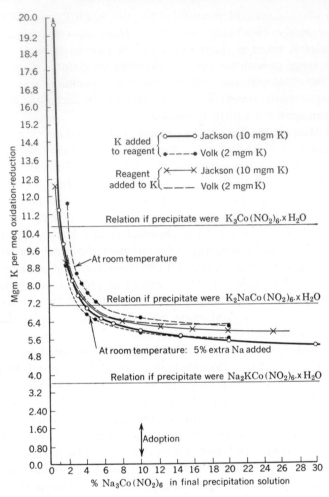

Fig. 6–1. Relation of oxidation-reduction reaction of K precipitate, $(K_nNa_{3-n})Co(NO_2)_6 \cdot xH_2O$, to concentration of precipitation solution, at 3°C and with no extra sodium added except as indicated. (Data from author's studies and Volk, *J. Am. Soc. Agron.*, 33:685, 1941.)

6–8. Lack of any inflexion of the curves for the hypothetical K_2NaCo $(NO_2)_6$ composition comes from the fact of isomorphism in the crystal (established by X-ray diffraction studies[10]) and shows the fallacy of the theory of adjusting[11] the $Na_3Co(NO_2)_6$ concentration and other factors to

---

[10] Data obtained in detailed studies by the author (1943).

[11] Carried out by Kramer and Tisdall, *J. Biol. Chem.*, 46:339 (1921) and many later workers, including Volk and Truog, *J. Am. Soc. Agron.*, 36:537 (1934), and Wilcox, *Ind. Eng. Chem., A.E.*, 9:136 (1937).

approximate the K_2Na composition. The precipitate composition is subject to great variation in this range as shown by the steep rise in the composition curves with small changes in conditions as they cross the K_2NaCo $(NO_2)_6$ composition line. The $K_3Co(NO_2)_6$ line lacks inflexion because the solubility product of the precipitate leaves appreciable K in solution with these low concentrations of Na^+ and $Co(NO_2)_6^{---}$ ions.

6–9. The pure $K_3Co(NO_2)_6 \cdot 1 \cdot 5\ H_2O$ salt can be prepared[12] with an excess of K^+ and NO_2^- in the presence of low Co^{++} and Na^+ concentrations, as a method for determining cobalt.

6–10. Choice of Procedure. The adoption of the 10 per cent final concentration of precipitating reagent (20 per cent original concentration) is based on the greater reproducibility[13] of precipitate composition, though nonstoichiometric, than is obtainable under greater or lesser concentrations. It greatly increases the sensitivity of the method with lower concentrations. Addition of the K solution to the precipitating solution (rather than the reverse) was adopted also for greater reproducibility. Adoption of 3°C precipitation is based on greater uniformity of composition over a wide range of K concentrations. The 10 per cent precipitating reagent concentration corresponds to 3.4 per cent Na in solution, which is sufficient to buffer out considerable differences in the Na content of the test solution, and permits greater reproducibility than higher Na concentrations.

6–11. Adding alcohol to the aqueous solvent increases the insolubility of the precipitate and substitutes for low temperature in effect, but alcohol is incompatible with formaldehyde in the precipitation system. The temperature effect on the K content is linear from 5° to 50°C, being -0.5 per cent per degree, but appears to be constant below 3° to 5°C. The pH of the supernatant liquid has no effect on the precipitate composition between pH 3.2 and 5.6. Above this the Co begins to precipitate as the hydroxide; below this the precipitate solubility increases rapidly. The cobaltinitrite reagent brings the pH within this range even though the solvent for the K may be considerably more acid in various procedures.

POTASSIUM DETERMINATION
(Precipitation as cobaltinitrite)

6–12. Determination of potassium is ordinarily quicker by the flame emission spectrophotometry (¶ 18–7) than by cobaltinitrite. In the absence of expensive emission equipment, cobaltinitrite is efficaceous for ex-

---

[12] Kolthoff and Sandell, *Textbook of Quantitative Inorganic Analysis* (New York: The Macmillan Company, 1938), p. 374.

[13] Greater reproducibility led to the adoption of procedures, in which the K content of the precipitate was lowered, by a number of workers, including Hibbard and Stout, *J.A.O.A.C.*, 16:137 (1933); Schueler and Thomas, *Ind. Eng. Chem., A.E.*, 5:163 (1933); Lohse, *Ind. Eng. Chem., A.E.*, 7:272 (1935); Brown *et al., Ind. Eng. Chem., A.E.*, 10:652 (1938); and Volk, *J. Am. Soc. Agron.*, 33:684 (1941).

changeable K (¶ 5–14 or 6–67), K in soluble salts (¶ 10–83), total K in minerals (¶ 6–75), and K in plant tissue (¶ 12–39). The key principle employed is the direct standardization in terms of standard KCl for the conditions of the analysis. The existence of (K,Na) isomorphous relations of the $(K_nNa_{3-n})Co(NO_2)_6 \cdot xH_2O$ precipitate dictates the choice of the most stable and reproducible conditions for its precipitation (¶ 6–7) rather than the conditions favoring a simulated stoichiometry. This principle is widely applied in spectrochemistry; for example, the stoichiometry is not known for the chromogen in the determination of phosphorus.

APPARATUS

6–13. Needed apparatus consists of beakers—150-ml for evaporation and 50-ml for precipitation, a centrifuge and 25-ml pointed tubes, test tubes or 50-ml conical flasks for cooling the K solution, a spot plate, a policeman and glass rod, a 500-ml volumetric flask, 15 and 10-ml pipets that deliver moderately rapidly, and a buret.

REAGENTS

6–14. Needed reagents include 10 per cent NaOH (low in K), ammonium-free 1 N HCl (tested), Nessler's reagent (¶ 8–43), phenolphthalein indicator, and the following special reagents.

6–15. Precipitation Reagent. A 20 per cent solution of sodium cobaltinitrite is prepared by dissolving 20 gm of reagent grade sodium cobaltinitrite, $Na_3Co(NO_2)_6$ (Mallinckrodt or Bakers) in 80 ml of cold distilled water (5°C) and making to 100 ml volume at 5°C. After standing 24 to 48 hours, the solution is filtered through a retentive paper or centrifuged in pointed centrifuge tubes to remove traces of insoluble matter including potassium precipitate (filtration under reduced pressure is avoided since a serious loss of nitrite results). The solution is tightly stoppered and stored in the refrigerator at this temperature, and may safely be used for 1 to 3 weeks. It has been stored in tightly stopped full bottles without change for 6 months.

6–16. Solvent for Potassium. The solvent for potassium is 0.17 N HOAc containing 4 per cent formaldehyde, prepared by dilution of 10 ml of glacial acetic acid and 100 ml of 40 per cent formaldehyde to 1 liter. The formaldehyde prevents traces of ammonia from interfering through coprecipitation with the potassium but does not eliminate the need for ammonium removal in the procedure.

6–17. Standard KCl Solution (2 mgm K per 10 ml). Exactly 0.1905 gm of dried KCl is dissolved in water. The solution is transferred to a 500-ml volumetric flask, made to volume, and mixed. Each ml contains 0.2 mgm of K.

6–18. Standardization. To obtain the standard curve and to establish the technique, aliquots (3.75, 7.5, 15, 30, and 45 ml) of the standard KCl solution are measured out with a buret into separate 150-ml beakers. The solutions are evaporated to dryness and each is carried, with blanks on reagents, through the procedure (¶ 6–20) and colorimetric evaluation (¶ 6–30).

6–19. In routine, 2 15-ml portions of the standard KCl solution are evaporated (later giving 2 mgm K in 2/3 aliquot precipitated), and treated as in the procedure (¶ 6–20). These 2 standards are used to establish a working calibration factor, which may vary slightly (but only slightly) according to the amount of Na introduced in the various procedures.

PROCEDURE

6–20. Removal of Ammonium. The sides of the beaker in which the potassium solution has evaporated are washed down thoroughly to dissolve any adhering ammonium. Two drops of 1 per cent phenolphthalein are added and 10 per cent NaOH then is added dropwise (usually 2 drops are required) until the phenolphthalein turns distinctly red. The use of over 1 ml of NaOH is avoided whenever possible, but the procedure accommodates more if necessary. The same quantities of NaOH are added to the blanks and K standards. The solution is then evaporated to dryness on a steam plate to drive off the last traces of ammonia. As evaporation proceeds, the solution color should remain pink. If fading occurs, more phenolphthalein and more drops of NaOH are added as required. Ammonia fumes *must be kept away*. When the evaporation is complete, 2 ml of ammonium-free 1 N HCl is added and 1 small drop of this HCl solution of the sample is added to a spot plate and tested for ammonium with Nessler's reagent.[14] (If ammonia is present, rarely the case, the solution is again evaporated to dryness, the above 10 per cent NaOH treatment is repeated, and the residue is taken up in 2 ml ammonium-free 1 N HCl as before.) The HCl solution is dried out to extract of the K completely from the siliceous residue and its conversion to KCl. The procedure is quickly continued until the solution is tightly stoppered.

6–21. Clarification of Solution. The beaker is cooled, and exactly 15 ml of the solvent for potassium (0.17 N HOAc, containing 4 per cent formaldehyde) is added. The sides and bottom of the beaker are policed (using no water), and the solution is immediately filtered through a dry filter paper into a dry test tube or a 50-ml conical flask, the latter then being stoppered to prevent evaporation. Instead of filtration, this solution may be clarified by centrifugation in a pointed 25-ml centrifuge tube just prior to precipitation.

---

[14] No trace of the Nessler's solution, which is high in potassium, must be allowed to come in contact with the test solutions.

(A 7.5-ml volume of solvent for the potassium may be used, and 5 ml of this solution may be used for precipitation.)

6–22. Potassium Cobaltinitrite Precipitation. The concentration of K in the solution for analysis is kept in the range of 0.5 to 20 mgm K in 10 ml. The 15 ml of K solution in the tube or conical flask is cooled in an ice bath to 3°C (this will take about 20 minutes). Then 10 ml of the precipitation reagent is pipetted into a dry 50-ml beaker and similarly cooled to 3°C in an ice bath. When both solutions have cooled to the proper temperature, an aliquot of exactly 10 ml of the test solution is pipetted into the beaker containing the precipitation reagent, *the precipitation reagent being stirred rapidly by rotation of the beaker during addition of the potassium solution.* The beaker is returned to the ice bath and kept at 4° to 6°C for 5 hours or preferably overnight.

6–23. Note. Various volumes of precipitation reagent and potassium solvent may be used as long as the volume ratio remains 1 : 1 and the potassium concentration does *not* exceed 2 mgm per ml. The K solution is added to the precipitation reagent so that the concentration of sodium and cobaltinitrite remain relatively high throughout the precipitation. The Na concentration of the precipitation reagent is adequately high to buffer out the effects of great variation in Na concentration in the K solution. Both solutions are cooled before precipitation so that the temperature is constant even for the precipitation of the last traces on standing. Cooling after the initial mixing would result in a gradient of precipitate composition as cooling took place.

6–24. Choice of Procedure for Evaluation of the Precipitate. Several procedures are described below for evaluation of the cobaltinitrite precipitate, and thus of potassium. The colorimetric method (as cobalt hydrocarbonate) is the most rapid; the titrimetric method (with cerate or permanganate) is popular and equally as accurate; the gravimetric method is most suitable for amounts of potassium of 5 mgm or above. The chief variables in the cobaltinitrite determination are the *conditions of precipitation,* which are satisfactorily controlled by the procedure given. A precision of 0.5 to 1 per cent is ordinarily obtained with any of the evaluation procedures herewith described, and the precipitation procedure as described is reproducible to 1 per cent.

6–25. Slightly different precipitate washing procedures are employed, according to the procedure to be followed for evaluating the precipitate, and therefore the washing procedure is detailed with each evaluation procedure below.

ALTERNATIVE PROCEDURE

6–26. For amounts of K less than 1 mgm, the precipitation may advantageously be carried out in a 15-ml or 25-ml centrifuge tube. Washing by means of centrifugation follows, and the precipitate is evaluated by oxidation in the tube. For quantities from 0.05 to 0.3 mgm, the centrifuge tube technique is much to be preferred.

COLORIMETRIC DETERMINATION OF POTASSIUM AS COBALT HYDROCARBONATE

(Evaluation of potassium cobaltinitrite precipitate)

6–27. The precipitate of K as $(K_nNa_{3-n})Co(NO_2)_6 \cdot xH_2O$, obtained in the previous section, is evaluated by dissolving the washed precipitate in acid and determining the cobalt contained. The washing procedure for the precipitate is given herewith. The standard curve is based on a series of K standards derived from the same procedure. This colorimetric determination is quantitative for cobalt in the range of 0.1 to 10 or more mgm of Co. This is ordinarily too insensitive for the range of Co in soils and plants. (Chapter 15 cites more sensitive methods.)

APPARATUS

6–28. Needed apparatus includes a colorimeter with 620-mu light maximum, colorimeter tubes with 40-ml calibration and stoppers to fit, fine fritted glass filter crucibles, a suction flask and crucible holder, a 60° funnel and rubber Gooch ring, a vacuum desiccator, a policeman, and a glass rod.

REAGENTS

6–29. Needed reagents are 70 per cent ethanol, absolute methanol or ethanol, 6 N HCl, 6 N KOH, 27 to 30 per cent U.S.P. grade H_2O_2 and 3 per cent H_2O_2 diluted from the concentrated reagent (made up fresh each week), and saturated $KHCO_3$ (46 gm in 100 ml of water, shaken repeatedly and allowed to settle out).

PROCEDURE

6–30. Filtration and Washing of Precipitate. The cobaltinitrite precipitate of K, formed at less than 5°C as directed above, is filtered on a fine porosity Pyrex fritted glass crucible with suction,[15] and the 50-ml beaker and precipitate are washed 3 times with 70 per cent ethanol. Then the crucible is removed and the underside is washed with 70 per cent ethanol. Finally the crucible is returned to the holder, the precipitate washed twice more with 70 per cent ethanol and once with absolute methanol or ethanol. The crucible is set in the 50-ml beaker and the apparatus and precipitate are dried for 5 minutes at 100° to 110°C.

---

[15] A centrifuge tube technique may be used to wash the precipitate, but that procedure is less rapid than the fritted glass filtration.

6–31. Development of Cobalt Hydrocarbonate Color.[16] The precipitate adhering to the walls of the dried 50-ml precipitation beaker is dissolved in 3 or 4 drops of 6 N HCl, a little heat being applied and the glass surface being rubbed with the policeman. Then about 5 ml of hot water is added to the beaker. Next the fritted glass crucible is placed upright in the beaker, and 2 ml 6 N HCl is pipetted into the crucible. The beaker and crucible are placed on the steam plate for a few minutes until the precipitate has dissolved.

6–32. A 60° funnel is arranged on a vacuum desiccator to deliver into an Evelyn colorimeter tube placed upright inside. This tube bears a 40-ml calibration mark and is colorimetrically standardized (Chapter 17). The crucible bearing some of the solution of the precipitate is set in the rubber crucible-holder in the funnel, suction is applied, and the cobalt solution in the 50-ml beaker is washed through the filter into the colorimeter tube. The transfer is completed with a few ml of water delivered from a fine-stream, wash bottle. (For amounts of K greater than 8 mgm, the color is made up in a volumetric flask.)

6–33. Now 1.5 ml 6 N KOH is added. The solution must remain slightly acid as evidenced by absence of precipitation; if it is not slightly acid, a little 6 N HCl is added dropwise with stirring. Next, 0.5 ml of 3 per cent H_2O_2 is added, and the tube is stoppered and inverted to mix. (If a brown precipitate begins to form, rarely the case, 2 to 5 drops 6 N HCl is added as required to clear the solution.) Finally 15 ml of saturated $KHCO_3$ is added and then water to make 40-ml total volume, followed by thorough mixing. After the solution has stood for a few minutes for bubbles to rise, the color is read in the colorimeter with 620-mu light maximum. The reagent blank tube is employed for the 100 per cent transmission setting of the colorimeter, automatically taking into account the potassium impurities in the reagents. The colorimeter readings are referred to the calibration curve (based on working standards) to find the mgm K in the test sample.

ALTERNATIVE PROCEDURES

6–34. The cobalt of the potassium precipitate has been colorimetrically determined[17] by the nitroso-R salt, a method that is well adapted to extremely small amounts of K below the range of the cobalt hydrocarbonate method. The nitrite has been extracted with 0.1 N NaOH and determined by diazotization.[18]

6–35. The cobaltinitrite precipitate has also been evaluated by oxidation in chromic acid, and the residual mixed color has been measured with 425-

---

[16] Colorimetric procedure is adapted from that of Blanchetiere and Pirlot, *Compt. rend. soc. biol.,* 101:858 (1929).

[17] Sideris, *Ind. Eng. Chem., A.E.,* 9:145 (1937), 14:821 (1942).

[18] Taylor, *J. Biol. Chem.,* 87:27 (1930).

mu light.[19] The residual dichromate color was measured later with 400-mu light.[20] It should be noted that any method based on residual color, in the lower range of the constituent, measures a small decrease in strong color, which is less accurate than measuring the first increment of color.

6–36. The cobaltinitrite precipitate can be estimated turbidimetrically for soil or tissue testing (Chapter 13), but this is difficult to make quantitative because of the variability in the number of precipitation nucleii.[21] A satisfactory procedure was devised[22] in which solid $Na_3Co(NO_2)_6$ was employed for the precipitation nucleii.

6–37. Centrifuge Washing of the Precipitate. In lieu of filtration on a fritted glass crucible, the precipitate may be washed by means of the centrifuge. The precipitate and supernatant liquid, in the tube (¶ 6–26) or transferred from the 50-ml beaker with a rubber policeman and 70 per cent ethanol dispensed from a wash bottle, are covered by a layer of 70 per cent ethanol. The precipitate is thrown down by centrifugation at 2000 rpm in a No. 2 International or other suitable centrifuge until clear, usually requiring 5 to 10 minutes or more. The supernatant liquid is removed by gentle suction (10–20 cm of Hg) through a glass needle with tip bent at a 90° angle. Then the precipitate is stirred with a fine jet of 70 per cent ethanol (completed with a pointed rod if necessary) and the washing volume made to 5 to 10 ml. The precipitate is thrown down by centrifugation, and the supernatant liquid is removed as before. Washing is repeated once with 70 per cent ethanol and then once with absolute methanol or ethanol. The tube is placed on its side to allow the alcohol to flow away from the precipitate, dried in an oven at 100°–110°C for 30 minutes, and cooled. The precipitate is then dissolved in 2 ml of 6 N HCl added to the centrifuge tube, and the color is developed by the cobalt hydrocarbonate procedure. The volume of colored solution is kept below 10 or 20 ml for small amounts of K.

6–38. The precipitate has been washed by means of a centrifuge by many workers, several of whom have shown that the washings may be limited to 1 if the procedure is so standardized that traces of residual precipitating reagent are represented in the calibration curve. Iced water and other washing solutions such as 0.01 N HNO_3[23] are satisfactory because the precipitate is relatively insoluble even in aqueous solvents, and the procedures are calibrated for any slight loss, even though in some cases the stoichiometric composition of the precipitate was in the end approximated by compensating factors. A 1 per cent solution of $Al_2(SO_4)_3$ has been

---

[19] Wander, *Ind. Eng. Chem., A.E.,* 14:471 (1942).
[20] Parks *et al., Ind. Eng. Chem., A.E.,* 15:530 (1943).
[21] Volk, *Proc. Soil Sci. Soc. Fla.,* 3:99 (1941).
[22] Garman, *Soil Sci.,* 56:101 (1943).
[23] Wilcox, *Ind. Eng. Chem., A.E.,* 9:136 (1937).

employed[24] as a washing solution to help keep the precipitate packed down, thus facilitating inversion of the centrifuge tube for complete drainage.

TITRIMETRIC DETERMINATION OF POTASSIUM

(Evaluation of potassium cobaltinitrite precipitate by cerate or permanganate titration)

6–39. As an alternative to the cobalt hydrocarbonate procedure, the precipitate of K as $(K_nNa_{3-n})Co(NO_2)_6 \cdot xH_2O$ (¶ 6–22) is dissolved in $2\ N\ H_2SO_4$ in the presence of an excess of cerate or permanganate, and the excess of oxidant is determined by back titration. Because the washing procedure varies according to the type of evaluation, it is detailed herewith.

APPARATUS

6–40. Needed apparatus includes a Gooch crucible suitable for holding asbestos, a crucible holder, a suction flask, a glass rod fitted with a stopper for tamping asbestos, a 100°–110°C oven, pipets, and burets.

REAGENTS

6–41. Needed reagents are 70 per cent ethanol, absolute methanol or ethanol, $2\ N\ H_2SO_4$, and the following special reagents.

6–42. Standard Oxidant. Approximately 50 gm of $(NH_4)_4Ce(SO_4)_4 \cdot 2\ H_2O$ is dissolved in 1 liter of $2\ N\ H_2SO_4$ to obtain a solution that is approximately $0.05\ N$ with respect to oxidation-reduction, $Ce^{4+} \longrightarrow Ce^{3+}$. (If permanganate is to be employed, a stock solution of $1\ N\ KMnO_4$ is prepared as described under manganese determination, ¶ 5–67, and an aliquot is diluted to $0.05\ N$ and standardized.)

6–43. Oxidation-Reduction Indicator. Orthophenanthroline-ferrous complex, $0.025\ M,$ is obtainable as "Ferroin" from G. F. Smith Chemical Co., Columbus, Ohio.

6–44. Standard Oxalate. Standard $Na_2C_2O_4$ is dried in an oven at 100°C and cooled. Then a 3.350-gm portion is weighed out and dissolved in $2\ N\ H_2SO_4$. The solution is made to a volume of 1 liter in a volumetric flask with this solvent. This primary oxidation-reduction standard is $0.0500\ N$.

6–45. Ferrous Reference Solution for Cerate Titration. Approximately 30 gm of $Fe(NH_4)_2(SO_4)_2 \cdot 6\ H_2O$ is dissolved in approximately 1 liter of $0.5\ N\ H_2SO_4$ to obtain a solution of approximately $0.075\ N$ with respect to oxidation-reduction, $Fe^{++} \longrightarrow Fe^{+++}$. The volumetric ratio (R) of cerate to iron is determined by titration at room temperature of 10 ml of the cerate with the ferrous reference solution to the end point, 1 drop of Ferroin being used as an internal indicator (red to faint blue color change). Apparatus has been designed[25] to protect the stock solution from oxidation, although daily determination of R is no disadvantage.

---

[24] Thrum, *Ind. Eng. Chem., A.E.,* 5:99 (1933).
[25] Schollenberger, *Ind. Eng. Chem., A.E.,* 7:199 (1935).

6–46. Asbestos for Filtering Precipitates. The commercial grade asbestos is ground in a water suspension with a rotary stirrer (drink mixer or blender) then digested in *aqua regia* for 10 minutes at boiling temperature, and finally washed with water on a Buchner funnel. The asbestos improves with use and is collected and repeatedly used for the potassium filtration.

PROCEDURE

6–47. Filtration and Washing of Precipitate. An asbestos pad is made by pouring a suspension of fairly fine purified asbestos through a Gooch crucible, tamping with a stopper attached to a glass rod, and finally pouring through an additional suspension of still finer asbestos[26] to give a total pad thickness of about 1.0 to 1.5 mm. (A fritted glass filter is not satisfactory with the titration procedure because some of the cobaltinitrite precipitate in the pores of fritted glass does not react with the oxidant before it is lost by side reactions with the acid and water, ¶ 6–50. This contrasts with oxalate, ¶ 5–33.)

6–48. The potassium precipitate (¶ 6–22) is suspended by stirring and poured into the center of the pad. The beaker is washed 3 times with small portions of 70 per cent ethanol and once with absolute ethanol. The Gooch (washed externally with ethanol) is dried with the beaker in the oven at 100°C for 10 to 30 minutes (while additional samples are filtered).

6–49. Titration Procedure (cerate). The Gooch is removed, and the pad and precipitate are transferred to the original 50-ml beaker with a stirring rod. Traces of precipitate adhering to the Gooch are washed into the beaker with a fine stream of water. To the 50-ml beaker containing the suspension of precipitate, approximately 1 ml of 2 N H_2SO_4[27] is added, followed immediately by an excess of cerate (15 ml of 0.075 N suffices for 6 mgm K), and the solution is rapidly heated to boiling while constantly being stirred. The reaction is complete after 30 seconds of boiling. (If the yellow color becomes rather faint, indicating insufficient excess of cerate, a measured additional quantity of cerate is quickly added. A large excess of cerate does no harm, so the procedure should be adjusted so that a sufficient excess is always added with the first pipetting.) The beaker with the solution is set aside to cool, while cerate is added to other samples. The excess cerate is back titrated with the ferrous ammonium sulfate reference solution to an end point with orthophenanthroline indicator.

6–50. The nitrite is oxidized to nitrate by the combined action of cerate

---

[26] Asbestos gives a much lower titration blank than paper, according to Curtis and Finkelstein, *Ind. Eng. Chem., A.E.,* 5:318 (1933), but its titration blank must be carefully taken into account. Sized talc particles have been successfully employed as a filter medium by Hibbard and Stout, *J.A.O.A.C.,* 16:137 (1933).

[27] It is important that the filter system be acidified prior to the addition of cerate, because ceric oxide otherwise precipitates at the interface of the acid cerate solution and the nearly neutral precipitate phase.

(Ce^{4+}) and cobalt (Co^{3+}), each of which is reduced by one valence charge.[28] The cobalt is stabilized as trivalent by sixfold nitrite coordination but is stable only as divalent in the absence of nitrite excess. The Co^{+++} ion is a strong enough oxidizing agent to liberate O_2 from water:

$$Co^{+++} + e \longrightarrow Co^{++} \tag{6-1}$$

$$2\,H_2O \longrightarrow 4\,H^+ + O_2 + 4e \tag{6-2}$$

On addition:

$$4\,Co^{+++} + 2\,H_2O \longrightarrow 4\,Co^{++} + 4\,H^+ + O_2 \tag{6-3}$$

This takes place in the absence of a more ready source of electrons, such as nitrite.

6–51. Strong acidification retards reactions 6–2 and 6–3 and liberates HNO_2 for stoichiometric reaction with the Co^{+++}. The essential reactions are as follows:

$$6\,NO_2^- + 6\,O^{--} \longrightarrow 6\,NO_3^- + 12e \tag{6-4}$$

$$Co^{+++} + e \longrightarrow Co^{++} \tag{6-5}$$

$$11\,Ce^{4+} + 11e \longrightarrow 11\,Ce^{+++} \tag{6-6}$$

On addition and doubling:

$$2\,(K, Na)_3Co(NO_2)_6 + 22\,H_4Ce(SO_4)_4 + 12\,H_2O \longrightarrow 6\,(K, Na)NO_3$$
$$+ 2\,Co(NO_3)_2 + 2\,HNO_3$$
$$+ 11\,Ce_2(SO_4)_3 + 55\,H_2SO_4 \tag{6-7}$$

6–52. The K determined cannot be calculated from equation 6–7 because the K content of the precipitate, represented by $(K, Na)_3$, must be evaluated by means of potassium standards, under precipitation conditions that hold the K/Na ratio in the precipitate constant (¶ 6-7). Then the computation of the mgm K is as follows:

$$\text{mgm K determined} = \frac{\text{mgm K (std)}}{\text{net ml cerate (std)}} \times \underset{\text{(unknown)}}{\text{net ml cerate}} \tag{6-8}$$

when mgm K (std) equals the number of mgm K precipitated in standard (usually 2 mgm K), net ml cerate is ml cerate pipetted into the determination minus ml Fe back titration time R, and R, the ratio Ce volume : Fe volume, is determined in a separate titration, in which 10 ml of the cerate is titrated to the Ferroin end point with the ferrous reference solution.

ALTERNATIVE PROCEDURES

6–53. Besides the sulfatocerate procedure for evaluating the potassium cobaltinitrite precipitate, detailed above, there are several other volumetric

---

[28] Intraction of cobalt with nitrite in stoichiometric proportions was noted by Drushel, *Am. J. Sci.*, 24:433 (1907), through removal of Co from the titration by NaOH treatment.

procedures that may be employed, the chief ones of which utilize nitrato- or perchloratocerate, permanganate, or chromate. The cerate procedures have advantages over permanganate. They have great stability even in very dilute solutions; no precipitate is formed in acid solutions and thus they are usable in large excess in routine constant volume, which is particularly convenient for use in centrifuge tubes with micro quantities of K. They give a very sharp end point with Ferroin and Nitroferroin indicators. The sulfatocerate in either 1 or 2 N H_2SO_4 solution, with oxidation potential of -1.44 volts, has the slight disadvantage of requiring the ferrous reference solution, and a temperature over 50°C for reaction with $Na_2C_4O_4$, and back-titration at less than 50°C. It is a slightly less active oxidizer than permanganate, which has an oxidation potential of -1.5 volts in 1 N H_2SO_4. Nitratocerate with an oxidation potential of -1.61 volts in 1 N HNO_3 and perchloratocerate with an oxidation potential of -1.71 volts in 1 N $HClO_4$, are stronger oxidizers than permanganate. Oxalate can be titrated with these cerates at room temperature. The permanganate is slightly cheaper, and more commonly called for in older procedures, but has the decided disadvantage of instability in storage and use.

6–54. Permanganate Titration of Cobaltinitrite. On the basis of an estimate of the amount of potassium present in the precipitate to be titrated, approximately 2-ml excess of 0.05 N $KMnO_4$ is dispensed from a buret into the 50-ml precipitation beaker (1 mgm K is equivalent to approximately 3 ml of 0.05 N $KMnO_4$). To the beaker is then added 20 ml of 2 N H_2SO_4. The crucible containing the precipitate is now washed on the outside with a fine stream of water. The asbestos pad is removed from the crucible with a glass rod, and transferred to the acid $KMnO_4$, and the solution is stirred vigorously as it is heated rapidly. *If the solution begins to turn colorless, more $KMnO_4$ is added at once to prevent loss of NO_2.* Heating is continued just to boiling. The crucible, containing traces of precipitate, is placed in the $KMnO_4$ solution and stirred continuously for about 1 minute, which usually suffices to complete the reaction as evidenced by no further change in the permanganate color. (If a larger titration volume is required than will go into the 50-ml precipitation beaker, the titration may be carried out in a larger beaker and a portion of the solution containing excess $KMnO_4$ can be used to wash the last traces of precipitate from the 50-ml beaker.)

6–55. Next a slight excess of 0.05 N sodium oxalate is added from a buret and stirring is continued until the excess of permanganate is consumed, and a water clear solution is obtained. The excess of oxalate is then back titrated with the 0.05 N $KMnO_4$ to a faint pink color. The volume of 0.05 N $Na_2C_2O_4$ used is subtracted from the total volume of 0.05 N $KMnO_4$, which has been dispensed from the buret, to obtain the net $KMnO_4$ used in oxidizing the precipitate.

6–56. The essential reactions with permanganate are similar to those with cerate:

$$6 \, NO_2^- + 6 \, O^{--} \longrightarrow 6 \, NO_3^- + 12e \qquad (6\text{–}9)$$

$$Co^{+++} + e \longrightarrow Co^{++} \qquad (6\text{–}10)$$

$$Mn^{7+} + 5e \longrightarrow Mn^{++} \qquad (6\text{–}11)$$

On addition:

$$5 \, (K, Na)_3Co(NO_2)_6 + 11 \, HMnO_4 + 11 \, H_2SO_4 \longrightarrow 15 \, (K, Na)NO_3 + 5 \, Co(NO_3)_2 + 5 \, HNO_3 + 11 \, MnSO_4 + 14 \, H_2O$$
$$(6\text{–}12)$$

Also:

$$5 \, Na_2C_2O_4 + 8 \, H_2SO_4 + 2 \, KMnO_4 \longrightarrow 5 \, Na_2SO_4 + K_2SO_4 + 2 \, MnSO_4 + 10 \, CO_2 + 8 \, H_2O \qquad (6\text{–}13)$$

6–57. The quantity of K is calculated by equation 6–8, the word "permanganate" being substituted for the word "cerate," when

Net ml of permanganate = ml of permanganate added — ml of $Na_2C_2O_4$ added $\times R$

in which $R = $ ratio $\left(\dfrac{\text{permanganate volume}}{\text{oxalate volume}} \right)$ determined in a separate standardization in which 10 ml of hot $Na_2C_2O_4$ solution is titrated with $KMnO_4$ solution. Ordinarily the strength of the $KMnO_4$ solution will not be exactly equal to that of the oxalate because the former is continuously changing. The quantity of K cannot be calculated from equation 6–13 because the content of K, represented by $(K, Na)_3$ (¶ 6–7), must be evaluated under the conditions of the precipitation.

6–58. Various procedures have been evolved for insuring good contact of the precipitate with the oxidant to prevent escape of unoxidized nitrogen oxides. One is to dissolve the precipitate in NaOH with precipitation of the cobalt as a hydroxide.[29] This is a satisfactory routine, which gives the same titer value as the direct acidification procedure above.

6–59. Centrifuge Washing Technique. When the volumetric evaluation of the cobaltinitrite precipitation is combined with the centrifuge method of washing the precipitate, the same washing procedure and solvents are employed as described in connection with Gooch filtration and colorimetric evaluation (¶ 6–30). The volumetric cerate procedure is the same, except that a more dilute cerate solution is used in the tube if the amount of K is less than 0.5 mgm. After the tube and precipitate have been oven-dried, the excess cerate is pipetted directly into the tube, the precipitate is stirred with a glass rod, and the suspension is heated by partly immersing the tube in a hot water bath to oxidize the cobaltinitrite. The excess cerate is back

---

[29] Klein and Mendel, *Ind. Eng. Chem., A.E.,* 12:687 (1940).

titrated with the ferrous solution, usually being more conveniently done after the solution is transferred to a 50-ml beaker.

6–60. Permanganate is much less suitable than cerate as an oxidant for use in excess in the centrifuge tube method.

GRAVIMETRIC DETERMINATION OF POTASSIUM

(Evaluation of potassium cobaltinitrite precipitate of over 5 mgm of K)

6–61. The weight of the potassium cobaltinitrite precipitate as $(K_nNa_{3-n})Co(NO_2)_6 \cdot xH_2O$ has been found to be as reproducible as the colorimetric or volumetric evaluation, and therefore the gravimetric method is highly satisfactory for macro amounts of K. The only precaution is that the concentration of K must not exceed 2 mgm per ml (as stated in ¶ 6–23). Any volume of the 2 solutions may be employed, so that this precaution places no upper limit on the amount of K that may be determined.

APPARATUS

6–62. Needed apparatus includes precipitation beakers, a fritted glass filter crucible, a holder, a suction flask, a policeman and glass rod, an oven at 100° to 110°C, and an analytical balance.

REAGENTS

6–63. Needed reagents include precipitation reagents as given in ¶ 6–15, and washing solutions—70 per cent ethanol and absolute methanol or ethanol.

PROCEDURE

6–64. The potassium is prepared and precipitated (¶ 6–20 and following) by adding the cooled K solution containing 5 mgm of K or more to the cooled 20 per cent solution of cobaltinitrite precipitating reagent in a 1 : 1 volume ratio of the 2 solutions. After standing over night, the precipitate is filtered on a fritted glass filter that has been dried at 100° to 110°C and weighed. The precipitation beaker and precipitates are washed 3 times with 70 per cent ethanol and once with absolute methanol or ethanol.

6–65. The crucible and precipitate are then dried at 100° to 110°C for 30 minutes, cooled, and weighed. Then:

$$\text{mgm K} = \text{Gravimetric factor} \times \text{weight of precipitate, mgm} \qquad (6\text{–}14)$$

$$\text{mgm K} = \frac{\text{K precipitated (std), mgm}}{\text{weight precipitate (std), mgm}} \times \text{weight of precipitate, mgm}$$

$$(6\text{–}15)$$

The gravimetric factor has been found to be 0.135 mgm K per mgm precipitate for the operating conditions specified, but should be redetermined for the actual operating conditions employed. A standard consisting of 10 to 20 mgm of K is suitable.

6–66. Precipitation and washing in a centrifuge tube is poorly suited for the gravimetric determination of potassium because of the large quantity of precipitate usually involved.

EXTRACTION OF EXCHANGEABLE POTASSIUM FROM SOILS

(Equilibrium extraction method in 1 N NH₄OAc)

6–67. Although the exchangeable K has been extracted by the 1 N NH₄OAc in the system for exchangeable cations (¶ 5–7), a separate rapid procedure is given here because of the frequent interest in exchangeable potassium, separately from other exchangeable metallic cations. The potassium obtained from this extraction may be determined by the cobaltinitrite procedure (or another). A slightly different extraction is ordinarily employed for determination of exchangeable potassium from soil or runoff by flame emission (¶ 18–24).

APPARATUS

6–68. Needed apparatus includes 500-ml conical extraction flasks and stoppers, a rotary shaker for flasks, a Buchner funnel attached to a suction flask (or a vacuum desiccator that holds a 400-ml beaker), 400-ml beakers, cover glasses, and glass hooks.

REAGENTS

6–69. Needed reagents are 1 N NH₄OAc (prepared by dilution of 57 ml of glacial HOAc to 800 ml, neutralization with concentrated NH₄OH to pH 7, and dilution to 1 liter), and 30 per cent H₂O₂.

PROCEDURE

6–70. A sample, consisting of 30.0 gm of field-moist soil (preferably freshly taken) that has passed a 5-mm sieve, is transferred to a 500-ml conical flask. Then 300 ml of 1 N NH₄OAc solution is added. The flask is stoppered and shaken for 30 minutes on a rotary shaker, or vigorously by hand intermittently every 5 minutes. A separate 20-gm moisture sample is weighed out and dried in an oven at 100°C, then reweighed.

6–71. The suspension is then filtered through a Buchner funnel on which a moistened filter paper has been tightly sealed by suction, the filtrate being collected in a suction flask or a 400-ml beaker in a vacuum desiccator. The extraction flask is rinsed with two 25-ml portions of N NH₄OAc, the washings being poured through the filter. The filtrate is evaporated to dryness on a steam hot plate overnight. (For greater speed, the solution may be boiled down gently to about 10 to 20 ml, but should not be allowed to go to dryness over a burner, because carbon is formed, which resists oxidation later.)

6–72. After the solution has evaporated to dryness, the sides of the beaker are washed down and the evaporation to dryness is repeated. The second evaporation gives any mechanically held NH_4OAc a chance to escape. Next, 5 ml of 30 per cent H_2O_2 is added, the beaker is covered with a watch glass, and the solution is digested for 30 minutes to oxidize residual organic matter. The refluxing that takes place in the closed beaker washes down the sides of the beaker, and makes the digestion much more effective than simple evaporation with H_2O_2. Finally the cover glass is lifted onto glass hooks, and the solution is evaporated to dryness. The H_2O_2 treatment is repeated if necessary to obtain a white residue indicating absence of organic matter. The beaker is protected from deposition of NH_4Cl. The residue is then ready for the potassium determination (¶ 6–20).

6–73. Calculation of Results. The mgm of K obtained in the potassium determination is converted to meq of K per 100 gm of soils:

$$\text{meq of K per 100 gm of soil} = \frac{\text{mgm of K} \times 100}{39.1 \times \text{weight of sample, gm}} \qquad (6\text{–}16)$$

"Weight of sample, gm" is identical to the net oven-dry weight of the 20-gm sample dried for a moisture determination, provided a 10/15 (or a 5/7.5) aliquot of potassium solution was taken for precipitation (¶ 6–22). The range of 0.05 to 0.3 meq per 100 gm (50 to 250 pp2m) is usual for unfertilized soils in the humid region (¶ 5–6). For pp2m of K in the soil:

$$\text{pp2m of K} = \frac{\text{mgm K} \times 2000}{\text{weight of sample, gm}} \qquad (6\text{–}17)$$

ALTERNATIVE PROCEDURE

6–74. An ordinary filter may be employed instead of the Buchner funnel, but it is advantageous then to use 40 gm of soil and exactly 400 ml of extraction solution. After the shaking period, the extraction solution is filtered through a dry filter into a dry receiving flask, and the rinsing of the flask is omitted. If the first portion of the extraction solution comes through cloudy, it is poured back through the filter. Finally, exactly 300 ml of the extraction solution (representing 30 gm of soil) is evaporated to dryness as in the regular procedure given.

TOTAL POTASSIUM IN SOILS OR MINERALS

6–75. Total K in soils or minerals is best determined by decomposition of the sample by means of HF (¶ 11–31 or 11–176) followed by determination by the emission spectrophotometric method (¶ 18–27) or by the cobaltinitrite precipitation (¶ 6–22). The total Na can be determined on the same sample as the total K when the HF decomposition is employed. The total K of soils may also be extracted by a Na_2CO_3 fusion (¶ 11–104) followed by disintegration of the melt with the addition of 30 ml of HCl (no $HClO_4$, ¶ 11–118) and removal of sesquioxides (¶ 11–180). Blanks are carried on all reagents. Two K standards which will yield 2 mgm of K in the final aliquot are analyzed with the addition of all reagents. (The 5 gm of Na_2CO_3 containing 0.002 per cent K carries 1 mgm of K into the sample, which must be taken into account by the blanks and standards.) The J. Lawrence Smith method for total K and Na involves fusion in $NH_4Cl\text{-}CaCO_3$ (¶ 11–181).

SOIL-POTASSIUM EQUILIBRIUM

6–76. As the exchangeable potassium of soils is removed by leaching or by crops, some of the reserve (or "total") potassium weathers from feldspars and micas and becomes exchangeable. The exchangeable potassium tends by equilibration to return to the original level.[30] The addition of soluble potassium salts to soils causes a reversal of this reaction. That is, some of the potassium is "fixed" in nonexchangeable form, more so when the soil is dried.[31] The equilibrium nature of this reaction is vividly illustrated by the *release* of potassium as a result of drying a soil that had been cropped severely to remove the readily exchangeable potassium.[32] Also, exhaustive cropping with oats resulted in a recovery of potassium that had been fixed in nonexchangeable form. In regions where soils have relatively high K supplying power, soil testing laboratories frequently dry the soil sample for a week or more at 95°F with low humidity to permit the release of K to exchangeable form before the testing is done. *Either* fixation or release of potassium occurs[33] as a result of freezing and thawing, depending on the equilibrium level of K.

6–77. Soil, NH_4-saturated and dried at 500°C, released[34] much more K than extractions with acids, bases, or salts without the heating. The "log K released" fell off linearly with successive NH_4-drying treatments.

6–78. Addition of colloidal alumina or use of a Na_2CO_3 boiling treatment[35] increased the quantity of K fixed by soil on drying, while removal of colloidal materials by H_2O_2 and $H_2S\text{-}HCl$ treatments decreased the quantity of K fixed. Addition of K_2SiO_3 to montmorillonite or illite greatly increased[36] the quantity of K fixed compared to that fixed with KOH added in equivalent amounts.

6–79. These findings and many others, clearly reveal the equilibrium

[30] Bray and DeTurk, *S.S.S.A. Proc.,* 3:101 (1939).

[31] Volk, *Soil Sci.,* 37:267 (1934).

[32] Attoe, *S.S.S.A. Proc.,* 13:112 (1949).

[33] Fine *et al., S.S.S.A. Proc.,* 5:183 (1941).

[34] Kolterman and Truog, *S.S.S.A. Proc.,* 17:347 (1953).

[35] Volk, *Soil Sci.,* 45:263 (1938).

[36] Mortland and Gieseking, *Soil Sci.,* 71:381 (1951).

nature of the reactions by which potassium is interchanged from exchange-able to nonexchangeable form. The equilibrium reaction with the layer silicate vermiculite[37] involves closure of the interlayer spaces by K ions, after which the K is not readily exchanged. Extending this concept, fixation of potassium by 2 : 1 layer silicate clays was attributed[38] to a frequency distribution of layer change density and K fixation in interlayer spaces in-volving high charge density. Potassium in interlayers surrounded by low charge density remains exchangeable. This mechanism accords with the evidence[39] that mixed layer structures are formed by K fixation. The equilibrium and rate functions of K fixation have been summarized.[40] Phosphate added to soils can also fix potassium by precipitation of potas-sium aluminum or iron phosphate salts.[41]

6–80. NH₄OAc Standard for Exchangeable K. Use of N NH_4OAc ex-traction (¶ 6–70) was advocated[42] as the standard for extraction of the exchangeable form of soil K because the level of exchangeable K of soils rose rapidly within an hour after replacement with H or Ca but did not after NH_4OAc replacement. Since $NH_4{}^+$ holds highly charged layers to-gether (¶ 8–35) just as K, the release of nonexchangeable K to exchange-able form is retarded during NH_4OAc extraction.

6–81. K-fixation Capacity of Soils. The following procedure for potas-sium fixation capacity of soils (wetting-and-drying basis) was suggested by N. J. Volk: to 10 gm of soil, 10 mgm of K is added in the form of 10 ml of KCl solution. The soil is dried and wetted 10 times on a steam plate. The K is then extracted in N NH_4OAc (¶ 6–70) and determined. A second 10-gm sample of soil is similarly treated with 10 mgm of K, and the soil is immediately extracted with N NH_4OAc and the K is determined. The difference, expressed as meq of K fixed per 100 gm of soil, is the K fixation capacity of the soil.

6–82. Nonreplacement of fixed K by NH_4 from vermiculite was demon-strated by Barshad.[43] Both of these ions are released by boiling in NaOH. The release may be attributed to the fact that the Na-vermiculite has expanded spacings from which the K may migrate out into solution. Deter-mination of the K-fixation capacity of soils (wet-fixation basis) was sug-gested as follows: of 2 samples, 1 is saturated with K, then both with am-monium. Then both are subjected to NaOH distillation of NH_4, and the difference (expressed as meq of K fixed per 100 gm of soil) in NH_4 held is

[37] Barshad, *Soil Sci.,* 72:361 (1951).
[38] Jackson *et al., S.S.S.A. Proc.,* 16:3 (1952).
[39] Dyal and Hendricks, *S.S.S.A. Proc.,* 16:45 (1952).
[40] Wiklander, *Potassium-Symposium* (Berne: Int. Pot. Inst., 1954), p. 109.
[41] Cole and Jackson, *S.S.S.A. Proc.,* 15:84 (1951); Haseman *et al., S.S.S.A. Proc.,* 15:76 (1951).
[42] Merwin and Peech, *S.S.S.A. Proc.,* 15:125 (1951).
[43] *Soil Sci.,* 72:361 (1951).

the K-fixation capacity. Wet fixation and dry fixation were measured by K saturation, 0.5 N Mg(OAc)$_2$ being used as a replacing agent.[44]

6–83. Acid-Soluble K of Soils. Extensive efforts have been made to develop a method of soil potassium extraction that is not exchangeable to begin with but is taken up by plants in the course of exhaustive cropping.[45] This form is sometimes called the "moderately available form." Some of these extractions involve various concentrations of acids and electrodialysis (¶ 6–85). Much more K is extracted[46] by 0.5 N HCl than is exchangeable with N NH$_4$OAc, and such extraction after drying of the H-saturated soil (cycle repeated 6 times) releases[47] an amount of K that was related to the K recovered by exhaustive cropping.

6–84. Extraction of soil with 1 N HNO$_3$ for 10 minutes[48] removed an amount of K that seemed to be correlated with removal by cropping. A 1 : 10 ratio of soil to the 1 N NHO$_3$ gave an amount of K extracted that was insensitive to dilution but was sensitive to time of boiling.[49] A 10-minute boiling time was adopted. The quantity of K released by this acid treatment was correlated significantly with the quantity removed by exhaustive cropping of several soils. A correlation was found[50] of the K thus extracted and the microcline content of the silt fraction of 12 Indiana soils. A correlation coefficient of 0.9 was obtained[51] between alfalfa uptake of K from some Iowa soils and the K released from 2 gm of soil in 25 ml of N NHO$_3$ on boiling 10 minutes after standing 15 minutes.

6–85. Electrodialysis Release of K. Electrodialysis for 30 days was used[52] to measure the supplying capacity of Hawaiian soils. Release of K by electrodialysis could be correlated with the K removal by exhaustive cropping.[53] The K removed by electrodialysis was related neither to the exchangeable K nor to the total K, but the total quantity of K removed when the rate leveled off and became constant was related to past K fertilization and potassium fertility level.[54] From 10 to 20 days of electrodialysis was required before the rate became constant.

---

[44] Marel, *Verslag. Landbouwk. Onderzoek.* No. 61, 8, S-gravenhage (1955).

[45] Drake and Scarseth, *S.S.S.A. Proc.,* 4:201 (1940); Olsen and Shaw, *J. Am. Soc. Agron.,* 35:1 (1942); Bear *et al., Soil Sci.,* 58:139 (1944); Chandler *et al., J. Am. Soc. Agron.,* 37:709 (1945); Evans and Attoe, *Soil Sci.,* 66:323 (1948); Gholston and Hoover, *S.S.S.A. Proc.,* 13:116 (1949); Legg and Beacher, *S.S.S.A. Proc.,* 16:210 (1952); Williams and Jenny, *S.S.S.A. Proc.,* 16:216 (1952).

[46] Attoe and Truog, *S.S.S.A. Proc.,* 10:81 (1946).

[47] Evans and Simon, *S.S.S.A. Proc.,* 14:126 (1950).

[48] DeTurk *et al., Soil Sci.,* 55:1 (1943).

[49] Rouse and Bertramson, *S.S.S.A. Proc.,* 14:113 (1950).

[50] Phillippe and White, *S.S.S.A. Proc.,* 16:371 (1952).

[51] Pratt, *Soil Sci.,* 72:107 (1951).

[52] Ayres *et al., S.S.S.A. Proc.,* 11:175 (1947).

[53] Reitemeier *et al., S.S.S.A. Proc.,* 12:158 (1948).

[54] Pearson, *Soil Sci.,* 74:301 (1952).

QUESTIONS

1. What are the principal methods for the determination of potassium of soils and plants?

2. Why is the flame emission method preferable to precipitation methods for K, and why are precipitation methods still widely employed?

3. Outline the principles of the cobaltinitrite method for the determination of potassium, including the role of Na.

4. How does the water solubility of potassium cobaltinitrite compare to that of $KClO_4$ and K_2PtCl_6?

5. Why must ammonium ions be removed before potassium is precipitated?

6. List several procedures available for evaluating the potassium cobaltinitrite precipitate, and give the principle involved in each.

7. What factor is involved in the gravimetric determination of potassium cobaltinitrite that is not involved in titrimetric determination, and how is this additional factor taken care of analytically?

8. What reagent is most commonly employed for the extraction of exchangeable K?

9. What are the chief methods for the extraction of total K from soil or clay for its determination?

10. Why is there a difference between wet fixation and dry K fixation capacity of soil?

11. What is the purpose of applying stronger extraction procedures such as with 0.5 N HCl, 1 N HNO_3 and electrodialysis in the extraction of K from soils?

7

Phosphorus Determinations for Soils

Availability, fixation, fractionation

7-1. Phosphorus determinations for soils have received extensive attention from soil chemists because of the importance of phosphorus in soil fertility.[1] The chemistry of phosphorus in solution as well as in soil is rather complex, and methods of analytical *determination* have required exacting attention to every controllable detail. The *extraction* of phosphorus from soils has received extensive study along 2 lines: (a) the extraction of more active or available phosphate with high specific surface, and (b) fractionation of the total of each chemical class or species of phosphate. The similarity of arsenic reactions to those of phosphorus and the fact that arsenic is added to soils through vegetation sprays and in studies of phosphorus reactions make the differentiation of arsenic from phosphorus an important consideration in the determination of phosphorus.

7-2. Methods for Phosphorus Determination. Phosphorus determination for soils was greatly expedited by the development of sensitive colorimetric methods, although less sensitive and more laborious precipitation-titrimetric[2] and gravimetric[3] methods have long been employed. The Osmond[4]

---

[1] Pierre and Norman, *Soil and Fertilizer Phosphorus* (New York: Academic Press, Inc., 1953); Pierre, ed., *Summary of Phosporus Research in the United States* (Beltsville, Md.: Natl. Soil and Fert. Res. Com., U.S.D.A. Soils Div., 1950); Waggaman, *Phosphoric Acid, Phosphate, and Phosphatic Fertilizers,* 2nd ed. (New York: Reinhold Publishing Corporation, 1952); DeMolon and Marquis, *Le phosphere et la Vie* (Paris: Presses Univ. de France, 1949).

[2] *Methods of Analysis,* 7th ed. (Washington, D.C.: A.O.A.C., 1950), p. 36.

[3] Washington, *Chemical Analysis of Rocks,* 3rd ed. (New York: John Wiley & Sons, Inc., 1919), p. 216.

[4] *Bul. soc. chim. biol.,* 47:745 (1887).

method, involving the molybdophosphoric blue color produced by selective reduction of the heteropoly molybdophosphoric acid, has been extensively adapted. Four widely used modifications:

    I. Chlorostannous-reduced molybdophosphoric blue color method, in a sulfuric acid system.
    II. Chlorostannous-reduced molybdophosphoric blue color method, in a hydrochloric acid system.
    III. Molybdenum-reduced molybdophosphoric blue color method, in a sulfuric acid system.
    IV. 1, 2, 4-aminonaphtholsulfonic-reduced molybdophosphoric blue method, in a perchloric or sulfuric acid system.

are described herein. Also included is method V, which is based on the yellow color of the unreduced vanadomolybdophosphoric heteropoly complex. Each of these methods offers its respective advantages of sensitivity, tolerance to various levels of interfering substances, speed, or stability of color. The choice of method for a given phosphorus analysis depends on the amount of phosphorus available for the determination, the acid system involved in the scheme of analysis, and the concentration of interfering substances present in the solution to be analyzed.

    7–3. Basic Principles. The heteropoly complexes are thought to be formed by coordination of molybdate ions, with phosphorus as the central coordinating atom,[5] the oxygen of the molybdate radicals being substituted for that of PO_4:

$$H_3PO_4 + 12\ H_2MoO_4 \longrightarrow H_3P(Mo_3O_{10})_4 + 12\ H_2O \qquad (7\text{--}1)$$

Ions besides (P^{5+}), which act as the central coordinating atom to form 12-fold heteropoly acids with molybdate, include arsenic (As^{5+}), silicon (Si^{4+}), germanium (Ge^{4+}), and under some conditions molybdenum (Mo^{6+}) and boron (B^{3+}). Also, wolframate[6] (also termed "tungstate") ions are coordinated about P as a central atom in a fashion analogous to molybdate ions, though with somewhat less avidity. The heteropoly complexes, before reduction, give a yellow hue to their water solution. With high P concentrations, a yellow precipitate is formed (eq. 7–1). In solutions of low enough concentration to be suitable for determination by reduction to form the blue color, the yellow color is so faint that it is not noticed. At about 100 times this concentration, the yellow color is suitable for spectrophotometry as for molybdosilicic acid color (¶ 11–72). The vanadomolybdophosphoric yellow color (method V) is greatly intensified by the vanadium component.

---

   [5] Boltz *et al.*, *Anal. Chem.*, 21:563 (1949); Kraus, *Z. Krist.*, 100:394 (1939); Keggin, *Proc. Roy. Soc. (London)*, *A* 144:75 (1934), *Nature*, 131:908 (1933); Hastings and Frediana, *Anal. Chem.*, 20:382 (1948).
   [6] International Union of Chemistry, *Sci. American*, 181, 5:30 (Nov. 1949).

7–4. A characteristic blue color (the "molybdenum blue reaction"[7]) is produced when either molybdate or its heteropoly complexes are partially reduced. Some of the molybdenum ions are reduced from $6+$ to a lower valence, probably $3+$ and/or $5+$, involving unpaired electrons from which spectrophotometric resonance (blue color) would be expected. The spectrophotometric absorption curves[8] for the blue color of molybdenum blue in the *presence or absence* of heteropoly complexes of phosphorus shows 2 wave lengths for characteristic light absorption, at 660 mu and 830 mu. Expressed as an extinction coefficient, E, in which $E = \log({}^{T}blank/{}^{T}test)$, the sensitivity at 660 is one-third that in the infrared at 830 mu. ${}^{T}blank$ and ${}^{T}test$ refer to the percentage transmission of the blank and test solution, respectively.

7–5. Optimum Concentration of Reagents. The optimum concentration of acid, molybdate, and reductant is that which will give the maximum of color per unit of P present (in accord with Beer's law), and the minimum

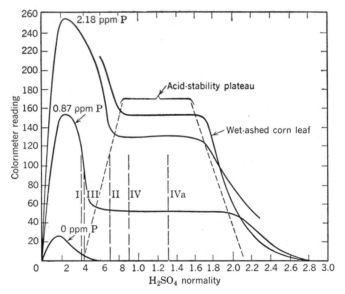

Fig. 7–1. Effect of acid concentration on molybdophosphoric heteropoly blue color intensity, with acid concentrations employed in methods I, II, III, IV, and IVa. The curves were made with 1,2,4-aminonaphtholsulfonic acid reduction, with 0.4 per cent ammonium molybdate as in method IVa. (Adapted in part from Cotton, *Ind. Eng. Chem., A.E.,* 17:736, 1945, and do not apply in detail to the other methods with different molybdate concentrations.)

[7] Berzelius, *Pogg. Ann.,* 6:380 (1826); McAlpine and Soule, *Qualitative Chemical Analysis* (New York: P. Van Nostrand Company, Inc., 1933), p. 239.
[8] Boltz and Mellon, *Anal. Chem.,* 19:874 (1947).

of fading.[9] The range of acidity over which the color is not affected by the acid concentration[10] may be termed the "acid-stability plateau" (Fig. 7–1). This plateau narrows as the phosphorus concentration increases and widens as it decreases, the low acidity boundary extending through 0.4 N H_2SO_4. The acid-stability plateau shifts position somewhat with different reductants, different molybdate concentrations, and in different acid systems. At low acid concentration, molybdate itself, as well as all of the heteropoly complexes, is easily reduced to form a blue color. The molybdate color (no P present) falls off above 0.35 to 0.6 N acid, depending upon the molybdate and reductant concentrations. The presence of phosphorus increases the molybdomolybdic blue color in the low (0.2 N) acidity range, but disproportionately to the phosphorus present. This disproportionate color development from molybdate and phosphorus extends to higher acidity progressively with higher phosphorus concentrations. At high acid concentration, the normality varying with the molybdate : acid ratio, the reduction of the molybdophosphoric complex itself falls off to zero.

7–6. Molybdoarsenic acid blue color is usually excluded from the phosphorus analysis (¶ 7–64) by reduction to arsenious acid prior to the addition of ammonium molybdate to form the heteropoly complex. The complex does not form with the arsenious radical. Also, the P can be precipitated[11] with $Al(OH)_3$ and the precipitate treated with HF, HBr, HCl, and H_2SO_4 to volatilize As, Ge, and Si, which may be coprecipitated, leaving the P for analysis. Usually, the molybdomolybdic and molybdosilicic complexes are separated by adjusting the acidity. In a 0.35 N H_2SO_4 solution, the molybdate is not reduced, but the heteropoly molybdosilicic and phosphoric acid complexes are still reduced. In method I, with 0.39 N acid, the molybdosilicic acid (with Si below 200 ppm) is not reduced. Molybdosilicic and molybdogermanic acid are reduced (as well as molybdophosphoric and molybdoarsenic acid) at acidity greater than 0.4 N under some conditions,[12] but are not a problem under suitable conditions. The acid strength is usually determined by the amount of acid added with the molybdate reagent. The test solution is previously brought to pH 2.7 to 3.0, 2, 4-dinitrophenol being used as the indicator. (The indicator 2, 6-dinitrophenol is preferred to 2, 4- except for its unavailability.)

7–7. Increasing the molybdate concentration increases the required concentration of acid to prevent molybdate reduction without altering the phosphorus concentration. That is, the acid-stability plateau (Fig. 7–1) is shifted to the right by increasing the molybdate concentration. Thus it extends[13] only from 1.7 to 2.1 N H_2SO_4 with a 0.75 per cent molybdate

9 Dickman and Bray, *Ind. Eng. Chem.*, *A.E.*, 12:666 (1940).
10 Cotton, *Ind. Eng. Chem.*, *A.E.*, 17:736 (1945).
11 Levine *et al.*, *Sci.*, 119:327 (1954).
12 Boltz and Mellon, *Anal. Chem.*, 19:873 (1947).
13 Fontaine, *Ind. Eng. Chem.*, *A.E.*, 14:77 (1942).

TABLE 7–1

Summary of the characteristics of 5 spectrophotometric methods for phosphorus described in text as methods I to V

Item compared	Molybdophosphoric blue color methods, reductant consisting of				Vanado-molybdo-phosphoric yellow color method
	Chlorostannous acid		Reduced molybdate system*	1, 2, 4 amino naphthol sulfonic acid*	
	In H_2SO_4 system*	In HCl system*			
	I	II	III	IV (IVa)	V
P conc at 50% transmission,‡ ppm P	0.4§	0.8	0.9	2.2	6
% Transmission, 1 ppm P, 660 mu	18	36	50	75	—
Range of conformity to Beer's Law, ppm P	0–1.0	0–2.5	0–4	0–10	0–20
Working range, ppm P	0.02–1	0.05–2	0.1–5	0.2–10	0.8–20
Time to develop color	5 min.	5 min.	30 min.	15 min.	5 min.
Temperature of color development	20°–25°C	25°C	100°C	25°C	25°C
Stability	15 min.	20 min.	24 hrs.	Changes**	Infinite
Final concentration of acid, N	0.39	0.7	0.44	0.9 (1.3)	0.2–1.6
Final concentration of molybdate, %	0.1	0.3	0.0506	0.4	0.5
Effect of excess molybdate-acid reagent	Slight decrease	Slight decrease	Slight decrease	None	None
Effect of excess reductant	Slight increase	Slight increase	Slight increase	Increase	—

* After Woods and Mellon, *Ind. Eng. Chem., A.E.,* 13:760 (1941).

† 1, 2, 4-aminonaphtholsulfonic acid is found to be more effective than 2, 5, 7-; 1, 4, 8-; 2, 6, 8-.

‡ For 1 cm cell at 700 mu for methods I to IVa; Evelyn tube at 440 mu for method V.

§ Calculated at 660 mu, from Fig. 1 of Woods and Mellon, *Ind. Eng. Chem., A.E.,* 13:760 (1941).

** Measurement must be made at a definite time.

concentration, compared to the wide range from 0.6 to 1.6 N with 0.4 per cent molybdate (Fig. 7-1). The plateau extends further to the left than in Fig. 7-1 under the conditions of method I with 0.1 per cent molybdate (zero color with no phosphorus, at 0.39 N acid). The sensitivity, final concentration of acid and molybdate, and other characteristics of methods I to V are listed in Table 7-1.

7-8. Many different reductant reagents can be used to develop the heteropoly blue color. Each has certain advantages, but it is doubtful if any one reductant is in every respect better than all others.[14] The calibration curve for each method fits only 1 fairly definite amount of reducing agent. A great excess cannot be employed because the reduction must be selective for the heteropoly complexes, and the excess molybdate reagent must not be reduced. There is usually a small plateau over which slight variation in the amount of reducing agent is permissible. The plateau depends upon the slight difference in reducibility between the heteropoly complex and the uncomplexed molybdate. The plateau is so small that the amount of reducing agent must be controlled closely.

7-9. Choice of Phosphorus Method. Sensitivity and freedom from interfering ions are the most important factors in the choice of phosphorus method for any given application. For example, method I has much the greatest sensitivity (Table 7-1) and is thus the most satisfactory for phosphorus extracted from infertile soils with relatively low soil : extractant ratios. Method II is suited for systems high in chlorides. Method III is relatively sensitive, eliminates the effect of arsenic, and has been used by the U.S.D.A. in regional cooperative studies.[15] Method IV, though less sensitive, permits the determination in the presence of 200 ppm of ferric iron, is little sensitive to moderate variations in acidity, and eliminates the effect of arsenate. Method V, though much less sensitive, provides the advantages of color stability, freedom from the reduction step, greater freedom from interfering ions and contamination from glassware and lower dilution required for a convenient size of soil or plant sample analyzed. The proper choice of analytical method is indicated with each type of soil phosphorus extraction procedure to be described.

---

[14] Reducing agents that have been employed include: chlorostannous acid (Osmond, *Chem. News,* 56:160, 1887), in methods I and II; gallic acid (Passerini, *Gazz. chim. ital.,* 41:182, 1911); hydroiodic acid (Wu, *J. Biol. Chem.,* 43:218, 1920); hydroquinone (Bell and Doisy, *J. Biol. Chem.,* 44:55, 1920) and (*Official Methods of Analysis,* 6th ed., Washington, D.C.: A.O.A.C., 1945, p. 127); sodium thiosulfate (Losana, *Giorn. chim. ind. applicata,* 4:60, 1922); 1, 2, 4-aminonaphtholsulfonic acid (Fiske and Subbarow, *J. Biol. Chem.,* 66:375, 1925), employed in method IV; benzidine (Feigl, *Z. anal. Chem.,* 74:386, 1928); molybdate reduced with a metal, usually Mo itself (Zinzadze, *Ann. agron., n.s.,* 1:321, 1931), employed in method III; p-methylaminophenol (Lingren, *Analyst,* 58:755, 1933); and hydrazine sulfate (Hague and Bright, *J. Research Nat. Bur. Standards,* 26:505, 1941).

[15] Peech *et al.,* U.S.D.A. Cir. 757 (1947).

7-10. Precautions Against Phosphorus Contamination. The glassware to be used must be free of contamination with phosphorus (or arsenic, which gives the same test unless reduced with $NaHSO_3$). Since Pyrex glass contains 0.7 per cent arsenic oxide, new glassware must be thoroughly weathered before use by treatment with warm sulfuric acid-dichromate solution for at least 24 hours. Washing soaps and powders, if used, must be completely removed by cleaning in strong acid, as they frequently contain phosphorus. As the last step in cleaning, the glassware is dipped or rinsed in 6 N HCl after *apparently clean,* then filled with tap water, and finally rinsed 3 times with distilled water. The reagents and filter paper selected should be as free of phosphorus as possible. Dust, saliva, perspiration, and tobacco ashes carry appreciable amounts of phosphorus and therefore should be excluded.

7-11. Primary Phosphate Standard, 50 ppm of P. Potassium dihydrogen phosphate (KH_2PO_4, Sorenson's standard, or recrystallized at pH 4.5) is dried at 40°C, and 0.2195 gm is dissolved in about 400 ml of distilled water in a 1000-ml volumetric flask. Then 25 ml of 7 N H_2SO_4 is added, and the solution made to 1000-ml volume and mixed, giving 50 ppm of P. Thus preserved with H_2SO_4, the solution keeps indefinitely,[16] but it should be stored in a weathered soft-glass bottle (rather than one of Pyrex), to minimize contamination with arsenic. This solution is diluted directly for the yellow colored solutions of the vanadomolybdophosphoric acid (method V, Table 7–2).

7-12. Secondary Standards, 2 and 20 ppm of P. For the 2 ppm standard, 20 ml of the 50 ppm stock solution is diluted to 500 ml. For the 20 ppm standard, 200 ml (pipetted or measured in a 200-ml volumetric flask) is diluted to 500 ml. These more dilute stock solutions, especially the 2 ppm solution, do not keep well, even with toluol[17] added, and must be made up fairly frequently. They are used in making the blue-colored solutions (methods I, II, III, and IV, Table 7–2).

7-13. Working Standards and Blank. All reagents including the extraction solution and sample processing chemicals must be included in each of the standard solutions *and in the blank* employed for any of the calibration curves (Table 7–2). The influence of the extraneous ions and the impurities thus are taken into account. A slight color in the blank does not interfere, since the photometer is set with the blank reading, G = 100 (L = 0), and the remaining solutions are read relative to this blank (¶ 17–39). The blank transmission percentage usually will be more than 95 per cent of a similar but uncolored solution. The "center setting" of the Evelyn colorimeter should be between 76 and 90 if the reagents are reasonably free from phosphorus and arsenic. If more than this slight trace of

---

[16] Bertramson, *Soil Sci.,* 53:135 (1942).
[17] Holman and Pollard, *J. Soc. Chem. Ind.,* 56T:339 (1937).

color is noted in the blank, the source of contamination should be located
(¶ 7–10).

TABLE 7–2

**Appropriate concentration ranges of phosphorus standard solutions
for various analytical methods**

Volume of stock* solution taken	Concentration obtained when stock solution is diluted to 50 ml final volume					% Transmission
	2 ppm stock		20 ppm stock		50 ppm stock	
	I	II	III	IV	V	
ml	ppm	ppm	ppm	ppm	ppm	
0 (Blank)	0	0	0	0	0	100.0
0.50	0.02	—	0.2	0.2	—	_____
1.00	0.04	0.04	0.4	0.4	1.0	_____
2.50	0.10	0.10	1.0	1.0	2.5	_____
5.00	0.20	0.20	2.0	2.0	5.0	_____
7.50	0.30	—	3.0	—	7.5	_____
10.00	—	0.40	—	4.0	10.0	_____
12.5	0.50	—	5.0	—	12.5	_____
15.0	0.60	0.60	—	6.0	15.0	_____
20.0	—	0.80	—	8.0	20.0	_____
25.0	—	1.0	—	10.0	—	_____

* Stock solution of KH_2PO_4 containing: for methods I and II, 2 ugm of P per ml (2 ppm of P); for methods III and IV, 20 ugm of P per ml (20 ppm of P); for method V, 50 ugm of P per ml (50 ppm of P).

CHLOROSTANNOUS-REDUCED MOLYBDOPHOSPHORIC BLUE COLOR METHOD, IN SULFURIC ACID SYSTEM[18] (METHOD I)

(Includes arsenate)

7–14. Method I has the highest sensitivity per unit of phosphorus present (Table 7–1), providing a working range from 0.02 to 0.6 ppm of P. It provides for noninterference of Si in solution up to 200 ppm, Fe^{++} up to 100 ppm, Fe^{+++} up to 2 ppm, Ti up to 20 ppm, Ca and Mg up to 500 or more ppm, NO_3 up to 100 ppm, F up to 5 ppm, Cl up to 250 ppm, SO_4 up to 1000 ppm—but it includes arsenate in chemical equivalence to P. Excess of nitrate or chloride prevents maximum color development and hastens color fading, and therefore is held to a minimum. Great excess of sulfate

---

[18] Adapted from Denigès, *Compt. Rend.,* 171: 802 (1920), Truog and Meyer, *Ind. Eng. Chem., A.E.,* 1:136 (1929); Woods and Mellon, *Ind. Eng. Chem., A. E.,* 13:760 (1941); and Bertramson, *Soil Sci.,* 53: 135 (1942).

intensifies the color. Preparation of the standard curve in the presence of the same amount of salts as will be present in the test sample permits determinations with Fe, Cl, SO_4, and NO_3 in much larger concentrations than the stated limits. Determination of P can be carried out with several hundred ppm of Fe if reduced (¶ 7–132).

APPARATUS

7–15. Apparatus needed consists of a special 2-ml pipet for sulfomolybdic acid; a special storage container for chlorostannous acid; 50-ml, 500-ml, and 1000-ml volumetric flasks; 125-ml conical flasks; a colorimeter with 660-mu light maximum or visual comparator tubes; pipets; and a buret.

REAGENTS

7–16. Needed reagents consist of 2 N H_2SO_4, 4 N Na_2CO_3, 2, 4-dinitrophenol indicator, standard phosphorus solution (Table 7–2), and the following special reagents.

7–17. Sulfomolybdic Acid Solution, 2.5 Per Cent. Exactly 25.0 gm of c.p. ammonium molybdate, $(NH_4)_6Mo_7O_{24} \cdot 4 H_2O$, is dissolved in 200 ml of distilled water and warmed to 60°C. The solution is filtered to remove sediment, if necessary. Then 275 ml of phosphorus-free and arsenic-free concentrated sulfuric acid (35 to 36 N) is diluted to 750 ml with distilled water. After both solutions have cooled, the ammonium molybdate solution is added slowly, with stirring, to the sulfuric acid solution. After the combined solution has cooled to room temperature, it is diluted with water to exactly 1000 ml. This is a 9.7 to 9.9 N sulfuric acid solution, containing 2.5 gm of ammonium molybdate per 100 ml. It is stored in an acid-weathered amber glass bottle,[19] with a 2-ml rapid-delivering pipet attached. Thus stored, protected from light, the solution keeps indefinitely.[20]

7–18. Chlorostannous Acid Reductant. Approximately 25 gm of reagent grade $SnCl_2 \cdot 2 H_2O$ is dissolved in 50 ml of concentrated HCl, with warming if necessary to dissolve. This solution is diluted (with rapid stirring) to approximately 500 ml with recently boiled distilled water, giving about 0.2 M Sn^{++}. The molar concentration of stannous in the solution is best determined (¶ 7–19) by titration of a 5-ml aliquot with 0.1 N standard iodine solution, although with reagents of known high purity, this stannous solution may be diluted with 1.2 N HCl (¶ 7–20) to 1 liter, giving 0.1 M Sn^{++}.

7–19. To standardize the stannous solution, an iodine solution is prepared by dissolving 12.7 gm reagent grade I_2 and 40 gm of iodate-free KI in 25 ml of water. This mixture is stirred until complete solution results and then is diluted to 1 liter and stored in an amber glass-stoppered bottle.

---

[19] Smith et al., Can. J. Research, B17:178 (1939).
[20] Holman and Pollard, J. Soc. Chem. Ind., T56:339 (1937).

The iodine solution is standardized against a 0.1 N arsenious solution, with starch as an indicator. The 0.1 N arsenious solution is prepared by weighing 2.4725 gm of pure, dry arsenious oxide, dissolving it in 20 ml of 1 N NaOH, then adding 1 N H_2SO_4 until the solution is neutral or very slightly acid to litmus paper, and finally diluting to 500 ml in a volumetric flask. A 25-ml aliquot is pipetted into a 250-ml conical flask, to which are then added 50 ml of water, 1 gm of $NaHCO_3$, and a few ml of starch solution (¶ 3–50). The iodine solution is titrated into the flask until a blue color results. The iodine solution is then titrated into a 25-ml aliquot of the chlorostannous acid solution in the presence of starch indicator to a blue color. An atmosphere of CO_2 may be maintained over the titration for most accurate results, as Sn^{++} is rapidly oxidized in air.

7–20. If the purity of the chlorostannous solution is less than 90 per cent, a fresh solution should be prepared or a new reagent obtained because the stannic ion will seriously affect the test.[21] The chlorostannous solution is next diluted with 1.2 N HCl to 0.1 M $SnCl_2 \cdot 2 H_2O$, (to about 1 liter), and stored in an amber glass bottle under a 1-cm layer of mineral oil, protected from oxygen by passing the entering air through two traps containing alkaline pyrogallol, or by means of a CO_2 generator. The original air in the bottle is removed by bubbling through natural gas or CO_2. The delivery of the chlorostannous acid solution is arranged by a siphon or bottom exit in the bottle, through a dropper tip calibrated to deliver almost exactly 0.15 ml in 3 drops,[22] and protected by a rubber cap (policeman) when not in use.

7–21. Precaution. A ml or so of the solution in the dropper is run out and discarded before use after it has stood exposed to the atmosphere for more than half an hour. To assure preservation of the $SnCl_2$ solution, it is desirable to check it occasionally against the standard iodine solution, which keeps indefinitely in a cool, dark place.

PROCEDURE

7–22. Preparation of Phosphorus Solution. The phosphorus solution (prepared according to Table 7–2 for the phosphorus standards, from the extract from a soil sample, or from stock solution resulting from a fusion, fertilizer, or plant tissue analysis) should have a phosphorus concentration in the final 50-ml dilution to be made, of 0.05 to 0.6 ppm P. This corresponds to 2.5 to 30 ugm of P per 50-ml volume. An aliquot is placed in a 50-ml volumetric flask. If its pH is appreciably at variance from pH 3, the reaction is adjusted to pH 3, using 2,4-dinitrophenol indicator[23]

---

[21] Pierce and Haenisch, *Quantitative Analysis* (New York: John Wiley & Sons, Inc., 1940), p. 199.

[22] 0.25 ml per 50 ml is recommended by Woods and Mellon, *Ind. Eng. Chem., A.E.,* 13:761 (1941). More than that leads to turbidity of the colored solution on standing.

[23] Zinzadze, *Ind. Eng. Chem., A.E.,* 7:228 (1935).

(0.25 per cent in H_2O). To do this, a few drops of indicator are added to the solution and if it gives a yellow color, 2 N H_2SO_4 is added dropwise until colorless. If the indicator gives a colorless solution, indicating a solution pH below 3, then 4 N Na_2CO_3 is added dropwise just until a yellow color appears and finally 2 N H_2SO_4 until yellow becomes faint.

7–23. Development of the Molybdophosphoric Blue Color. The test solution aliquot (of pH 3) is placed in a 50-ml volumetric flask. Then 2 ml of the sulfomolybdic acid solution is added with the pipet. The solution is made to volume, mixed, and poured into a drained 125-ml conical flask. The working temperature is kept at 25° ± 5°C, and the volume ratios are adhered to strictly, to maintain a 0.4 N H_2SO_4 solution, 0.1 per cent in ammonium molybdate. Next, 3 drops (0.15 ml) of the chlorostannous acid reductant solution is added, and the solution is mixed thoroughly. The full color intensity develops in 3 to 4 minutes and begins to fade in 10 or 12 minutes. It is read photometrically with a 660-mu light maximum, within that interval. The blue solution cannot be diluted if too strongly colored; the color is developed in a new aliquot if further dilution is needed.

7–24. Calibration Curve. The transmission percentage readings of the standards are plotted (¶ 17–16). The photo response follows Beer's law up to 0.4 ppm, or somewhat more with some types of colorimeters. The transmission percentage readings of the test samples are referred directly to this calibration curve to obtain the ppm of P in solution in the test sample. *Precautions: For a satisfactory phosphorus procedure, maintain constant conditions in the blank, standard, and test solutions.* Contamination must be scrupulously avoided (¶ 7–10). The standard curve should be repeated as necessary to obtain all the data points on the straight line calibration curve and a consistent position of the curve.

7–25. Instead of a photoelectric colorimeter and calibration curve, the standard colors (0.1 and 0.25 ppm P) may be visually compared to those in the test solutions. In this case, the development of the standard colors is delayed until several test solutions are prepared; then the color is developed in the series of solutions simultaneously, and is compared by means of comparator tubes or a visual colorimeter (¶ 17–42).

CHLOROSTANNOUS-REDUCED MOLYBDOPHOSPHORIC BLUE COLOR METHOD, IN HYDROCHLORIC ACID SYSTEM[24] (METHOD II)

(Includes arsenate)

7–26. Method II has approximately one-half the sensitivity of the sulfuric acid system (method I), and a working range from 0.05 to 1 ppm of

---

[24] After Dickman and Bray, *Ind. Eng. Chem., A.E.,* 12:665 (1940), and Woods and Mellon, *Ind. Eng. Chem., A.E.,* 13:760 (1941).

P (Table 7–1). Concentrations of 2000 ppm or more of Cl, 15 ppm of Fe^{+++}, 1000 ppm of Al, 200 ppm of Ca or Mg, 600 ppm of SO_4, 50 ppm of ClO_4, or 25 ppm of NO_3 do not interfere. The method is thus eminently suited for application in the Na_2CO_3–HCl system (¶ 7–133) for total elemental analysis of soils. Sulfates or other anions (except chloride) in gross amounts do interfere, just as chloride does in the sulfuric acid system. Determination of P can be carried out with several hundred ppm of Fe if reduced (¶ 7–32).

APPARATUS

7–27. Apparatus needed consists of a special storage container for the chlorostannous acid (¶ 7–20), 50-ml and 1000-ml volumetric flasks, 125-ml conical flasks, a colorimeter with 660-mu light maximum or visual comparator tubes, pipets, and a buret.

REAGENTS

7–28. Needed reagents consist of 4 N NH_4OH, 4 N HCl, 2, 4-dinitrophenol indicator, standard phosphorus solution (Table 7–2), and the following special reagents.

7–29. Chloromolybdic Acid Reagent, 1.5 Per Cent. Exactly 15.0 gm of c.p. ammonium molybdate, $(NH_4)_6Mo_7O_{24} \cdot 4 H_2O$, is dissolved in about 300 ml of distilled water warmed to about 50°C, and the solution is filtered to remove sediment, if necessary. The molybdate solution is cooled and 350 ml of 10.0 N HCl is added slowly with rapid stirring. When this solution has cooled again to room temperature, it is diluted with distilled water to exactly 1000 ml in a volumetric flask, mixed thoroughly, and stored in an amber, glass-stoppered bottle. This is a 1.5 per cent ammonium molybdate solution in 3.5 N HCl; it should be replaced every 2 months.

7–30. Chlorostannous Acid Reductant. The same reagent is employed as for the sulfuric acid system (Method I) except that 0.25 ml is used per 50 ml of colored solution.

PROCEDURE

7–31. Development of the Molybdophosphoric Blue Color. An aliquot of the phosphorus-containing test solution is pipetted into a 50-ml volumetric flask, adjusted to pH 3 with 4 N NH_4OH or 4 N HCl, 2,4-dinitrophenol being used as an indicator (becomes yellow as pH 3 is approached from the acid side). Then 10 ml of the chloromolybdic acid solution is added by means of a pipet. The solution is diluted to the 50-ml volume mark, mixed and poured into a drained 125-ml conical flask. The temperature throughout the determination is maintained at 25° ± 5°C. Next, 5 drops (0.25 ml) of the chlorostannous acid reductant solution is added to the solution in the flask and mixed thoroughly. The color intensity is nearly constant between 4 and 20 minutes, and is read photometrically after 5 minutes with a 660-mu light. For greater rapidity, the solution may of course be mixed in 25 × 200-mm test tubes calibrated for the appropriate volume.

ALTERNATIVE PROCEDURES

7–32. Reduction of Large Amounts of Ferric Iron. If greater than 15 ppm Fe^{+++} in the final dilution are encountered, an aliquot of the acid test solution is passed through a small Jones reductor. A convenient size is a 15-cm column of amalgamated zinc supported on 5 mm of glass wool in a 50-ml buret. The solution is rinsed from the reductor with three small portions of 0.25 N HCl, and the combined effluent is adjusted to pH 3 by the addition of 4 N NH_4OH, with care to avoid exceeding that pH— otherwise a precipitate forms. If this happens, the turbid solution is discarded and a new aliquot is reduced. When over 30 ppm of iron is present, the reduced solution should be used for a blank reading, since it has an appreciable color. The color is developed as in the previous paragraph.

7–33. Elimination of Fluoride Interference[25] **in the Molybdenum Blue Reaction.** Fluoride ions, if present in greater than about 5 ppm,[26] produce a negative interference with the molybdenum blue reaction used for the determination of phosphorus. The interference of F ion is eliminated by the addition of boric acid,

$$4\,F^- + H_3BO_3 + 3\,H^+ \longrightarrow (BF_4)^- + 3\,H_2O \qquad (7\text{--}2)$$
$$\text{(fluoroborate, very slightly ionized)}$$

Neither the boric acid ions or the fluoroborate interfere. An aliquot of the test solution, containing less than 0.15 mole of fluoride ion is pipetted into a 50-ml volumetric flask, and 15 ml of 0.8 M H_3BO_3 (50 gm of H_3BO_3 per liter) is added. The color is then developed as usual (¶ 7–31). A less convenient method[27] is the removal of F by evaporation with $HClO_4$, the excess $HClO_4$ being neutralized before the determination of phosphorus.

MOLYBDENUM-REDUCED MOLYBDOPHOSPHORIC BLUE COLOR METHOD, IN SULFURIC ACID SYSTEM[28] (METHOD III)

(With reduction to exclude arsenate)

7–34. Method III is about one-third as sensitive as Method I, and requires heating for 30 minutes for color development (Table 7–1). The

---

[25] Kurtz, *Ind. Eng. Chem., A.E.,* 14:855 (1942).

[26] Woods and Mellon, *Ind. Eng. Chem., A.E.,* 13:762 (1941).

[27] Robinson, *Ind. Eng. Chem., A.E.,* 13:465 (1941).

[28] After Zinzadze, *Zts. Pflanzenerdhr. Dung. Bodenk.,* 16A:129 (1930), *Ann. Agron.,* n.s., 1:321 (1931), *Ind. Eng. Chem., A.E.,* 7:227 (1935), as modified by Gerritz, *J.A.O.A.C.,* 23:321 (1940), and Peech *et al.,* U.S.D.A. Cir. 757, p. 3 (1947).

color, once developed, is stable for 24 hours. Over 2, 25, 100, and 25 ppm respectively of iron, arsenate, arsenite, and silicate interfere.[29]

APPARATUS

7–35. Needed apparatus includes an 800-ml Kjeldahl flask and heating rack, a 50-ml volumetric flask, a 125-ml conical flask, pipets, a buret, a 100°C water bath, a colorimeter with 660-mu light maximum, and tubes.

REAGENTS

7–36. Needed reagents consist of 99.5 to 100 per cent pure and phosphorus-free MoO_3, 99.5 to 100 per cent pure Mo metal powder (passed an 80-mu or 200 meshes per inch sieve), concentrated and 2 N H_2SO_4, 0.1 N $KMnO_4$, 4 N Na_2CO_3, 0.25 per cent 2,4-dinitrophenol, standard phosphorus solution (Table 7–2), and the following special reagents.

7–37. Sulfomolybdic Acid "Molybdenum Blue"[30] (Reagent A). Approximately 19.5 gm of MoO_3 is placed in an 800-ml Kjeldahl flask and 500 ml of 36 N H_2SO_4 added. The mixture is heated gently with occasional mixing until solution is complete, and then is cooled to 150°C. Next, 1.25 gm of finely powdered Mo metal is added. The temperature is kept at 140° to 150°C, and the solution is mixed vigorously until all of the metal is dissolved except possibly a few large particles. The solution is cooled and a 5-ml aliquot (a previously wetted pipet is used and the aliquot is washed out to transfer the proper aliquot of this viscous solution) is placed in a 125-ml conical flask. Next, 20 ml of distilled water is added and the solution is titrated with 0.1 N $KMnO_4$ to a pink that persists for 1 minute. The reagent should be 0.11 N; if less than 0.109, a calculated amount of the Mo powder is added and dissolved by reheating in the Kjeldahl flask at 150°C. Evolution of fumes and loss of acid concentration is avoided. The reagent is cooled, then transferred to a dark Pyrex, glass-stoppered bottle without dilution. This solution keeps indefinitely.

7–38. Dilute Sulfomolybdic Acid "Molybdenum Blue"[31] (Reagent B). One volume of *reagent A* is diluted with 3 volumes of water and cooled. Since this reagent deteriorates rapidly upon standing, it is freshly prepared as needed.

7–39. Sodium Bisulfite-H_2SO_4 Solution, 8 Per Cent. Approximately 40 gm of $NaHSO_3$ (meta, powder) is dissolved in 500 ml of 1.0 N H_2SO_4. This reagent is freshly prepared each week.

---

[29] Woods and Mellon, *Ind. Eng. Chem., A.E.,* 13:763 (1941).

[30] Peech *et al.,* U.S.D.A. Cir. 757 (1947).

[31] The concentration of molybdate expressed as $(NH_4)_6Mo_7O_{24} \cdot 4 H_2O$ is 1.28 per cent; the hexavalent molybdate, similarly, expressed is 1.19 per cent. Thus, a lower molybdate concentration is employed in method III than in methods I and II.

7–40. Preparation of the Phosphorus Solution. The appropriate volume of the standard phosphorus solution (Table 7–2), the blank, and an extract from the soil sample, fertilizer, or plant tissue analysis, is taken to give 0.2 to 3 ppm of P (final concentration) in a 50-ml volumetric flask. This corresponds to 10 to 150 ugm P. If the pH is appreciably at variance from pH 3, the reaction is adjusted to pH 3, using 2,4-dinitrophenol indicator (0.25 per cent in H_2O), with $2 N H_2SO_4$ added dropwise just to colorless or $4 N Na_2CO_3$ added dropwise just to a faint yellow.

7–41. Reduction of Arsenic to Arsenious and Ferric to Ferrous. The phosphorus solution (of pH 3) is diluted to a 35-ml mark on the flask and then 4 ml of the sodium bisulfite-H_2SO_4 solution is added.[32] The solution is mixed with a swirling motion and heated in a water bath at 100°C for 40 minutes. This treatment reduces As_2O_5 to As_2O_3, the latter form of which does not give the heteropoly blue reaction, but does not reduce the P_2O_5. Ferric iron is, within limits, reduced to ferrous. Arsenate should be limited[33] to 25 ppm and iron to 2 ppm.

7–42. Development of Molybdophosphoric Blue Color. To each flask containing a 39-ml total volume of phosphorus-containing solution, at 100°C, 2 ml of the dilute molybdenum blue (reagent B) is added by means of a pipet, the stream being directed to the center of the flask, not being allowed to run down the sides. The solution is quickly mixed by swirling, and the heating is continued for 25 minutes. Next the solution is cooled in cold running water, diluted to 50 ml, and mixed. The color is stable for as long as 24 hours and is measured at 660 mu. A calibration curve is prepared in the usual way, with transmission percentage plotted on a log scale against the P concentration on a linear scale. If the color in a test sample is too strong, the determination is repeated, since dilution of the final solution is not permissible.

1, 2, 4-AMINONAPHTHOLSULFONIC ACID-REDUCED MOLYBDOPHOSPHORIC BLUE COLOR METHOD, IN PERCHLORIC ACID SYSTEM[34] (METHOD IV)

(With a modification to exclude arsenate)

7–43. Method IV is unique in that the perchloric acid is added separately to the test solution near the end of the formulation, the reductant and

---

[32] Zinzadze, *Ind. Eng. Chem., A.E.,* 7:221 (1935), added 5 ml of $NaHSO_3$ following separate addition of 5 ml of $1 N H_2SO_4$.

[33] Woods and Mellon, *Ind. Eng. Chem. A.E.,* 13:763 (1941).

[34] After Sherman, *Ind. Eng. Chem., A.E.,* 14:182 (1942), as modified from King, *Biochem. J.,* 26:292 (1932), the reductant of Fiske and Subbarow, *J. Biol. Chem.,* 66:375 (1925), being employed.

sodium sulfite for arsenate elimination having been mixed previously. Finally the molybdate is added to develop the color. This permits separate adjustment of the final acidity in solutions containing an appreciable residual acidity.The total acidity is 0.9 N in the final solution, which is 22 per cent greater than that used by King (0.7 N), the latter being too low to be in the acid-stability plateau (¶ 7–5) for amounts of phosphorus above 2 ppm.

7–44. Method IV is about one-sixth as sensitive as method I, ranging 0.4 to 2.4 ppm (Table 7–1). The chief advantage of method IV is that 200 parts per million of ferric iron do not interfere with the development of the blue color, and it is thus eminently suited to the determination of total phosphorus (¶ 7–134) of soils following perchloric acid digestion of the sample.[35] The iron gives the solution a greenish cast, but that effect is eliminated by the light filter. Ti and V do not interfere, nor does Mg from the magnesium nitrate ashing procedure. Silica and nitrate are eliminated by $HClO_4$ predigestion.

APPARATUS

7–45. Needed apparatus includes a 5-ml pipet, 2 burets, 50-ml volumetric flasks, a colorimeter with 660-mu light maximum, and tubes. Additional apparatus needed for the purification of the reagents includes a 2-liter conical flask and 32-cm suction filter apparatus.

REAGENTS

7–46. Required reagents include 60 per cent and 2 N $HClO_4$, 2 N Na_2CO_3, 0.25 per cent 2,4-dinitrophenol indicator, and standard phosphorus solutions (Table 7–2). To exclude arsenates, $NaHSO_3$ crystals are needed as well. To purify the reagents, concentrated HCl, $NaHSO_3$, Na_2SO_3, and 95 per cent ethanol are needed. The following special reagents are prepared freshly every 2 weeks.

7–47. Ammonium Molybdate, 5 Per Cent. Five gm of ammonium molybdate are dissolved in 100 ml of distilled water, and allowed to stand over night. The solution is then filtered into an amber glass bottle.

7–48. 1, 2, 4-Aminonaphtholsulfonic Acid Reductant. The commercial reagent 1-amino, 2-naphthol, 4-sulfonic acid (Eastman Kodak Co.) is recrystallized as follows:[36] to 1000 ml of water in a 2-liter conical flask, heated to 90°C, in which there have been dissolved 150 gm of $NaHSO_3$ and 10 gm of crystalline Na_2SO_3, 15 gm of the crude 1,2,4-aminonaphtholsulfonic acid is added. The flask is stoppered and shaken until all but the "amorphous" impurity is dissolved. Next the hot solution is filtered through a large filter paper (about 32 cm), and the filtrate is then cooled promptly

---

[35] Bray and Kurtz, *Soil Sci.*, 59:39 (1945).
[36] Fiske and Subbarow, *J. Bio. Chem.*, 66:375 (1925).

under a water tap. Then 10 ml of concentrated HCl is added to the solution. Finally the solution is filtered with suction and washed with about 300 ml of water followed by 95 per cent ethanol until the washings are colorless. The purified aminonaphtholsulfonic acid is dried in air with the least possible exposure to light, then powdered and transferred to a brown bottle.

7–49. The 1,2,4-aminonaphtholsulfonic acid may be synthesized[37] from B-naphthol and the crystalline product so prepared, while still wet on the filter, may be washed further with 95 per cent ethanol as long as any color is extracted.

7–50. The reductant reagent[38] is prepared by mixing 0.125 gm of the purified 1,2,4-aminonaphtholsulfonic acid crystals with 44 ml of 15 per cent $NaHSO_3$ solution in a dark glass stopped bottle. A 20 per cent solution Na_2SO_3 is then added drop by drop until the solution is clear, usually requiring 5 to 7 ml.

PROCEDURE

7–51. Development of the Molybdophosphoric Blue Color. An aliquot of phosphorus solution (less than 25 ml containing 20 to 120 ugm of P, 0.4 to 2.4 ppm in the 50 ml) is pipetted into a 50-ml volumetric flask. The pH, if appreciably at variance from pH 3, is adjusted to pH 3 with 2 N Na_2CO_3 or 2 N $HClO_4$, 2,4-dinitrophenol being used as an indicator. (In certain routines, the amount of $HClO_4$ in the aliquot, if accurately known, may be subtracted from that to be added and the pH adjustment dispensed with.) Then 5 ml of 60 per cent $HClO_4$ is added and the solution volume is adjusted to approximately 40 ml. The solution is thoroughly mixed after each successive reagent addition. The temperature is maintained at $25° \pm 4°C$, throughout the color development. Next, 1.6 ml of the 1,2,4-aminonaphtholsulfonic acid reagent is added. Exactly 15 minutes before the colorimetric reading, 4.0 ml of the ammonium molybdate solution is added, the volume quickly adjusted to 50 ml with distilled water, and the solution mixed. At the end of 15 minutes, transmission percentage is read with a 660-mu light maximum. The photo response is linear to 2.4 ppm.

7–52. A convenient routine[39] is to prepare as many as 20 or 30 samples at once through the addition of the aminonaphtholsulfonic acid. Then, when the colorimeter is ready, the ammonium molybdate is added at intervals of 2 minutes; and the samples are made to volume and mixed. When 7 samples are prepared (14 minutes), the first is read. Subsequently additional samples are prepared, and readings are taken alternately, so that the 15-minute reading interval is maintained between color development and

---

[37] Folin, *J. Biol. Chem.*, 51:386 (1922).
[38] Sherman, *Ind. Eng. Chem., A.E.,* 14:182 (1942).
[39] Cole, Ph.D. Thesis, Department of Soils, University of Wisconsin (1950).

reading. Carefully matched tubes (or the same tube) are used to avoid variance. A standard solution and blank are included with each run to re-check the calibration curve.

7–53. Modification to Exclude Arsenate.[40] To eliminate arsenates, which may be present in amounts equal to phosphorus in soils sprayed with arsenic to control insects, an aliquot of the test solution is placed in the volumetric flask, and the perchloric acid is added as in the regular de-termination. Then 0.8 gm of crystalline $NaHSO_3$ is added by means of a scoop of appropriate size. The neck of the flask is washed down with water and the total volume brought to 40 ml. The flask is agitated a little to hasten solution of the solid, and the solution is allowed to stand on the bench for 3 hours, after which the color is developed (¶ 7–51). Heat is unnecessary[41] for the reduction of arsenate in the presence of perchloric acid; in fact the solution must not be heated because it affects the reading.

ALTERNATIVE PROCEDURE

7–54. Modification for Mid-Range of Acid-Stability Plateau in Sulfuric Acid System[42] **(Method IVa).** Although method IV (above) utilizes 0.9 N $HClO_4$, which is well within the acid-stability plateau, phosphorus of plants has been determined at[43] the mid-range of acid-stability (¶ 7–5). In acid digestions for the oxidation of organic matter of tissue, the residual acidity may be utilized as a part of the total acidity of the formulation, without detailed adjustments for losses by volatilization.

7–55. To eliminate the effect of arsenate from the sample or contamina-tion from glassware, approximately 0.03 gm of crystalline $NaHSO_3$ is added to a 5-ml aliquot of plant digest solution; the solution is heated to 80°C for at least 30 minutes and cooled. The total acidity is adjusted to give 1.3 N H_2SO_4 in the final 50-ml volume, after which the determination is carried out according to method IV[44] (¶ 7–51). The color is read at 25 minutes; it varies slowly after this.

VANADOMOLYBDOPHOSPHORIC YELLOW COLOR METHOD, IN NITRIC ACID SYSTEM (METHOD V)

7–56. The exact nature of the yellow chromogen of the vanadomolybdo-phosphoric system (method V) is not known, but the color is attributed to

[40] Sherman, *Ind. Eng. Chem., A.E.,* 14:182 (1942).
[41] Sherman, *Ind. Eng. Chem., A.E.,* 14:182 (1942).
[42] Woods and Mellon, *Ind. Eng. Chem., A.E.,* 13:762 (1941).
[43] Cotton, *Ind. Eng. Chem., A.E.,* 17:734 (1945).
[44] Woods and Mellon employed the equivalent of 5 ml of 5 per cent ammonium molybdate per 50 ml, but stated that the amount was not critical; Cotton, according to King, *Biochem. J.,* 26:292 (1932), employed 3.3 ml, and Sherman (method IV) employed 4 ml of 5 per cent per 50 ml final volume.

substitution[45] of oxyvanadium and oxymolybdenum radicals for the O of PO_4 to give a heteropoly compound that is chromogenic. The method has long been used in steel analysis[46] and biological materials.[47] The advantages of method V are extreme simplicity, lower sensitivity (1 to 20 ppm of P, or about one-tenth the sensitivity of the blue-color methods, Table 7–1, permitting applications on a more macro scale), stability of color, freedom from interferences with a wide range of ionic species in concentrations up to 1000 ppm, and adaptability to HNO_3, HCl, H_2SO_4, or $HClO_4$ systems. Ions that do not interfere in concentrations up to 1000 ppm are: Al, Fe^{+++}, Be, Mg, Ca, Ba, Sr, Li, Na, K, NH_4, Cd, Mn, Pb, Hg^+, or Hg^{++}, Sn^{++}, Zn, Cu and Ni only by a change in hue, Ag, U, Zr, OAc, As (ite), Br, CO_3, ClO_4, cyanide, pyrophosphate, molybdate, tetraborate, selenate, iodate, silicate, nitrate, nitrite, sulfate, sulfite, benzoate, citrate, oxalate, lactate, tartrate, formate, and salicylate. Positive interference is caused by silica and arsenic with heating; negative interferences are caused by As (ate), F, Th, and Bi; blue color is caused by Fe^{++} (but without interference up to 100 ppm), sulfide, thiosulfate, thiocyanate, or excess molybdate. Chloride over 75 ppm interferes in HNO_3 system.

APPARATUS

7–57. Required apparatus includes a buret, 50-ml and 1000-ml volumetric flasks, and a colorimeter with facilities for light maxima at 400 to 490 mu (variable according to sensitivity needed, ¶ 7–61).

REAGENTS

7–58. Needed reagents include standard phosphorus solutions (Table 7–2), and the following special combined HNO_3-vanadate-molybdate[48] reagent: Solution A is prepared by dissolution of 25 gm of ammonium molybdate in 400 ml of water. Then solution B is prepared by dissolving 1.25 gm of ammonium metavanadate in 300 ml of boiling water. Solution B is cooled and then 250 ml of concentrated HNO_3 is added and the solution is again cooled to room temperature. Finally solution A is poured into solution B and the mixture is diluted to 1 liter.

PROCEDURE

7–59. Preparation of the Test Solution. An aliquot of the phosphorus solution (standard, or test sample from plant tissue, soil, fertilizer, or rock analysis) that contains 0.05 to 1.0 mgm of P, in acid not exceeding the equivalent of 0.2 N in the final 50 ml, is placed in a 50-ml volumetric flask in a volume not exceeding 35 ml.

---

[45] After Kitson and Mellon, *Ind. Eng. Chem., A.E.,* 16:379 (1944).
[46] Mission, *Chem. Ztg.,* 32:633 (1908).
[47] Koenig and Johnson, *Ind. Eng. Chem., A.E.,* 14:155 (1942).
[48] After Barton, *Anal. Chem.,* 20:1068 (1948).

7–60. Acidity. The acid concentration in the determination is not critical, but the final concentration of 0.5 N is recommended. It must be above 0.2 N (to eliminate the yellow nitric acid color), but not over 1.6 N above which there is less color produced. Color development is slowed up in the higher portion of this range; and to obtain full color development in 5 minutes, the acidity should be less than 1 N. The acidity obtained from the combined reagent in the following procedure is approximately 0.8 N. Although this system is in HNO_3, equivalent systems in HCl, H_2SO_4, or $HClO_4$ are satisfactory.

7–61. Vanadomolybdophosphoric Yellow Color. To the phosphorus solution in a 50-ml volumetric flask, 10 ml of the vanadomolybdate reagent is added, and the solution is diluted to 50 ml with distilled water and mixed well. The color develops rapidly but is usually read after 10 minutes to assure full strength. A blank must be prepared and read with the samples because the blank vanadate color itself is noticeable even when phosphorus impurities have been carefully excluded. Variation in room temperature has a negligible effect on the color intensity. The color is read in the colorimeter with a light maximum from 400 to 490 mu, according to the sensitivity needed. The sensitivity varies 10-fold with wave lengths from 400 to 490 mu, but ferric ion causes interference with the lower wave lengths, particularly at 400 mu. The 470 filter is generally employed. Concentration ranges for different light maxima are:

Range, ppm P	Light maximum, mu
0.75–5.5	400
2.0–15	440
4–17	470
7–20	490

When ferric ion is low enough not to interfere, a convenient practice is to plot a family of calibration curves of 1 series of solution concentrations with a number of light maxima. A suitable selection of light maximum can be then made with any given test solution according to the transmission percentage found. This permits a wide latitude in the concentrations in one series of determinations.

ALTERNATIVE PROCEDURES

7–62. A procedure[49] employing 2 reagent solutions has been widely employed. A 0.25 per cent ammonium metavanadate solution is prepared in dilute HNO_3 by dissolving 2.5 gm of NH_4VO_3 in 500 ml of boiling water, cooling the solution somewhat and adding 20 ml of concentrated HNO_3. The solution is cooled, diluted to 1 liter, and stored in an amber glass bottle. The vanadate concentration is moderately critical (within 10 per cent); the effect of an excess is a slight vanadate reagent color at a similar

---

[49] Kitson and Mellon, *Ind. Eng. Chem., A.E.,* 16:379 (1944).

wave length of absorption. A 5 per cent solution in water of ammonium molybdate is prepared by dissolving 25 gm of $(NH_4)_6Mo_7O_{24} \cdot 4 H_2O$ in 400 ml of distilled water warmed to 50°C. The solution is cooled and filtered if cloudy, and diluted to 500 ml, mixed, and stored in an amber glass bottle. The molybdate concentration is not critical but should be held constant for a given series of determinations.

7–63. To the phosphorus solution (with acid equivalent[50] to 0.5 N figured on the basis of a final volume of 50 ml, but contained in a solution not to exceed 35 ml) 5 ml of 0.25 per cent ammonium vanadate solution is added. The solution is mixed, 5 ml of 5 per cent ammonium molybdate solution is added, and the mixing is repeated. The solution is made to volume and mixed well. The yellow color is read as before.

7–64. Phosphorus Determination After Removal of Arsenic by Bromide Distillation. Gross amounts of arsenic are removed from the solution in which the phosphorus is to be determined[51] rather than being reduced to suppress the arsenic-derived color as applicable to small amounts of As (¶ 7–6). To remove the As as $AsBr_3$, a 10-ml aliquot of the clear slightly acid test solution is placed in a 70-ml Kjeldahl flask, 10 ml of 48 per cent HBr is added, and the contents of the flask is brought *just* to dryness with moderate heating. Then the neck of the flask is washed down with 10 ml of 1.5 N HNO_3, and the contents is boiled gently until colorless. The cooled solution is transferred to a 50-ml volumetric flask and brought to about 35 ml, and the vanadomolybdophosphoric yellow color is developed and read (¶ 7–61).

DILUTE ACID SOLUBLE PHOSPHORUS OF SOILS

7–65. A number of dilute acid extraction methods have been proposed for measuring a fraction of the soil phosphorus ("available" phosphorus), that could be correlated with field response of crops. The degree of correlation varies according to the nature of the soil. In general, the phosphorus extractable from acid soils by dilute solutions of strong acids can be correlated with crop yield response to phosphate fertilizers. The correlation is lower with neutral soils, but little or no correlation is obtained for soils that are alkaline, calcareous, or that have been fertilized with phosphate rock. The strongly dissociated acids that have been employed by different investigators[52] include 0.5 N H_2SO_4 (¶ 7–74), 0.2 N HNO_3,[53] and 0.002

[50] Obtained by the addition of 5 ml of 5 N HNO_3 less the equivalent of residual acidity if over 0.1 N.

[51] Rubins and Dean, *Soil Sci.,* 63:392 (1947), found that the usual molybdophosphoric blue color methods are not satisfactory following this removal of arsenic used in large amounts as a replacing reagent. Residual impurities, particularly Sb, present in most commercially obtainable arsenates, apparently interfered.

[52] Reviewed in detail by Nelson *et al.,* "Soil and Fertilizer Phosphorus," *Agronomy* (New York: Academic Press, 1953), Vol. 4, ch. 6, p. 153.

[53] Fraps, *Tex. Agr. Exp. Sta. Bul.* 126 (1909).

N H$_2$SO$_4$[54] corresponding to a range from pH 0.7 to pH 3. Solutions of weakly dissociated acids (¶ 7–73) have been used for extraction of phosphorus in efforts to correlate with crop yield responses to phosphate fertilization. The procedure for pH 3 extractable phosphorus is given in this section. A higher correlation of soil test with crop response is obtained with dilute acid-fluoride extraction (¶ 7–86) or NaHCO$_3$ extraction (¶ 7–99) when all soils are considered, including acid, neutral, alkaline, and calcareous soils.

7–66. Effect of Drying the Soil. Freshly taken field-moist samples are recommended for measurement of the chemical conditions existing in the field. Storage in the moist condition may decrease the dilute acid extractable phosphorus. At the same time air-drying the sample, especially if the soil is acid, may increase the extractable phosphorus test found by 10 to 30 per cent. Oven-drying the sample, especially if acid, may increase the extractable phosphorus found by over 100 per cent. With limed and highly fertilized soils, T. M. Yu and the author found the dilute acid extractable phosphorus was decreased by drying.

APPARATUS

7–67. Needed apparatus includes a 2-mm (10 meshes per inch) sieve, a drying oven, moisture dishes, an analytical balance, 500-ml conical extraction flasks fitted with rubber stoppers, a rotary shaker, 10-cm filter funnels and phosphorus-free filter paper, and a 50-ml graduated cylinder.

REAGENTS

7–68. Extraction Reagent. A stock solution of exactly 0.1 N H$_2$SO$_4$ is prepared by titration against standard alkali. A convenient volume of this is diluted to 0.002 N and buffered by addition of 3 gm of (NH$_4$)$_2$SO$_4$ or K$_2$SO$_4$ per liter to produce a pH of 3 in the final solution.

PROCEDURE

7–69. Extraction of Soil.[55] The freshly taken field-moist soil sample is passed through a screen having 2-mm openings (or 10 meshes per inch), mixed, bottled tightly, and the moisture content determined by oven-drying. Then a sample is weighed out equivalent to 1.000 gm oven-dry soil and placed in 200 ml of the buffered 0.002 N H$_2$SO$_4$ extraction solution in a 500-ml conical flask. The suspension is shaken on the rotary shaker for exactly one-half hour. The suspension is immediately filtered through a retentive, P-free paper (the first of the filtrate being discarded, the clear filtrate saved). Then 50-ml of the clear filtrate is taken for determination of

[54] Truog, *J. Am. Soc. Agron.*, 22:874 (1930).
[55] After Truog, *J. Am. Soc. Agron.*, 22:874 (1930), modified for application to freshly taken field-moist soils samples.

the molybdophosphoric blue color (¶ 7–22). For soils extremely high in pH 3 extractable phosphorus (over 100 ppm), a 10-ml aliquot of this solution is diluted to 50 ml prior to development of the color.

7–70. Interpretations. The concentration of P in the test solution is read as ppm from the standard curve. Then:

$$\underset{\text{(pH 3 extractable)}}{\text{ppm P in soil}} = \text{ppm P in solution} \times \frac{\text{total ml extraction solution used}}{\text{gm soil extracted}}$$

$$= \text{ppm P in solution} \times 200 \qquad (7\text{–}3)$$

when 1 gm of soil and 200 ml of extraction solution are employed. For slightly acid to acid soils tested, under 5 ppm is very low in terms of crop response to phosphate fertilizers, 5 to 15 ppm is low, 15 to 25 ppm is medium, and over 25 ppm is adequate to high.

ALTERNATIVE PROCEDURES

7–71. Air-dry soil samples may be tested for pH 3 extractable phosphorus, but a change from the field analysis should be recognized.

7–72. A modification of the Truog 1 : 200 soil to extractant ratio was employed by Peech *et al.*[56] It consisted of doubling the soil suspension concentration to a 1 : 100 ratio. The phosphorus was determined by method III (¶ 7–40). Peech *et al.* also suggest extraction of coarse textured soils after they have been through a 1-mm sieve, in order to decrease the sampling error. The results were corrected to the 2-mm basis by assuming no P to be extractable from the 1 to 2 fraction.

7–73. The list of weak acids used for the extraction of soil phosphorus includes saturated carbonic acid[57] (usually employed with calcareous soils), dilute acetic acid[58] of pH 4.8 buffered with NaOAc, and 1 per cent citric acid.[59] Stelly and Pierre [60] employed the whole range of pH values from acid to alkaline to characterize the soil inorganic phosphorus. Calcium phosphate of phosphate rock dissolves in extraction solutions of pH 3 or lower.[61] Even neutral ammonium citrate solution dissolves 5 to 34 per cent of the phosphate of phosphate rock, but 2 per cent citric acid dissolves 2 to 3 times more.[62] Water soluble and neutral ammonium citrate

---

[56] U.S.D.A. Cir. 757 (1947), p. 3.

[57] Daubeny, *Roy. Soc. (London) Phil. Trans.* 179 (1845); McGeorge, *Ariz. Agr. Exp. Sta. Tech. Bul.* 82 (1939); Ensminger and Larson, *Soil Sci.,* 58:253 (1944); Smith, *J. Am. Soc. Agron.,* 40:1045 (1948).

[58] Morgan, *Conn. Agr. Exp. Sta. Bul.* 392 (1937); Spurway and Lawton, *Mich. Agr. Exp. Sta. Bul.* 132 (1949); Lunt *et al., Conn. Agr. Exp. Sta. Bul.* 541 (1950).

[59] Dyer, *J. Chem. Soc.,* T65:115 (1894); Wiley, *Principles and Practices of Agricultural Analysis,* 3rd. ed., Vol. 1 (Easton, Pa.: Chemical Publishing Co., 1926), p. 429.

[60] *S.S.S.A. Proc.,* 7:139 (1943).

[61] Fraps and Fudge, *J. Am. Soc. Agron.,* 37: 532 (1945).

[62] Jacob *et al., J.A.O.A.C.,* 30:529 (1947), 19:449 (1936).

soluble phosphate is defined[63] as the available phosphate of fertilizers. The use of citrate with $Na_2S_2O_4$ reduction is presented below (¶ 7–105).

7–74. Extraction of Calcium Phosphate of Soil in 0.5 N H_2SO_4. In the soil phosphorus fractionation system (¶ 7–106), the 1-gm soil sample, from which aluminum phosphate (¶ 7–92) and iron phosphate (¶ 7–104) have been extracted, is washed twice with 25-ml portions of saturated NaCl solution. It is then extracted with 50 ml of 0.5 N H_2SO_4 on a rotary shaker for 1 hour[64] and the suspension is centrifuged. The supernatant solution is decanted into a clean, dry flask and the soil sample is saved for further extraction with citrate-$Na_2S_2O_4$ (¶ 7–109). To test for noninterference of Fe in the P determination, 2 identical aliquots (usually 1 to 5 ml each) are taken from the decanted solution. To 1 aliquot, enough standard P solution (¶ 7–12) is added to give 0.2 ppm final concentration of added P. Then P is determined in both aliquots (¶ 7–22). The complete recovery of the 0.2 ppm of P (difference between the 2 determinations) establishes noninterference (usually the case) by Fe present. Low recovery, indicating Fe interference, can be eliminated by adding chlorostannous acid (¶ 7–120) or using a Jones reductor (¶ 7–132).

WATER SOLUBLE AND pH 3 EXTRACTABLE PHOSPHORUS IN RUNOFF WATERS

7–75. The water soluble and "loosely bound" (¶ 7–91) phosphorus in runoff is obtained in the clear solution after flocculation of the soil with NaCl solution. The concentration of P is determined by means of method I (¶ 7–22). The pH 3 extractable phosphorus is then determined with a 200 to 1 extractant : solids ratio. The sum of the water soluble phosphorus and the pH 3 extractable phosphorus is considered to be the available phosphorus in runoff.

APPARATUS

7–76. Needed are a graduated cylinder cut to contain 60-ml; a 50-ml and other graduated cylinders, a 250-ml conical flask, a centrifuge and 100-ml centrifuge tube, and apparatus for the colorimetric determinations (¶ 7–15).

REAGENTS

7–77. In addition to the reagents regularly used in the determination of available phosphorus (¶ 7–16), 5 N NaCl is needed. It is prepared by dissolving 293 gm of NaCl in water and making the solution volume to 1 liter.

---

[63] *Methods of Analysis,* 7th ed. (Washington, D.C.: A.O.A.C., 1950), p. 10.
[64] Dean, *J. Agr. Sci.* 28:234 (1938).

PROCEDURE

7–78. The Sample. The amount of runoff is calculated which will give between 100 and 200 mgm of solids, based on a separate determination of the solids content (¶ 10–66). The first 60-ml increment of well-mixed runoff is poured into a 100-ml centrifuge tube, and 10 ml of 5 N NaCl is added and mixed. The tube is placed in a hot water bath until the suspension is flocculated, and the solids are then thrown down by centrifugation for 5 minutes at 2000 rpm. Of the clear supernatant liquid, 50 ml is decanted into a graduated cylinder and the rest is discarded. The soluble phosphorus as ppm P in solution is determined (¶ 7–22) with a separate calibration curve made up with 1 N NaCl present in the standards, since the slope of the curve is affected by chloride.

7–79. If less than 100 mgm of solids is obtained in the first 60-ml of runoff, 1 or more additional increments are taken and flocculated as before. The solids are thrown down as before, in the same centrifuge tube, the clear supernatant solutions being discarded.

7–80. Extraction of pH 3 Extractable Phosphorus. The pH 3 extractable phosphorus is extracted with a 200 : 1 ratio of the extractant volume to solids weight exactly as for soils (¶ 7–69). A variable volume of extracting solution is employed, 20 ml per 100 mgm of solids. The extraction is carried out in the 100-ml centrifuge tube if the extractant volume is under 75 ml, otherwise in a 250-ml conical flask. If less than 50 ml of extractant is employed, the solution is diluted with extraction solution to 50 ml after extraction, and the dilution factor represented is then (50 / ml extractant used in the determination). The ppm P in the pH 3 extraction solution is determined by reference to the calibration curve.

7–81. Calculations. The soluble phosphorus is calculated, as pounds per acre inch (ppai) of runoff:

$$\underset{\text{(soluble P)}}{\text{ppai}} = \underset{\text{(curve)}}{\text{ppm P in solution}} \times \frac{7}{6} \times 0.227 \qquad (7\text{–}4)$$

The ppai is multiplied by the correction factor (¶ 10–69). The parts of soluble P per 2 million solids (pp2ms) is calculated:

$$\text{pp2ms} = \frac{\text{ppai (soluble P)}}{\text{ppai (solids)}} \times 2{,}000{,}000 \qquad (7\text{–}5)$$

Similarly, for the pH 3 extractable P:

$$\underset{\text{(extractable P)}}{\text{pp2ms}} = \underset{\text{(curve)}}{\text{ppm P in solution}} \times 200 \times 2 \times \text{dilution factor} \qquad (7\text{–}6)$$

in which the dilution factor is 1.0 if 50 ml of extractant was analyzed (otherwise as defined in ¶ 7–80). Finally, the pounds of extractable P per acre inch of runoff is calculated:

$$\underset{\text{(extractable P)}}{\text{ppai}} = \underset{\text{(solids)}}{\text{ppai}} \times \frac{\text{pp2ms (extractable P)}}{2,000,000} \qquad (7\text{--}7)$$

FLUORIDE EXTRACTABLE PHOSPHORUS OF SOILS

7–82. The F^- ion has the special property of complexing Al^{+++} and Fe^{+++} ions in acid solution, with consequent release of phosphorus held in the soil by these trivalent ions.[65] The reaction *in acid solution* may be represented as follows:

$$3\,NH_4F + 3\,HF + AlPO_4 \longrightarrow H_3PO_4 + (NH_4)_3AlF_6 \qquad (7\text{--}8)$$

$$3\,NH_4F + 3\,HF + FePO_4 \longrightarrow H_3PO_4 + (NH_4)_3FeF_6 \qquad (7\text{--}9)$$

The formula $AlPO_4$ represents various hydrated and hydroxyl phosphates of aluminum, including any adsorbed or precipitated surface layers on oxides and aluminosilicates. The formula $FePO_4$ similarly represents various hydrated and hydroxyl phosphates of iron, including adsorbed or precipitated surface layers on iron oxides. The reaction with $FePO_4$ (eq. 7–9) does not go to completion for concretionary or iron-oxide coated iron phosphate (¶ 7–105). Also the fluoroferrate is unstable in neutral or alkaline system, so phosphorus from $AlPO_4$ can be fractionated by 0.5 N NH_4F extraction (¶ 7–91). The $(NH_4)_3AlF_6$ may precipitate with large excess of fluoride.

7–83. The dilute acid-fluoride procedure[66] given here for extraction of available phosphorus of soils with 0.03 N NH_4F in 0.025 N HCl (Bray and Kurtz, No. 1 solution) has been employed widely and has been found to give results that are highly correlated with crop response to phosphate fertilization. Inclusion of acid results in the dissolution of the more active calcium phosphates and prevents the precipitation (as calcium phosphate) of phosphorus dissolved by equations 7–8 and 7–9. The method removes, in the words of Bray and Kurtz, "proportional parts of [or] . . . the more readily soluble portion of each form of available soil phosphorus." Also, "the term 'available forms' [of soil phosphorus] is restricted to those which are of most immediate significance to crop growth and whose variations in amount are responsible for variation in crop growth and response to added phosphates."

APPARATUS

7–84. Needed apparatus includes a 50-ml extraction bottle or tube fitted with stopper; 20-ml, 2-ml and 1-ml pipets (preferably automatic); a filter tube or funnel and 7-cm filter paper (Whatman No. 42), and a colorimeter with 660-mu light maximum and comparator tubes.

---

[65] Swenson *et al.*, *Soil Sci.*, 67:3 (1949); Turner and Rice, *Soil Sci.*, 74:141 (1952).
[66] Bray and Kurtz, *Soil Sci.*, 59:39 (1945).

7–85. Needed reagents include the $0.03\ N\ NH_4F$ in $0.025\ N$ HCl extraction solution (1.11 gm of solid NH_4F and 4.16 ml of $6\ N$ HCl per liter) and ammonium molybdate, in HCl as specified for method II (¶ 7–28). The extraction solution may be stored in a glass container for a year without appreciable deterioration. Also needed is a stannous chloride stock solution prepared by dissolution of 10 gm of reagent grade $SnCl_2 \cdot 2\ H_2O$ in 25 ml of concentrated HCl. Kept in a dark, tightly stoppered bottle, this solution need be replaced only at 2-month intervals. For each 4-hours work, a freshly diluted stannous chloride solution is prepared by pipetting 1 ml of the stock solution into 330 ml of freshly boiled, cooled, distilled water.

7–86. Dilute Fluoride-Dilute Acid Soluble P. A 2.85-gm sample of crushed, sieved soil is weighed out (or measured, about 2.5 ml) into a 50-ml extraction bottle or tube. Then 20 ml of the extraction solution ($0.03\ N\ NH_4F$ in $0.025\ N$ HCl) is added from a pipet (preferably arranged as an automatic dispenser), and the bottle is stoppered and shaken for 1 minute.[68] The suspension is immediately filtered on a moist Whatman No. 42 filter paper held in a filter tube or funnel. The filtrate should be clear. If not, the solution is quickly poured back through the same filter. A 2-ml aliquot[69] of the clear filtrate is transferred to a colorimeter test tube by means of an automatic pipet, after 1 ml has previously been discarded to rinse the pipet. Then 5 ml of distilled water is added. The determination is next carried out essentially in accord with method II (¶ 7–31). First 2 ml of ammonium molybdate (chloromolybdic acid) reagent (¶ 7–85) is added and the solution is mixed, conveniently accomplished in routine by an air jet stirrer. Finally, 1 ml of freshly diluted stannous chloride reagent (¶ 7–85) is added with immediate mixing. After 5 to 6 minutes and before 15 to 20 minutes the color is read in a colorimeter. The P standards are made up in the range of 0.1 to 1 ppm of P through the same steps as in this procedure, including 2 ml of the extraction solution in each 10 ml final volume since the F^- content of the final solution is slightly above the 5 ppm limit[70] of noninterference (¶ 7–33) and would be expected to shift the curve slightly. A reagent blank is made with each series of determinations and is employed for the 100 per cent transmission setting.

7–87. The concentration of dilute fluoride-dilute acid soluble soil phosphorus is calculated:

---

[67] Adapted from Bray and Kurtz, *Soil Sci.,* 59:39 (1945).

[68] More dilute soil : extractant ratios also have been employed (¶ 7–88).

[69] For unusually high or low tests another aliquot size is employed to give proper range of P concentration; the aliquot volume plus the distilled water must total 7 ml

[70] Woods and Mellon, *Ind. Eng. Chem., A.E.,* 13:762 (1941).

$$\text{ppm of P in soil} = \text{ppm of P in solution} \times \frac{10}{2} \times \frac{20}{2.85}$$

$$= \text{ppm of P in solution} \times 35 \qquad (7\text{--}10)$$

As a general guide to crop response, below 3 ppm is very low, 3 to 7 ppm is low, 7 to 20 is medium, and above 20 ppm is adequate to high. Different crops shift the scale some because of different root characteristics.

ALTERNATIVE PROCEDURES

7–88. A soil extractant ratio of 3 : 20 is substituted, for the 2.85 : 20 (1 : 7) ratio of Bray and Kurtz, by the Nebraska Soil Testing Laboratory.[71] A 5-minute shaking time is also employed. Soil extractant ratios of 1 : 10 and 1 : 50[72] also have been employed, and the more dilute extraction is thought to raise the correlation with yield response on some kinds of soils.

7–89. 0.1 N HCl and 0.03 N NH₄F. To include more of the soil apatite (for example, that in near neutral or calcareous soils or that remaining from phosphate rock additions) in the extraction, a higher concentration of HCl is included (Bray and Kurtz, No. 2, acid-soluble and "adsorbed" phosphorus). The procedure is the same (¶ 7–86) except that the 0.1 N HCl and a 40-second shaking period are employed. Some workers have employed 0.2 N HCl instead of 0.1 N HCl and considered that all of the apatite was thereby dissolved during the 40-second shaking period.

7–90. For a "quick test," the soil is allowed to settle with either No. 1 or No. 2 solution instead of being filtered, and the color is developed in the clear supernatant by the addition of 0.30 ml of concentrated molybdate and stirring with a tin rod. The color range of this undiluted solution is usually too intense for use in a colorimeter.

7–91. Extraction of Aluminum Phosphate of Soil in Neutral 0.5 N NH₄F. In neutral or alkaline solutions, the fluoride complex of Al (¶ 7–82) forms, but that of iron does not to any appreciable extent. Neither is calcium phosphate appreciably dissolved in this reagent (¶ 7–106). Therefore, the phosphate extracted by neutral 0.5 N NH₄F[73] is mainly $AlPO_4$, and the method is therefore an important step in the soil phosphorus fractionation system (¶ 7–106). A 1-gm sample of soil is placed in a 100-ml centrifuge tube and extracted with 50 ml of 1 N NH₄Cl for 30 minutes on a rotary shaker to remove water soluble and loosely bound phosphorus and exchangeable calcium. The suspension is centrifuged, and the supernatant solution is discarded. Water soluble P could be determined on this solution, but the amount is generally very low.

---

[71] Information courtesy Dr. R. A. Olson, Agron. Dept., University of Nebraska, Lincoln.

[72] Information courtesy Dr. Floyd Smith, Agron. Dept., Kansas State College, Manhattan, Kansas.

[73] Reagent of Bray and Dickman, *S.S.S.A. Proc.*, 6:312 (1942) and Bray and Kurtz, *Soil Sci.*, 59:39 (1945), extractant No. 3, adapted to a somewhat different procedure

7–92. To the NH_4-soil in the centrifuge tube, 50 ml of neutral 0.5 N NH_4F (18.5 gm solid NH_4F per liter of water adjusted to pH 7 and stored in a wax-lined bottle) is added and the suspension is shaken for 1 hour. The suspension is then centrifuged and an aliquot (usually 10 ml) is taken for analysis. The soil sample is saved for the iron phosphate extraction in 0.1 N NaOH (¶ 7–104). The extract may be slightly colored with organic matter, but a slight color usually does not interfere with readings at 660 mu. With strong coloration, an aliquot may be prepared without the reductant and used as a blank (the reagent blank in this case is handled separately and the ppm P therein is subtracted from the analysis). In extreme cases, the organic matter may be flocculated in HCl and filtered off, with or without the aid of aqua regia-purified charcoal. Boric acid is added (¶ 7–33) to remove fluoride interference, and the total volume is made to 50 ml during the P analysis. Then:

$$\text{ppm P in soil} \atop \text{(neutral NH}_4\text{F extractable)} = \text{ppm P in solution} \times \frac{50}{\text{aliquot, ml}}$$
$$\times \frac{\text{ml extraction solution}}{\text{gm soil extracted}} \qquad (7\text{--}11)$$

The aluminum phosphate removed includes much that is only slowly available to crops, and therefore the results are not as highly correlated with yield responses to phosphate fertilization as the dilute acid-fluoride extraction (¶ 7–86). It is correlated with phosphate released by liming acid soils and the resultant low response to phosphate fertilizer on such soils.

7–93. Acid–0.5 N NH_4F Extraction. A separate 1-gm soil sample is shaken in 50 ml of 0.1 N HCl for 30 minutes. Then 1 gm of solid NH_4F is added and the shaking is continued for an additional 60 minutes (Bray and Kurtz, No. 4). The suspension is filtered on Whatman No. 2 paper, and the P is determined on a 10-ml aliquot in the presence of H_3BO_3 (¶ 7–33). Calcium phosphate and some of the iron phosphate (¶ 7–82) is included with the aluminum phosphate by this extraction.

HYDROXYL AND CARBONATE EXTRACTABLE PHOSPHORUS OF SOILS

7–94. Two general types of alkaline extraction of soil phosphorus have been employed: (a) moderately alkaline solutions such as sodium bicarbonate[74] or potassium carbonate (¶ 7–103) have been employed to extract a portion of the soil phosphorus that could be correlated with the response of crops to the addition of phosphate fertilizers, and (b) strongly alkaline solutions such as NaOH have been employed for the extraction of phosphorus from aluminum and iron phosphates (¶ 7–104) and organic forms of soil phosphorus (¶ 7–112). The organic phosphorus extracted by al-

---

[74] Olsen *et al.,* U.S.D.A. Cir. 939 (1954).

kaline solutions is flocculated and excluded from the analysis of the inorganic phosphorus brought into solution.

7–95. The 0.5 N NaHCO$_3$ method employs a solution of pH 8.5, designed to control the ionic activity of Ca, through the solubility product of CaCO$_3$, during the extraction of calcareous soils. As the carbonate activity in the soil is raised by this solution, the calcium activity is decreased. Thus some phosphate from the surface of calcium phosphates is extracted through the solubility product of calcium phosphate. As Ca activity decreases, phosphate activity increases. The importance of buffering carbonate during extraction is illustrated by the 2 trends produced by carbonic acid in calcareous soils; (a) a trend toward increased solubility of calcium phosphate as expected with an acid, and (b) a trend toward decreased solubility of calcium phosphate owing to the increased calcium activity as CaCO$_3$ is dissolved by the carbonic acid. The reagent also extracts some phosphate (¶ 7–143) from the surface of aluminum and iron phosphates, which are more abundant (¶ 7–106) in acid and neutral soils. By repression of the Al and Fe activities (the Al,[75] by aluminate complex formation and Fe,[76] by precipitation as the oxide) the phosphate activity is increased. By the solubility product principle,[77] the activity of phosphate ions must rise as a_{Al} and a_{Fe} decrease in the presence of AlPO$_4$ and FePO$_4$. Also, the carbonate ion added in the reagent, by the solubility product of CaCO$_3$, maintains the Ca activity low enough in all soils (acid, neutral, or alkaline) to prevent reprecipitation of the liberated phosphate as calcium phosphate. The secondary precipitation of calcium phosphate during the extraction is a problem with dilute acid extractions (¶ 7–73) including CO$_2$ extractions. The procedure of Olsen *et al.,* with NaHCO$_3$ can be likened to the brief extraction with dilute acid-dilute fluoride (¶ 7–86), since the most reactive (high specific surface) phosphate is extracted from phosphates of aluminum, iron, and calcium.

APPARATUS

7–96. Needed apparatus consists of a weathered 250- or 300-ml soft glass extraction bottle or conical flask fitted with a stopper, an end-over-end shaker, a filter funnel and Whatman No. 40 filter paper, a 50-ml volumetric flask, and a 10-ml pipet.

REAGENTS

7–97. Needed reagents include the extraction solution, activated charcoal, and the colorimetric phosphorus reagents. The extraction solution is 0.5 M NaHCO$_3$ (42.0 gm per liter) adjusted to pH 8.5 with NaOH. The

---

[75] Cole and Jackson, *S.S.S.A. Proc.,* 15:84 (1951).
[76] Chang and Jackson, *S.S.S.A. Proc.,* 21:265 (1957).
[77] Kittrick and Jackson, *J. Soil Sci.,* 7:81 (1956).

pH of the solution tends to increase on standing exposed to the atmosphere, but this change can be prevented by the addition of a layer of mineral oil. To remove phosphorus from the activated charcoal (Darco G–60), it is preleached with $NaHCO_3$ and then is washed with water and dried.

7–98. The Dickman and Bray chloromolybdic acid reagent (¶ 7–29) is modified by the addition of 60 ml more of 10 N HCl per liter (for a total of 410 ml) to neutralize the $NaHCO_3$ in the 10-ml aliquot. The 0.1 M chlorostannous acid (¶ 7–30) is employed.

PROCEDURE

7–99. In the procedure of Olsen *et al.,* a 5-gm sample of soil is suspended in 100 ml of the $NaHCO_3$ extraction solution of pH 8.5 along with 1 teaspoon of carbon black. The suspension is shaken for a period of 30 minutes. The solution is filtered through a Whatman No. 40 or other suitable filter paper. If the filtrate is not clear, it is returned to the soil and more carbon black is added to the flask followed by a quick shaking and a second filtration.

7–100. A 10-ml aliquot of clear filtrate is pipetted into a 50-ml volumetric flask. The P is determined by method II (¶ 7–31) except that the modified molybdate reagent (¶ 7–98) containing extra HCl is employed. Ten ml of the acid molybdate is added down the side of the flask containing the aliquot, and the flask is allowed to stand quietly lest too rapid evolution of CO_2 result in some loss of the solution. After CO_2 evolution has subsided (following a final swirling of the solution), the neck of the flask is washed down, and the solution is diluted to 40-ml volume. Then 0.25 ml (5 drops) of the 0.1 M chlorostannous acid solution is added, followed by immediate shaking, dilution to volume, and mixing. Failure to observe these precautions with respect to the chlorostannous acid addition causes erratic results.

7–101. If the concentration of P found is above the range of the method, an aliquot of less than 10 ml is taken, and additional extraction solution is added to make up a total of 10 ml of $NaHCO_3$ solution, in order to maintain the proper acidity during color development. The standard curve is prepared with the same quantity of $NaHCO_3$ included.

7–102. The quantity of P extracted is calculated as ppm of the soil:

$$\text{ppm of P in soil} = \text{ppm of P in solution} \times \frac{50}{10} \times \frac{100}{5} \qquad (7\text{–}12)$$

As a general guide to crop response, 5 ppm of P (25 pounds P_2O_5 per acre) is low, and response to phosphate is likely, 5 to 10 ppm of P (25 to 50 pounds P_2O_5 per acre) is medium and response is probable, and over 10 ppm of P (50 pounds P_2O_5 per acre) is adequate and response is unlikely. Values in the range of 18 to 25 ppm of P (90 to 125 pounds of P_2O_5 per acre) are characteristic of fertile soils.

ALTERNATIVE PROCEDURES

7–103. A more alkaline carbonate solution, 1 per cent K_2CO_3, was used[78] to measure the available phosphorus in calcareous soils. With acid and neutral soils, this method causes the dissolution of so much of the strong alkali soluble phosphate (¶ 7–104) that a poor correlation was obtained with yield response to phosphate fertilization on such soils.[79] A 1.5 per cent Na_2CO_3 solution was employed[80] to measure the quantity of phosphate rock converted to soil phosphate in acid soils. A 0.01 N Na_2CO_3 and H_3BO_3 buffer, adjusted to the pH of the soil, was employed[81] for available phosphorus. An 8-hydroxy quinoline reagent was employed[82] to repress the activity of Fe and Al in dilute acid extracts of the soil.

7–104. Extraction of Iron Phosphate of Soil in 0.1 N NaOH. In the soil phosphorus fractionation system (¶ 7–106), the 1-gm soil sample extracted with 0.5 N NH_4F (¶ 7–92) is washed twice with 25-ml portions of saturated NaCl solution. It is then extracted with 50 ml of 0.1 N NaOH on a rotary shaker at room temperature for 17 hours.[83] The soil suspension is centrifuged for 15 minutes at 2400 rpm (and recentrifuged, if necessary) to obtain a clear supernatant solution. The solution is decanted into another centrifuge tube and the soil sample is saved for the extraction with 0.5 N H_2SO_4 (¶ 7–74). Two ml of 2 N H_2SO_4 is added to the decantate and then 1 or more drops of concentrated H_2SO_4 until the organic colloids begin to flocculate. Then the suspension is centrifuged and an aliquot (usually 1 to 5 ml) of the supernatant liquid is taken for analysis (¶ 7–22).

DITHIONITE-CITRATE EXTRACTABLE PHOSPHORUS OF SOILS

7–105. The residual soil phosphorus not extracted by successive fluoride (¶ 7–91), alkali (¶ 7–104), and acid (¶ 7–74) treatments—often around 40 per cent of the soil phosphorus—was sometimes termed[84] "insoluble phosphorus" and attributed to phosphorus in the structure[85] of layer silicate clays. All or nearly all of this residual, so-called "insoluble" phosphorus is extracted[86] when the iron oxides are removed by an effective re-

[78] Das, *Soil Sci.,* 30:33 (1930).

[79] Gardner and Kelley, *Soil Sci.,* 50:91 (1940).

[80] Joos and Black, *S.S.S.A. Proc.,* 15:69 (1951).

[81] Rhoades, *Nebr. Agri. Exp. Sta. Bul.* 113 (1939).

[82] Ghani, *Ind. J. Agr. Sci.,* 13:562 (1943).

[83] After Williams, *J. Agr. Sci.,* 40:233 (1950), who used 40 ml per gm of soil.

[84] Bray and Kurtz, *Soil Sci.,* 59:39 (1945); Allaway and Rhoades, *Soil Sci.,* 72:119 (1951).

[85] Marshall, *J. Soc. Chem. Ind.* (London), 54:393 (1935).

[86] Bauwin and Tyner, *S.S.S.A. Proc.,* 21:250 (1957); Lancaster, Ph.D. thesis, Univ. Wis. (1954).

duction-chelation procedure (¶ 7–109). Since a reduction-chelation treatment is rather specific for iron oxide removal, the phosphate released by such treatment is attributable to forms *occluded* in the iron oxides rather than to tetrahedral P, and may aptly be termed "reductant soluble" P. Iron oxides, unlike aluminum hydroxides, are not dissolved by NaOH or neutral NH_4F solutions and therefore coatings of iron oxides would be expected to remain on the surfaces of iron oxide aggregates or concretions during the process of extraction with these reagents, thus preventing the dissolution of phosphate occluded in the interior. The phosphate of freshly precipitated aluminum or iron phosphate is largely extractable by NaOH. Also, phosphate accumulated in soil as residues from fertilizers is all or largely extracted by NaOH-acid treatment.[87] The occluded phosphate thus must be so insoluble as to be highly unavailable to plants.

7–106. Soil Phosphorus Fractionation System. Soil phosphorus long ago was classified[88] into the categories:

> 1. Inorganic phosphorus in near neutral soils, probably calcium phosphate.
> 2. Inorganic phosphorus in acid soils, presumably in combination with aluminum and iron.
> 3. Organic phosphorus compounds.

Fractionation was carried out[89] by 0.2 N NaOAc, 0.25 N NaOH, and 0.5 N H_2SO_4 treatments; and later[90] by 0.2 N HOAc, cool 0.25 N NaOH and 2 N H_2SO_4 treatments. Also, functional acid and alkali treatments were applied.[91] A soil phosphorus fractionation procedure[92] (flow sheet, Fig. 7–2) has been developed which measures discretely the total of each chemical form, aluminum phosphate (¶ 7–91), iron phosphate (¶ 7–104), calcium phosphate (¶ 7–74), and reductant soluble phosphate (¶ 7–109). It is now known[93] that calcium, aluminum, and iron phosphates, and reductant soluble phosphates occur in varying proportions in most neutral, alkaline, and acid soils. Controls with the different chemical species showed that the NH_4F and NaOH treatments must precede the H_2SO_4 treatment since the latter removes considerable aluminum and iron phosphate as well as all of the calcium phosphate. Knowledge of the distribution of soil phosphorus among chemical forms should prove useful in the development of soil chemistry, even though the objective of such fractionation is completely distinct from the measurement of the amount of available phosphate (¶

---

[87] Dean, *J. Agr. Sci.*, 28:234 (1938).

[88] Russell, *Soil Conditions and Plant Growth* (New York: Longmans Green & Co. Inc., 1932), p. 238.

[89] Dean, *J. Agr. Sci.*, 28:234 (1938).

[90] Ghani, *Ind. J. Agr. Sci.*, 13:29 (1943).

[91] Stelley and Pierre, *S.S.S.A. Proc.*, 7:139 (1943).

[92] Chang and Jackson, *Soil Sci.*, 84:133–144 (1957).

[93] Chang and Jackson, *J. Soil Sci.*, (1958), presented before the North Central Branch, American Society of Agronomy, Lafayette, Ind., Aug. 1956.

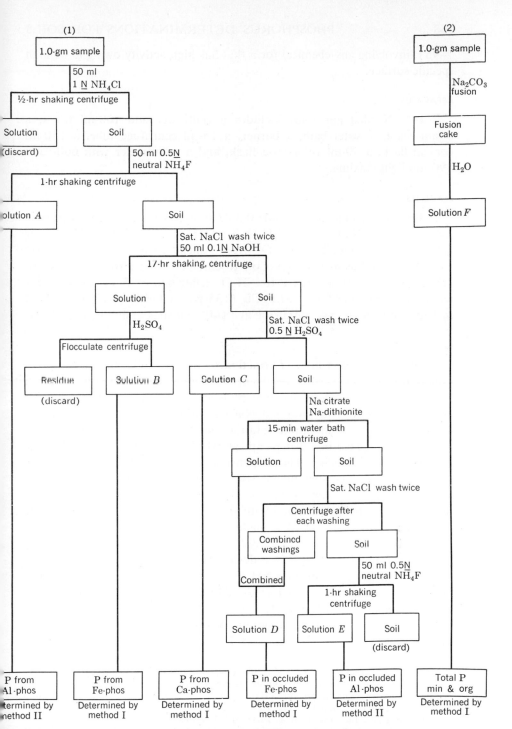

Fig. 7–2. Flow sheet for soil phosphorus fractionation system. Organic phosphorus is not included in this fractionation, but is determined separately (see Fig. 7–3).

7–95), involving any chemical form that has high activity owing to its high specific surface.

7–107. Needed apparatus includes a centrifuge and 100-ml tubes, a steam plate, a water bath, a burner, a 15-ml centrifuge tube, a 150-ml conical flask, a 50-ml volumetric flask, and a colorimeter with 660- and 490-mu light maxima.

7–108. Needed reagents include 0.3 M sodium citrate (88 gm of tribasic sodium citrate, $Na_3C_6H_5O_7 \cdot 2 H_2O$ per liter) 1 M $NaHCO_3$ (84 gm per liter), sodium dithionite ($Na_2S_2O_4$, from Amend Drug and Chemical Co., New York, or Eastman Kodak Co., Rochester, N.Y.; also called sodium "hydrosulfite"), 30 per cent P-free H_2O_2 (obtained by 3 successive treatments with kaolinite[94]), 0.5 M $FeCl_3$ (135 gm of $FeCl_3 \cdot 6 H_2O$ dissolved in 1 liter of water), and saturated NaCl (400 gm shaken in a liter of H_2O).

7–109. Dithionite-Citrate Extraction.[95] In the soil phosphorus fractionation system (¶ 7–106), the 1-gm soil sample, just previously extracted in 0.5 N H_2SO_4 to remove calcium phosphate (¶ 7–74), is washed twice with 25-ml portions of saturated NaCl solution. It is then suspended in 40 ml of 0.3 M sodium citrate solution and 5 ml of M $NaHCO_3$, and the suspension is heated in a water bath at 80°C. Then 1.0 gm of $Na_2S_2O_4$ is added with rapid stirring. The suspension is kept at 80°C for 15 minutes and centrifuged. The supernatant solution is collected in a 100-ml volumetric flask. The soil is washed twice with 25-ml portions of saturated NaCl, the 2 washings being combined with the extract in the 100-ml volumetric flask. The solution in the flask is made to volume and an aliquot (usually 1 to 5 ml) is taken for the determining P (¶ 7–110). Another aliquot is taken for Fe determination (¶ 7–111) if desired. For soils high in iron oxides, the residue is extracted with neutral NH_4F (¶ 7–91) to remove occluded aluminum phosphate or with NaOH (¶ 7–104) to remove occluded aluminum-iron phosphate (barrandite-like).

7–110. Phosphorus Determination. A suitable aliquot (usually 1 to 5 ml) of the dithionite citrate extract (¶ 7–109) is placed in a 150-ml conical

---

94 Chang and Jackson, *Sci.,* 124:1209 (1956); this procedure gives nearly full strength H_2O_2 and little loss in volume. Serious losses of concentration occur with distillation under reduced pressure, Baumann, *J. Biol. Chem.,* 59:667 (1924), and Dickman and DeTurk, *Soil Sci.,* 45:29 (1938).

95 Aguilera and Jackson, *S.S.S.A. Proc.,* 17:359 (1953), 18:223, 350 (1954); procedure for removal of free iron oxides from soils and clays. Modified for inclusion of $NaHCO_3$ buffer by Mehra and Jackson.

flask. About 10 ml of distilled water and 5 to 10 ml of the 30 per cent P-free H_2O_2 (5 ml for 1- to 2-ml aliquot and 10 ml for 3- to 5-ml aliquot) are added, and the solution is heated cautiously on a burner. Vigorous splashing must not occur. The burner is moved under or away from the flask as needed. One drop of 0.5 M $FeCl_3$ (or 10 ml of 100 ppm Fe solution) is added to moderate the oxidation. The cessation of foaming (gas evolution) and the beginning of ordinary boiling indicate the completion of oxidation. Complete drying must be avoided before the oxidation is complete, otherwise the very concentrated H_2O_2 and the high temperature will ignite the organic matter, leaving some carbon particles. Small amounts of distilled water are added as necessary. After completion of oxidation, the solution is boiled for an additional 1 or 2 minutes, and then dried on a steam plate. About 10 ml of 2 N NaOH is added. The solution is boiled for 1 to 2 minutes and digested on a steam plate for 5 minutes. The suspension is poured into a 15-ml centrifuge tube and centrifuged to throw down the iron oxide precipitate. The supernatant liquid is decanted into a 50-ml volumetric flask. The original 150-ml flask is washed with 10 ml of water into the same 15-ml centrifuge tube. The precipitate is resuspended by shaking and again thrown down by centrifugation. The supernatant solution is poured into the same 50-ml volumetric flask. The washing is repeated once more and the supernatant solution placed in the same flask. The combined supernatant solutions are made to volume, and the phosphorus is determined by method I (¶ 7–22).

7–111. Iron Determination.[96] An aliquot of the dithionite-citrate extract (¶ 7–109), which will make a final solution containing 0.5 to 3 ppm Fe, is placed in a 50-ml volumetric flask. Water is added to make 35 ml, then 1 drop of 30 per cent H_2O_2, 5 ml of 6 N HCl, and 5 ml of 20 per cent KSCN solution are added. The solution is made to volume with water. The color is measured with a 490-mu light maximum.

ORGANIC PHOSPHORUS OF SOILS

7–112. Organic phosphorus of soils has been extracted and determined by several methods, but these can be classified into two general types; (a) alkaline extraction in NaOH or NH_4OH after acid pretreatment, and (b) dilute acid extraction after oxidation of organic matter by H_2O_2 or ignition. In *either* type of method, the phosphorus is determined colorimetrically, and the difference between the inorganic phosphorus in the extract before and after oxidation of the organic matter represents organic phosphorus. In the colorimetric determination of phosphorus, only the inorganic orthophosphate yields the blue or yellow color. In method (a) the oxidation of organic matter is carried out after extraction, in method (b), before ex-

---

[96] Aguilera and Jackson, *S.S.S.A. Proc.*, 17:359 (1953), 18:223 and 350 (1954).

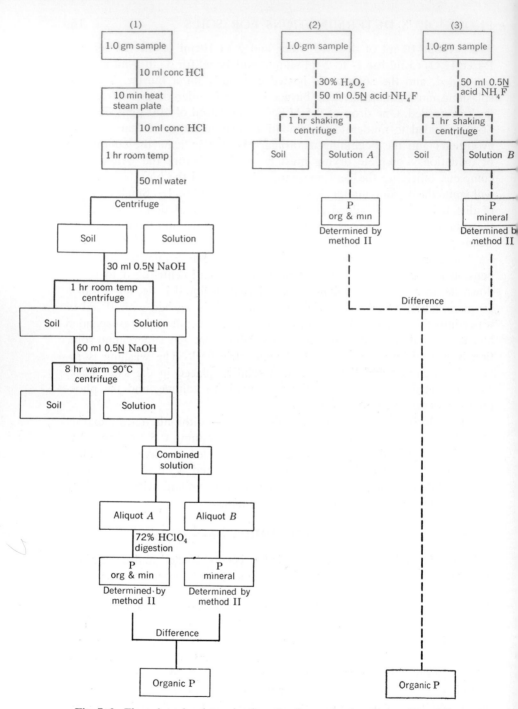

Fig. 7–3. Flow sheet for determination of soil organic phosphorus. Dotted lines indicate an alternative procedure.

170

traction (Fig. 7–3). Release of phosphorus from mineral form (either before or after extraction, the latter from suspended mineral colloids) by the oxidation procedure gives a (+) inference with the organic phosphorus determination. Release of orthophosphate from organic matter by hydrolysis before the initial inorganic phosphorus determination gives a (−) interference with the organic phosphorus determination. The HCl–NaOH extraction, method[97] (a), is given in the procedure. The dilute acid extraction, method (b), after H_2O_2 oxidation or ignition, is considered in the alternative procedures (¶ 7–125). The first NaOH extraction is given at room temperature to minimize the hydrolysis of organic phosphorus.

APPARATUS

7–113. Needed apparatus includes a 100-ml centrifuge tube and centrifuge; 250-ml and 50-ml volumetric flasks; a 50-ml beaker; 15-, 10-, and 5-ml pipets; an oven at 90°C; a suitable fume hood for $HClO_4$ fumes; an electric plate; a rubber policeman; and a colorimeter and tubes, with 660-mu light maximum.

REAGENTS

7–114. Needed reagents include concentrated HCl, 0.5 N NaOH, 72 per cent $HClO_4$, 6 N NH_4OH, 0.5 N HCl, 0.5 per cent p-nitrophenol indicator in water, and the following special reagents.

7–115. Chloromolybdic Acid. Twenty-four gm of ammonium molybdate is dissolved in 300 ml of water. Then 560 ml of 10 N HCl is added slowly with stirring. The solution is then diluted to 1 liter with water.

7–116. Chlorostannous Acid. Forty gm of $SnCl_2 \cdot 2H_2O$ is dissolved in 100 ml of concentrated HCl, and 40 ml of water is added. The solution is protected from oxidation (¶ 7–20).

PROCEDURE

7–117. Extraction. In the procedure of Mehta et al., 1 gm of soil is placed in a 100-ml centrifuge tube and 10 ml of concentrated HCl is added. The suspension is heated on a steam plate for 10 minutes (final solution temperature about 70°C), then removed, and an additional 10 ml of concentrated HCl is added and mixed. This suspension is allowed to stand at room temperature for 1 hour. Then 50 ml of water is added and mixed. The suspension is centrifuged, and the clear supernatant liquid is poured into a 250-ml volumetric flask containing about 50 ml of water.

7–118. Thirty ml of 0.5 N NaOH is added to the tube, the soil is stirred, and the suspension is allowed to stand at room temperature for 1 hour. The suspension is then centrifuged and the supernatant liquid is poured into the volumetric flask containing the acid extract. Then 60 ml of 0.5 N

---

[97] Mehta et al., S.S.S.A. Proc., 18:443 (1954).

NaOH is added to the tube, the soil is stirred, and the tube is covered with an inverted 50-ml beaker, followed by warming in an oven at 90°C for 8 hours. The tube is cooled, the suspension centrifuged, and the supernatant liquid is poured into the 250-ml flask containing the previous extracts. The combined extracts are diluted to volume with water and mixed thoroughly.

7–119. Total Phosphorus Extracted. The flask containing the mixed extracts is shaken thoroughly to suspend the flocculated material, and immediately a 15-ml aliquot is pipetted into a 50-ml beaker. To the aliquot is added 1 ml of 72 per cent $HClO_4$, followed by evaporation to a residue of $HClO_4$ on a steam plate. The temperature is raised (with care to avoid spattering due to a rapid temperature change) until fumes of $HClO_4$ appear (use a suitable fume hood for $HClO_4$ fumes) after which the beaker is covered with a watch glass to reduce further loss of the acid. The digestion is continued until the color of the solution no longer changes. When the temperature of the digest approaches the boiling point, the organic matter is oxidized rapidly. After oxidation, extracts low in iron usually become colorless; those high in iron retain a light yellow color. Care is taken not to dry the solution completely. The beaker is cooled and the contents are transferred quantitatively to a 50-ml volumetric flask with the aid of a rubber policeman to insure complete transfer of the silica. The solution is diluted to volume with water and mixed thoroughly. An aliquot, usually 10 ml of the clear supernatant liquid, is pipetted into a test tube graduated at 35 ml.

7–120. Determination. The phosphorus solution in the test tube graduated at 35 ml is neutralized with 6 N NH_4OH to yellow with p-nitrophenol and then with 0.5 N HCl just to colorless. Then water is added to 35-ml volume, followed by addition of 5 ml of chloromolybdic acid and thorough mixing. Finally 3 drops of chlorostannous acid solution is added, followed by immediate mixing. A blank is carried through the same steps. The percentage transmittance is read with 660-mu light after 10 minutes. If more than 75 ppm of Fe is present, the quantity of $SnCl_2$ is increased to give noninterference. The standards are made up with the same reagents and procedure, in the range from 0.05 to 0.6 ppm of P. The total phosphorus extracted is calculated as ppm of P in the soil.

7–121. Inorganic Phosphorus Extracted. After the aliquot of the combined soil extracts has been taken for total extracted phosphorus, the suspended material is allowed to flocculate and settle out. Then an aliquot of the clear, colorless (¶ 7–122) supernatant liquid (usually 5 or 10 ml) is pipetted into a test tube graduated at 35 ml. The inorganic phosphorus is then determined (¶ 7–120) and expressed as ppm of P in the soil.

7–122. Compensation for Brown Coloration. To compensate[98] for brown color, if present (a problem with peat soils), a separate aliquot is taken

---

98 Dyer and Wrenshall, *Can. J. Research,* 16B:97 (1938).

of the supernatant solution and treated as in the determination (¶ 7–120) except for omission of the $SnCl_2$ reagent. This solution is then employed for the 100 per cent transmission setting for the test sample. (The test sample may be used for the 100 per cent transmission setting after the addition of all reagents except $SnCl_2$. The rest point of the galvanometer is immediately recorded; then the colorimeter is reset at this rest point 10 minutes after addition of the $SnCl_2$ and the test sample is then read.) The optical density of both the sample P and the P in the reagents (blank) are represented in the test reading. The standard phosphorus curve is made with solutions containing the proper aliquots of all reagents employed in the determination, including a reagent blank (zero P added). The transmission percentage is read for each solution including the reagent blank against a colorless solution including all of the solvents and solutes except $SnCl_2$. The standard curve does not pass through 100 per cent transmission at zero P added, to the extent of P impurities in the reagents. The transmission percentage of the test sample, when referred to the standard curve made up in this way, excludes the P from the blank and gives the net ppm of P attributable to the determination.

7–123. Calculation. The organic phosphorus is calculated as follows:

$$\text{ppm of P} = \text{ppm of P} - \text{ppm of P} \qquad (7\text{–}13)$$
$$\text{(organic)} \qquad \text{(total extracted)} \qquad \text{(inorganic)}$$

ALTERNATIVE PROCEDURES

7–124. Soil organic phosphorus has also been extracted with cold 0.1 N NH_4OH,[99] with hot 0.5 N NH_4OH,[100] and with hot 4 per cent NH_4OH.[101] The NH_4OH extractions are less complete than the NaOH extraction.

7–125. Organic Phosphorus Estimation by Means of Hydrogen Peroxide.[102] One gm of soil having passed a 0.5-mm sieve is placed in a tube with a 50-ml graduation. (The carbonates should be removed by acidification prior to application of the H_2O_2 method to calcareous soils.) To the soil is added the phosphorus-free H_2O_2 equivalent to 15 ml of phosphorus-free[103] 30 per cent H_2O_2. The suspension is thoroughly mixed and placed on a steam bath for 0.5 hour. Then to the solution are added 15 ml of water, 10 ml of 0.5 N HCl, and water to give a 50-ml total volume. The tube is stopped and shaken for 30 minutes. Then 1 gm of solid NH_4F is added and the shaking is continued for 1 hour. Finally the solution is filtered on a small Buchner funnel. An aliquot of 5 or 10 ml of this solution

99 Schollenberger, *Soil Sci.*, 6:365 (1918).

100 Pearson, *Ind. Eng. Chem., A.E.*, 12:198 (1940).

101 Dyer and Wrenshall, *Soil Sci.*, 51:159 (1941).

102 Bray and Kurtz, *Soil Sci.*, 59:39 (1945); as adapted to HCl by Dickman and Bray, *Ind. Eng. Chem., A.E.*, 12:665 (1940) instead of H_2SO_4 used by Dickman and DeTurk, *Soil Sci.*, 45:29 (1938).

103 Chang and Jackscon, *Sci.*, 124:1209 (1956).

is placed in a 250-ml beaker, 15 ml of 0.8 M H_3BO_3 is added, and this solution is evaporated to dryness. Approximately 10 ml of 0.1 N HCl is added and the solution is again evaporated to dryness. The residue is taken up in 10 ml of 0.1 N HCl and the P is determined (¶ 7–31) on this aliquot in the presence of the H_3BO_3 therein. The organic phosphorus is taken as the difference between the phosphorus removed by this procedure and that by acid-0.5 N NH_4F without H_2O_2 (¶ 7–93) removed from a duplicate sample. Disadvantages of the method are that the H_2O_2 may not release all of the organic phosphorus and may change the status of the inorganic phosphorus and thus introduce an error in the difference attributed to organic phosphorus.

7–126. Ignition Method. Extraction of the phosphorus with acid before and after ignition has been employed to estimate organic phosphorus. The increase due to ignition is attributable to organic phosphorus.[104] Complicating factors are the release to acid soluble form of some phosphorus from mineral form by ignition[105] and the possible hydrolysis of some phosphorus from organic forms to orthophosphate during the acid extraction.

7–127. Chemical Characterization of Soil Organic Phosphorus Compounds. The determination of the chemical nature of the various soil organic phosphorus compounds is also important. The 3 general classes of soil organic phosphorus compounds include phospholipids, nucleic acids, and inositol (including phytin and related compounds). Phospholipids are indicated by the presence of organic phosphorus in the ether and alcohol extracts of soils and are confirmed by the isolation of choline.[106] The presence of nucleic acids is indicated[107] by the identification, in the hydrolysates of soil phosphorus preparations, of constituent parts of nucleic acid such as pentose sugar, cytosine, adenine, guanine, uracil, xanthine, and hypoxanthine, as well as H_3PO_4. Support is also found in the known susceptibility of nucleic acids to dephosphorylation and the lability observed of the nucleic acid portion of soil organic phosphorus compared to the stability of inositol-like soil organic phosphorus compounds. Analysis[108] of the organic phosphorus of several groups of soils shows that soil organic phosphorus is abundant in inositol-like compounds. Of these, phytin or inositol hexaphosphate (precipitated by ferric iron) is the most abundant, and inositol triphosphate (precipitated by Ca) is next most abundant. How-

---

104 Legg and Black, *S.S.S.A. Proc.*, 19:139 (1955).

105 Fraps, *J. Ind. Eng. Chem.*, 3:335 (1911).

106 Aso, *Coll. Agr. Tokyo Imp. Univ. Bul.*, 6:277 (1905); Shorey, *Bul.* 88 (1913).

107 Black and Goring, "Soil and Fertilizer Phosphorus," *Agronomy* (New York: Academic Press, 1953), Vol. 5, ch. 5, p. 123.

108 Bower, *Soil Sci.*, 59:277 (1945); Yoshita, *Soil Sci.*, 50:81 (1940); Dyer *et al.*, *Sci.*, 91:319 (1940); Dyer and Wrenshall, *Soil Sci.*, 51:159 (1941); Young, *Biochem. J.*, 28:1435 (1934); Anderson, *J. Biol. Chem.*, 18:441 (1914), 20:463, 475 (1915).

ever, anion exchange chromatography and P^{32} tracer techniques[109] show that the two-thirds or more of the organic phosphorus-containing material from soil that behaves chemically as phytin does not behave chromatographically as inositol hexaphosphate. The preparations were extracted in 0.5 N NaOH, treated with alkaline hypobromite, precipitated with Fe^{+++} and Ca, and washed thoroughly in N HCl, the standard procedure for separation of phytin.

TOTAL ELEMENTAL PHOSPHORUS

7–128. The total content of the element phosphorus in silicates and other solids can be extracted and determined by several methods: (a) by a Na_2CO_3 fusion, (b) by perchloric acid digestion followed by colorimetric or titrimetric determination, (c) by heating of the soil sample with Mg $(NO_3)_2$, followed by titrimetric determinations as the yellow ammonium molybdophosphate;[110] or (d) by digestion in the HF followed by gravimetric determination as the $Mg_2P_2O_7$.[111] Methods a, b, and d are satisfactory for most soils and rocks, but method c apparently does not extract[112] all of the soil phosphorus. The perchloric acid method (¶ 7–134) has been widely used for total P in soils, although less recovery is sometimes obtained[113] than with the Na_2CO_3 or HF methods.

APPARATUS

7–129. Needed apparatus consists of a platinum crucible and cover, a filter funnel and paper, a 50-ml volumetric flask, and pipets.

REAGENTS

7–130. Reagents required are analytical grade Na_2CO_3, 1 N H_2SO_4, and the reagents for method I (¶ 7–14).

PROCEDURE

7–131. Total P of Soils by Na_2CO_3 Fusion. A 0.1- to 1-gm sample is fused in Na_2CO_3 (¶ 11–104 to 11–106) followed by disintegration of the melt in distilled water, and filtration to remove the curd containing the iron and much of the silica.[114] The filtrate is diluted to a volume appropriate to give 5 to 30 ugm of P in an aliquot to be taken. The aliquot is placed in a 50-ml volumetric flask, neutralized with 1 N H_2SO_4 to pH 3 and brought to 50 ml by method I (¶ 7–22). This method works well for silicious soils

---

[109] Clark and Smith, *Soil Sci.,* 72:353 (1951).

[110] *Methods of Analysis,* 7th ed. (Washington, D.C.: A.O.A.C., 1950), p. 37.

[111] Washington, *Chemical Analysis of Rocks* (New York: John Wiley & Sons, Inc., 1919); Robinson, U.S.D.A. Cir. 139 (1930).

[112] Sherman, *Ind. Eng. Chem., A.E.,* 14:182 (1942).

[113] Muir, *Analyst,* 77:313 (1952).

[114] Pearson *et al., J. Am. Soc. Agron.,* 32:685 (1940).

and rocks, but if the silica does not exceed the quantities of F plus Ca present (as with highly calcareous soils, rock phosphate, etc.), some of the P is retained in the curd and *the determination is not successful* (¶ 7–132).

ALTERNATIVE PROCEDURES

7–132. An alternative Na_2CO_3 procedure, employed (1945) by S. C. Chang and the author, is to take up Na_2CO_3 fusion cake (¶ 11–105) in 30 ml of 9 N H_2SO_4, with care to avoid loss by effervescence. The crucible and cover are boiled in a little 2 N H_2SO_4 in a separate small beaker and this solution is added to the main solution. The solution and suspended material are then transferred to a 200-ml volumetric flask, made to volume, and mixed, giving approximately 1 N H_2SO_4. To eliminate ferric iron, if present in interfering amounts (a test is given in ¶ 7–74), an aliquot of the clear supernatant liquid remaining after the silica settles out is passed through a small amalgamated Zn Jones reductor (¶ 11–144), made up in a 50-ml buret, followed by determination by method I (¶ 7–14). Full recoveries of phosphorus were obtained at a concentration of 0.25 ppm of P in the presence of 100 to 1000 ppm of iron, after reduction in the Jones reductor in from 0.25 to 2 N H_2SO_4.

7–133. Use of HCl to decompose the melt and method II (¶ 7–26) permits up to 15 ppm of ferric before interference occurs, and the upper limit can be extended by the use of a Jones reductor (¶ 7–32 or 7–120). Hydrazine sulfate has been employed[115] as the reducing agent and ferric iron did not cause interference up to 150 ppm.

7–134. $HClO_4$ Method for Total P.[116] A 2-gm sample of soil (5 gm of soil low in phosphorus) that has passed an 0.5-mm sieve is weighed and transferred to a 300-ml conical flask. A smaller sample of a rock material high in phosphate is employed. If the sample is high in organic matter, 20 ml of HNO_3 is added to effect preliminary oxidation on a steam plate. For ordinary soil or rock, fairly low in organic matter, the HNO_3 treatment is omitted. Then 30 ml of 60 per cent $HClO_4$ is added and the digestion is carried out at 130°C in a special digestion apparatus (¶ 12–23) designed to remove $HClO_4$ fumes. A funnel can also be used to reflux the $HClO_4$ during the digestion in the flask.

7–135. The $HClO_4$ digestion of the sample is carried out until the solution appears colorless, with a slight increase of temperature if necessary. Usually about 40 minutes of digestion suffices. As the digestion is completed, dense white fumes of $HClO_4$ appear and the silica becomes white. Additional $HClO_4$ may be employed to wash down any dark particles that stick to the sides of the flask.

---

[115] Sheldon and Harper, *Iowa State Coll. J. Sci.,* 40, 4:403 (1941).

[116] Digestion in $HClO_4$ was used by Volk and Jones, *S.S.S.A. Proc.,* 2:197 (1938), with a titrimetric procedure; Sherman, *Ind. Eng. Chem., A.E.,* 14:182 (1942), with method IV; and Bray and Kurtz, *Soil Sci.,* 59:39 (1945), with method III.

7–136. When the digestion is completed, the flask is removed. When it has cooled sufficiently to avoid spattering, 50 ml of distilled water is added, and the solution is transferred through a filter to a 200-ml volumetric flask. The residue is washed to bring the volume of solution to the mark. An aliquot is taken for analysis by the vanadomolybdophosphoric (¶ 7–59) or the perchloric acid methods (¶ 7–51). The silica has been removed by the $HClO_4$ treatment, and ferric iron does not generally interfere.

PRECIPITATION AND IDENTIFICATION OF ALUMINUM AND IRON PHOSPHATE

7–137. It is often desirable to prepare precipitates of amorphous or crystalline phosphates of aluminum or iron for study in the laboratory or greenhouse. Characterization of the solid phases precipitated can be effected by X-ray diffraction, elemental, thermal, and infrared analyses. The precipitates may be compared in behavior to soil phosphates by the several extraction methods given above (¶ 7–106).

APPARATUS

7–138. Needed apparatus includes 1-liter beakers, pipets, burets, a steam plate, a centrifuge and tubes, and apparatus for characterization of the precipitates.

REAGENTS

7–139. Needed reagents consist of 1 M $AlCl_3$, 1 M $FeCl_3$, 1 M NaH_2PO_4, 0.1 N NaCl, and acetone.

PROCEDURE

7–140. Aluminum Phosphates. To precipitate aluminum phosphate, 500 ml of distilled water is placed in a 1-liter beaker and 30 ml of 1 M $AlCl_3$ is added. Then, with stirring, 90 ml of 1 M NaH_2PO_4 is added. The beaker is covered with a cover glass and placed on the steam plate. After a period of heating, a precipitate of aluminum phosphate begins to form. Digestion for about 40 hours makes the precipitated crystalline. To determine the identity of the solid phase, the suspension is stirred, an aliquot is removed, and the precipitate is thrown down by centrifugation, washed twice with 0.1 N NaCl to remove saloid-bound phosphate, then with water until free of chlorides, and finally with acetone. The precipitate gives an analytical composition of $AlPO_4 \cdot 2 H_2O$ or $Al(OH)_2H_2PO_4$, and an X-ray diffraction pattern of the mineral variscite. To follow the process of precipitation and crystallization, the pH values of the unmixed and mixed solutions are measured at the beginning (about pH 2.2) and at 8-hour intervals (a slight decrease occurs with time). Also at 8-hour intervals, a portion of the precipitate is removed, washed, and X-rayed. Usually a precipitate having the analytical composition $AlPO_4 \cdot 1\frac{1}{2}\ H_2O$ and a distinctive X-ray diffraction pattern appears first, then gradually disappears as variscite becomes predominant. Removal of fine colloidal material from the sample by size separation aids in the separation of pure crystalline variscite in the coarser fraction. Use of low pH values hastens the growth of crystals (greater solubility of the phosphate) and prevents the precipitation of hydroxides or oxides of aluminum.

7–141. Iron Phosphates. To 540 ml of water in a 1-liter beaker, 10 ml of $1\ M$ $FeCl_3$ is added and then, with rapid stirring, 30 ml of $1\ M$ NaH_2PO_4. A precipitate forms rapidly and becomes crystalline with digestion on the steam plate for about 24 hours. The composition is $FePO_4 \cdot 2\ H_2O$, or $Fe(OH)_2H_2PO_4$, and the crystalline diffraction pattern is that of the mineral strengite. The precipitate is washed as for the aluminum phosphates and is then ready for X-ray diffraction analysis and other tests.

ALTERNATIVE PROCEDURES

7–142. Inclusion of a K or NH_4 ions in the mixture results in formation of crystalline products with these cations contained in the crystals; for example, crystals of minerals such as minyulite and taranakite. There is an extensive series of relatively insoluble aluminum and iron phosphates,[117] the compositions of which include the ions K, NH_4, Na, H, and Ca in varying proportions depending on the ions present and their source, concentrations, acidity, and the temperature of the precipitation solution. Colloids of Fe and Al oxides, hydroxides, and silicates, when placed in phosphate solutions at steam plate temperatures, result in crystalline iron and aluminum phosphate precipitates.[118]

PHOSPHATE EXCHANGE CAPACITY OF SOILS

7–143. Of the plant nutrient anions, only phosphate shows much anion exchange in soils. Sulfate may exchange some, but chlorides and nitrates exchange little or none. Anion exchange, therefore, must be thought of as having a different general character from cation exchange, which occurs more or less the same for all of the common cations. Phosphate "exchange," "adsorption," or "precipitation" involves change of the phosphate from solution to solid phase (¶ 7–95), and when the phase change is examined in detail, any distinction in the meaning of the 3 terms as applied to the phosphate soil system is difficult and probably useless. The fraction

---

[117] Haseman *et al., Soil Sci.,* 70:257 (1950), *S.S.S.A. Proc.,* 15:76 (1951); Cole and Jackson, *S.S.S.A. Proc.,* 15:84 (1951), *J. Phys. Colloid Chem.,* 54:128 (1950); Larsen, *Am. Mineral.,* 25:315 (1940); McConnell, *Am. Mineral.,* 25:719 (1940), *Bul. Geol. Soc. Am.,* 54:707 (1945), *J. Geol.,* 58:16 (1950).

[118] Kittrick and Jackson, *Sci.,* 120:508 (1954); *S.S.S.A. Proc.,* 19:292 and 455 (1955), *Soil Sci.,* 79:415 (1955); *J. Soil Sci.,* 7:81 (1956).

of fixed phosphate that is available for "exchange" can be calculated from the specific surface (particle size) of the phosphate phase.[119] The amounts of phosphate present on surfaces can be measured by the P^{32} exchange.[120] The reaction rates increase with temperature and therefore chemical bonding rather than physical (the usual adsorption) bonding is responsible.[121] The phase change appears to be controlled by the formation of chemical bonds with Fe, Al, and Ca ions that are on mineral surfaces or in solution. All of these cations are known to form insoluble phosphate salts, and the "exchange" is of the nature of a chemical double decomposition reaction. Authors agree unanimously that measurement of phosphate exchange capacity (phosphate fixation capacity) is dependent upon the conditions such as time, reference pH, and pretreatment, and that these conditions must be stated with the report of phosphate exchange capacity.

7–144. To eliminate precipitation of phosphate by divalent cations, the soil was prewashed[122] with 0.5 N NaOAc of pH 5.7, saturated with the 0.5 M salt solution of the anion to be tested, and adjusted to pH 5.7. To Ca soil (from which the free $CaCO_3$ has been removed), the cation exchange equivalent of dilute H_3PO_4 (on the basis of the first hydrogen) was added[123] to measure the phosphate reaction. The iron and aluminum extracted from acid soils in 0.5 M citric acid was shown[124] to be related to the phosphate exchange capacity as measured by J. S. Hosking[125] with 0.5 M KH_2PO_4 plus H_3PO_4 at pH 3.4.

APPARATUS

7–145. Needed apparatus includes 400- and 250-ml beakers, a 500-ml volumetric flask, a 250-ml conical flask, $HClO_4$ digestion apparatus (¶ 12–23), a filter funnel and Whatman No. 40 or 41 and 42 filter papers, a 25-ml pipet, and the apparatus for colorimetric phosphorus determination.

REAGENTS

7–146. Needed reagents are 0.5 M citric acid (91 gm per liter), 1 and 20 per cent NaCl, 60 per cent $HClO_4$, 0.03 M KH_2PO_4, approximately N NaOH and N HCl, 0.1 per cent methyl orange indicator (¶ 3–42), and the reagents for colorimetric phosphorus determination.

[119] Kittrick and Jackson, *J. Soil Sci.*, 7:81 (1956).
[120] Olsen and Watonabe, *S.S.S.A. Proc.*, 21:144 (1957).
[121] Hemwall, *Soil Sci.*, 83:101 (1957).
[122] Rubins and Dean, *Soil Sci.*, 63:389 (1947).
[123] Mehlich, *Soil Sci.*, 66:429 (1948).
[124] Bass and Sieling, *Soil Sci.*, 69:269 (1950).
[125] Piper, *Soil and Plant Analysis* (New York: Interscience Publishers, Inc., 1944), p. 191.

PROCEDURE

7-147. In the procedure of Bass and Sieling for the phosphate exchange capacity of acid soils, a 20-gm soil sample is weighed into a 400-ml beaker, mixed with 75 ml of 0.5 M citric acid, and digested in a boiling water bath for 1 hour with periodic stirring. The suspension is then filtered through Whatman No. 40 or 41 filter paper into a 500-ml volumetric flask, followed by washing with hot water. When the filtrate has cooled to room temperature, it is made to volume, mixed, and a 25-ml aliquot is pipetted into a 250-ml conical flask. The aliquot is evaporated nearly to dryness, then 10 ml of concentrated HNO_3 is added. The mixture is heated on a steam plate for about 20 minutes and then 5 ml of 60 per cent $HClO_4$ is added. Heating is continued on an electric hotplate with a digestion manifold to collect the $HClO_4$ fumes in water (¶ 12–23). Heating is continued until heavy white fumes of $HClO_4$ appear, then an additional 20 minutes to insure complete oxidation of the organic matter and iron. The sample is sufficiently cooled to avoid spattering, and then is diluted with 20 ml of distilled water.

7-148. The digested solution (organic matter free), containing 0.05 to 1.0 millimol of Fe plus Al or either element separately, is transferred to a 250-ml beaker. Then 100 ml of 0.03 M KH_2PO_4 and 10 ml of 20 per cent NaCl are added. Two drops of methyl orange indicator are added, and the solution is heated to boiling. The solution is then titrated with approximately N NaOH until a color change to yellow is observed. Dilute HCl is then used to back titrate the solution to a slight orange color, giving a pH of approximately 3.4 to 3.5. The sample is then digested at near boiling temperature on a steam plate for 30 minutes. After digestion, the hot solution is filtered through Whatman No. 42 filter paper, and the filtrate is discarded. The precipitation beaker is washed thoroughly with hot 1 per cent NaCl adjusted to pH 3.4, and this washing liquid is poured over the precipitate on the filter. The solution is allowed to drain completely from the filter and the filter and precipitate are washed 2 additional times with hot 1 per cent NaCl solution. Care is taken to direct the wash solution around the top of the filter so as to disturb the precipitate as little as possible. When the third washing has completely drained through the filter (the precipitate must not be allowed to dry), the precipitate is dissolved with a hot 0.2 N acid solution, the acid being the one to be employed in the colorimetric determination (H_2SO_4 for method I, HCl for method II, $HClO_4$ for method IV, or HNO_3 for method V). The solution resulting from dissolution of the precipitate is washed into a 500-ml volumetric flask. The solution is cooled, made to volume, mixed, and an aliquot is taken for colorimetric analysis of the phosphorus.

7-149. The number of millimols of phosphorus found is equivalent to the number of millimols of Fe plus Al present in the original citric acid extract of the soil and represents the phosphate exchange (fixing) capacity of the soil. It is calculated in terms of millimols (mgm atoms) of P per 100 gm of soil.

ALTERNATIVE PROCEDURES

7–150. In the Bass and Sieling procedure for measurement of phosphate exchange capacity by direct addition of phosphate, 5 gm of soil is weighed into a 50-ml centrifuge tube and enough $0.5 M KH_2PO_4$ (brought to pH 3.4 with H_3PO_4) is added to bring the total volume to 40 ml. The mixture is stirred thoroughly and then digested on a water bath for 4 hours. At the end of this time the centrifuge tube is removed and centrifuged for 15 minutes to clarify the solution. The supernatant liquid is poured off and 40 ml of hot 1 per cent NaCl is added to each sample. The tubes are thoroughly shaken, heated for 3 minutes in a water bath, and then centrifuged again. The supernatant liquid is poured off and the second washing with 1 per cent NaCl made. Following this, 3 washings are made with 70 per cent ethanol containing 2 per cent NaCl. Samples are shaken thoroughly each time and centrifuged without being heated. All the liquid is drained out of the centrifuge tubes after each centrifuging.

7–151. To displace the phosphate, the sample is digested on the hot water bath for 1 hour with $0.5 M$ citric acid. The suspension is filtered into a 250-ml volumetric flask, and the solution is cooled and made to volume. A 25-ml aliquot is taken for oxidation with HNO_3 and $HClO_4$ as in the procedure (¶ 7–147). When the oxidation has reached the stage of dense $HClO_4$ fumes, the solution is cooled, diluted, and filtered into a 250-ml flask. An aliquot is taken for the colorimetric phosphorus determination. The phosphate extracted is calculated as millimols (mgm atoms) of P per 100 gm of soil, the phosphate exchange capacity.

QUESTIONS

1. Distinguish between the analytical determination of phosphorus as opposed to the principles and problems involved in the extraction of various forms of soil phosphorus.

2. What is the relation of the phosphorus atom to the molybdate radicals in the heteropoly complex ion?

3. What chemical principle is employed in the elimination of the interference by silica in the phosphorus determination?

4. What is the "acid-stability plateau" with reference to the heteropoly blue color methods for phosphorus?

5. What factors dictate the choice of phosphorus method?

6. By what means is the interference of fluoride eliminated in the chlorostannous-HCl method?

7. State the advantages of the vanadomolybdophosphoric yellow color phosphorus method.

8. What forms of soil phosphorus are extracted by dilute acid?

9. What chemical form of phosphorus is extracted by neutral fluoride solution?

10. Why is $NaHCO_3$ of pH 8.5 effective in the measurement of available phosphorus of calcareous soils? Of acid and neutral soils?

11. Why is citrate-dithionite an effective extractant of acid and alkali insoluble soil phosphate?

12. What chemical principles are applied in the extraction of the total organic phosphorus of soils?

13. List 4 different methods for the release of the total phosphorus from soils.

14. Why do the phosphates of Fe and Al quickly become crystalline when formed at pH 2 to 3 but not when precipitated at higher pH values?

15. Explain the equivalence of citric acid soluble Fe and Al and the phosphate exchange capacity of acid soils.

8

Nitrogen Determinations
for Soils and Plant Tissue

Nitrogen—essential link in protein

8–1. Most of the nitrogen in soils is in organic form. Relatively small amounts ordinarily occur in ammonium and nitrates, the available forms. Two general types of analytical procedures are widely used—the Kjeldahl conversion of nitrogen to $(NH_4)_2SO_4$ and the Dumas conversion to nitrogen gas. The Kjeldahl method is employed in macro, micro, and ultramicro procedures. The macro procedure is given here.

8–2. Microbiological conversion of organic nitrogen to ionic forms is an important aspect of the nitrogen chemistry of soils. The Kjeldahl method includes both organic and ammonium forms, and with modifications (¶ 8–14) includes the nitrate form. Nitrate nitrogen should be included in the total nitrogen of soils that contain appreciable amounts. For example, 100 ppm N in nitrate form is 0.01 per cent of the soil and 10 per cent of the total nitrogen in the soil containing 0.10 per cent nitrogen (expected in a soil containing 2 per cent organic matter). Procedures for the separate determination of ammonium and nitrate are also detailed herein.

8–3. A general approximation of total soil nitrogen content can be made from organic matter content (O.M. $\times$ 0.05 = N) and ignition loss at 400°C (loss $\times$ 0.022 to 0.03 = N). These approximate factors are subject to great change with widely different soils.

TOTAL NITROGEN DETERMINATION
(Modified Kjeldahl method)

8–4. Although the original Kjeldahl procedure has been modified many times, the determination of total nitrogen is still not as simple as it is often thought to be.[1] It is subject to many difficulties, any of which may lead to low results. For example, an hour of digestion may be necessary after the digest turns clear, to release all of the nitrogen, the most important considerations being the catalyst selected and the digestion temperature. If the temperature is too low (below 360°C), the release is slow or incomplete, and if too high (over 410°C), some loss of NH_3 from the mixture results.[2] The soil should be more finely ground[3] than the sample size would ordinarily require in order to assure complete oxidation of the organic matter within the small aggregates, especially in the case of heavy clay soils. Soaking[4] clay soils in water also aids in achieving complete oxidation.

APPARATUS

8–5. Needed apparatus consists of the Kjeldahl digestion manifold (¶ 8–6), a Kjeldahl NH_3 distillation rack, 800-ml or 500-ml Kjeldahl flasks, a 25-ml pipet, 500-ml conical receiver flasks with 8-mm diameter receiver tubes long enough to reach from the bottom of the conical flask to the distillation condenser, burets, and analytical balance.

8–6. Kjeldahl Digestion Rack with Fume Aspirator. The special type of

Fig. 8–1. Kjeldahl digestion apparatus for disposal of acid fumes through water pump and sewer, successfully operated at the University of Wisconsin for over 20 years.

---

[1] Bal and Meter, *Anal. Chem.,* 23:1632 (1951), show wide variation between laboratories in both the Kjeldahl and Dumas determination of total nitrogen of petroleum products, which are somewhat more difficult materials to analyze than soils and plants.

[2] Lake *et al., Anal. Chem.,* 23:1634 (1951).

[3] Walkley, *J. Agr. Sci.,* 25:598 (1935); Prince, *Soil Sci.,* 59:48 (1945).

[4] Bal, *J. Agr. Sci.,* 15:454 (1925); Ashton, *J. Agr. Sci.,* 26:239 (1936).

H_2SO_4 fume disposal by evacuation[5] through a large lead water pump (Fig. 8–1) is much preferred to the less satisfactory H_2SO_4 fume chimney type that is commonly featured commercially. The shut-off and regulator valves for the water line, which flushes condensed acid out of the lead manifold, is seen in the upper right of Fig. 8–1. A similar set of valves regulates the flow through the lead suction pump at the end of the manifold. Details of the manifold and pump are shown in Fig. 8–2.

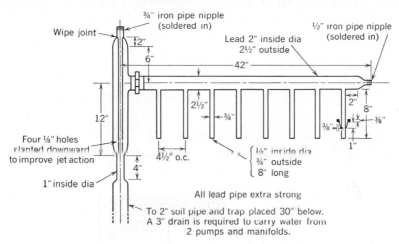

Fig. 8–2. Pump and manifold for Kjeldahl digestion apparatus. (Lead fabricated by Crown Metal Products Co., 117–119 Washington Street, Milwaukee, Wis.)

REAGENTS

8–7. Needed reagents include concentrated H_2SO_4, granulated zinc or pumice, reductant for mercuric compounds, standard $\dfrac{N}{14}$ H_2SO_4, and the special reagents listed in the following paragraphs. If Na_2S or K_2S is to be employed for reduction of mercuric compounds, 40 gm of the commercial grade is dissolved in 1 liter of water. If $Na_2S_2O_3 \cdot 5 H_2O$ is to be employed, it is dissolved in the NaOH (¶ 8–9).

8–8. Digestion Accelerators. Approximately 20 gm of $CuSO_4 \cdot 5 H_2O$ (previously ground and dried in an oven at 110°C), 3 gm HgO, and 1 gm of Se powder are mixed[6] by grinding in a mortar. *Caution:* The Se powder

---

[5] Kjeldahl fume disposal through the sewer has been successfully employed by Prof. H. A. Schuette of the University of Wisconsin by an apparatus after which the one described here was designed. Tyner, *Anal. Chem.*, 20:273 (1948), described a slightly different apparatus that successfully achieved the same results.

[6] Mixture proportions after Poe and Nalder, *Ind. Eng. Chem.*, *A.E.*, 7:189 (1935), and Lauro, *Ind. Eng. Chem.*, *A.E.*, 3:401 (1931), who found a greatly accelerated digestion rate over copper alone. Patel and Sreenivasan, *Anal. Chem.*, 20:63 (1948) noted the value of Hg in helping prevent loss of N, which may occur with Se alone as a catalyst.

must not be dried at 110°C since this element is volatile and toxic. One part of this mixture is thoroughly mixed with 20 parts of anhydrous Na_2SO_4 and the mixture labeled "Na_2SO_4-plus-catalyst." The purpose of the Na_2SO_4 salt is to raise the boiling temperature of the H_2SO_4 digestion; K_2SO_4 works as well as Na_2SO_4 and may be substituted. Alternatives to the dry mixture of digestion accelerators is the separate addition of each component; for example, 5 ml of 1 N $CuSO_4$ solution has been used instead of the crystals.

8–9. 40 per cent NaOH, for NH_3 Distillation. First 50 per cent NaOH solution is made up and impurities are allowed to settle out. To do this, 3 kgm of NaOH (technical, low N) is dissolved in 3 liters of distilled water in a heavy-walled Pyrex flask or bottle. The solution is allowed to stand several days for the Na_2CO_3 to settle out. Then the clear supernatant liquid is siphoned (caution) into 1.5 kgm of water; the solution is then mixed and placed in the 40 per cent NaOH bottle (Fig. 8–3) with a glass

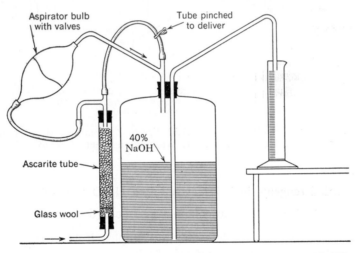

Fig. 8–3. Arrangement for delivery of 40 per cent ($10N$) NaOH and protection from CO_2 contamination.

delivery tube that is too short to act as a siphon, and an Ascarite tube to prevent absorption of CO_2. If $Na_2S_2O_3$ is to be employed to precipitate mercuric compounds, 360 gm of $Na_2S_2O_3 \cdot 5\ H_2O$ is dissolved in the 1.5 kgm of water prior to addition of the 50 per cent NaOH.

8–10. Mixed Indicator Solution. Brom cresol green (0.5 per cent) and methyl red (0.1 per cent) mixed indicator[7] is prepared by dissolving 0.5

---

[7] Indicator proportions after Ma and Zuazaga, *Ind. Eng. Chem., A.E.,* 14:280 (1942); but brom cresol green concentration 5-fold greater, was found to be more efficacious in the author's laboratories.

gm of brom cresol green and 0.1 gm methyl red in 100 ml of 95 per cent ethanol, and adjusting the solution to the bluish purple midcolor at pH 4.5, with dilute NaOH or HCl. This indicator is pink at pH 4.2 or lower and bluish green as the pH rises to pH 4.9 and above.

8–11. Boric Acid. Approximately 40 gm of H_3BO_3 is dissolved in 1 liter of distilled water containing 5 ml of the mixed indicator. This boric acid stock solution is adjusted by dilute H_2SO_4 or HCl titration until the bluish color of the indicator weakens toward pink. The equilibrium constant of H_3BO_3 (6.4×10^{-10}) shows that pH 8.6 is reached when 20 per cent of the first H has been neutralized with NH_3, which corresponds to 48 mgm of N per 25 ml. The solution is 0.65 M H_3BO_3 and thus its pH is 4.7 when all of the H_3BO_3 has been reformed in the acid titration. Therefore the pH 4.5 midcolor of the indicator permits a sharp end point on titration with a strong acid.

8–12. The reagents are tested for nitrogen by digestion of a filter paper blank, all steps of the procedure being carried out as in the determinations. The blank determination is subtracted from each determination.

PROCEDURE

8–13. For Soils or Plant Tissue. A soil sample of 5.00 gm (1.000 gm of muck or peat, or 20.00 gm of sandy soil) that has been ground to pass a 0.15 mm (100 mesh per in.) screen, or 0.500 gm of dried plant tissue that has been ground to pass a 0.4 mm (40 mesh per in.) screen is wrapped in a 11-cm qualitative filter paper and dropped as a package into a 800-ml Kjeldahl digestion flask. Then 20 ± 1 gm[8] of the Na_2SO_4-plus-catalyst digestion mix is added.

8–14. Nitrates may be included, (¶8–2, 8–15) but usually are not, since they are often negligible in relation to the total nitrogen. The procedure for plant tissue or sandy soil samples is to add 35 ml of concentrated H_2SO_4 and to mix the contents by swirling the flask, with care not to throw the sample onto the sides. The digestion is then commenced (¶ 8–18). The procedure for medium and fine textured soils is to add 50 ml of water[9] and to allow the sample to soak for 30 minutes. Then 35 ml of concentrated H_2SO_4 are added and digestion follows (¶ 8–18).

---

[8] This quantity of Na_2SO_4 controls the boiling point of the digestion as shown by Lake *et al., Anal. Chem.,* 23:1634 (1951), between 360° and 410°C, which is the critical range for efficacious digestion. Since the boiling temperature is affected by altitude and the rate of H_2SO_4 discharge during digestion, some control work on completeness of digestion and recovery is suggested by each laboratory. The 20-gm quantity, adopted by Lake *et al.,* and used in this procedure, is double the conventional 10 gm.

[9] Bal modification, *J. Agr. Sci.,* 15:454 (1925), which raises the N recovery considerably, especially in clayey soils.

8–15. If soil nitrates[10] are to be included in the determination, 35 ml of concentrated H_2SO_4 containing 1 gm of commercial salicylic acid is added to the sample in the flask (¶ 8–13). The flask is swirled until the acid is thoroughly mixed with the soil, and the mixture is allowed to stand for 30 minutes for the nitrates to react with the salicylic acid. Then 5 gm of $Na_2S_2O_3 \cdot 5 H_2O$ (or 2 gm of zinc dust—granulated zinc will not do) and 50 ml of H_2O[11] are added and the mixture is heated slowly and with care at first to avoid frothing over. When this danger is past, the digestion is continued as usual (¶ 8–18).

8–16. Procedure for Runoff Suspensions. The runoff suspension is shaken thoroughly and a 250-ml aliquot (100 ml if over 5 gm of solids occurs in 100 ml) is quickly measured out in a calibrated (¶ 10–64) beaker. The aliquot is transferred to an 800-ml Kjeldahl flask, a few glass beads and 20 ± 1 gm of the Na_2SO_4-plus-catalyst are added, and finally 35 ml of concentrated H_2SO_4. The suspension is mixed cautiously by swirling the flask, and heated gradually to evaporate the water. The heat is then increased and digestion in the H_2SO_4 is effected (¶ 8–18).

8–17. The above procedure for runoff does not include the nitrates. Separate determination of nitrates by the phenoldisulfonic acid (¶ 8–59) is simpler, and permits addition of the nitrate equivalent to the Kjeldahl nitrogen excluding nitrates. The salicylic acid method (¶ 8–15) works only in concentrated H_2SO_4 and will not recover nitrates from aqueous solution.

8–18. Digestion in H_2SO_4. Digestion is effected on the Kjeldahl digestion rack with low flame for the first 10 to 30 minutes, until frothing stops, and then gradually more strongly until the sample is completely charred. The heat is gradually raised until the acid reaches a boil, and condensation of acid reaches approximately one-third the way up the neck of the digestion flask.[12] The flame is not allowed to touch the flask above the part occupied by liquid; otherwise there may be a loss of NH_3 in consequence of decomposition of $(NH_4)_2SO_4$. Heating at an excessive rate may be a disadvantage because of undue volatilization of acid before the organic matter is all oxidized. Some NH_3 may be lost if the acid is largely volatilized, because the temperature may rise above 410°C. The flask is rotated at intervals and heating is continued until the organic matter is destroyed,

---

[10] Nitrates are ordinarily lost by volatilization of HNO_3 during the H_2SO_4 digestion. In this procedure, the nitrate is combined with salicylate in concentrated H_2SO_4. According to the work of Dr. J. C. Kaudy and the author at this laboratory (1948), nitrates in runoff in aqueous H_2SO_4 are virtually impossible to reduce quantitatively by means of granulated zinc, Davada's alloy, or iron powder, although one quantitative result was reported by Ashton, *J. Agr. Sci.,* 26:239 (1936), with 2 gm of colloidal iron reduced from the oxide. The ferrous sulfate formed from iron powder has the advantage over zinc sulfate of solubility in the H_2SO_4.

[11] Combination of the Bal modification and the salicylate procedure, after Ashton, *J. Agr. Sci.,* 26:239 (1936).

[12] Lake *et al., Anal. Chem.,* 23:1634 (1951).

best judged by timing the digestion for 1 ± 0.25 hour after the solution has cleared (light yellow or gray color). According to Lake *et al.,* the best assurance of complete digestion is careful regulation of the digestion temperature so that it exceeds $360°C$ but does not reach $410°C$. Extra digestion time may be substituted for higher temperature only to a limited extent.

8–19. At the end of the digestion, the heating is stopped, but the fume exhaustion is continued *until fuming stops.* When the flasks are cooled just to the point where crystals start to form (not cooled completely, as the salts redissolve only slowly), 300 ml of NH_3-free water is added as the solution is cautiously mixed. This solution is further cooled (heat of dilution).

8–20. If large quantities of sand are present, particularly from runoff, bumping during distillation is sometimes severe. This can be avoided by washing the acid solution into another flask, the sand being left in the original flask.

8–21. Several pieces of granulated zinc or a teaspoon of pumice is added, followed by 25 ml of K_2S (reducing agent for mercuric salts; may be replaced by Na_2S or $Na_2S_2O_3$, the latter being most effectively added in the 40 per cent NaOH as in the next paragraph). The solution is mixed, and is then ready for determination of the ammonium content.

8–22. Distillation of NH_3 into Boric Acid.[13] Approximately[14] 25 ml of 4 per cent boric acid is pipetted into a 500-ml conical flask, and 4 drops of brom cresol green-methyl red indicator solution are added. A glass receiver tube is attached to the still and placed in the flask so that its end is below the surface of the boric acid in the flask. The cooling water is then started flowing in the condenser. The contents of the Kjeldahl flask are mixed by rotation, and the flask is placed on the distillation stand and checked for a good fit with the condenser connection. Then, with the Kjeldahl flask held at a 45° angle, about 125 ml (or 100 ml, if bumping is a problem) of 40 per cent NaOH are poured so that it runs down the neck to the bottom of the flask without mixing. The burner is then lighted, the flask is attached to the still, and the solution is *mixed thoroughly* by swirling. Immediately after this mixing, the flask is set to rest on the still support and is heated to avoid the danger of "sucking back."[15] The flame

---

[13] Wrinkler modification, Scales and Harrison, *Ind. Eng. Chem.,* 12:350 (1920), *J.A.O.A.C.,* 8:455 (1925).

[14] Neither the volume nor the strength of the boric acid need be known exactly, because the NH_4-borate formed is titrated back to H_3BO_3 in the titration. Twenty-five ml of boric acid will absorb 48 mgm of nitrogen as NH_3, which is approximately equivalent to 0.9 per cent N in soil (5 gm sample), or 4.8 per cent N in peat (1 gm sample), or 9.6 per cent N in vegetation (0.5 gm sample), or about 34 meq per 100 gm exchange capacity (10 gm sample).

[15] If sucking back occurs, it is only necessary to wash all of the boric acid into the digestion flask and redistill the NH_3 into a fresh lot of boric acid.

is increased gradually. About 150 ml is distilled over and then the receiver flask and tube are disconnected to prevent sucking back.

8–23. The boric acid is back titrated with a standard acid, preferably $\frac{N}{14}$ H_2SO_4 or HCl in routine soil analysis (0.0788 N acid for runoff). At the end point the blue color just disappears. One drop in excess (0.02 to 0.05 ml) turns the solution pink.

8–24. For soil or plant tissue, the percentage of nitrogen[16] is calculated as follows:

$$\% \text{ N in soil or plant tissue} = (T - B) \times N \times \frac{1.4}{s} \qquad (8\text{–}1)$$

in which

$T =$ sample titration, ml standard acid

$B =$ blank titration, ml standard acid

$N =$ normality of standard acid

$s =$ sample weight, gm

For runoff (¶ 8–16), pounds N per acre inch of runoff (ppai) is calculated for a 250-ml sample of suspension analyzed as follows:

$$\text{N in runoff (ppai)} = (T - B) \times 1.0 \text{ (for 0.0788 } N \text{ } H_2SO_4)$$

$$= (T - B) \times 0.906 \text{ (for } \frac{N}{14} H_2SO_4)$$

$$= (T - B) \times 1.27 \text{ (for 0.10 } N \text{ } H_2SO_4)$$

$$(8\text{–}2)$$

in which

$T =$ sample titration, ml standard acid

$B =$ blank titration, ml standard acid

ppai $=$ pounds N per acre inch runoff

Then the nitrogen in the soil solids present in the runoff is calculated:

$$\underset{\text{(pp2ms)}}{\text{N in runoff}} = \frac{\text{ppai nitrogen in runoff}}{\text{ppai solids in runoff}} \times 2,000,000 \qquad (8\text{–}3)$$

in which, pp2ms = parts N per 2 million parts of soil solids in runoff. These values, for greatest precision, are multiplied by the correction factor (¶ 10–69, eq. 10–21).

---

[16] Approximations:

% N × 6.25 = % crude protein in plant tissue

% N × 20 = % organic matter in soil

% N × 20,000 = pounds nitrogen per acre in soil

8–25. A number of suggestions have been made for insuring complete liberation of the organic nitrogen in the form of ammonium sulfate. Greater completeness is claimed[17] through the addition of $HClO_4$ near the end of the digestion followed by warming below boiling, but loss of nitrogen by this treatment will occur if the solution is brought to boiling. Another procedure calls for the addition at the end of the digestion (after cooling slightly) of $KMnO_4$ crystals in pinches until the solution remains green or purple. Loss of nitrogen occurs if the solution is heated after this treatment. It is believed that the elevated temperature employed in the procedure given is the most satisfactory method.

8–26. Acid-Base Titration of Distilled Ammonia. An alternative procedure is to collect the ammonia in dilute (about 0.1 N) H_2SO_4 or HCl, the excess acid being back titrated with standard NaOH. A common error is made in thinking that this dilute acid need be of standardized strength, whereas only its volume need be known exactly. The ammonia is distilled over (¶ 8–22) into exactly 25 ml of approximately 0.1 N H_2SO_4 or HCl, containing 3 drops of methyl red-methylene blue indicator. Twenty-five ml of $\dfrac{N}{14}$ acid is equivalent to 0.5 per cent N in 5 gm of soil; or 18 meq of exchange capacity per 100 gm, when a 10 gm sample is employed. The excess acid is back titrated with standard $\dfrac{N}{14}$ NaOH (0.0788 N NaOH may be used for runoff) to an end point of about pH 6.0 with methyl red-methylene blue indicator (0.6 gm methyl red and 0.4 gm of methylene blue in 500 ml of 95 per cent ethanol). The color change is from lavender to colorless to green. For soils or plant tissue, the percentage of nitrogen is calculated as follows:

$$\% \text{ N in soil or plant tissue} = (S - T) \times N \times \frac{1.4}{s} \qquad (8\text{–}4)$$

in which

S = standardization titration, ml standard NaOH for 25 ml H_2SO_4 used for receiving the distillation of the blank

T = titration of sample, ml standard NaOH for 25 ml H_2SO_4 receiving the sample

N = normality of standard alkali

s = sample weight, gm

For runoff, lbs. N per acre inch runoff (ppai) is calculated:

$$\underset{\text{(ppai)}}{\text{N in runoff}} = (S - T) \times 1.0 \text{ (for 0.788 } N \text{ NaOH)} \qquad (8\text{–}5)$$

---

[17] Pepkowitz *et al., Ind. Eng. Chem., A.E.,* 14:856 (1942).

$$= (S - T) \times 0.906 \text{ (for } \frac{N}{14} \text{NaOH)}$$

$$= (S - T) \times 1.27 \text{ (for } 0.10 \, N \text{ NaOH)}$$

8–27. Titration of Ammonium in Digest. Instead of being distilled the ammonium, as NH_3, may be titrated directly,[18] under suitable conditions, in the Kjeldahl flask after the usual H_2SO_4 digestion. The principle is based on the fact that the excess H_2SO_4 can be neutralized with strong NaOH while the ammonium, previously displaced from the mercuric complex by the addition of NaBr, which complexes the mercuric ions as $HgBr_4^{--}$, is left as $(NH_4)_2SO_4$ as follows:

$$NH_4HSO_4 + H_2SO_4 + NaOH \xrightarrow[\text{(to pH 5.7)}]{} (NH_4)_2SO_4 + Na_2SO_4 \quad (8\text{–}6)$$

This reaction is controlled by methyl red indicator, and the addition of 10 N NaOH is stopped at the point at which the indicator turns from pink to yellow (after the solution is boiled to remove CO_2). Then 30 ml of 18 per cent formaldehyde is added to complex the ammonium as hexamethylenetetramine (slight reversal of indicator color to pink is ignored) and standard 0.1 N NaOH is added to yellow and then further added to pink with 8 drops of 1 per cent phenolphthalein indicator. The total titer of standard NaOH between methyl red and phenolphthalein is equivalent to the ammonium present:

$$(NH_4)_2SO_4 + 2 \, NaOH \xrightarrow[\text{(to pH 8.3)}]{} Na_2SO_4 + 2 \, H_2O + 2 \, NH_2$$

$$(8\text{–}7)$$

$$4 \, NH_2 + 6 \, CH_2O \xrightarrow{\hspace{3cm}} (CH_2)_6N_4 + 6 \, H_2O \quad (8\text{–}8)$$

The procedure is facilitated by digestion in 500 ml, round bottom or slightly flattened bottom, Pyrex flasks with 29/42 standard-taper openings that fit 20-cm (eight-inch) detachable necks.[19]

8–28. As would be expected, some materials in the sample may interfere with titration in the presence of the entire digest. Precipitates of iron and aluminum tend to obscure the end points, and phosphorus tends to undergo conversion that gives a positive error. Zirconyl chloride, however, precipitates the phosphate in nonreactive form. Silica impurities in the NaOH also interfere by buffering the solution near the phenolphthalein end point if more than 15 ml of concentrated H_2SO_4 must be neutralized.

---

[18] Marcali and Rieman, *Ind. Eng. Chem., A.E.,* 18:709 (1946), *Anal. Chem.,* 20:381 (1948).

[19] Available from Fisher Scientific Co., Pittsburgh 19, Pa.

TOTAL AMMONIUM AND NITRATE NITROGEN IN WATERS

8–29. To determine the ammonium and nitrate nitrogen in drainage waters, the nitrate is reduced to ammonium with H_2 in alkaline solution, and the total ammonium is volatilized as NH_3 into boric acid.

PROCEDURE

8–30. A 250 ml (or other) volume of filtered runoff or drainage water is placed in an 800-ml Kjeldahl flask, and the flask is fitted to the Kjeldahl distillation rack. Boric acid solution is placed in the receiver flask as in the total nitrogen procedure (¶ 8–22). Then, 2 gm of Davarda's alloy (Cu, 50 per cent; Al, 45 per cent; Zn 5 per cent) and 10 ml of 40 per cent NaOH are added. The flask is attached to the still and the heating is started while the solution is simultaneously mixed by swirling the flask.

8–31. Distillation is continued until approximately 225 ml of the distillate has been collected. It is necessary to carry the distillation nearly to dryness to obtain complete reduction of all nitrate.

8–32. Quantitative tests with standard nitrate samples are suggested as a measure of the percentage recovery being obtained, since full recovery is frequently difficult to obtain.

EXCHANGEABLE AMMONIUM DETERMINATION

8–33. Because the ammonium ion is subject to oxidation to nitrite and nitrate in soils stored warm and moist, its determination should quickly follow the taking of the soil samples. The samples may be extracted moist, a separate determination of moisture being made, or they may be spread out in a thin layer and dried rapidly in an oven at 50°C.

8–34. Care must be exercised to prevent hydrolysis of the organic compounds of the soil to ammonium. This precludes a satisfactory direct displacement of ammonium by distillation as ammonia through treatment of the soil with hot alkali. Use of an acidified salt solution for displacement purposes appears to be a satisfactory precaution. Exchangeable ammonium ion has been determined by aeration of the soil at room temperature in the presence of a solution containing 4 per cent K_2CO_3 and 20 per cent KCl in a suitable apparatus,[20] but the method is more tedious than extraction.

8–35. The ammonium ion is held in exchangeable form in soils just as are the exchangeable metallic cations (Chapter 5). It must be extracted by some other exchangeable cation. Ammonium ion undergoes equilibrium fixation in the 2 : 1 layer silicates, particularly in the highly charged vermiculite interlayer spaces, in exactly the same way as K^+, by closure of the

---

[20] Mathews, *J. Agr. Sci.*, 10:72 (1920).

interlayer space. The ammonium ion thus fixed undergoes only slow exchange and is reluctant to nitrify.[21] The sodium ion has been selected for the replacing ion because it is among the best for replacing ammonium and potassium from the slow exchange positions.[22]

8–36. The amount of exchangeable NH_4^+ frequently falls in the range of 0.01 to 0.1 meq per 100 gm of soil, which range corresponds to 1.4 to 14 ppm or 2.8 to 28 pp2m. The upper limit of this range corresponds to 1 per cent of an exchange capacity of 10 meq per 100 gm of soil, and therefore, the exchangeable NH_4^+ usually may be neglected in the calculation of percentage cation saturation (¶ 5–4). The possibility of an exchangeable ammonium content of 10 or more times the upper limit of this range in some circumstances should not be overlooked. Equivalent to the value 0.1 meq per 100 gm soil, are the values 28 pp2m of NH_4^+ and 78 pp2m of K^+, and thus the percentage saturation with K^+ will generally exceed that of NH_4^+ in most soils.

APPARATUS

8–37. Needed apparatus includes a torsion balance, a 500-ml conical flask, a 11-cm Buchner funnel and suction flask, 11-cm Whatman No. 42 filter paper, a 800-ml Kjeldahl flask, and ammonia distillation apparatus.

REAGENTS

8–38. Needed reagents include 10 per cent (1.7 N) NaCl, acidified to pH 2.5 with HCl,[23] standard $\frac{N}{14}$ or $\frac{N}{56}$ H_2SO_4, 40 per cent (10 N) NaOH, N-free (¶ 8–9), methyl red-brom cresol green mixed indicator (¶ 8–10), and 4 per cent boric acid solution (¶ 8–11).

PROCEDURE

8–39. Extraction of Ammonium. A 100-gm, freshly taken soil sample is weighed out and placed in a 500-ml conical flask. (A separate moisture determination is made.) Then 200 ml of the acidified NaCl solution is added. The suspension is shaken thoroughly at first and then intermittently for 0.5 hour. Then it is poured onto the Buchner funnel on which a 11-cm Whatman No. 42 filter paper has been moistened and seated firmly by suction. Finally 250 ml more of the acidified NaCl solution is passed through the soil in increments, the first increment being used to rinse out the conical flask.

8–40. The entire leachate from 100 gm of soil is generally needed for

[21] Bower, *S.S.S.A. Proc.*, 16:119 (1951).
[22] Barshad, *Soil Sci.*, 72:361 (1951).
[23] Peech *et al.*, U.S.D.A. Cir. 747, p. 9 (1947).

the distillation determination of ammonium because of the small quantities of ammonium usually present in soil (¶ 8–36). If much less than 10 ppm of N is expected, the Nessler procedure (¶ 8–43) may be elected for greater sensitivity. Since 25 ml of 4 per cent boric acid, used to collect the ammonia, will hold the equivalent of 48 mgm of N, it will collect the NH_4 equivalent of up to 960 pp2m of N in the soil.

8–41. Determination of Ammonium. The NaCl leachate, containing 1 to 48 mgm of N, is transferred to a 800-ml Kjeldahl flask. *Caution:* the still should be scrupulously clean, conveniently insured by distilling 50 ml of distilled water through it prior to the ammonia distillation. A reagent blank is run. Also, the pH of the boric acid should be carefully adjusted to the end point. Next, 80 ml of 40 per cent NaOH is added carefully down the side of the flask so as to collect at the bottom of the flask. The ammonia is then distilled into 25 ml of 4 per cent boric acid by means of Kjeldahl still (¶ 8–22). The boric acid is back titrated with standard $\frac{N}{56}$ H_2SO_4 (or $\frac{N}{14}$, if the amount of ammonia is expected to be large).

8–42. The meq of ammonium is the product: (ml of standard acid) × (normality). The nitrogen in ammonium form, expressed as pp2m (pounds per acre) may be calculated:

$$N \text{ (pp2m)} = (T - B) \times \frac{500}{s} \qquad (\text{for } \frac{N}{56} \text{ acid})$$

$$= (T - B) \times \frac{2000}{s} \qquad (\text{for } \frac{N}{14} \text{ acid})$$

(8–9)

when

$N = $ nitrogen, in ammonium form, pp2m

$T = $ sample titration, ml standard acid, $\frac{N}{56}$ or $\frac{N}{14}$

$B = $ blank titration, ml standard acid, $\frac{N}{56}$ or $\frac{N}{14}$

$s = $ sample weight, gm

ALTERNATIVE PROCEDURES

8–43. Nessler Method for Ammonium.[24] The ammonium may be determined by means of the Nessler reagent. This reagent is prepared[25] by dissolving 45.5 gm of mercuric iodide and 35.0 gm of KI in a few ml of water:

$$HgI_2 + 2 KI \longrightarrow K_2HgI_4 \qquad (8\text{–}10)$$

[24] Peech *et al.*, U.S.D.A. Cir. 757, p. 10 (1947).
[25] Vanselow, *Ind. Eng. Chem., A.E.,* 12:516 (1940); Peech, *Soil Sci.,* 59:27 (1945).

The solution is washed into a 1-liter volumetric flask. Then, 112 gm of KOH is added and the volume is brought to about 800 ml. The solution is mixed well, cooled, and diluted to 1 liter with water. The solution is allowed to stand for a few days, and the clear supernatant liquid (Nessler's reagent) is decanted off into an amber colored bottle for use.

8–44. Other reagents needed are 10 per cent sodium tartrate (100 gm of $Na_2C_4H_4O_6 \cdot 2 H_2O$ per liter of solution), and standard NH_4Cl solution (1.337 gm of NH_4Cl in 1000 ml of water containing 1 ml of chloroform as a preservative). A dilute NH_4^+ standard, containing 0.001 meq of NH_4^+ per ml, is prepared from 20 ml of the first standard solution diluted to 500 ml.

8–45. Aliquots of 3 to 30 ml of the dilute standard are placed in a series of 100-ml volumetric flasks together with 2 ml of 10 per cent tartrate solution and the same amount of acidified NaCl solution (¶ 8–38) as will be employed in the determinations on soil extract:

$$2 K_2HgI_4 + 3 KOH + NH_3 \longrightarrow Hg_2O(NH_2I) + 7 KI + 2 H_2O$$
$$\text{(orange)} \qquad \qquad (8\text{–}11)$$

Water is added to make about 93 ml total volume. Then 5 ml of the Nessler reagent is added with rapid mixing. The solution is brought to volume, mixed, and read at the end of 25 minutes in a colorimeter with 410-mu light maximum. Transmission percentage is plotted on a log scale against concentration on a linear scale to obtain the calibration curve.

8–46. To determine the NH_4^+ in the extract, the leachate is washed into a 500-ml volumetric flask and made to volume, and the solution is mixed. Then a 50-ml aliquot is taken for Nesslerization as for the standards. A greater or lesser volume of aliquot may be taken if the NH_4^+ present is out of range of the curve. For the 50-ml aliquot:

$$NH_4^+ \text{ (meq per 100 gm soil)} = 10 \times \text{(meq } NH_4^+ \text{ from curve)}$$
$$(8\text{–}12)$$

$$N \text{ (pp2m)} = 2800 \times \text{(meq } NH_4^+ \text{ from curve)}$$
$$(8\text{–}13)$$

8–47. Equilibrium Extraction. An equilibrium extraction of exchangeable ammonium is satisfactory and more rapid. The 100-gm soil sample is placed in a liter flask. Exactly 500 ml of 10 per cent solution acidified to pH 2.5 is added, and the suspension is shaken for 30 minutes in a mechanical shaker. The solution is filtered on an 11-cm Buchner funnel into a dry suction flask. Then 400 ml of the filtrate is added to a Kjeldahl flask. A small piece of paraffin is added to prevent foaming. An excess (3 to 4 gm) of MgO is added,[26] and the ammonia is distilled into boric

[26] Harper, *Soil Sci.,* 18:409 (1924); McLean and Robinson, *J. Agri. Sci.,* 14:548 (1924); Prince, *Soil Sci.,* 59:47 (1945). The regular NaOH distillation (¶ 8–22) also may be used.

acid (¶ 8–22), followed by back titration. A correction factor of 1.25 for the aliquot taken is applied in the calculation (¶ 8–42).

NITRATE DETERMINATION
(Colorimetrically with nitrophenoldisulfonic acid[27])

8–48. Several common chemical reactions are available for the determination of soil nitrates, the most important of which is the *nitrophenoldisulfonic-yellow color method*. *Reduction of nitrate* with H_2 generated by iron filings in H_2SO_4 has been employed to include nitrate with total nitrogen (¶ 8–15); Davarda's alloy in alkaline solution has been similarly used (¶ 8–30). The *diphenylamine-blue color method* is as used in the qualitative test for nitrates in the sap of green plants (¶ 13–12). The *alpha naphthylamine-pink color method* may be employed if the nitrate is reduced to nitrite (¶ 13–22). The *brucine-blue or -yellow color methods* have been used in qualitative tests for nitrates in soils.

8–49. The phenoldisulfonic acid method for nitrates depends upon the nitration of position 6 of 2, 4-phenoldisulfonic acid in fuming H_2SO_4:

$$C_6H_3 OH(HSO_3)_2 + HNO_3 \longrightarrow C_6H_2 OH(HSO_3)_2NO_2 + H_2O$$

$$(8\text{–}14)$$

The nitrate solution is dried out previous to determination since the reaction must be effected in the virtual absence of water. The product behaves as a nitrophenolic type indicator with C–Y–Y reaction (¶ 3–40), that is, is colorless in acid and yellow when neutralized or in alkaline solution. A hydroxide such as KOH or NH_4OH is therefore employed to shift the pH to the yellow range for the colorimetric determination.

APPARATUS

8–50. Needed apparatus includes a torsion balance, a 500-ml extraction bottle and tight-fitting rubber stopper, an 18-cm filter paper and funnel, 8-cm evaporating dishes, 3 by 70 mm glass stirring rods, a 3-ml pipet with its tip cut off to deliver rapidly, volumetric pipet, colorimeter tubes with 40-ml calibration marks (or Nessler tubes), and a colorimeter with 420-mu light maximum.

REAGENTS

8–51. Needed reagents (all tested to be nitrate-free) include 6 N NH_4OH, $Ca(OH)_2$, $MgCO_3$, activated charcoal (G Elf or Darco G 60), approximately 1 N $CuSO_4$ (125 gm of $CuSO_4 \cdot 5 H_2O$ per liter), and the following special reagents.

8–52. Phenol 2, 4-Disulphonic Acid. Twenty-five gm of pure phenol (crystal white in color) is dissolved in 150 ml of concentrated H_2SO_4. Then

---

[27] Adapted for photometric determination from Harper, *Ind. Eng. Chem.,* 16:180 (1924) and Prince, *Soil Sci.,* 59:47 (1945).

75 ml of fuming H_2SO_4 is added. This solution is mixed and heated by placing the flask in boiling water for 2 hours. The resulting phenoldisulfonic acid, $C_6H_3OH(HSO_3)_2$, solution is stored in a brown bottle. *Caution: this reagent is highly corrosive.*

8–53. Standard Nitrate Solution. Exactly 0.7221 gm of pure dry KNO_3 is dissolved in water and the solution is diluted to exactly 1 liter, giving 0.1 mgm N per ml, or 100 ppm stock solution. This stock solution is then diluted, 20 ml to 200 ml in a volumetric flask. This latter solution contains 0.01 mgm N per ml, or 10 ppm. Aliquots (2, 5, 10, and 15 ml) of the 10 ppm N standard nitrate solution are placed in separate 8-cm porcelain evaporating dishes and evaporated to dryness on the steam bath in an atmosphere free from HNO_3 fumes. Color development follows (¶ 8–61).

8–54. Ag_2SO_4 Solution, to Remove Chlorides. Six gm of Ag_2SO_4 is dissolved in 1 liter of H_2O. This gives a 0.6 per cent solution.

8–55. Nitrate Extraction Solution. This is prepared by mixing 200 ml of 1 N $CuSO_4$ solution and 1 liter of 0.6 per cent Ag_2SO_4 solution (¶ 8–54) and dilution to 10 liters with H_2O. The Ag_2SO_4 is equivalent to 338 ppm Cl^- present in 50 gm soil, or 0.03 per cent Cl^-. If less than 10 ppm of Cl^- is present in soil, the Ag_2SO_4 may be omitted from the extraction solution. If more than 0.03 per cent Cl^- is present, as in saline soils, 2.25 gm of powdered Ag_2SO_4 salt for each 1 per cent Cl^- present is mixed with the soil prior to extraction; or, the Cl^- in the soil is determined and a Cl^- correction factor is established by addition of Cl^- to a standard nitrate series.

PROCEDURE

8–56. Soil Sampling and Preparation. Composite soil samples are obtained (¶ 2–7) freshly from the field or pot. The soil is mixed thoroughly by passing it through a 6-mm sieve. Clayey soils that have dried and contain hard granules are pulverized to pass a 2-mm sieve, to facilitate complete wetting of the sample by the extractant in the time allowed.

8–57. Rapid changes in the nitrate and ammonia contents of soil samples occur after removal of the samples from field or pot, because of the increased aeration and rise in temperature. It is, therefore, desirable that the extraction of nitrates and ammonium follow the collection of the samples closely. If this is not possible, nitrification and ammonification in the samples is retarded by adding 3 ml of toluene per kgm of soil and sealing and refrigerating the samples. Retardation by this means is only moderately satisfactory. If the elapsed time is to be greater than a day or two, the samples are dried at a temperature not exceeding 55°C.

8–58. Extraction of Nitrate from Soil. Fifty gm of soil (25 gm of peat) is weighed out and placed in a 500-ml, wide-mouthed bottle, and 250 ml of extraction solution is added. (At the same time, a 25-gm sample is weighed out for moisture determination.) The suspension is shaken for 10 minutes and then 0.4 gm $Ca(OH)_2$ is added. This is followed by 5 minutes further shaking and the addition of 1 gm of $MgCO_3$. These 2 reagents precipitate the copper and silver and clarify the suspension. The suspension is filtered on a dry filter paper, and the first 20 ml of filtrate discarded. A 10-ml portion of the clear filtrate[28] (25 ml if the soil nitrate nitrogen content may be less than 10 ppm) is pipetted into an 8-cm evaporating dish and evaporated to dryness in an atmosphere free of HNO_3 fumes. Color development follows (¶ 8–61).

8–59. Extraction of Nitrate from Evaporated Runoff. Samples of runoff on which nitrate is to be determined are made alkaline by the addition of 0.25 gm of $CaCO_3$ and evaporated to dryness immediately after collection. (Denitrification in runoff suspensions is not prevented by the addition of 1 ml of toluol.) To the evaporated residue from runoff, 100 ml of the extraction solution is added, and the solids are suspended by thorough agitation for 10 minutes with a rotary stirrer or an end-over-end shaker. Then 0.2 gm $Ca(OH)_2$ is added, and the shaking is continued for 5 minutes Finally, 0.5 gm of $MgCO_3$ is added, and the suspension is shaken, allowed to stand for a few minutes, and filtered on dry filter paper. The first 10 ml are discarded to rinse the apparatus and about 40 ml is collected. If this filtrate is colored[29] with organic matter, 1 gm of nitrate-free carbon black or activated charcoal (G Elf or Darco G 60) is added to the filtrate, followed by shaking and filtration.

8–60. A 20-ml aliquot of the clear filtrate is placed in an 8-cm evaporating dish, evaporated to dryness (with protection from HNO_3 fumes), and analyzed (¶ 8–61).

8–61. Development of the Nitrophenoldisulfonic Color. The 8-cm evaporating dishes are allowed to cool, and 3 ml of phenoldisulfonic acid is added rapidly directly in the center of each. The dish is rotated to effect contact with all of the residual salt, and the reagent is allowed to act for 10 minutes. Then 15 ml of cold water are added, and the solution is stirred with

---

[28] For certain acid soils that give a colored extract, the soil is allowed to settle before the addition of the $Ca(OH)_2$ and $MgCO_3$. Then about 150 ml of the supernatant liquid is decanted off. To this are added 0.2 gm of $Ca(OH)_2$ and 0.5 gm of $MgCO_3$. It is then shaken for 5 minutes and filtered on a dry filter. The first 20 ml of filtrate may be discarded.

For certain (usually alkaline) soils that give highly colored soil extracts that cannot be decolorized by this treatment of the decanted supernatant liquid, 1 gm of carbon black or activated charcoal (Darco G. 60) is added to 100 ml of the supernatant liquid, and the suspension is shaken 15 or 20 minutes before the addition of the $Ca(OH)_2$ and $MgCO_3$ to the solution. If the soil is calcareous, 5 ml of $1 N$ copper sulfate is added to the soil extract with the carbon black or charcoal to insure enough copper hydroxides to remove the colloidal carbon completely on filtration.

[29] Although organic matter that may color the filtrate can be removed by treatment with 30 per cent H_2O_2, the treatment tends to result in an off color in the final nitrate solution, and therefore is not recommended.

a glass rod until all the residue is in solution. After the dishes are cool, 6 N NH$_4$OH is added slowly until the solution is distinctly alkaline as indicated by the development of a yellow color, then 3 ml more is added. This solution is then diluted to volume with water. The standard series is diluted to 100 ml and contains 0.2, 0.5, 1, and 1.5 ppm of nitrate nitrogen. Soils extract is usually diluted to 100 ml. Runoff nitrate is conveniently diluted to 40 ml in calibrated tubes.

8–62. The transmission percentage of the nitrate solutions is read in a colorimeter with 420-mu light maximum. Alternately, the color may be evaluated by visual comparison to the standard solution by means of Nessler tubes (¶ 8–65).

8–63. Preparation of Standard Colorimetric Curve. A calibration curve is plotted from the standard nitrates on semilogarithmic paper, the log scale being employed for the transmission percentage readings. This curve is usually not exactly linear, and thus it is best to refer to the graph to determine nitrate concentration in the test sample.

8–64. Calculation of Results. The results are reported in parts of N (nitrate form) per million parts of oven-dry soil. The concentration of the nitrate test solution as ppm N is obtained from the standard curve. Then the calculation is as follows:

$$\text{ppm N in soil} = \text{ppm N in test solution} \times \text{Aliquot dilution} \times \text{Soil dilution}$$
$$\small \text{(nitrate form)} \qquad\qquad \text{(from curve)}$$

$$(8\text{–}15)$$

$$= \text{ppm N in test solution} \times \frac{\genfrac{}{}{0pt}{}{\text{ml final}}{\text{color volume}}}{\genfrac{}{}{0pt}{}{\text{ml aliquot}}{\text{evaporated}}} \times \frac{\genfrac{}{}{0pt}{}{\text{ml extraction}}{\text{solution}}}{\genfrac{}{}{0pt}{}{\text{gm O.D. soil}}{\text{extracted}}}$$

$$= \text{ppm N in test solution} \times \frac{100}{10} \times \frac{250 + \text{ml H}_2\text{O}}{50 - \text{ml H}_2\text{O}}$$

The dilution of the extracting solution by the soil moisture present in the original moist sample is taken into account in equation (8–15) as (+) and (−) ml H$_2$O. In this way the results are based on the oven-dry weight of the soil.

8–65. For visual comparison in Nessler tubes:

$$\text{ppm N in test solution} = \frac{\text{ml standard solution}}{\text{ml test solution matched by standard}}$$
$$\times \text{ppm N in standard solution} \qquad (8\text{–}16)$$

Then computations are continued (eq. 8–15).

8–66. For runoff, the nitrate content is expressed as parts N per million parts of original runoff suspension and also per million parts solids in the runoff. The quantity of N removed per unit area of field from which the runoff was collected is calculated:

$$\begin{matrix} \text{ppm N in} \\ \text{original} \\ \text{runoff} \\ \text{suspension} \end{matrix} = \begin{matrix} \text{ppm N} \\ \text{from} \\ \text{working} \\ \text{curve} \end{matrix}$$

$$\times \frac{\begin{matrix} \text{ml final} \\ \text{analytical solution} \end{matrix}}{\begin{matrix} \text{ml extracting so-} \\ \text{lution analyzed} \end{matrix}} \times \frac{\begin{matrix} \text{ml extracting} \\ \text{solution} \end{matrix}}{\begin{matrix} \text{ml runoff} \\ \text{evaporated} \end{matrix}} \qquad (8\text{–}17)$$

The runoff from each tank is sometimes evaporated separately. The composite nitrate analysis is calculated by proportion of each runoff suspension needed to form a composite. Then:

$$\underset{\text{(nitrate-N)}}{\text{ppai}} = \text{ppm N in composite runoff} \times 0.227 \qquad (8\text{–}18)$$

This value is next corrected by factors for dilution of runoff by rain and for the volume of the runoff occupied by solids (¶ 10–68, 10–69). Finally, the nitrate concentration on a solid basis is:

$$\text{pp2ms} = \frac{\text{ppai, nitrate-N in runoff}}{\text{ppai, solids in runoff}} \times 2,000,000 \qquad (8\text{–}19)$$

NITRITE DETERMINATION

8–67. Nitrites accumulate in soils that are above a critical pH value of 7.7 ± 0.1.[30] Thus, in somewhat alkaline soils that have been fertilized heavily with ammonium fertilizers, nitrites may accumulate instead of nitrates and in similar amounts,[31] up to almost 100 ppm. Otherwise, the accumulation of nitrites is generally so neglible that they can scarcely be detected.

8–68. No formal procedure is given here for nitrite determination. In principle, the nitrite is extracted from soils by the same water extraction employed for nitrate. In practice it is difficult to obtain a clear, colorless extract without oxidation of some of the nitrite. The standard procedure for its chemical determination is that employing sulfanilic acid and alpha-naphthylamine.[32] The nitrite standard is prepared from $AgNO_3$ and $NaNO_2$, from which $AgNO_2$ is prepared.

---

[30] Martin *et al.*, *S.S.S.A. Proc.*, 7:223 (1942).

[31] Chapman and Liebig, *S.S.S.A. Proc.*, 16:276 (1952).

[32] Prince, *Soil Sci.*, 59:50 (1945); Fraps and Sterges, *Tex. Agr. Exp. Sta. Bul. 439* (1931); Rider and Mellon, *Ind. Eng. Chem., A.E.*, 18:96 (1946). An alternative procedure has also been proposed by Shinn, *Ind. Eng. Chem., A.E.*, 13:33 (1941).

NITRIFICATION RATE OF SOILS

8–69. The nitrification rate of a soil is a measure of the rate of release of available nitrogen by the organic matter in the soil. The nitrogen in nitrate form is released by microbiological activity (a) from fresh organic residues from crops and (b) from soil organic matter. Fresh organic matter, if succulent and with a relatively low C : N ratio, releases nitrate more rapidly than does dry carbonaceous material that may depress nitrate release temporarily. Nitrate release from soil organic matter may be less rapid but continues over a longer period, with as much as 10 per cent of the total N being converted to the nitrate form. This determination assumes that the NH_4^+ formed in the decomposition of organic matter is converted to NO_3^-, so that the NO_3^- formed is a measure of both processes.[33] The actual rate of nitrification may be higher under conditions of nearly complete nitrate removal by a crop than under conditions of accumlation as nitrate. The measurement of nitrification in the field is not meaningful unless the amount of nitrate used by the crop and lost by leaching is accounted for. When incubated under optimum conditions, the accumulation of nitrogen in nitrate form may go to 100 pp2m in 6 weeks and exceed 200 pp2m in 4 months.

APPARATUS

8–70. Sampling tube or spade, 6-mm (4 meshes per inch) sieve, a sample container, a knife or scissors, a torsion balance with capacity of at least 3 kgm, a 2-liter crock, a mixing table, a paper towel for the crock cover, string or rubber bands.

REAGENTS

8–71. Reagents needed include only those for NO_3^- determination (¶ 8–51).

PROCEDURE

8–72. Field Sampling. The soil samples are obtained by one of two methods: (a) For bare soil, random cores are taken well distributed over the area (¶ 2–7), to a depth of the plow-layer, and (b) to obtain a representative sample of the tops and roots of vegetation such as grass, clover, or small grain, the vegetation is tramped down flat on the ground, a slanting hole is dug to the plow-layer depth with a sharp flat spade, and a thin slice (1 cm) of the vegetation and soil is taken to obtain a representative sample. Several random samples are composited.

---

[33] Russel *et al.*, *Soil Sci.*, 19:381 (1925).

8–73. Mixing and Potting. As soon as possible after the field sampling, the samples are mixed thoroughly by being passed through a 6-mm sieve. Any plant material present is cut up into small pieces so that a uniform mixture can be made. The soil (in 4 replications) is filled into a weighed crock to within an inch of the top, and the crock and contents are weighed. The soil moisture percentage is determined on a 25-gm sample taken at the time of filling the crock. Sufficient water is added to the soil in the crock to bring it to approximately 0.7 or 0.8 of field-moisture capacity. At the time of potting, soil nitrate and total N are determined.

8–74. Incubation and Sampling. The crock is covered with a paper towel secured by a rubber band or string, and stored at a constant temperature of 28° to 30°C. Water is added to the soil in the crocks twice weekly to maintain the moisture level, the surface crust being pulverized by hand before watering. Weekly mixing of the soil provides aeration, which is an important factor affecting the rate at which nitrification takes place. At the end of the first week, the soil is removed, broken up, and mixed thoroughly. Care is taken not to lose any soil or to contaminate it. The crock is jarred to settle the soil, and water is added to the required weight. If the soil is watered 2 or 3 days before sampling, it can be mixed more easily and a more uniform sample can be taken for the NO_3^- determinations. At the end of the second week, the above mixing procedure is repeated, and 50 gm of soil is removed for NO_3^- determination (¶ 8–58) and 25 gm for moisture determination. The new constant weight is recorded.

QUESTIONS

1. What forms of nitrogen in the soil are determined by the Kjeldahl method?

2. What is the role of the HgO in the catalyst mixture?

3. How is the complete liberation of nitrogen insured without undue danger of nitrogen loss in the Kjeldahl digestion process?

4. How is the digestion temperature controlled?

5. What are the advantages of the disposal of fumes in water to the sewer as compared to disposal in air by means of a fume chimney?

6. How is the Kjeldahl procedure for soils and plant tissue modified to include nitrates in the determination?

7. Why is the NaOH added so that it runs down to form a layer on the bottom of the flask just prior to the distillation?

8. In the exchangeable ammonium or nitrate determinations, what precautions must be observed in handling the sample prior to the extraction process?

9. Why is it not satisfactory to distill off the NH_3 directly by treatment of the soil with hot alkali?

10. How is NH_4^+ held in the soil, and how can it be extracted?

11. What is the usual range of NH_4^+ concentration in soils?

12. What is the purpose of each of the following in the extraction of soil nitrates: $CuSO_4$, Ag_2SO_4, $Ca(OH)_2$, and $MgCO_3$?

13. Why is the aliquot of the extract evaporated to dryness in the nitrate test, and what is the action of phenoldisulfonic acid on the residue?

14. What is the role of the NH_4OH in the nitrate procedure?

15. Why is it important to include a representative amount of vegetation in soil samples to be used for nitrification rate determinations?

Organic Matter Determinations for Soils

Organic matter . . . a distinction of soil from rock

9–1. Carbon occurs in soils in 4 forms of mineral and organic matter:

1. Carbonate mineral forms, chiefly $CaCO_3$ and $MgCO_3 \cdot CaCO_3$ (¶ 10–121); but highly active and important small amounts also occur as CO_2, and HCO_3^- and CO_3^{--} ions of more soluble salts (¶ 10–87).

2. Highly condensed, nearly elemental organic carbon (charcoal, graphite, coal).

3. Altered and rather resistant organic residues of plants, animals, and microorganisms, sometimes termed "humus" or "humate," but not, as these latter terms tend to suggest, a single compound.

4. Little altered organic residues of plants and animals, and living and dead microorganisms, subject to rather rapid decomposition in soils.

9–2. The total carbon of soils obviously includes all 4 forms. Total *organic* carbon includes the latter 3, the mineral form being eliminated by treatment with dilute reducing acid prior to the organic carbon determination. The most *reproducible* soil organic carbon determination is one that includes all 3 forms of organic carbon without any attempt at fractionation. The chemically active organic matter that is related to soil genesis and fertility includes forms 3 and 4. Some effort is sometimes made, therefore, to exclude 2, the carbon in highly condensed form, from soil organic matter determinations. Also, a distinction may be made between the older, more resistant organic matter which is the *humus* proper, 3, and the freshly added *organic residues,* 4, which are subject to rapid decomposition and release of their nutrient elements to the current crop (¶ 9–73). Although fractionation, or distinction between forms of soil organic matter, involves loss in reproducibility of measurement, when perfected, it may promote more *significant* interpretations of the analyses.

9–3. Total Organic Carbon of Soils. Organic carbon determination is carried out (after removal of carbonate) by (a) dry combustion in a furnace (¶ 9–9), or (b) by chromic acid oxidation (¶ 9–21), followed by measurement of the CO_2 evolved. The CO_2 evolved may be measured by volume, weight, or titration. The organic carbon content of soil may be reported directly as percentage of C; or calculated as organic matter by multiplication by a factor. The conventional carbon to organic matter factor of long standing is 1.724, based on the assumption that soil organic matter is 58 per cent C. This factor is sometimes referred to as the "Van Bemmelen factor," although it is of older origin. Russel and Engel[1] state that ". . . organic matter calculated by multiplying carbon content by the conventional factor 1.724 agrees closely with the direct determination by means of hydrogen peroxide, individual discrepancies being within the range of experimental error. . . ." Several other studies on the factor have been reported.[2] The factor for a conversion of the carbon content of many surface soils to organic content has been found[3] to be 1.9, and the factor for many subsoils is about 2.5. The variation in the carbon to organic matter ratio makes it desirable to report the *organic* content rather than the *carbon* content for comparisons between different horizons or between dissimilar soils. Comparisons of organic carbon content as such may be satisfactory for comparisons between similar soil horizons.

9–4. Oxidizable Soil Organic Matter Determination. The oxidizable matter of soils is determined by (a) chromic acid oxidation with heat applied (¶ 9–33), or (b) by chromic acid oxidation with spontaneous heating (¶ 9–57). It can be carried out without prior carbonate removal because the CO_2 evolved is not measured. The meq of chromic acid reduced may be measured by titration or by the green color formed. The meq may be related to the total carbon or the total organic matter by calibration with other methods. Oxidizable matter determination by chromic acid methods is the most rapid and popular type of analysis and has the advantage of moderately satisfactory discrimination of humus from highly condensed forms including graphite and charcoal. The determination of oxidizable matter is often termed the determination of "organic carbon"; however, since the highly condensed forms of organic carbon are excluded, the term "oxidizable matter" should be given preference. The total organic carbon thus would be reserved for those methods (¶ 9–3) that do in fact measure all forms of organic carbon without a correlation factor. Oxidizable matter

---

[1] *Proc. 1st Intern. Congr. Soil Sci.,* 4:343 (1928).

[2] Leighty and Shorey, *Soil Sci.,* 30:257 (1930); Lunt, *Soil Sci.,* 32:27 (1931); and Wilson and Staker, *J. Am. Soc. Agron.,* 24:477 (1932).

[3] Broadbent, *Adv. Agron.,* 5:176 (1953).

can be reported conveniently as the meq of oxidizable matter per 100 gm of soil. Conversion factors from oxidizable matter to carbon and organic matter are often employed, and greatly facilitate comparison with the contents of these constituents in various soils. The use of carbon to organic matter factors other than conventional 1.724 factor (¶ 9–3) would not influence the net results of the chromic acid methods, because it would merely change the assumed percentage recovery of organic matter, leaving the over-all factor for conversion of titer to organic carbon or organic matter the same.

9–5. Total Soil Organic Matter by Weight Loss. The total organic matter content of soils is determined by (a) oxidation with H_2O_2 (¶ 9–74), (b) ignition at moderate temperatures (¶ 9–85), or (c) ignition after decomposition of silicates with HF-HCl (¶ 9–86). Distinction between the determination, by these methods, of organic *matter* and organic *carbon* (¶ 9–3) is based on the fact that the total organic matter weight is measured by the former, while only that of carbon is represented by the latter. Serious errors enter into the various weight-loss methods for measuring the organic matter weight because other constituents—such as salts including CO_2 of carbonates, H_2O, and OH (¶ 9–85)—also influence the weight change. Also, the organic matter may not be completely oxidized.

9–6. Other Estimates of Soil Organic Matter. Soil organic matter has been shown to correlate (a) with total nitrogen content, (b) with climate, and (c) with clay content. Multiplication of the total nitrogen content of soil by 20 roughly approximates the organic matter content. This assumes 5 per cent N in the organic matter of a C : N ratio of 11.6 since the organic matter is conventionally assumed to contain 58 per cent carbon (¶ 9–3). The estimation of soil organic *matter* from the nitrogen content may be as accurate as from the carbon content.[4] Likewise, a correlation of organic matter with the climate[5] and with the clay content of the soils of a given region has been suggested by some investigators.

9–7. Determination of the specific compounds, organic structure, and functional groups of organic matter in soils is a soil chemical analysis field in itself. Organic exchange capacity (¶ 4–19), carboxyl, phenolic, acetyl, methoxy, and other functional properties can be measured. Specific molecular species carrying phosphate, such as phytin and inositol monophosphate, have been isolated. Solubility classes include fats and waxes, carbohydrates, lignins, and proteins. Alcohol, acetyl bromide, alkali, and pyrophosphate dissolution techniques—coupled with acid and other types of precipitation —give information on undecomposed plant residues, black pigment, brown pigment, and other *humus* fractions.

---

[4] Read and Ridgell, *Soil Sci.*, 13:1 (1922).
[5] Jenny, *Soil Sci.*, 27:169 (1929).

9–8. The age of organic matter in soils can be determined[6] up to about 50,000 years through the natural tagging of CO_2 of the air with C^{14} formed by cosmic ray neutron bombardment of N^{14}. Turnover of organic *matter* added to soils similarly can be studied by radiochemically tagged carbon of CO_2 photosynthetically incorporated in plants.

ORGANIC CARBON DETERMINATION AS CO_2

(Dry combustion by Fisher induction carbon apparatus)

9–9. The organic carbon of soil is determined after the removal (¶ 9-14) or separate determination (¶ 10–121) of carbonate, the subsequent ignition of the soil in a furnace, and the determination of the CO_2 evolved by a gravimetric or titrimetric method. Robinson[7] employed oxygen to sweep the CO_2 from the silica combustion tube, the latter being heated with a multiple-unit electric furnace. The dry combustion method includes elemental carbon such as in charcoal, graphite, or coal (¶ 9–1).

9–10. The ignition in the Fisher induction carbon apparatus is carried out in a stream of purified oxygen, and the gases released are purified so that only CO_2 is measured. The purification of the oxygen includes absorption of water vapor in $Mg(ClO_4)_2$, and of CO_2 in an adsorbant. The oxygen stream containing the gases released by combustion of the sample is passed through a colloidal MnO_2 absorption bulb to remove SO_2 and other absorbable gases, and through $Mg(ClO_4)_2$ again to remove water vapor. A platinum oxidizer converts any CO remaining to CO_2. The CO_2 is then collected. No special provision is made other than the colloidal MnO_2 for the absorption of compounds of chlorine, nitrogen, or other acidic compounds released, but no difficulty has been experienced with nonsaline of soils of widely variable carbon content.[8] Zinc, silver, $CaCl_2$ and H_2SO_4 absorbants have been employed.[9] Concordant results by a variety of dry combustion methods were found by the Organic Carbon Committee of the International Society of Soil Science.[10]

APPARATUS

9–11. Needed apparatus includes the Fisher induction carbon apparatus (Fig. 9–1) equipped with gas train tubes, CO_2 absorption bulb (Nesbitt gravimetric type) filled with "Caroxite" absorbant, special alundum ("Combax") combustion boats and sleeve, and an analytical balance.

---

[6] Libby, *Radiocarbon Dating* (Chicago: University of Chicago Press, 1952).
[7] U.S.D.A. Cir. 139 (1930).
[8] Jackson, *S.S.S.A. Proc.*, 16:370 (1952).
[9] Piper, *Soil and Plant Analysis* (New York: Interscience Publishers, Inc., 1944), p. 219.
[10] *Trans. 3rd Intern. Congr. Soil Sci.*, 1:114, 3:82 (1935).

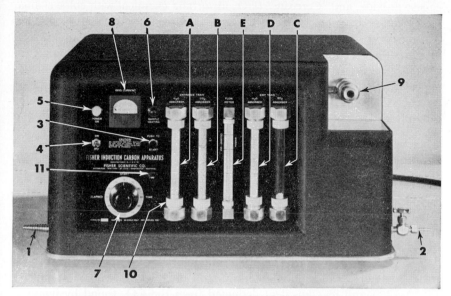

Fig. 9–1. Fisher Induction Carbon Apparatus. The sample in a combustion boat is placed in a combustion tube at 9 and oxygen is passed into 1 and out at 2, sweeping the CO_2 along. Other features are explained in Fig. 9–2 and the text.

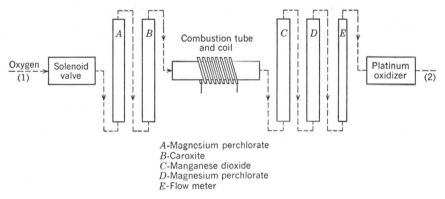

A-Magnesium perchlorate
B-Caroxite
C-Manganese dioxide
D-Magnesium perchlorate
E-Flow meter

Fig. 9–2. Schematic diagram of gas train of Fisher Induction Carbon Apparatus. Letters and numbers also refer to Fig. 9–1.

(Complete apparatus is available from Fisher Scientific Co., Pittsburgh, Pa.) If carbonates are to be removed by SO_2, 50-ml beakers and capillary aspirator tubes are required.

REAGENTS

9–12. Needed reagents include tank oxygen; the three absorbants (¶ 9–10), including granular magnesium perchlorate, a special grade of manganese dioxide, and "Caroxite" (CO_2 absorbing chemical with color change to indicate exhaustion); electrolytic iron powder; granulated tin, passing 0.5 mm sieve (30 meshes per inch); and alundum, passing 0.2-mm sieve (90 mesh per inch). (All reagents are available from Fisher Scientific Co., Pittsburgh, Pa.) A mixture is prepared, 50 per cent each by weight, of the granular tin and electrolytic iron powder; 0.5 gm of the mixture is required for each determination. If carbonates are to be removed by SO_2, tank SO_2 is required.

PROCEDURE[11]

9–13. The soil sample is air-dried, ground to pass a 0.2-mm sieve (80 meshes per inch), and thoroughly mixed. Samples containing the chloride equivalent of 1 per cent NaCl or more are preleached to prevent positive interference. Such interference is not prevented by the inclusion of Ag_2SO_4-H_2SO_4-saturated pumice or silver wool in the train. The preleaching can be combined with the carbonate removal procedure that follows.

9–14. Removal of Carbonate. If carbonate is present, either it must be removed prior to the ignition, or its amount must be determined separately (¶ 10–121) and its equivalent deducted from the CO_2 found by ignition. Carbonate can be removed readily without oxidizing the organic matter by treating the soil with sulfurous acid.

9–15. A soil sample equivalent to 2-gm or more of carbonate-free material is placed in a 50-ml beaker, 15 ml of water is added, and then SO_2 gas is bubbled through the suspension with a capillary tube until all carbonates are destroyed. The reaction may be hastened by warming the suspension slightly. The reaction is allowed to proceed over night. Then the soil is dried at 100°C and thoroughly mixed, and the sample for the determination is weighed out. In the presence of high amounts of MnO_2, the addition of $FeCl_2$ aids in the prevention of oxidation of any organic matter.

9–16. Combustion. The alundum boat is lined with granular alundum until it is half filled. Then approximately 0.5 gm of powdered electrolytic iron is spread evenly over the alundum. The soil sample (0.2727 gm for samples containing over 5 per cent carbon; 1.364 gm for samples containing less than 5 per cent carbon) is thoroughly mixed with approximately 0.5 gm of a 50-50 mixture of granular tin and electrolytic iron powder combustion accelerator (¶ 9–12). The mixture is transferred quantitatively to the bed of electrolytic iron in the boat. The sample with the accelerator is then covered with an additional 0.5 gm (approximate) of electrolytic iron powder. The boat and sleeve are positioned in the induction carbon apparatus with the special tool provided.

9–17. The apparatus is fired according to the directions supplied with

---

[11] Results with this procedure have been published by the author, *S.S.S.A. Proc.*, 16:370 (1952).

the instrument, and the CO_2 is collected and weighed in the weighing tube. Each 10 mgm of CO_2 collected equals 1 per cent C for a sample weighing 0.2727 gm; each 50 mgm of CO_2 collected equals 1 per cent C for a sample weighing 1.364 gm.

9–18. Each ignition cycle with a Fisher induction carbon apparatus re-, quires 2 minutes. With rapid weighing conveniences such as the "Gram-atic" balance, the complete carbon determination for a soil sample can be effected within 3 minutes.

ALTERNATIVE PROCEDURES

9–19. The CO_2 may also be collected in standard alkali and titrated (¶ 9–28).

9–20. The Lindberg high frequency combustion apparatus has been employed[12] for the carbon in steel, and could undoubtedly be adapted for carbon in soils. The CO_2 was measured gasometrically in a buret, the walls of which were treated with a silicone to hasten volumetric equilibrium.

ORGANIC CARBON DETERMINATION AS CO_2

(Wet oxidation by chromic acid and determination by titration)

9–21. The soil organic matter may be wet oxidized by chromic acid and the CO_2 collected for determination as in the dry combustion method. The wet-oxidation method to be described differs from the chromic acid methods (¶ 9–49, 9–65) for the determination of oxidizable matter in soils; the CO_2 is measured in the present method, whereas the amount of chromic ion reduced is measured in the methods for oxidizable matter. Though the results may be shown to be highly correlated with each other, the deter-minations are quite different in principle.

9–22. The carbonate carbon must be excluded with the wet-oxidation method just as for the dry combustion method, by separate determination (¶ 10–121) or expulsion by means of sulfurous acid (¶ 9–14).

9–23. Although gravimetric and titrimetric determination of the CO_2 are both appropriate for either the dry combustion or wet-oxidation pro-cedures, the titrimetric determination is employed with the procedure given here.

APPARATUS

9–24. Needed apparatus includes a small gas burner and wind shield, a 25-ml pipet, a buret, and a special apparatus (Fig. 9–3). The sample flask is a 200-ml conical flask fitted with a 3-hole stopper. The condenser tip is drawn out and a hole is blown in the side to permit free passage of the gases without interference from condensation at the tip. The U-tube has glass beads on the bottom, a layer of glass wool on each side, and 20-mesh pumice filling each arm. The pumice in the left arm is saturated with

---

[12] Pepkowitz and Chebiniak, *Anal. Chem.,* 24:889 (1952).

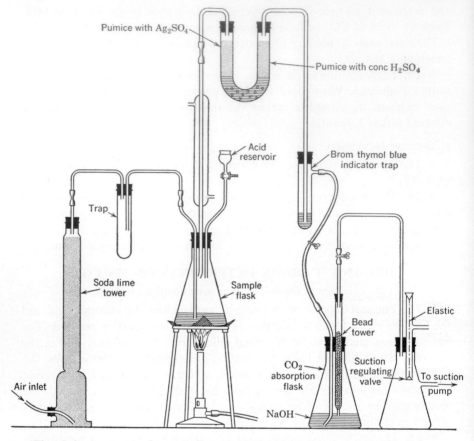

Fig. 9–3. Apparatus for organic matter determination by wet-oxidation procedure and titrimetric determination of the CO_2 evolved. (After Heck, *Soil Sci.,* 28:225, 1929.)

concentrated Ag_2SO_4, and in the right arm with freshly boiled, concentrated H_2SO_4. The brom thymol blue trap is a side arm test tube. The bead tower is constructed of a 2×25 cm test tube, the bottom of which is drawn out and the sides pinched to hold the beads away from the bottom opening. The beads are 4 to 6 mm in diameter. A little glycerol is applied to the outside of the bead tower to facilitate raising and lowering it. The soda lime (or Ascarite) tower admits CO_2-free air to the apparatus.

REAGENTS

9–25. Required reagents include standard 0.5 N HCl, 1 per cent alcoholic phenolphthalein indicator, 0.04 per cent brom thymol blue indicator (1 ml of this in 10 ml of water in the trap, Fig. 9–3), CO_2-free water, approximately 0.5 N NaOH (20 gm per liter), approximately 1 M $BaCl_2$

(244 gm of $BaCl_2 \cdot 2 H_2O$ per liter of CO_2-free water), and the following special digestion acids.

9–26. Chromic Acid. Approximately 340 gm of chromic oxide, CrO_3, is dissolved in 400 ml of hot water and made to a volume of 1 liter with 85 per cent H_3PO_4.

9–27. Sulfuric Phosphoric Acid. Equal volumes of concentrated H_2SO_4 and 85 per cent H_3PO_4 are mixed together and stored in a glass-stoppered bottle.

PROCEDURE[13]

9–28. A 1-gm sample of 0.2-mm soil is weighed out and transferred to the sample flask, after pretreatment with sulfurous acid (¶ 9–14) if carbonates are present. (If the organic matter content is between 4 and 20 per cent, a 0.5 gm sample is employed. A 0.2-gm sample of muck and peat is employed.) The sample flask is then attached to the apparatus. To free the train of CO_2, a flow of CO_2-free air is sent through for 1 or 2 minutes longer than required for the brom thymol blue in the trap to turn from yellow to blue. Then 25 ml of approximately 0.5 N NaOH is pipetted into the CO_2 absorption flask followed by 50 ml of CO_2-free water. The condenser cooling water is next started. While the air flow continues, the bead tower is lowered into the NaOH until the solution reaches the top of the beads, and then raised so that no more NaOH solution enters. The air flow is regulated to about 3 to 5 bubbles per second.

9–29. Next, 10 ml of the chromic acid solution is added through the separatory funnel, followed by 50 ml of the H_2SO_4-H_3PO_4 mixture. A small flame with a wind shield is placed under the sample flask, and the suspension is brought to boiling as rapidly as is possible without danger of frothing over. The boiling is continued for 5 minutes longer than required for the brom thymol blue in the trap to change from yellow to blue.

9–30. Back Titration. The clamp on the suction side of the CO_2 absorption flask is closed and the flask is detached. The NaOH is washed from the bead tower and entrance tube with CO_2-free water. Next, 15 ml of 1 M $BaCl_2$ solution is added to precipitate the carbonate. The excess NaOH is then back titrated with standard 0.5 N HCl, 3 drops of 1 per cent phenolphthalein indicator being employed. A standardization blank is made to measure the NaOH concentration.

9–31. Calculation of Results. Since the carbonate is all precipitated as $BaCO_3$ the net titration is as follows:

$$NaOH + HCl \longrightarrow NaCl + H_2O \qquad (9-1)$$

---

[13] Heck, *Soil Sci.*, 28:225 (1929); Friedemann and Kendall, *J. Biol. Chem.*, 82:45 (1929); White and Holben, *Ind. Eng. Chem.*, 17:83 (1925). Robinson, U.S.D.A. Cir. 139 (1939), employed this titration procedure in combination with ignition to liberate the CO_2.

The CO_2 evolved may be calculated to its equivalent value as follows:

$$\text{meq of } CO_2 = (S - T) \times N \qquad (9\text{-}2)$$

in which S is the standardization blank titration of 25 ml of NaOH, T is the back titration, and N refers to the normality of the standard HCl.

$$\% \text{ organic C} = \text{meq } CO_2 \times \frac{0.6}{s} \qquad (9\text{-}3)$$

in which s is the sample weight in gm and the factor 0.6 is the meq weight $(12/2000) \times 100$.

ALTERNATIVE PROCEDURE

9–32. The CO_2 may be passed through a $Mg(ClO_4)_2$ bulb to remove water vapor and then may be collected in a gravimetric absorption bulb and weighed instead of being titrated.

OXIDATION MATTER BY CHROMIC ACID WITH EXTERNAL HEAT APPLIED

(Schollenberger)

9–33. To avoid the laboriousness of conventional carbon determination methods involving ignition, collection of CO_2, and weighing, various rapid approximate methods of determining organic matter in soils have been developed. These methods involve the oxidation of the organic matter by an oxidizing agent added to the soil in excess, and the subsequent titration or colorimetric determination of the excess oxidizing agent.

9–34. In the Schollenberger[14] method, oxidizable matter in soil is oxidized by chromic acid in the presence of excess H_2SO_4, with external heat applied, the excess of standard chromic acid being back titrated with ferrous solution. This is a rapid method for approximating the organic matter content, since a linear relationship between the titer and organic content can be established for a given procedure. Moreover, the arbitrary measurement of "oxidizable" material, expressed as meq per gm soil, has a direct interpretation of its own, without regard to total organic content, as a measure of the active organic content of soil. By these methods, carbon from carbonate does not interfere, and also the various forms of elemental carbon (graphite, charcoal, coal, etc.) are only attacked in part and thus are mainly excluded from the measurement. In this regard, Allison[15] gave an example that indicated discrimination between organic matter of soil and the carbon in the form of cinders and coal by his modification of the Schollenberger procedure. The Walkley-Black method which involves less heating has been shown (¶ 9–58) to give almost complete discrimination.

---

14 Schollenberger, *Soil Sci.*, 24:65 (1927).
15 *Soil Sci.*, 40:311 (1935).

9–35. The following consideration of the effect of chloride, manganese dioxide, and ferrous iron applied equally to the Schollenberger and the Walkley-Black (¶ 9–57) chromic acid procedures.

9–36. Effect of Chloride. The reaction of $Cr_2O_7^{--}$ with Cl^-:

$$Cr_2O_7^{--} + 6\,Cl^- + 14\,H^+ \longrightarrow 2\,Cr^{+++} + 3\,Cl_2 + 7\,H_2O$$

$$(9-4)$$

is quantitative, thus permitting an accurate use of an approximate chloride factor[16] of $1/12$ (from eq. 9–6 below, $C/4Cl^- = 12/4 \times 35.5$) as follows:

$$\text{Soil C content in } \% = \text{Uncorrected soil C content in } \%$$
$$- \frac{\text{Soil Cl content in } \%}{12} \qquad (9-5)$$

The correction factor has been found to be valid up to a $Cl : C$ ratio of $5 : 1$.

9–37. Alternatively, the chloride may be leached out[17] on an asbestos filter and the asbestos and sample together placed in the determination. The oxidation of Cl^- can be prevented by the use of Ag_2SO_4 in the digestion mixture. HgO and $HgSO_4$ have also been found effective.

9–38. Effect of Higher Oxides of Manganese. Although the presence of active higher oxides of manganese causes an error in the chromate titer of the soil, inactive higher manganese oxides such as occur in ores cause no interference. Ordinarily the content of higher oxides of manganese in soils will cause no interference. However, any possible interference of highly reactive (as freshly precipitated higher oxides of manganese) can be nullified by preliminary treatment of the soil with $FeSO_4$. Such active oxides react rapidly in the cold with acidified N $FeSO_4$, and their amount can be determined by preliminary titration.[18] Two ml of H_3PO_4, 5 ml of water, and 1 ml of diphenylamine indicator are added to the soil followed by sufficient N $FeSO_4$ to give an excess as judged by the color of the indicator (5 ml usually suffices). The mixture is allowed to stand with occasional agitation for 10 minutes, and then the excess $FeSO_4$ is back titrated with $K_2Cr_2O_7$. The amount of $FeSO_4$ oxidized by the MnO_2, as determined by this titration, is then added to the fresh soil sample together with 2 ml of H_3PO_4. The mixture is allowed to stand about 5 minutes, whereupon most of the MnO_2 will have been dissolved and what remains may be neglected. The $K_2Cr_2O_4$ solution is then added, and the digestion of soil organic matter is carried out by the usual procedure.

9–39. The use of H_2O_2 by Degtjareff[19] in his modification would cause

---

[16] Walkley, *J. Agr. Sci.*, 25:398 (1935); *Soil Sci.*, 63:257 (1947).
[17] Schollenberger, *Soil Sci.*, 59: 53 (1945).
[18] Walkley, *Soil Sci.*, 63:257 (1947).
[19] *Soil Sci.*, 29:239 (1930).

the decomposition of the MnO_2 but would still involve the quantitative error.

9–40. Effect of Ferrous Iron. Ferrous iron in soils, if present, leads to high results for the chromic acid titer of soil organic matter.[20] However, soil samples that have been air-dried for 1 or 2 days contain insignificant amounts of soluble ferrous compounds, even though the ferrous had been high in the fresh sample. Thus no interference with the organic matter determination is caused by the ferrous iron.

9–41. Use of an iron or steel mortar is avoided because of the introduction of reducing material in the form of metallic iron.

9–42. The Chromic Oxidation Equivalent of Soil Organic Matter. The reactions of dichromic acid with soil organic matter may be represented, separately with organic carbon and organic hydrogen, as follows:

$$4 \, Cr^{6+} + 3 \, C^\circ \underset{(acid)}{\longrightarrow} 4 \, Cr^{+++} + 3 \, C^{4+} \qquad (9\text{--}6)$$

$$2 \, H_2Cr_2O_7 + 3 \, C^\circ + 6 \, H_2SO_4 \longrightarrow 2 \, Cr_2(SO_4)_3 + 3 \, CO_2 + 8 \, H_2O \qquad (9\text{--}7)$$

$$2 \, H_2Cr_2O_7 + 3 \, H^\circ_4 + 6 \, H_2SO_4 \longrightarrow 2 \, Cr_2(SO_4)_3 + 14 \, H_2O \qquad (9\text{--}8)$$

The H and O content of the organic matter is ordinarily not considered in the stoichiometric relationships. However, in methane, CH_4, the organic H would require (eq. 9–8) as much dichromic acid as would the carbon. As the carbon chain length increases, the H drops to the ratio 2H : C; in phenolic compounds, to H : C. Iso-linked carbon compounds have still less hydrogen present. The oxygen in groups attached to the organic matter complex, R, lowers the dichromate titer that would be required by the carbon:

$$RCOOH \underset{(acid)}{\longrightarrow} RH + CO_2 \qquad (9\text{--}9)$$

Thus the presence of organic oxygen tends to counterbalance the effect of organic hydrogen in the titration. Also, some of the carbon may not be oxidized.

9–43. These various compensating factors apparently summate to give 74 to 100 per cent of a 4-electron change equivalent for each carbon. A report[21] that the CO_2 evolved by wet oxidation with chromic acid correspond closely with the quantity of reduction of chromic acid, suggest a near balance of organic oxygen and hydrogen effects. External heat was applied, so the procedure is similar to that of Schollenberger. An oxidation factor[22] of 90 per cent approximates the results of the dry combustion method; 84

---

[20] Walkley, *Soil Sci.*, 63:257 (1947).
[21] Aldrich *et al.*, *Soil Sci.*, 59:299 (1945).
[22] Schollenberger, *Soil Sci.*, 59:53 (1945).

to 91 per cent oxidation factors were found for a number of soils in this laboratory by the procedure described here (¶ 9–49).

APPARATUS

9–44. Needed apparatus includes an electric hot plate with adjustable temperature; 250-ml and 400-ml beakers; 30×200 mm Pyrex test tubes; a 2-liter Pyrex beaker (bath); a 1-liter shallow Pyrex tray (bath); a thermometer, 0° to 250°C; a torsion balance, ±0.05 gm; a capillary tube stirrer and compressed air supply; stirring rods with ends flattened; volumetric pipets; and a 50-ml buret.

REAGENTS

9–45. Needed reagents include 85 per cent H_3PO_4, both for the baths and as a reagent, and the following special reagents.

9–46. Standard 0.4 N Chromic Acid Solution. Exactly 19.61 gm $K_2Cr_2O_7$ (oven-dry) is dissolved in about 50 ml of water and then the solution is diluted to one liter with concentrated H_2SO_4.

9–47. Ferrous Ammonium Sulfate Solution, 0.2 N. Exactly 78.44 gm of $Fe(NH_4)_2(SO_4)_2 \cdot 6 H_2O$ is dissolved in 300 ml of water containing 20 ml of concentrated H_2SO_4, and the solution is diluted to 1 liter with water. This solution is made freshly, or titrated against the standard chromic acid each day.

9–48. Orthophenanthroline Indicator. 0.025 M solution ("Ferroin" from G. F. Smith Chemical Co., Columbus, Ohio).

PROCEDURE[23]

9–49. The Soil Sample. The soil sample is ground to pass a 0.2-mm (80 meshes per inch) sieve and 0.25 gm of mineral soil (0.05 gm of peat, 1.00 gm of soil having less than 1 per cent organic matter) is placed into a 250-ml beaker (or 30×200 mm test tube).

9–50. The Runoff Sample. If the beaker in which the runoff was dried (¶ 10–71) contains more than 1 gm of solids, they are transferred from the beaker, ground to pass the 0.2-mm (80 meshes per inch) sieve, and a 0.25 gm sample (more if the organic matter content is less than 2 per cent) is weighed out into a 250-ml beaker or 30×200 ml test tube. Eight test tubes can be digested simultaneously in the H_3PO_4 bath in a 2-liter beaker.

9–51. If the beaker containing the dried runoff (¶ 10–72) contains less than 1 gm, the entire residue is analyzed directly in the 250-ml beaker, the shallow Pyrex tray with H_3PO_4 being employed for the heating bath.

---

[23] The procedures given are modified from Schollenberger, *Soil Sci.*, 24:65 (1927), 59:53 (1945); Allison, *Soil Sci.*, 40:311 (1935); Wilde and Patzer, *J. Am. Soc. Agron.*, 32:551 (1940). Dr. H. F. Massey studied the heating rate and bath procedures with soils of standard organic carbon contents.

9–52. Oxidation of Organic Matter. From a pipet, 20 ml of 0.4 N chromic acid solution (50 ml for peats) is added to the soil sample in the 250-ml beaker or test tube, and a similar quantity is taken for the standardization blank. The vessel with mixture is placed in the H_3PO_4 bath and heated on an electric hot plate at such a rate that a temperature of 155°C is reached in 20 to 25 minutes.[24] The contents of the tube or beaker are mixed every 5 minutes during the heating period. The temperature is held at 155° to 160°C for an additional 5 minutes. The thermometer is kept in the blank, which is simultaneously heated, to follow the solution temperature.

9–53. The vessels with samples and blank are then removed from the bath, are allowed to drain in air for 30 seconds, and are then placed in a water bath at room temperature for 2 minutes. The thermometer is removed with care not to break it by thermal shock.

9–54. Back Titration. The chromic acid solution, now cooled to room temperature, is diluted with water to 75 to 200 ml, either in the tube or 250-ml beaker. Then 5 ml of 85 per cent H_3PO_4 and 4 drops of ortho-phenanthroline indicator are added. The solution is back titrated with the 0.2 N ferrous ammonium sulfate until the solution color turns from green to red at the end point. An air-jet stirrer is used with the tubes. The color at the start is dark brownish, and then shifts sharply from blue to red at the end point. The blank is similarly titrated. More chromic acid should be added to fresh samples if the amount added proves to be inadequate; not over one-half of the chromic acid should be consumed by oxidation of the organic matter.

9–55. Calculation of Results for Soils. The percentage of organic matter in soil is estimated as follows:

$$\% \text{ OM (in soil)} = 20(1 - \frac{T}{S}) \times 0.92 \qquad (9\text{–}10)$$

S = Standardization blank titration, ml of approximately 0.2 N ferrous solution

T = sample titration, ml of approximately 0.2 N ferrous solution

0.92 is an empirical factor derived as a product:

$$(0.4\ N) \times \frac{12}{4000} \times \frac{1.724}{0.90} \times \frac{100}{0.25} = 0.92$$

when 0.4 N is the normality of the chromic acid and 0.25 is the sample weight in gm. In deriving the factor, it is assumed a 4 valence change of carbon occurs, 58 per cent carbon occurs in soil organic matter, only carbon

---

[24] Heating the chromic acid in an electric oven has been described by Purvis and Higson, *Ind. Eng. Chem., A.E.,* 11:19 (1939).

is oxidized, and only 90 per cent of the total soil organic matter is oxidized, the assumed figures being somewhat arbitrary.

9–56. Calculation of Results for Runoff. The percentage of organic matter in the runoff solids is calculated as for soils, as percentages of organic matter, the appropriate sample weight being inserted in equation 9–10. Then the pounds of organic matter per acre inch of runoff is calculated from this percentage and the pounds of solids per acre inch (¶ 10–73).

OXIDIZABLE MATTER BY CHROMIC ACID WITH H_2SO_4 HEAT OF DILUTION

(Walkley-Black)

9–57. The chromic acid method based on spontaneous heating by dilution of H_2SO_4 (Walkley-Black method) involves essentially the same procedure as that of Schollenberger (¶ 9–49) except that the heating is less than that externally supplied. For this reason, somewhat less of the total organic matter is oxidized, and this is held by some workers to be an advantage, since the less active organic matter is not measured.

9–58. Exclusion of Elementary Carbon. The lesser heating largely differentiates soil humus matter from extraneous sources of organic carbon such as graphite and charcoal, a distinct advantage. While dry combustion methods include all of the elementary carbon, the Walkley-Black method excludes 90 to 95 per cent of it.[25] Oxidation of flake graphite stopped at the graphite oxide stage as indicated by its typical swelling reaction when warmed while moistened with water. The method of Tiurin,[26] involving greater oxidation intensity, gave 84 per cent recovery of charcoal, according to Walkley.

9–59. The effects of chloride, manganese dioxide, and ferrous iron on the chromic acid titration methods are discussed in ¶ 9–36 to 9–41.

APPARATUS

9–60. Needed apparatus includes 500-ml conical flasks, pipets of 10-ml and 20-ml volume and preferably self-adjusting to zero, a buret for the ferrous solution, and an analytical balance. A storage vessel to prevent oxidation of ferrous iron is a convenience and may be arranged to keep hydrogen or CO_2 over the solution. For convenience, the chromate solution is employed as the standard of reference and the ferrous concentration is determined only in ratio to the chromic acid.

REAGENTS

9–61. Required reagents include 85 per cent H_3PO_4, solid NaF, concentrated H_2SO_4 not less than 96 per cent, and the following special reagents.

[25] Walkley, *Soil Sci.*, 63:251 (1947).
[26] *Pedology*, 26:36 (1931); *Trans. Dokuchaev Soil Inst.* (U.S.S.R.), 10:27 (1934).

9–62. Standard 1 N K$_2$Cr$_2$O$_7$. Exactly 49.04 gm of K$_2$Cr$_2$O$_7$ is dissolved in water, and the solution is diluted to 1 liter.

9–63. Diphenylamine Indicator. Approximately 0.5 gm of reagent grade diphenylamine is dissolved in 20 ml of water and 100 ml of concentrated H$_2$SO$_4$.

9–64. Ferrous Solution. The ferrous concentration may be made standard and preserved or made approximate and the chromate used as the standard of reference. A 0.5 N solution of ferrous is prepared by dissolution of 196.1 gm of Fe(NH$_4$)$_2$(SO$_4$)$_2$ · 6 H$_2$O in 800 ml of water containing 20 ml of concentrated H$_2$SO$_4$ and dilution to 1 liter. Walkley[27] employed 278.0 gm of FeSO$_4$ · 7 H$_2$O per liter with 15 ml of concentrated H$_2$SO$_4$, a 1 N solution.

PROCEDURE[28]

9–65. Pretreatment to eliminate readily oxidizable MnO$_2$ (¶ 9–38) is given if needed.

9–66. Oxidation of Organic Matter. The 0.5-gm soil sample (0.05 gm for peat; 2.00 gm for soils less than 1 per cent organic matter), having passed a 0.2-mm (80 meshes per inch) nonferrous sieve, is placed in a 500-ml conical flask. Next, exactly 10 ml of 1 N K$_2$Cr$_2$O$_7$ solution is pipetted onto the soil, and the 2 are mixed by swirling the flask. Then 20 ml of concentrated H$_2$SO$_4$ is added and mixed by gentle rotation for 1 minute, to insure complete contact of the reagent with the soil, with care to avoid throwing soil up onto the sides of the flask out of contact with the reagent. The mixture is allowed to stand 20 to 30 minutes. A standardization blank (without soil) is run in the same way.

9–67. Back Titration. The solution is diluted to 200 ml with water, and 10 ml 85 per cent H$_3$PO$_4$, 0.2 gm NaF, and 30 drops of diphenylamine indicator are added. The solution is back titrated with ferrous ammonium sulfate solution delivered from a buret. The color is dull green with chromous ion at the beginning, then shifts to a turbid blue as the titration proceeds. At the end point, this color sharply shifts to a brilliant green, giving a 1-drop end point. If over 8 of the 10 ml of chromic acid has been consumed, the determination is repeated with a smaller soil sample.

9–68. Calculation of Results. The results are calculated by the equation:

$$\% \text{ OM} = 10(1 - \frac{T}{S}) \times 1.34 \qquad (9\text{–}11)$$

S = standardization blank titration, ml ferrous solution

T = sample titration, ml ferrous solution

---

27 Walkley, *Soil Sci.,* 63:251 (1947).

28 After Walkley and Black, *Soil Sci.,* 37:29 (1934); Walkley, *J. Agr. Sci.,* 25:598 (1935); *Soil Sci.,* 63:251 (1947).

The factor 1.34 is derived as follows:

$$(1.0\ N) \times \frac{12}{4000} \times \frac{1.72}{0.77} \times \frac{100}{0.5} = 1.34$$

in which 0.5 is the sample weight, 1.72, the factor for organic matter from carbon, and 12/4000, the meq weight of carbon. The 77 per cent recovery factor found by Walkley[29] is used; a recovery factor of 74 per cent had been suggested by Smith and Weldon[30] for Nebraska soils. Good correlation of the Walkley-Black method with the dry combustion method was obtained for Florida soils when the 77 per cent recovery factor was employed.[31]

9–69. If the results are expressed in terms of readily oxidizable organic matter, the recovery factor (1/0.77) is omitted, thus giving:

$$\% \text{ OM (readily oxidizable)} = 10(1 - \frac{T}{S}) \times 1.03 \qquad (9\text{–}12)$$

The readily oxidizable organic matter may be calculated by the equation:

$$\text{meq per 100 gm} = 10(1 - \frac{T}{S}) \times \frac{100}{s} \qquad (9\text{–}13)$$

wherein s is the sample weight.

9–70. The correction for chloride (¶ 9–36 and eq. 9–5) is applied if Cl^- is present.

ALTERNATIVE PROCEDURES

9–71. Colorimetric Chromic Acid Procedures. The quantity of chromic acid reduced by the soil organic matter has been measured colorimetrically instead of titrated.[32] The soil is filtered off[33] after dilution with water, and the green chromous color is measured with a photoelectric colorimeter and a light maximum of 645 mu. Under these conditions the amount of chromate added need not be measured accurately. The change in the orange chromic color may be measured instead, but that procedure is not as satisfactory from several standpoints. The color changes may be approximated visually[34] as a rapid test of soil organic matter (orange color—low, green color—high).

9–72. Permanganate Use in the Titration. The Walkley-Black procedure was slightly modified[35] by addition of an excess of ferrous solution to the chromic acid after the digestion, then back titrating the ferrous with stand-

[29] Walkley, *Soil Sci.,* 63:251 (1947).
[30] *S.S.S.A. Proc.,* 5:177 (1941).
[31] Dyal and Drosdoff, *Proc. Soil Sci. Soc. Fla.,* 3:91 (1941).
[32] Graham, *Soil Sci.,* 65:181 (1948).
[33] Carolan, *Soil Sci.,* 66:241 (1948).
[34] Wilde, *S.S.S.A. Proc.,* 7:393 (1943).
[35] Smith and Weldon, *S.S.S.A. Proc.,* 5:177 (1941).

ard $KMnO_4$. So long as the same volume of ferrous and dichromate are added to the blank and to the determination, no solution need to be standardized except the $KMnO_4$. This method was further extended[36] to smaller samples consisting of 0.1 to 0.3 gm of soil.

9–73. Readily Oxidizable Organic Matter Fractions of Soils. Oxidation of the more readily available organic matter (¶ 9–2) by means of a more dilute chromic acid solution or more dilute H_2SO_4 has been considered as a means of measuring the readily oxidizable organic matter that is possibly related to current crop production. However, the content of fresh organic matter may not be correlated with its supplying power for available nitrogen, if it has a high carbon : nitrogen ratio. Thus the content of readily available organic matter might be correlated with an adverse effect on crop production. Even the measurements of ammonium ion released through the action of mild oxidants is a difficult method to calibrate to measure the effect of fresh organic matter on nitrogen supplying power.

TOTAL ORGANIC MATTER BY H_2O_2 OXIDATION AND WEIGHT LOSS[37]

9–74. Decomposition of organic matter by treatment with 30 per cent H_2O_2 is effected at temperatures below 110°C, and total organic matter is estimated gravimetrically by the weight loss. This low temperature permits the retention of the hydroxyl and strongly sorbed water in the mineral colloids. Thus the determination of organic matter is more accurate than can be achieved by ignition temperatures high enough to oxidize the organic matter thermally, because H_2O and OH are also lost by the latter procedure (¶ 9–85).

9–75. Elemental carbon and resistant, paraffin-like organic material is not attacked by the H_2O_2 (¶ 9–2). To some extent structural (nonhumified) organic matter is not attacked, especially if the H_2O_2 is more dilute than 6 per cent. Up to 16 per cent of the original carbon content has been found[38] in the residues from the H_2O_2 method. In this respect, the H_2O_2 method is comparable to the chromic acid methods for oxidizable matter.

9–76. The free MnO_2 present in soil is changed by the procedure to Mn^{++} and finally to Mn_3O_4. The $CaCO_3$ is decomposed with acid, the soil being brought to pH 5.8 or less to increase the effectiveness of the organic matter oxidation with H_2O_2. The carbonates are formed again at the end of the procedure.

---

[36] Chesnin, *Agron. Jour.,* 42:385 (1950).

[37] After procedure of Robinson, *J. Agr. Res.,* 34:339 (1927), as modified by J. C. Russel and described by Judd and Weldon, *J. Am. Soc. Agron.,* 31:217 (1939).

[38] Alexander and Byers, U.S.D.A. Tech. Bul. 317 (1932).

9–77. Needed apparatus consists of tall-form 250-ml Pyrex beakers and closely fitting cover glasses; a gas or electric hot plate; 100-ml centrifuge tubes and centrifuge; 75-ml platinum or rhotanium dishes; an analytical balance and counterpoised scoop; a 110°C oven; and a series of 50-ml glass-stopped weighing bottles, numbered in ascending order of weights, arranged so the odd numbered bottle of each pair is slightly lighter. The even numbered bottles are dried and weighed to the nearest mgm.

REAGENTS

9–78. Needed reagents consist of 0.1 N HCl; 30 per cent H_2O_2, reagent grade, residue free, in wax-lined bottles; 10 per cent $(NH_4)_2CO_3$ prepared by dissolving 10 gm of reagent grade salt in 100 ml of water. The latter solution is filtered if not entirely clear; 10 ml should not leave a weighable residue after evaporation to dryness and heating in an oven at 110°C.

PROCEDURE

9–79. The Samples. A system of weighing is employed that minimizes systematic errors, number of calculations, and time. Two successive 2-gm samples of air-dry soil having been passed through a 0.15 mm (100 mesh per inch) screen are weighed out on a counterpoised scoop and transferred to 2 paired weighing bottles that have stood open to weight-equilibrium in air. (For soils containing over 5 per cent organic matter, a 1-gm sample is employed. A 0.2-gm sample of peat or other organic material is employed.) The bottles are tightly stoppered as filled. When the series of samples has been weighed out, the pair of bottles containing samples of 1 soil is placed on the balance, the odd numbered on the right pan, and the other on the left. The difference in their weights is then determined to the fourth decimal. The even-numbered bottle is set aside for the time and the sample from the odd-numbered bottle is transferred to a 250-ml tall-form beaker, a little water being employed to rinse out traces of soil. The weighing bottle is set aside.

9–80. Acidification of the Sample and Removal of Carbonates. Ten ml of water is added to the soil and then 4 ml of 0.1 N HCl. If the soil is calcareous, 4 additional ml of 0.1 N HCl is added for each 1 per cent of $CaCO_3$ present. The suspension is stirred to facilitate reaction, and finally is warmed on the hot plate for an hour. A drop of *salt-free* brom cresol green indicator is added, which should remain yellow or green, indicating acidity greater than pH 5.8 (BCG is blue at pH 5.8 and above). If the indicator turns blue, additional 0.1 N HCl is added and digestion is continued until the pH remains below 5.8. The sample is then slightly acid and carbonate-free, ready for organic matter oxidation.

9–81. Oxidation of Organic Matter. To the 250-ml tall-form beaker containing the slightly acid soil suspension, 10 ml of 30 per cent H_2O_2 is added, the beaker is covered with a tightly fitting watch glass, and the suspension is digested on a gas or electric hot plate that is carefully regulated to avoid frothing over of the sample. From time to time the suspension is mixed by rotation of the beaker. After all the peroxide is decomposed, and the solution has evaporated to a volume of approximately 5 ml (beaker uncovered briefly if necessary), 5 ml additional 30 per cent H_2O_2 is added to rinse down the sides of the beaker. The digestion is continued until all peroxide is decomposed. Oxidation is usually complete at this point, but further additions of H_2O_2 may be required for complete oxidation of the organic matter of some soils.

9–82. After digestion is complete, the cover glass is scrubbed with a policeman and rinsed into the beaker. The contents of the beaker are transferred to a 100-ml centrifuge tube into which 5 ml of the 10 per cent $(NH_4)_2CO_3$ solution has been previously placed, a policeman being used to complete the transfer. The beaker is covered and set aside to be used again, to receive the soluble salts from the sample. Finally the suspension in the tube is mixed with a strong jet of water, and the tube is set aside for the soil to flocculate. The $(NH_4)_2CO_3$ serves also to reconvert the $CaCl_2$ and $MgCl_2$ formed by the HCl treatment back to $CaCO_3$; each 5 ml is equivalent to 25 per cent $CaCO_3$ in the soil. After flocculation has occurred, the suspension is centrifuged until the supernatant liquid is entirely clear. This clear liquid is decanted into the original beaker in which the soil was digested, and saved for the procedure in the next paragraph. Two additional washings are given the residue by resuspending with a water jet, adding 5 ml of 10 per cent $(NH_4)_2CO_3$, flocculating, centrifuging, and decanting it into the beaker. Finally it is resuspended with a jet of water, and quantitatively rinsed into the respective original weighing bottle with the aid of a policeman. With care and a fine water jet, the transfer can be made with 1 filling of the weighing bottle. The weighing bottle and contents are placed in the oven, the liquid evaporated to dryness, and the bottle and cover finally placed beside the companion bottle (even-numbered) containing the moisture sample. Drying at $110°C$ is continued for 8 hours or over night. The pair of weighing bottles is cooled in the same desiccator and the difference in their weights is determined (even-numbered bottle on left pan as before) to the nearest 0.1 mgm. The odd-numbered bottle is removed and the other bottle and contents weighed to the nearest 1 mgm. The net oven-dry weight is determined by subtracting the weight of the weighing bottle.

9–83. To determine the weight of the soluble salts removed from the sample, a series of platinum or rhotanium dishes is weighed, cooled in a desiccator, and weighed again to the nearest 0.1 mgm. Then the supernatant solution from the beakers is transferred to the dishes, evaporated to dryness, and ignited at 550°C (medium red) in a muffle furnace for a few minutes. The soluble salts are thus dried, excess NH_4Cl is removed (formed from the HCl treatment), and the solublized soil organic matter volatized. The dishes are cooled in a desiccator and weighed, and the weight of the ignited residue is calculated.

9–84. Calculation of Results. The weight of organic matter is calculated as follows:

$$\text{Weight of organic matter} = \frac{\text{Final weight difference}}{\text{in weigh bottles}} - \frac{\text{Initial weight difference}}{\text{in weigh bottles}} - \frac{\text{Ignited residue}}{\text{in dish}}$$
$$(9\text{–}14)$$

$$\% \text{ Organic matter} = \frac{(\text{weight of organic matter}) \times 100}{(\text{oven dry sample weight})} \quad (9\text{–}15)$$

ALTERNATIVE PROCEDURES

9–85. Ignition at Low Temperature. A procedure for the oxidation of organic matter at moderate temperature is described by Mitchell.[39] Discrimination of organic matter loss from weight loss of H_2O and OH is based on selection of temperature ranges: the H_2O is driven off at 110°C; the organic matter is oxidized by heating at 350° to 400°C for 7 to 8 hours; and the mineral matter is assumed to be unchanged at these temperatures. Unfortunately, the discrimination between organic and mineral matter is far from complete, particularly for soils containing amorphous materials.

9–86. HF-HCl Pretreatment. A proposal was made by Rather[40] to decompose the hydrous silicates prior to heating to oxidize the organic matter, and thus to eliminate the heating weight loss due to water and hydroxyl. The silicate is decomposed by HF-HCl treatment and the residue is then weighed. The organic matter is driven off by heat, and the weight loss in the absence of H_2O and OH effects is noted. Complete preservation of the organic matter while the silicate is being decomposed presents a problem, and loss of some organic matter during the process of washing out the salts presents another. The method, while requiring much time, is worthy of consideration for some purposes. Alexander and Byers[41] give a modified Rather procedure, but consider it long and tedious. Gottlieb and Hendricks[42] employed the Rather procedure for extraction of organic matter for comparison to that extracted with NaOH.

---

[39] *J. Am. Soc. Agron.,* 24:256 (1932).
[40] *Ark. Exp. Sta. Bul.* 140 (1917).
[41] U.S.D.A. Tech. Bul. 317 (1932).
[42] *S.S.S.A. Proc.,* 10:117 (1946).

QUESTIONS

1. List the 4 general forms in which carbon may occur in soils.

2. State representative ratios of carbon to organic matter of soils.

3. What is the ratio of organic matter to nitrogen in the more resistant stabilized portion of the organic colloids of soils?

4. How is carbonate excluded from the determination of organic carbon of soils?

5. Why is the determination of soil organic carbon as CO_2 by means of the dry combustion method or the wet oxidation method a fairly reproducible determination?

6. What methods are available for the determination of CO_2 evolved from the soil organic carbon?

7. Why is it more proper to speak of the chromic acid methods as determinations of "oxidizable matter" rather than as methods for organic carbon determination? In what sense are they estimates of total organic carbon?

8. What are the percentages of recovery of total organic carbon for (a) the chromic acid method in which external heat is applied, and (b) the chromic acid method in which no external heat is applied?

9. Why is it possible to employ a ferrous solution of a concentration not known exactly in the back titration of the chromic acid?

10. Why may the hydrogen peroxide method be termed a direct determination of soil organic matter as distinguished from the CO_2 measurement methods?

11. What principles are applied in the ignition loss method for organic matter to distinguish the organic from H_2O and OH constituents? To what extent is it successful?

10

Soluble Salt Analysis for Soils and Waters

The salt of the earth
—FROM AN OLD PROVERB

10–1. All fertile soils have at least small amounts of soluble salts in them. The exchangeable cations equilibrate with the H_2CO_3 dissolved in soil moisture, yielding soluble carbonates and bicarbonates of the metallic cations and leaving the corresponding amount of hydrogen ion on the exchange. Traces to 100 ppm or more of nitrogen occur as nitrate salts in soils. Natural waters from rivers, lakes, and wells contain varying amounts of dissolved salts. Runoff waters from soil carry soluble salts as well as suspended solids. Lysimeter leachates contain dissolved salts. The accumulation of soil salts in larger amounts is mainly through influx of seepage, runoff, and irrigation waters, followed by concentration by evapotranspiration. Varying amounts arise from the processes of nitrification, sulfofication, acidification, and fertilization.

10–2. Soil Salinity. When a soil contains an excess of soluble salts, it is termed a *saline* soil. Sometimes it is called a "white alkali" soil because of the white saline crust that sometimes appears on drying. Occurrence of soil salinity problems fall into 2 main classes:

1. Natural occurrence of excess salts in soil, in the absence of adequate drainage, usually in semiarid or arid regions,[1] but also through marine waters or sediments even in humid and tropical areas.

---

[1] The salt problem in irrigation agriculture is reviewed by Richards, ed., *Diagnosis and Improvement of Saline and Alkali Soils,* U.S.D.A. Agr. Handb. 60 (1954); and by Hayward and Magistad, U.S.D.A. Misc. Publ. 607 (1946).

2. Occurrence of excess salts in soil as a result of fertilization, troublesome in highly fertilized greenhouse soils[2] and in fertilizer bands. This situation occurs frequently, even in humid soil regions, and includes the problem of salt *index* of fertilizers.

10–3. Soluble salt analysis for soils and waters generally concerns whether enough salt is present to cause interference with normal seed germination, plant growth, or plant intake of water. The determination of the actual amount of each ionic species in the soil salts is also important in the interpretation of the extent of their interference with plant function. Besides the determination of both concentration and composition of salts in the soil solution and natural waters, soluble salt analysis includes the analysis of salt crusts and salt deposits such as $CaSO_4 \cdot 2 H_2O$ (gypsum) and $CaCO_3$ (calcite) in the soil profile.

10–4. Water soluble salts occurring in soils in total amounts of over 0.1 per cent usually consist principally of the four cations Na^+, K^+, Ca^{++}, and Mg^{++}, linked mainly to Cl^- and SO_4^{--}, sometimes to NO_3^- and CO_3^{--}, and to a limited extent to HCO_3^-. Usually 98 per cent of the soluble salts of saline soils consist of these ions. Soil salinity problems[3] frequently arise from Na^+, Cl^-, SO_4^{--} but seldom from Ca^{++}, Mg^{++}, or CO_3^{--}. Chlorosis is sometimes associated with high HCO_3^- concentration coupled with high pH (¶ 10–5). Toxicity to plants of borate ion even in small amounts is important in irrigation waters and in saline soils. The ions Mn^{++} and Al^{+++} are also toxic to plants if present in soil as soluble salts at more than quite low concentrations.

10–5. Soil Alkalinity. Associated with the occurrence of salinity or its aftermath is the occurrence of soil *alkalinity,* which in general is evidenced by sufficiently high soil pH to turn phenolphthalein pink or red (pH 8.3 to 10 or 11). This range is frequently associated with a high percentage (15 to 85 per cent or more) of exchange saturation with Na in soils.[4] The percentage of exchange saturation with Na is called the *degree of alkalization* (¶ 4–44). Poor permeability of the soil to water (under 1 cm/hr) frequently develops in association with over 15 per cent of Na saturation when the salinity is low. The poor permeability often persists as a detriment to productivity after the alkalinity has dropped to near neutral and even after the percentage Na saturation has been decreased. Saline and alkaline soils taken collectively are often termed *alkali soils,*[5] although this meaning of the term "alkali" is not entirely acceptable in a chemical sense. A dis-

---

[2] A problem in 20 per cent of the greenhouse soils examined by Merkle and Dunkle, *J. Am. Soc. Agron.,* 36:10 (1940).

[3] Scofield, *Soils and Men,* U.S.D.A. Yearbook, p. 712 (1938).

[4] Fireman and Reeve, *S.S.S.A. Proc.,* 13:494 (1949).

[5] Kelley, *Alkali Soils* (New York: Reinhold Publishing Corporation, 1951); Richards, *op. cit.,* p. 5.

persive effect on the soil, somewhat like that of Na saturation, is thought[6] to result from Mg saturation in excess of 30 per cent.

DIRECT SEMIQUANTITATIVE TEST FOR SOIL SALINITY— CONDUCTOMETRICALLY ON SOIL PASTE

10–6. A semiquantitative estimate of the salt content of a soil, by the electrical resistance of the soil paste, may be made by means of the salt bridge. The soil paste method gives a fair semiquantitative approximation except for soils low in salts but high in exchangeable Na.[7] Appreciable variations occur[8] in resistance found with different soils having the same percentage of salts. Soils at the saturation moisture percentage gave conductances 0.5 to 4.8 times the conductance of the corresponding extracted solutions.[9] Nonetheless, the approximate measurement of the salt content by soil paste resistance is simple and rapid, and has been found to be extremely useful in field work, such as soil surveys,[10] where wide variance in soil salt content occurs in short distances. The soil paste-salt bridge technique has been indispensable for the survey and reclamation of soils of arid regions.

APPARATUS

10–7. Needed apparatus includes a thermometer and salt bridge. A standard soil paste "salt bridge" apparatus, consisting of an A.C. potentiometer with standard Bureau of Soils hard rubber soil resistance cup is suitable. Also, a standard conductance meter (¶ 10–21) and separate soil resistance cup (Fig. 10–1) are suitable. The ohm resistance range needed is from about 10 to 10,000. The principles of resistance or conductance measurements are presented in ¶ 10–22.

REAGENTS

10–8. Needed are distilled water, 1 per cent phenolphthalein indicator solution, and carefully collected and representative soils samples, the soluble salt content of which are to be determined.

PROCEDURE

10–9. The soil sample is sieved through 6-mm screen (0.25 inch) and thoroughly mixed on a rubberized sheet. Pebbles and large root fragments are discarded. The rubber resistance cup is filled about half full of distilled

---

[6] Gill and Sherman, *Pac. Sci.,* 6:137 (1952); Smith *et al., Soil Sci.,* 68:451 (1949).

[7] Richards, U.S.D.A. Agr. Handb. 60, p. 16 (1954).

[8] Magistad *et al., Soil Sci.,* 59:70 (1945).

[9] Reitemeier and Wilcox, *Soil Sci.,* 61:281 (1946).

[10] Davis and Bryan, U.S.D.A. Bur. Soils Bul. 61 (1910); Kellogg, U.S.D.A. Misc. Pub. 274, p. 123 (1937); U.S.D.A. Agr. Handb. 18, p. 343 (1951).

Fig. 10–1. Standard Bureau of Soils soil resistance cup. (Photo courtesy Industrial Instruments, Inc., Jersey City 5, N.J.)

water (or somewhat less if the soil is rather moist, and somewhat more if the soil is dry and of very fine texture). The soil is added with stirring until the paste is wet enough to glisten on the surface, but thick enough so that no free water stands on the surface. The cup is tapped to remove air bubbles. The top of the soil is struck off to leave the cup just level full, and the cup (clean externally) is placed between the spring clips of the salt bridge. The soil-water mixture may be made in a beaker and transferred to the cup. The mixture is equilibrated for a period of 20 minutes.

10–10. The knife switch of the "salt bridge" is set in the "out" position (the "in" position places an extra resistance of 100 ohms in series with the soil cup). Then the coil resistance knob is turned to 10, the phone placed to the ear and the button depressed. An electronic eye replaces the buzzer in some bridges. If a buzzing is heard, the dial resistance knob is turned back and forth until the point of minimum sound is located. If such a position cannot be found, the coil resistance knob is turned to 100 and the dial resistance knob again turned back and forth to the position where the sound is the faintest. An adjustment of the soil resistance to the 1000 factor may be necessary to get a minimum with the knob. When the minimum point sound is found, the dial reading is observed and multiplied by the setting of the coil resistance factor 10, 100, or 1000 as the case may be. The product is the ohms resistance in the cup. For example, if the dial reading is 1.45 and the coil resistance factor is 100, the cup resistance is 145 ohms.

10–11. Soils containing large amounts of soluble salts may have a resistance below the range of the dial. To obtain the resistance of these soils, the knife switch is thrown to the "in" position to throw 100 ohms in series with the soil cup, and the dial is adjusted to minimum sound. From the product obtained as in the preceding paragraph, 100 is subtracted. The 100 ohms resistance controlled by the knife switch is also used to test the bridge, and when in the "in" position should balance the 100 ohm bridge setting when the cup contacts are short circuited with a buss bar.

10–12. Temperature Correction. The temperature of the soil suspension is measured and corrected to 15.8°C (60°F), which is the conventional temperature for soil paste resistance comparisons. Each degree centigrade away from 15.8°C represents a 2.49 per cent resistance change[11] (1.38 per cent per degree F away from 60°F). The resistance (R) corrections may be made by fairly tedious calculations from tables,[12] or more conveniently (and with fewer arithmetical steps), by the formula,

$$R_{15.8}°C = R_T(T - 15.8) \times 0.0249 + R_T \qquad (10\text{--}1)$$

in which R_T refers to observed resistance at $T°C$. The approximation is to within ± 2 per cent of table values from 0° to 33°C (32° to 92°F) and within ± 5 per cent up to 40°C.

10–13. The specific conductance of the soil paste is $0.25/R$ wherein 0.25 is the constant for the Bureau of Soils cup, and R is the resistance of the soil paste in ohms. The ratio of electrical conductance of the saturation extract (mmho/cm) to the electrical conductance of the soil paste in the standard cup was found[13] to be 2.71 for some muck soils and a silty clay loam.

10–14. Interpretation of Resistance of Soil Paste in Terms of Salt Content. The soil paste resistance values corrected to 15.8°C (60°F) are interpreted in terms of salt content as percentage by weight of the soil, by means of the chloride and sulfate column of Table 10–1. These data were based on average saline soils encountered in the field, for which the soluble salt contents were determined by extraction and weighing (¶ 10–17). The data

---

[11] Derived graphically from table values of Whitney and Means, U.S.D.A. Div. of Soils, Bul. 8 (1897).

[12] Whitney and Means, U.S.D.A. Div. of Soils, Bul. 8 (1897); Davis and Bryan, U.S.D.A. Bur. Soils Bul. 61 (1910); or Kellogg, U.S.D.A. Misc. Pub. 274, p. 123 (1937); U.S.D.A. Agr. Handb. 18, p. 343 (1951).

[13] Campbell and Richards, *Agron. Jour.*, 42:582 (1950).

of Davis and Bryan (Tables 10–1 and 10–2) agree well with those of Whitson and King.[14] Salt contents as parts per 100,000 (as they are sometimes expressed) may be obtained by multiplying by 1000. A soil having a salt content of less than 0.1 per cent is considered nonsaline except for the more sandy soils (¶ 10–35). A higher percentage ranging up to 0.3 per cent is the upper limit for nonsaline clay soils (¶ 10–42). The salt content of water or soil solutions may be estimated by the determination of the resistance when the soil cup is filled with it (Table 10–2).

TABLE 10–1

Approximate amounts of salts in soils of various textures with given electrical resistance of soil paste in standard soil cup*

| Resistance of soil paste at 15.8°C (60°F), in ohms | Percentage salt content of soils containing salts consisting | | | | | | | |
| | predominantly of chlorides and sulfates | | | | in part of sodium carbonate (turn phenolphthalein pink) | | | |
	Sand	Loam	Clay loam	Clay	Sand	Loam	Clay loam	Clay
18	3.0	3.0	...	...	...	...	...	...
19	2.4	2.6	3.0	...	...	...	...	...
20	2.2	2.4	2.8	3.0	...	...	...	...
25	1.5	1.7	1.9	2.2	2.9	3.0	3.0	...
30	1.2	1.3	1.4	1.6	2.1	2.2	2.2	3.0
35	1.0	1.1	1.2	1.3	1.6	1.9	1.9	2.6
40	0.86	0.94	1.0	1.1	1.4	1.7	1.7	2.3
50	0.67	0.71	0.77	0.86	1.3	1.4	1.4	1.9
60	0.55	0.58	0.63	0.70	0.87	1.2	1.2	1.6
70	0.48	0.50	0.53	0.59	0.74	0.98	1.0	1.4
80	0.42	0.44	0.47	0.51	0.64	0.86	0.90	1.2
90	0.37	0.39	0.41	0.45	0.56	0.77	0.82	1.1
100	0.33	0.35	0.37	0.39	0.51	0.69	0.75	0.97
120	0.27	0.28	0.29	0.32	0.43	0.57	0.64	0.79
140	0.22	0.23	0.24	0.26	0.38	0.49	0.55	0.66
160	0.20	0.20	0.21	0.22	0.34	0.43	0.49	0.56
180	...	...	...	...	0.31	0.38	0.44	0.49
200	...	...	...	...	0.29	0.34	0.40	0.43
240	...	...	...	...	0.21	0.28	0.34	0.33
300	...	...	...	...	...	0.22	0.28	0.29
380	...	...	...	...	...	...	0.20	0.20

* Adapted from data of Davis and Bryan, U.S.D.A. Bur. Soils Bul. 61 (1910).

[14] *Wis. Agr. Exp. Sta. Bul.* 85 (1901).

TABLE 10–2

Approximate salt content of water with given resistances in standard soil cup*

Resistance of water at 15.8°C (60°F), in ohms	Salt content of water containing salts consisting	
	predominantly of chlorides and sulfates	in part of sodium carbonate (turn phenolphthalein pink)
	p.p.t.†	p.p.t.†
30	7.5	7.5
35	6.7	6.7
40	6.0	6.0
45	5.3	5.3
50	4.6	4.6
55	4.0	4.3
60	3.6	4.0
65	3.1	3.8
70	2.7	3.6
75	2.3	3.4
80	2.1	3.2
85	2.0	3.0
90	1.95	2.9
95	1.88	2.8
100	1.81	2.6
110	1.70	2.5
120	1.60	2.3
130	1.50	2.1
140	1.41	2.0
150	1.32	1.87
160	1.24	1.76
170	1.16	1.65
180	1.09	1.54
190	1.02	1.44
200	0.96	1.38
220	0.87	1.22
240	0.79	1.10
260	0.71	1.00
280	0.65	0.90
300	0.59	0.83
340	0.50	0.71
380	0.44	0.60
400	0.41	0.55
450	0.35	0.46
500	0.31	0.38
550	0.28	0.32
600	0.25	0.27
700	0.22	0.23
800	0.20	0.20
1000	0.18	0.18
1500	0.16	0.16
2500	0.15	0.15

* Adapted from data of Davis and Bryan, U.S.D.A. Bur. Soils Bul. 61 (1910).
† Parts per thousand parts water.

10–15. Davis and Bryan checked for the presence of Na_2CO_3 by addition of drops of 1 per cent phenolphthalein solution to the soil or solution. If a pink color was obtained, indicating pH 8.3 or above, the salts were in part sodium carbonate, and the corresponding columns in Tables 10–1 or 10–2 were used. In practice, the estimate of salt content based on the sulfate and chloride columns (Table 10–1) is better[15] than from the carbonate columns for all soils, even of alkali soils above pH 8.3.

10–16. Care of the Salt Bridge. The salt bridge is carefully protected from mechanical shock and kept clean. Particularly, the contact metals are kept clean, bright, and free from grease. After use, the soil cup is washed, rinsed, and dried.

ALTERNATIVE PROCEDURES

10–17. Standardization. It is possible to standardize soil paste resistance in terms of the salts occurring under the particular field conditions. The salt content of 10 or 12 representative soils is determined by the conductance of the saturation extract (¶ 10–27) or gravimetrically (¶ 10–75). The accuracy of the soil resistance method seldom justifies this refinement. For greater accuracy, the salt content is determined on the saturation extract of all samples (¶ 10–27).

DETERMINATION OF ELECTRICAL CONDUCTANCE OF SOIL SOLUTIONS AND WATERS AS A MEASURE OF SALT CONTENT

10–18. A fairly quantitative estimate of the salt content of solutions extracted from soils or of natural waters can be made from their electrical conductance. Extracts of soils, particularly those made with high water to soil ratios, are a less accurate measure of the solute content of the soil itself because more salts may be removed than are ever present in the soil at field moisture contents. Also, the ionic species extracted may be different from those present in the soil solution. For example, the amount of calcium and sulfate from a gypsum-bearing soil is about 5 times as much in a 1 : 5 extract as in a 1 : 1 extract. If $CaCO_3$ is present, HCO_3^- and Na^+ increase with dilution, the latter being displaced by Ca^{++} dissolved from $CaCO_3$.[16] The content of Na^+ may be twice as great in the 1 : 5 extract as the 1 : 1 extract; likewise, the dissolved Ca^{++}, SO_4^{--}, and Na^+ are greater in the 1 : 1 extract than in the soil saturation extract. To some extent, hydrolysis of the exchangeable sodium increases with the extent of

---

[15] Fireman and Reeve, *S.S.S.A. Proc.,* 13:495, Fig. 2 (1949); Richards, *op. cit.,* p. 16.

[16] Magistad *et al., Soil Sci.,* 59:65 (1945).

dilution. Chloride and nitrate concentrations decrease more than proportionately by dilution of the suspension,[17] an effect attributed to "negative adsorption" (Donnan distribution) or to bound water of the colloids not acting as a solvent. Increased quantities of sulfate extracted with more dilute suspensions in one soil was attributed to anion replacement by hydroxyl.

10–19. Because the soil : water ratio influences the amount and composition of salts extracted, the soil : water ratio employed must be specified with the analyses. Extraction of soil at natural field moisture contents (¶ 10–45) gives the most accurate measure of soluble soil salts. The soil moisture saturation percentage (¶ 10–27) is related to soil moisture constants, and field moisture content, provides a simply interpreted soil salinity scale based on electrical conductance of the extract at this moisture content (¶ 10–35), and is the highest soil moisture content at which the soil itself may be employed to regulate the soil : water ratio for extraction.

10–20. Definitions. Electrical *resistance* is defined by the equation.

$$E = IR \qquad (10\text{--}2)$$

in which E is the electrical potential in volts, I is the current in amperes and R is the resistance in ohms. Electrical *conductance, C,* or conductivity of a solution in mhos is the reciprocal of resistance, R, in ohms,

$$C = \frac{I}{R} \qquad (10\text{--}3)$$

For convenience, conductance is often expressed as millimhos (1000 times mhos). *Specific conductance, L,* of a solution is the conductance that would be measured at 25°C between electrodes 1 cm² in cross section and placed one cm apart, and may be visualized as the conductance across a cm³, or mhos/cm. Specific conductance may be measured with a cell of various dimensions by means of a *cell constant* (¶ 10–32). Because the numbers obtained expressing specific conductance of soil solutions are generally small, it has been found convenient to express specific conductance as millimhos/cm[18] (1000 times mhos/cm) and this unit has been adopted widely. Other units such as[19] $10^5 \times$ mhos/cm, and[20] micromhos/cm ($10^6 \times$ mhos/cm) have been employed (Table 10–3).

---

[17] Reitemeier, *Soil Sci.,* 61:195 (1946).

[18] Fireman and Reeve, *S.S.S.A. Proc.,* 13:495 (1949).

[19] Magistad *et al., Soil Sci.,* 59:65 (1945).

[20] Employed by Wilcox, U.S.D.A. Cir. 784 (1948), the Rubidoux Laboratory, and also several agencies, such as U.S. Geol. Surv., Quality of Water Branch; U.S. Fish and Wild Life, and Reclamation Research Laboratory, Denver.

TABLE 10–3

Various units which have been employed for electrical conductance
of soil solutions and other waters

Relative size of unit	Factor for calculation	Example, L of moisture saturation extract of a moderately saline soil	
1	$1 \times$ mhos/cm	0.006	mho/cm
10^{-3}	$10^3 \times$ mhos	6	millimhos/cm (adopted)
10^{-5}	$10^5 \times$ mhos	600	mhos $\times$ 10^5/cm*
10^{-6}	$10^6 \times$ mhos	6000	micromhos/cm

* Some writers have stated "mhos $\times$ 10^{-5}/cm" when the numerical value reported was mhos $\times$ 10^5/cm.

APPARATUS

10–21. Needed apparatus consists of an AC "salt bridge" or electrical resistance bridge[21] (Fig. 10–2 and 10–3), conductance cell (Fig. 10–4) with platinum-blackened electrodes, a Buchner or special[22] vacuum funnel with a vacuum flask or desiccator, a suction pump (a centrifuge and tubes may be used) for separation of the soil extract, large test tubes, bottles or beakers for collection of the extract, and a thermometer.

10–22. Principles of the Salt Bridge. In a salt bridge (a resistance or conductance bridge) 2 fixed resistances R_1 and R_2 and a variable resistance R_v are connected in a branched circuit with the conductance cell having resistance R_x (Fig. 10–5). An AC potential is applied at C and D. An AC potential is employed to prevent electrolysis of the solution and polarization of the electrodes in the conductance cell at R_x. Ordinarily a 1000-cycle source is used, but some bridges operate on a 60-cycle power line source. As the frequency rises, capacitance effects become important and are compensated for with the variable condenser in parallel with R_2. The variable resistance R_v is adjusted until there is no current passing in the phone circuit from A to B, as indicated by a minimum sound or shift in the electric eye. Then A and B are at the same potential, and the voltage drop IR_x (eq. 10–2), between BD must equal $I'R_2$, the voltage drop between AD:

$$IR_x = I'R_2 \qquad (10\text{–}4)$$

Also:

$$IR_v = I'R_1 \qquad (10\text{–}5)$$

---

[21] Bouyoucos and Mick, *Mich. Agr. Expt. Sta. Tech. Bul.* 172 (1940), available from Wood and Metal Products Co., Bloomfield Hills, Mich.

[22] Richards, *Agron. Jour.*, 41:446 (1949), available from Instrument Development and Manufacturing Corp., Box 191, East Pasadena, Calif.

Fig. 10–2. Conductance bridge suitable for the measurement of soluble salt content of soil solutions (as well as gypsum block resistances). (Available from Industrial Instruments, Inc., Jersey City 5, N.J.)

Fig. 10–3. Conductance bridge and cell suitable for measurement of electrical conductance from 0.1 to 10 millimhos/cm (nonsaline to strongly saline soil extracts). (Available from the Industrial Instruments, Inc., Jersey City 5, N.J.)

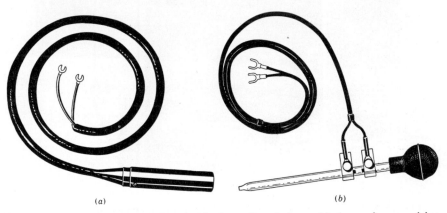

(a)   (b)

Fig. 10–4. Conductance cells suitable for soils solutions: (*a*), large size, requiring about 35 ml of solution; (*b*), small size, requiring only a few ml of solution. (Both available with a cell constant range of 0.1 to 2.0, from Industrial Instruments, Inc., Jersey City 5, N.J.)

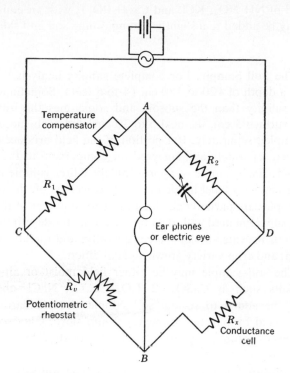

Fig. 10–5. Schematic diagram of salt bridge. The dial of R_v is calibrated in terms of resistance or conductance of R_x, the conductance cell, as explained in text.

Then division of equation 10–4 by 10–5 gives:

$$\frac{IR_x}{IR_v} = \frac{I'R_2}{I'R_1} \qquad (10\text{–}6)$$

Whence:

$$R_x = \frac{R_2}{R_1} R_v \qquad (10\text{–}7)$$

Since R_1 and R_2 are fixed, the dial on R_v can be calibrated to read R_x, the resistance of the test sample. Or, the dial on R_v can be calibrated to read $1/R_x$, that is, directly in conductance of the solution.

REAGENTS

10–23. Needed reagents consist of 0.02 M KCl (1.4912 gm of KCl per liter of solution), CO_2-free distilled water, and filter paper.

10–24. For purposes of the standardization work, salts such as $CaSO_4 \cdot 2 H_2O$, $CaCO_3$, NaCl, Na_2CO_3, and 3–12–12 fertilizer (commercial or compounded of NH_4NO_3, KCl, and $Ca(H_2PO_4)_2$ with an equal amount of gypsum) may be added to a slightly acid nonsaline soil and saline soils.

PROCEDURE

10–25. The Soil Sample. For complete salinity analysis,[23] soil samples are taken to a depth of 120 to 180 cm (4 to 6 feet). Sometimes the surface has greater salinity than the subsoil, and sometimes this situation is reversed. The surface 5 cm, the next 5 to 30 cm, and each succeeding 30-cm layer are sampled separately. If 1 portion of the field produces good crops, this is sampled separately and analyzed for comparison to the troublesome area (¶ 2–54). Each sample of approximately 1-liter volume is placed in a strong paper bag with label inside on a tag, as well as on the outside of the bag. Wet samples are partially air-dried prior to shipment to the laboratory. The label is supplemented with data on location, soil description, area represented; depth to water table; source, quantity, and quality of water used for irrigation; and crop variety grown and condition.

10–26. The soil sample may be either field moist or air-dry, but not oven-dry. Salts such as $CaSO_4 \cdot 2 H_2O$, $CaCO_3$, NaCl, or fertilizer (¶ 10–24) may be added to various soil samples for standardization work. The soil is mixed by passage through a 2-mm sieve. Clay soils can more easily be sieved before they are completely air-dry. Stones and coarse roots are discarded.

10–27. Moisture Saturation Extract of Soil. The soil saturation moisture content is defined[24] as the maximum amount of water held in the puddled soil without free water collection in a depression made in the soil mass. The quantity of soil sample to be extracted depends on the soil texture (Table 10–4) and the volume of the conductance cell to be employed. The approximate weight of soil to provide the needed filtrate volume is placed in a beaker. The first half or two-thirds of the water is added down the side of the beaker so that it passes through the large capillaries. The soil is not disturbed during this process because water movement through puddled soil is very slow. Increments of water are added until the soil mass is fully wetted by capillarity. It is convenient to add increments of water to several successive samples to be analyzed, time being allowed for full imbibition of one increment before more is added to each sample. The soil is then stirred with a spatula, and more water or soil is added to give the final adjustment of water content. The water content is right when the soil barely flows together into a hole made with spatula, the mixture slides off the spatula, and the soil surface is wet enough to glisten. Free water does not collect in the depressions on the surface on standing a few minutes. If free

---

[23] Magistad and Christiansen, U.S.D.A. Cir. 707 (1944).
[24] Scofield, U.S.D.A. Cir. 232 (1932).

TABLE 10–4

Quantity of soil to be taken for each ml of saturation extract in relation
to soil texture and moisture properties

Soil texture	Wilting percentage	Field capacity percentage	Moisture saturation percentage	Sample weight in gm, oven-dry equivalent, per ml filtrate
Sand	1	2	4	50.0
Sandy loam	4	8	16	12.5
Silt loam	10	20	40	5.0
Clay	25	50	100	2.0
Peat	35	70	140	1.4
Relative*	1	2	4	—

* Relative values for 3 soil moisture conditions pointed out by Dr. L. A. Richards (lecture at the University of Wisconsin, 1949).

water stands on the surface, too much water has been added, and a little more soil is added to blot up the excess. With a little practice, the characteristic moisture saturation percentage can be reproduced.

10–28. For many purposes the percentage moisture at saturation need not be determined. It may be determined by oven-drying a sample, or it may be estimated (¶ 10–44).

10–29. Equilibration Time. For conductance measurements, the saturated soil is equilibrated for 10 minutes if gypsum is absent or for 2 hours if gypsum is present. If the extract is to be analyzed chemically for ionic composition (¶ 10–78), the moisture-saturated soil is equilibrated for 6 hours to permit ionic-exchange equilibrium to be attained (¶ 10–18), but no longer because of changes in composition that result from bacterial activity.

10–30. Filtration. The soil is placed on a suitable size of Buchner funnel with tightly seated filter paper, and the "saturation extract" filtrate is removed by suction. The soil saturation extract also may be obtained by the pressure membrane (¶ 10–47) or by centrifugation.[25] A porous tube device has been employed for sampling soil solutions during water-spreading operations.[26]

10–31. Coloration of the extract by dissolved organic matter does not appreciably affect the conductance or chemical analysis, so may generally be ignored. Turbidity, on the other hand, may lead to an appreciable error in the chemical analysis. Turbid solutions may clear on standing, or may be cleared up by passage through a Pasteur-Chamberland filter (¶ 10–53).

10–32. Determination of Cell Constant. The cell constant, *k,* of a con-

[25] Chesnin and Johnson, *Soil Sci.,* 69:497 (1950).
[26] Krone *et al., Soil Sci.,* 73:211 (1952).

ductance cell is determined by measurement of the electrical conductance, C, of a standard KCl solution, and use of the equation:

$$k = \frac{L}{C} \qquad (10\text{--}8)$$

in which

L = known specific electrical conductance of standard solution, usually 0.02 M KCl, mmhos/cm

C = conductance of the standard solution measured in the given cell, mmhos

The specific conductance, L, of the 0.0200 M KCl is 2.39 mmhos/cm at 18°C, and 2.768 mmhos/cm at 25°C. Various standard conductance solutions are available.[27] The measured conductance, C, of a test solution (¶ 10–33), in millimhos, multiplied by the cell constant gives the specific conductance, $L_{mmho/cm}$, of the test solution:

$$L = kC \qquad (10\text{--}9)$$

10–33. Determination of Solution Conductance. The conductance cell is ordinarily stored immersed in distilled water. The cell is usually rinsed twice with the test solution, but if insufficient solution is at hand, the cell may be rinsed with and dried from acetone to prevent dilution of the extract with water. The cell is filled with the test solution (¶ 10–30, 10–79) to immerse the electrodes completely. The bridge is balanced and the reading is recorded as resistance or conductance (specify units, ¶ 10–20). The specific conductance as $L_{mmho/cm}$ is calculated (eq. 10–9). The "Solubridge" with its conventional cell reads directly in specific conductance,[28] no cell constant thus being needed.

10–34. The temperature of the solution is taken into account in the calculation of the result. Electrical conductance of a solution increases approximately 2 per cent per degree C. Temperature corrections may be avoided by use of a temperature bath at 25°C, or approximately by use of a reference solution at the same temperature as the test solution.

10–35. The Soil Salinity Scale. Soluble salts decrease the availability of the soil water by contributing osmotic pressure[29] to the integrated soil moisture stress, and the latter decreases yields if it exceeds low values.[30] As the soil moisture content is changed from the wilting percentage to field

---

[27] *Handbook of Chemistry and Physics* (Cleveland, Ohio: Chemical Rubber Pub. Co., 1930–1957); Jones and Bradshaw, *J. Am. Chem. Soc.* 55:1780 (1933).

[28] In some dials (Fig. 10–3) "mhos × 10⁻⁵" means "mhos × 10⁵/cm" (¶ 10–20).

[29] Magistad, *Bot. Rev.*, 11:181 (1945).

[30] Wadleigh, *Soil Sci.*, 61:225 (1946).

capacity or saturation percentage, the salts present in the soil solution are diluted. Conversely, the salts become more concentrated in the soil solution as the soil moisture is used up and the wilting percentage is approached. Greater salt damage to crops is often observed in hot summers than in cooler summers, presumably because the wilting percentage is approached more frequently. Since the wilting percentage is smaller for sandy soils than for finer textured soils, a given absolute amount of salts per unit weight of a sandy soil creates a greater concentration of salts in its soil solution at the wilting percentage than that same amount of salts would create in a finer textured soil (¶ 10–42). For all soil textures, the concentration of salts in the soil moisture saturation extract is approximately one-fourth that in the soil solution at the wilting percentage and one-half that present in the soil solution at the field capacity, owing to the fundamental relation of the saturation moisture percentage to soil moisture constants (Table 10–4, above). The saturation extract is thus an "equipotential" soil moisture content for various soils. The specific electrical conductance of the saturation extract, which is linearly related to osmotic pressure as well as concentration of salts in solution (¶ 10–37), can be interpreted directly in terms of plant growth, by means of the salinity scale[31] (Table 10–5). Although different plants vary in their tolerance to the presence of soluble salts,[32] the salinity scale is found applicable to plants classified into relatively few groups. Workers of long experience with saline soils tend to prefer electrical conductance units to units of concentration of salts in solution. The relative conductance units of the salinity scale can be interpreted as readily as the relative numbers of the soil pH scale.

10–36. Irrigation waters should range from 0.1 to 0.75 mmhos per cm or below. High salinity hazard is incurred in the use of irrigation water having conductance much above this range (¶10–80).

10–37. Calculation of Specific Electrical Conductance to Salt Concentration in Solution. A linear relationship exists[33] between the specific electrical conductance in a water extract of soils or irrigation water and the concentration of salts as found by analysis (¶ 10–78) and expressed as meq of anions (or cations) per liter of solution,

$$\text{meq of salt per liter} = \text{equiv. per million} = 12.5 \, L_{\text{mmho/ cm}} \qquad (10\text{–}10)$$

The factor for the single salt solutions of $NaCl$, $CaCl_2$, $MgCl_2$, Na_2SO_4, $CaSO_4$, $MgSO_4$, and $NaHCO_3$, according to data published in the International Critical Tables,[34] ranges from 8 to 20.

---

[31] Scofield, U.S.D.A. Cir. 232 (1932).
[32] Ali and Powers, *Plant Physiol.*, 13:767 (1938); Ayers *et al., J. Am. Soc. Agron.*, 35:796 (1943); for boron, Wilcox, U.S.D.A. Cir. 784 (1948).
[33] Fireman and Reeve, *S.S.S.A. Proc.*, 13:494 (1949).
[34] Richards, U.S.D.A. Agr. Handb. 60, p. 10–12 (1954).

TABLE 10–5
The salinity scale*

Specific conductance of the saturation extract of soil, millimhos per cm.

0		2		4		8		16	

Nonsaline	Very slightly saline	Moderately saline	Strongly saline	Very strongly saline
Salinity effects mostly negligible.	Yields of very sensitive crops may be restricted.	Yield of many crops restricted. Alfalfa, cotton, sugar beets, cereals, and grain sorghums adapted.	Only tolerant crops yield satisfactorily. Bare spots appear because of injury to germination.	Only a few very tolerant crops yield satisfactorily. Only salt tolerant grasses, herbaceous plants, shrubs, and trees grow.

0		0.1		0.3		0.5		1.0	

Percentage of salts in moisture saturation extract

* Adapted from descriptions of Scofield, *Reports of Participating Agencies*, Part III, Sec. 6, U.S. National Resources Planning Board, June (1942), pp. 263–334; Richards, ed., *Diagnosis and Improvement of Saline and Alkali Soils*, U.S.D.A. Agr. Handb. 60, p. 9 (1954); and Campbell and Richards, *Agron. Jour.*, 42: 582 (1950).

10–38. The effects of salts on plants is more closely related[35] to the equivalents of salts per million parts of solution (¶ 10–37) than gravimetric weight units per million. However, the latter can be estimated[36] for waters in the alkaline soil regions:

$$\text{ppm of salts} = 640\, L_{mmho/\,cm} \tag{10–11}$$

$$\%\ \text{salts in solution} = 0.064\, L_{mmho/\,cm} \tag{10–12}$$

$$\%\ \text{salts in soil} = 0.064\, L_{mmho/\,cm} \times \frac{\%\ \text{water in soil at extraction}}{100} \tag{10–13}$$

Equivalents per million multiplied by the gm-equivalent weight gives the parts per million. Equation 10–11 involves the assumption of an average gm-equivalent weight of 51 for the various salts present. The conversion factor to percentage salts for highly fertilized soils of the humid region is approximately 0.1 (¶ 10–51), or somewhat higher than 0.064, and signifies that the average equivalent weight is greater than 51.

10–39. Osmotic Pressure of Solutions. Specific conductance can be converted to osmotic pressure:

$$\text{Osmotic pressure of solution, atm.} = 0.36\, L_{mmho/\,cm} \tag{10–14}$$

The factor 0.36 applies well for NaCl and for solutions extracted from alkali and saline soils[37] and should be applicable to irrigation waters in arid regions. The factor is 0.3 for common MX_2 and M_2X salts and 0.28 for $MgSO_4$, and thus a factor of about 0.3 would be expected for highly fertilized soils of the humid region.

10–40. The salt concentrations of the soil extract or water may be checked by gravimetric determination through evaporation (¶ 10–75). The anion and cation species in the solution may be determined (¶ 10–78).

10–41. The salt index of a fertilizer may be estimated by electrical conductance:

$$\text{Salt index} = \frac{\substack{\text{Specific conductance of} \\ \text{solution when 1 gm of fertilizer is} \\ \text{suspended in 1 liter of water}}}{\substack{\text{Specific conductance of 0.1\% NaNO}_3 \\ \text{solution}}} \times 100 \tag{10–15}$$

---

[35] Magistad, *Bot. Rev.*, 11:181 (1945).

[36] Richards, U.S.D.A. Agr. Handb. 60, p. 16 (1954); and Magistad *et al.*, *Soil Sci.*, 59:70 (1945), used the factor 700.

[37] These factors are derived from freezing point depression data reported in the International Critical Tables, 4:254–260, based on $O.P. = 12.06\,\Delta\,T - 0.021\,(\Delta\,T)^2$, as reported by Richards, *op. cit.*, p. 10, 17; Bouyoucos and McCool, *J. Agr. Res.*, 15:331 (1918); Campbell, *Soil Sci.*, 73:221 (1952).

10–42. Toxic Limit Percentage of Salt in Soil. The salt content of soil expressed as percentage or ppm of the dry soil is not simply related to the salt toxicity to plants grown there (¶ 10–35). For example, in 2 soils, 1 a loamy sand and the other a clay, both with same salt content on the dry soil weight basis, the salt concentration in the soil solution at the wilting percentage will be approximately 10 times as high in the sandy soil, because its wilting percentage is about 0.1 as great as that of the clay soil. Thus no 1 definite percentage of salts in soils can be given at which toxicity begins in all soils. If the moisture saturation percentage of the clay soil happened to be 100 per cent, the concentration of salts in the soil solution would be equal to that in the dry soil. Supposing $L = 10$ mmho/cm in the saturation extract, from equation 10–12:

$$\% \text{ salts in soil} = L \times 0.064 = 10 \times 0.064 = 0.64$$
$$(= \text{that in solution})$$

This value of 0.64 per cent is plotted as point A (Fig. 10–6) at a saturation extract conductance of 10 mmho/cm. A line drawn through point A from the origin is the locus of salt percentages for all values of specific conductance for soils having 100 per cent moisture saturation percentage. For a second soil, having a saturation moisture percentage of 80 per cent, the concentration of salts in the dry soil would be 80/100 of that in the saturation extract from it, and for $L = 10$ mmho/cm in the saturation extract, from equation 10–13:

$$\% \text{ salts in soil} = \frac{L \times 0.064 \times \% \text{ water at sat.}}{100}$$

$$= \frac{10 \times 0.064 \times 80}{100} = 0.51$$

which is plotted at point B (Fig. 10–6). The various lines show the relationship of salt content (of soils having the stated saturation moisture percentages) to specific conductance of the saturation extract. Taking Scofield's value of 4 mmhos/cm as the upper limit of salinity that is harmless to plants (Table 10–5), the toxic limit percentage of soil salts is 0.35 per cent for a peat soil (Fig. 10–6), about 0.1 per cent for a silt loam, and about 0.05 per cent for a coarse loamy sand. Salt contents in soils in excess of these percentages would be harmful to some plants. Double these values may be taken as the toxic limit for more resistant plants (limit of moderate salinity, Table 10–5).

10–43. A fertile soil may contain 0.02 to 0.05 per cent (200 to 500 ppm) of soluble salts. A content of 0.1 per cent salts in a silt loam corresponds to 1000 ppm in the soil or 4000 ppm in the soil solution at the field moisture capacity of 25 per cent. For a silt loam soil, 1500 ppm in the soil is often found to be the maximum salt content for growth of soft-stemmed plants,

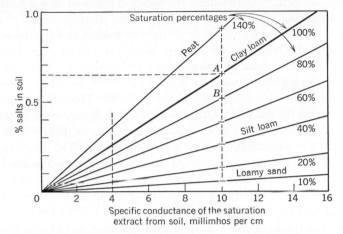

Fig. 10–6. Relationship of percentage of soluble salts to specific conductance of the saturation extract of soils of varying texture. The moderately saline limit at 4 mmho/cm falls at widely varying percentages of salts, depending on the soil texture. (After Richards, *op. cit.*, p. 17.)

and 2500 ppm of the soil is the maximum for growth of woody plants such as rose bushes.

ALTFRNATIVE PROCEDURES

10–44. Determination of Saturation Moisture Percentage. It is often desirable to determine the saturation moisture percentage. To do this, a small portion of the soil paste is removed, and the moisture content is determined by oven-drying. Alternatively, Wilcox[38] has published a formula for the calculation of the saturation moisture percentage from the weight of a known volume of saturated soil paste, as follows:

$$\text{Saturation moisture percentage} = 37.74 \frac{(2.65V - W)}{W - V} \quad (10\text{–}16)$$

in which V is the volume in ml of the saturated paste, and W is its weight in gm. The density of water is taken as unity and that of the soil particles as 2.65. The formula is suitable for mineral soils but not for organic soils; the estimate was found to be 4 to 6 per cent low for those mineral soils that swell considerably.

10–45. Displacement of the Soil Solution. Water or other displacing liquid appears to replace the sorbed films of the soil solution, pushing it ahead through the column. The displacement method has been employed to study the effect of fertilizers on the concentrations of the soil solution[39] and

[38] *Soil Sci.*, 72:233 (1951).
[39] White and Ross, *S.S.S.A. Proc.*, 1:181 (1937).

other soil conditions,[40] and to study the solution phase of mixed fertilizers.[41] Various displacing liquids[42] used include water, alcohol, acetone, and oil. The soil with the desired moisture content is passed rapidly through a 2- or 3-mm screen. Quartz gravel or glass beads are placed over the opening in the glass leaching tube or metal cylinder[43] (inverted 1-liter glass bottle with gently sloping neck and with bottom cut off, ¶ 1–23). A 5-mm layer of glass wool is next laid over the gravel or beads. The soil is then packed to three-fourths fill the tube, with a wooden rod. Sandy soils or peats are packed as firmly as possible at all moisture contents, as there is little danger of making them impervious to the displacing liquid. The finer classes of soil are packed more lightly and used at a moisture content somewhat below the field capacity to insure adequate rate of solution displacement. A silt loam is best used at a moisture content of about 20 per cent, and when properly packed has an apparent specific gravity of 1.50 to 1.60.

10–46. The leaching tube is suspended from a ring stand and 300 to 500 ml of water containing 0.5 per cent of KCNS is added. This solution displaces or pushes the soil solution ahead of it without rapid mixing of the 2 solutions, making it possible to get a portion of the actual soil solution (usually 20 to 50 per cent) before any of the displacing solution comes through. After about 20 per cent of the soil solution has come through, the remainder is caught in successive 25-ml portions and a few drops are tested on a spot plate with 4 per cent $FeCl_3$ solution. The first appearance of a pink or red color in this test indicates CNS^- ions of the displacing solution are coming through and collection of the solution is stopped.

10–47. Soil Solution Obtained with a Pressure Membrane.[44] Extraction of the soil solution by means of the pressure membrane is slower and requires a larger soil sample than do water extracts, but has the advantage that the soil solution is obtained without dissolution of additional materials from the soil. The method serves well for more exacting studies and as a means to check the extent that the results are being affected by water extraction procedures.[45] In the event that air-dried soil is to be examined, the soil first is sprayed with a fine mist of water while being rapidly turned in a can or on a rubberized mixing sheet. The soil is equilibrated with the water by storage at high humidity and constant temperature for a period of 2 weeks, with occasional mixing. The field-moist, or moistened soil after

[40] Burd and Martin, *J. Agr. Sci.,* 13:265 (1923).

[41] Rader, *Anal. Chem.,* 19:229 (1947).

[42] Parker, *Soil Sci.,* 12:209 (1921).

[43] Anderson *et al.,* U.S.D.A. Tech. Bul. 813 (1942); White and Ross, *J. Agr. Res.,* 59:81 (1939).

[44] Reitemeier and Richards, *Soil Sci.,* 57:119 (1944).

[45] Reitemeier, *Soil Sci.,* 61:195 (1946).

storage, is packed by hand into the pressure membrane cylinder[46] to a depth of 5 to 10 or more cm. The cylinder is then closed, and the extraction process carried out at 15 kgm per cm^2 (15 atmospheres, or 225 lbs. per sq. inch).

10–48. The 1 : 1 Soil : Water Extraction of Soluble Salts. A soil sample consisting of 50 to 1500 gm of dry soil or its equivalent of field-moist soil is added to an equal weight of CO_2-free water (the water in the soil being included in this total) in a bottle of suitable size. (A small sample is employed if only conductance measurements are to be made.) The bottle is stoppered and shaken for a period of 2 hours, preferably in a rotary shaker. The suspension is then filtered on a large Buchner funnel fitted with a carefully sealed medium porosity filter paper. The filter paper is sealed by wetting it with a little distilled water and pulling it down with suction. The excess water pulled through is discarded before the filtration is begun. The first portion of the filtrate may be cloudy, and is either discarded or poured back through the filter. The filter is covered with a glass during the filtration process to retard evaporation. The conductance is measured (¶ 10–33) and then the concentration of salts in the 1 : 1 extract solution is automatically the concentration in the soil, oven-dry basis.

10–49. As a simple alternative[47] a 50-gm soil sample is placed in a Collodian bag suspended in 50 ml of water in an extraction flask. Gentle agitation gives chloride equilibrium into the outer solution within 24 hours.

10–50. The 1 : 2 Soil : Water Extraction of Soluble Salts. The 1 : 2 soil : water extraction has been employed extensively by research workers in the humid soil region, particularly in connection with highly fertilized greenhouse soils.[48] One hundred gm of dry soil or its equivalent of field-moist soil (more if ionic analyses are to be made) is placed in 200 ml of water in a 500-ml conical flask. The flask is stoppered and the suspension is shaken for a period of 2 hours or over night. The solution is filtered, and the conductance is measured (¶ 10–33). The concentration of soluble salts in the 1 : 2 extract, multiplied by 2 is the concentration in the soil, oven-dry basis.

10–51. The factor (¶ 10–38, eq. 10–12) calculated for the 1 : 2 extract data from greenhouse soils[49] was 0.073 (instead of 0.064) after 2 weeks equilibration of fertilizer salts with soil before extraction, but increased to 0.094 after 4 weeks equilibration; and this value was also the "best fit" for

---

[46] Available commercially from the Instrument Development and Manufacturing Corporation, P.O. Box 191, East Pasadena, California.

[47] Hester, *Sci.,* 107:99 (1948); Pierre and Parker, *Soil Sci.,* 23:13 (1927).

[48] Merkle and Dunkle, *J. Am. Soc. Agron.,* 36:10 (1944); Sweet and Peech, *Farm Research,* 11:4 (April 1945), and Industrial Instruments, Litho. circular, Jersey City, N.J.

[49] Dunkle and Merkle, *S.S.S.A. Proc.,* 8:185 (1944).

a large number of collected soils.[50] Data in the author's laboratory gave a factor of 0.12 for the filtrate of a soil equilibrated with 4–10–10 fertilizer, based on the gravimetric weight of solutes in the filtrate. It appears that a factor of about 0.1 for $L_{mmho/\ cm}$ to % salts in solution is applicable to 1 : 2 extracts from highly fertilized soils in which calcium and sulfate are in fairly high proportion.

10–52. The interpretation of specific conductance of solutions derived from 1 : 2 or other fixed soil : water ratios is subject to variation with the wilting percentage or soil texture (¶ 10–35). The literature reveals attempts to set a limit for the 1 : 2 extract without reference to soil texture. A 1 : 2 extract of a sand involves much more dilution of the soil solution at wilting than does a 1 : 2 extract of a silt loam. The relation between the specific conductance of the 1 : 2 and the saturation extracts may be calculated (Table 10–6) by the equation:

$$L_{sat.\ ext.} = L_{1\ :\ 2} \times \frac{200}{\%\ \text{water in soil at saturation}} \qquad (10\text{–}17)$$

except for additional $CaSO_4 \cdot 2\,H_2O$ and $CaCO_3$ dissolved (¶ 10–18) in the more dilute extraction. The upper limit of conductance for 1 : 2 soil extract appeared to be 0.75 to 1.25 mmhos/cm for best growth of tomato seedlings,[51] 1.0 mmho/cm for correction of salinity due to flooding of soils by sea water,[52] and 2 to 4 mmho/cm for freedom from repression of germination and growth in greenhouse soils.[53] These values correspond (Table 10–6) to satisfactory values on the salinity scale (Table 10–5) for good growth on fine textured soils, but would be excessive on coarse tex-

TABLE 10–6

**Relationship of specific conductance in 1 : 2 soil : water extract to that
in the saturation extract for 2 soil textures**

Specific conductance of the 1 : 2 extract (observed)		Specific conductance of the saturation extract (calculated)	
Expressed as millimhos/cm	Expressed as mhos × 10⁵/cm	For silt loam (sat. % = 40)	For clay loam, high organic matter (sat. % = 100)
0.75	75	3.75	1.5
1.0	100	5.0	2.0
2.0	200	10.0	4.0
3.0	300	15.0	6.0
4.0	400	20.0	8.0

[50] Merkle and Dunkle, *J. Am. Soc. Agron.*, 36:10 (1944).
[51] Sweet and Peech, *Farm Research*, 11:4 (April 1945).
[52] Industrial Instruments, Litho. circular, Jersey City, N.J.
[53] Dunkle and Merkle, *S.S.S.A. Proc.*, 8:185 (1944).

tured soils. The 1 : 2 extracts from fertilized greenhouse soils undoubtedly involved extraction of considerable gypsum that did not actually occur in the soil solution. Thus the conductance values found are higher than would be found in the saturation extract. It is indeed striking, nonetheless, how similar the conductance ranges are for the saline soil studies of the otherwise contrasting alkaline and humid soil regions.

10–53. The 1 : 5 Soil : Water Extraction of Soluble Salts.[54] Field-moist or air-dry soil is weighed out equivalent to 140 gm of oven-dry soil, and transferred to a 1-liter bottle. Then 700 ml of CO_2-free water (less the calculated amount of water in the soil sample) is added. The bottle is stoppered and placed in the rotary shaker for 2 hours, and then allowed to settle for 0.5 hour, after which the supernatant liquid is filtered. A Pasteur-Chamberland filter may be employed. To insure cleanness of the filter tubes, distilled water is passed through until the collected filtrate shows a very low electrical conductance. The filters are then disconnected and drained. The supernatant liquid in the extraction flask is decanted into the Pasteur-Chamberland filter cup, and filtration is effected under 10 or 15 pounds per square inch pressure. The first 30 to 50 ml of filtrate is discarded and then 250 or more is collected for analysis. The clay filter tubes are cleaned and rinsed under pressure, and air-dried, ready for use again. The concentration of the soluble salts in the 1 : 5 extract multiplied by 5 is the concentration in the soil, oven-dry basis.

10–54. The factor (0.064 × % water in soil at extraction) of equation 10–13 for a 1 : 5 extract becomes 0.320, or, for L in mhos, 320. Joseph and Martin[55] used the factor 250 based on the specific resistance of 50 ohms for a 1 per cent salt solution (50 per cent NaCl and 50 per cent Na_2SO_4); Piper[56] used the factor 375 (equivalent to 0.075 in equations 10–12 and 10–13, and to 750 in equation 10–11). The range in these values is some measure of the uncertainties of the analysis.

MEASUREMENT OF EFFECTS OF SOIL SALINITY ON SEED GERMINATION

10–55. Many crop plants are especially sensitive to soil salinity during the seed-germination stage. This sensitivity occurs even with plants that are relatively salt tolerant during later stages of growth, examples being sugar beets and alfalfa.[57] Adverse effects of salinity during germination are

---

[54] Dilution was employed at the Division of Soils, University of Nebraska (1936), and the Waite Agricultural Research Institute, Adelaide, Australia according to Piper, *Soil and Plant Analysis* (New York: Interscience Publishers, Inc., 1944). Comparison of the 1 : 5 extract to Lipman's pressure extract has been reported by Burgess, *Soil Sci.,* 14:191 (1922).

[55] *J. Agr. Sci.,* 13:52 (1923).

[56] Piper, *op. cit.,* p. 32.

[57] Ayers and Hayward, *S.S.S.A. Proc.,* 13:224 (1949).

largely responsible for the bare spots contrasting to good growth with only a few cm transition in the field. The literature on this subject has been extensively reviewed.[58]

APPARATUS

10–56. Needed apparatus includes a constant temperature room, 20-cm culture dishes, a 4-mm sieve, rubberized cloth or Cellophane, a mixing spatula, moist soil containers, and an electrical conductance bridge to test the final salinity of samples.

REAGENTS

10–57. Needed reagents include NaCl and other salts, including fertilizer salts. Barley and other seeds and saline and nonsaline soils are also needed.

PROCEDURE

10–58. The soil is passed through a 4-mm sieve, and the salt content is adjusted by the addition of with NaCl (or other salt to be tested) so as to give in successive lots, 0, 0.1, 0.15, 0.2, 0.25, and 0.3 per cent salt on a dry soil basis. The soil-moisture content is then brought into the moisture range from wilting percentage to field capacity as follows: the soil sample is spread out in a thin layer on rubberized sheet or waterproof Cellophane,[59] and the calculated amount of water is sprayed on the soil in small increments, after each of which the soil is mixed with a spatula with care to avoid puddling. If wetted lumps appear, the soil is placed on the 4-mm sieve and gently shaken to pass only the fine soil, the lumps being retained on the sieve. When the calculated amount of water has been added, the whole sample of soil is mixed and placed in a container, which then is tightly closed. The soil is stored in a constant temperature room at 70°C for about two weeks for equilibration.[60] Occasional rotation of the container to mix the soil speeds up the equilibration of moisture and salts throughout the soil mass.

10–59. After equilibration, 1.4-kgm soil samples are weighed and placed in 20-cm culture dishes. A definite number of seeds is planted, 20 in the case of barley. The dishes are covered and maintained at constant temperature to prevent distillation and condensation of moisture. The number of emerging seedlings is counted each day. The results are expressed as the percentage of emergence at various time intervals.

10–60. The electrical conductance of the saturation extract is determined (¶ 10–27) from subsamples of the moistened soil (¶ 10–58) taken at the time of planting. From this and the measured soil moisture content of the

---

[58] Uhvits, *Am. J. Bot.,* 33:278 (1946).
[59] Technique described to the writer by Dr. G. M. Volk (1946).
[60] Ayers and Hayward, *S.S.S.A. Proc.,* 13:224 (1949).

soil, the osmotic pressure of the soil solution may be calculated (¶ 10–39). If the relation of moisture stress to soil moisture content is known, the total moisture stress may be calculated.[61]

10–61. The procedure may be adapted to the determination of the influence of different single salts, cation exchange status, germination temperatures, and the effect of different fertilizer salts[62] on germination. Critical percentages of NaCl (dry soil basis), above which germination was greatly retarded were found by Ayers and Hayward to be 0.1 per cent for barley, and 0.04 to 0.05 per cent for corn and beans. Expressed as percentage of NaCl in solution,[63] the critical percentage for hemp was 0.25 per cent and 0.5 for clover, wheat, rye, beans, and peas, which agree well with the above values for the dry soil basis.

COMPOSITING RUNOFF WATERS AND DETERMINATION OF TOTAL SUSPENDED SOLIDS OF RUNOFF WATERS

10–62. The analysis of runoff waters differs somewhat from that of well, lake, and river waters (¶ 10–81), because they contain rather high amounts of suspended solids in addition to the dissolved solids ordinarily determined in waters. The determination of total suspended solids of runoff waters is carried out (¶ 10–71) to provide a base for the calculation of the chemical constituents in terms of soil material lost by erosion, as well as to determine the amount of physical erosion that has taken place. In addition, a few special procedures are given here for getting the runoff waters in condition for the respective chemical determinations given elsewhere in the text in the respective sections where the analysis of soil for the same constituent is given.

10–63. Of interest in the interpretation of runoff analyses in terms of soil fertility is the "enrichment ratio":

$$\text{Enrichment ratio} \atop {\scriptstyle \text{(of a soil constituent)}} = \frac{\text{Concentration in soil material in runoff}}{\text{Concentration in soil from which runoff originated}}$$

$$(10\text{--}18)$$

APPARATUS

10–64. Needed are an electric stirring apparatus with collapsible paddle (Fisher Scientific Co., Pittsburgh, Pa.) and a set of graduated beakers each of which holds, when level full, the size of aliquot wanted for a particular determination. The beaker volume is adjusted with melted paraffin at the bottom.

---

[61] Wadleigh, *Soil Sci.*, 61:225 (1946).

[62] Lundstrom, Research report 134, Division of Fertilizers and Agricultural Lime, Bur. Plant Ind., Soils Agric. Eng., U.S.D.A. (1948) as cited by Ayers and Hayward, *S.S.S.A. Proc.*, 13:224 (1949).

[63] Harris, *Soil Alkali, Its Origin, Nature, and Treatment* (New York: John Wiley & Sons, Inc., 1920).

10–65. Reagents needed are toluene and precipitated $CaCO_3$ (for treatment of the nitrate samples).

PROCEDURE[64]

10–66. Compositing of Runoff Water Samples. Each suspension is thoroughly mixed and the volume of each is taken in proportion to the fraction of runoff from a given plot it represents. A few samples are readily composited by agitation of the bottles by hand, but if many samples are to be composited, an electric stirring motor is employed. The proper amount of each suspension to give a total 3 liters of composited suspension volume is measured in a graduated cylinder with caution to keep the suspension of uniform concentration during the process. The composited suspension is placed in a 4-liter (1-gallon) jug, and 1 ml of toluene is added to suppress bacterial activity.

10–67. Nitrate Samples. Since nitrates are subject to denitrification in solution, a 1-liter sample of the runoff water from each tank is treated with 0.25 gm of $CaCO_3$ and dried immediately after collection. When separate samples are dried from each of several tanks that are to be reported as 1 composite sample, data are submitted with the samples showing the percentage from each tank for the composite sample. Nitrates are determined according to ¶ 8–59.

10–68. Correction Factor. The amount of dilution caused by precipitation that falls in the tanks is calculated from the exposed area of the tank, and the "corrected runoff volume" in the tank is calculated. The analytical results for the diluted runoff are corrected by a "dilution factor" calculated as follows:

$$\text{Dilution factor} = \frac{\text{Uncorrected runoff volume measured}}{\text{Corrected runoff volume calculated}} \quad (10\text{--}19)$$

10–69. The runoff volume measured also includes the volume of the solids present. For runoff containing more than 1.5 gm of solids per 100 gm, a correction is made for the volume of solids:

$$\% \text{ water in runoff} = 100 - \frac{(\text{gm solid per 100 gm runoff})}{2.65}$$

$$(10\text{--}20)$$

The total correction factor to be applied to analyses of runoff (¶ 10–73) is then calculated:

---

[64] The writer is indebted to Dr. H. F. Massey, J. C. Kaudy, and J. Dana-Bashian at the University of Wisconsin for their participation in the runoff analysis through which these procedures were developed. Also, helpful suggestions were made by O. E. Hays of the U.S.D.A., and Dr. H. Kohnke of Purdue University.

$$\text{Correction factor} = \frac{\text{Dilution factor} \times 100}{\% \text{ water in runoff}} \qquad (10\text{--}21)$$

10–70. Subsampling for Analysis. In subsampling of a composite runoff water for analysis, the suspension is first thoroughly mixed. Since it is easier to measure out a constant volume, a calibrated (¶ 10–64) beaker is used that holds just the desired quantity of suspension for a given analysis. This allows the sample to be poured quickly without settling, the excess merely spilling over the top.

10–71. Total Solid Content of Runoff. Two separate 100-ml samples are measured out and poured into the same tared 250-ml beaker, the solids being rinsed out of the measuring beaker with distilled water. The 250-ml beaker is placed on the steam plate and brought to dryness at 100°C. (The process may be hastened by boiling the liquid down to low volume on an electric hot plate.) The sample is not allowed to bake on the hot plate after drying, as organic matter may be decomposed. The beaker is allowed to cool and then is weighed.

10–72. When the beaker contains less than 1 gm of solids, it is weighed on an analytical balance to the nearest mgm. Otherwise, a torsion balance sensitive to 0.05 gm is satisfactory. At least 0.25 gm of solids is required for the organic matter determination (¶ 9–50), and it may sometimes be necessary to dry down more than 200 ml of runoff to obtain this amount of solids. If additional volume is necessary, the sample is removed from the hot plate just prior to dryness, 2 additional 100-ml aliquots are added, and the beaker is again placed on the hot plate.

10–73. The concentration of solids as gm per 100 ml of runoff is calculated, and from this the pounds solids per acre inch of runoff (ppai) is calculated:

$$\text{Solids (ppai)} = \text{gm solids per 100 ml} \times 2270 \times \text{correction factor} \qquad (10\text{--}22)$$

The correction factor is obtained from equation 10–21. The factor 2270 is derived for the pounds of water per acre inch as follows:

$$43560 \text{ sq. ft. per acre} \times \frac{62.4 \text{ pounds per cu. ft.}}{12 \text{ inches per foot}} = \frac{226512 \text{ pounds of water}}{\text{per acre inch}} \qquad (10\text{--}23)$$

The conversion factor for percentage to ppai is therefore 2270, and for ppm to ppai is 0.227.

10–74. The chemical analyses usually made on runoff waters include: organic matter (¶ 9–50), combined organic and ammonium nitrogen (¶ 8–16), nitrate nitrogen (¶ 8–59), soluble and extractable phosphorus (¶ 7–75), and exchangeable potassium (¶ 18–26).

DETERMINATION OF TOTAL DISSOLVED SOLIDS
OF SOIL EXTRACT OR WATER

10–75. The soil extract or water is evaporated to dryness and the quantity of dissolved solids is determined gravimetrically. The method is a direct measure of total salinity, and serves as a check on the results by the more rapid electrical conductance methods (¶ 10–18) and on the chemical analysis for individual ions (¶ 10–78). Two procedures have been widely employed, 1 involving drying at 110°C and the other at 550° to 600°C for 5 minutes. The object of the latter is to remove organic matter and measure only salts; prolonged heating is avoided because of losses of salts, particularly $MgCl_2$.

APPARATUS

10–76. Needed apparatus includes platinum or porcelain evaporating dishes, pipets, a 110°C oven, a muffle furnace, and an analytical balance.

PROCEDURE[65]

10–77. An evaporating dish, preferably of platinum, is carefully cleaned, ignited, and weighed to 4 places. Then 50 ml of the clear extract or water is measured out by means of a pipet. The solution is evaporated to dryness at 110°C (the platinum dish being set on a cloth-wrapped ring, not on metal or porcelain) then is cooled and weighed. The total dissolved solids are reported as ppm in solution.

DETERMINATION OF INDIVIDUAL CATIONS AND ANIONS
OF SOLUBLE SALTS IN SOILS AND WATERS

10–78. Analyses are often made of soil extracts (¶ 10–18, 5–3), of lysimeter[66] percolates, and of waters from rivers, lakes, wells, and runoff. The determinations of the individual cations of the soluble salts and waters include those of Na^+, K^+, Ca^{++}, Mg^{++} (¶ 10–82 to 10–86). The soil : water ratio used in the extraction of soils affects the ionic composition of the extract (¶ 10–18). Procedures for the dissolved anions CO_3^{--}, HCO_3^-, Cl^-, SO_4^{--}, gypsum, and carbonate carbon are given in following sections. Other anions in solutions are determined by procedures given in appropriate places: NO_3^- (¶ 8–48), BO_3^{---} (¶ 14–7), PO_4^{---} (¶ 7–14) and SiO_3^{--} (¶ 11–72).

10–79. Water Samples.[67] Because representative waters have been analyzed, an inquiry from the state chemist or engineer, or Agricultural Experi-

---

[65] *Official and Tentative Methods of Analysis,* 6th ed. (Washington, D.C.: A.O.A.C., 1945).

[66] Lysimeter technique has been reviewed by Kohnke *et al.,* U.S.D.A. Misc. Pub. 372 (1940) and Harrold and Dreibelbis, U.S.D.A. Tech. Bul. 1050 (1951).

[67] Magistad and Christiansen, U.S.D.A. Cir. 707 (1944).

ment Station should be made prior to water sampling from common sources. If sufficient information is not available, 4 liters (1 gallon) of water sample is collected for analysis. The container is thoroughly washed and then rinsed several times with the water to be sampled. In sampling a stream, water is taken from a rapidly flowing part. The kind of water (spring, stream, lake, well) should be specified, together with location, depth, temperature, odor, color, use to be put to, users opinion of its quality, and other pertinent information. Collection of rain water (particularly for sulfur studies) by means of a frost-proof rain and snow gauge has been described.[68]

10–80. Interpretation of Quality of Irrigation Waters. The quality of irrigation waters is dependent on the total salt content, on the nature of the salts (particularly of Na and B) present in solution, and the proportions of meq of Na to meq of other metallic cations, and of Ca to Mg to bica bonates. The total salt content as parts per million can be estimated rather accurately from the specific conductance (¶ 10–33). The ppm multiplied by 0.00136 gives the tons of salt per acre foot of water. Also ppm × 0.0586 equals grains of salt per U.S. gallon. The quality of irrigation water can be evaluated in terms of the conductance and the sodium adsorption ratio (Fig. 10–7). A guide to the quality of water in terms of specific conductance, sodium percentage, boron content,[69] and residual Na_2CO_3[70] is given in Table 10–7. The sodium percentage is the percentage of Na meq of the total meq of cations by analysis. The range of concentration of boron is given for the more sensitive crops such as lemons, grapefruit, and navy beans (low number of the range) to the more tolerant crops such as carrots, cabbage, and alfalfa (higher number in the range). The "residual Na_2CO_3" of water is defined as follows:

$$\text{Residual } Na_2CO_3 = (CO_3^{--} + HCO_3^{-}) - (Ca^{++} + Mg^{++}) \quad (10\text{–}24)$$

TABLE 10–7

Guide to the quality of irrigation water

Specific conductance, mmho/cm	Sodium percentage	Boron, ppm	Residual Na_2CO_3 meq/l	Quality of irrigation water
<0.75	<65	0.3–1	$<<1.25$	Excellent to good
0.75–2.0	50–65	0.7–2	<1.25	Good to permissible
2.0–3.0	92	1–3	1.25–2.5	Doubtful to unsuitable
>3.0	>92	1.2–3.8	>2.5	Unsuitable

[68] Fried and Jackson, *Sci.*, 106:19 (1947).
[69] Wilcox, U.S.D.A. Cir. 784 (1948) (condensed and rearranged from this source).
[70] Wilcox *et al.*, *Soil Sci.*, 77:259 (1954).

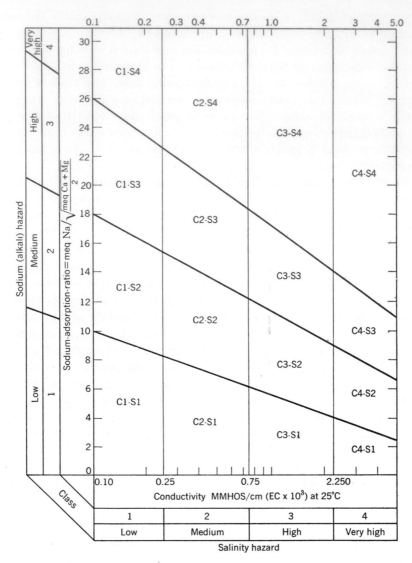

Fig. 10–7. Guide to quality of irrigation waters. (After Richards, ed., U.S.D.A. Agr. Handb. 60, 1954, p. 80.)

when all quantities are expressed as meq/liter. The salt content of river water tends to increase with distance from the source, especially if the water is repeatedly used for irrigation en route.

10–81. The following are representative analyses[71] of river water for conductance and individual ionic species.

---

[71] Wilcox, U.S.D.A. Tech. Bul. 962, Table 2 (1948).

	North Platte R. Scottsbluff, Nebr., 1945	Gila R. Amhurst-Hyden Dam Ariz., 1933
L mmho/cm	0.28	1.33
Per cent Na	22.	60.
B, ppm	0.03	0.20
Silica, SiO_2, ppm	15.	15.
Cations: meq/l.		
Ca	1.61	3.39
Mg	0.57	1.59
Na	0.63	7.75
K	0.07	0.25
Total	2.88	12.98
Anions: meq/l.		
CO_3	0.0	0.30
HCO_3	1.59	2.75
SO_4	1.12	2.29
Cl	0.09	7.07
NO_3	0.03	0.01
Total	2.83	12.42

10–82. Sodium Determination. An aliquot for Na analysis is transferred to a small beaker and the Na is determined by emission spectrophotometry (¶ 18–16). Determination of Na can also be made by the sodium magnesium uranyl acetate procedure. An aliquot of extract equivalent to 1 to 5 mgm of Na is transferred to a small Pyrex beaker, neutralized with HOAc, and evaporated to a volume of 1 ml, with care not to evaporate to dryness with consequent dehydration of silica. The Na is precipitated from this solution (¶ 5–81). The change in specific gravity caused by uranyl acetate precipitation of Na has been adapted to rapid testing.[72]

10–83. Potassium Determination. An aliquot for K analysis is transferred to a small beaker and determined by emission spectrophotometry (¶ 18–16). Determination of K can also be made by precipitation as the cobaltinitrite. An aliquot containing 0.5 to 5 mgm of K is transferred to a Pyrex beaker, ammonia is removed, and the precipitation is effected (¶ 6–20). The K can be estimated in rapid testing by the turbidimetric cobaltinitrate procedures (¶ 13–56).

10–84. Combined Sodium and Potassium Determination. A simple approximation method[73] for the estimation of combined Na and K is provided by their combined weight as the chlorides and the chloride content (similar to the titration of the combined alkali carbonates, ¶ 4–49). Bray's alcoholic $(NH_4)_2CO_3$ solution is prepared by dissolution of 100 gm of powdered $(NH_4)_2CO_3$ in 190 ml of water and addition of 210 ml of concen-

[72] Bower, *J. Am. Soc. Agron.*, 40:1100 (1948).
[73] Division of Soils, University of Nebraska (1935).

trated NH_4OH. This solution is then diluted with an equal volume of 95 per cent ethanol as needed. The filtrate from the precipitation of sulfate as $BaSO_4$ (¶ 10–102) is evaporated to dryness in a porcelain dish and 5 ml of water and 20 ml of Bray's reagent are then added. The mixture is stirred occasionally for a half hour or more (or over night) and then is filtered through a dry paper. The filter is washed with Bray's reagent and then discarded. The filtrate is evaporated to dryness in a weighed platinum or rhodium dish and ignited to faint redness (540°C) to expel ammonium salts. The residue is taken up in water and a few drops of HCl and brought to dryness again, then dried in an oven at 110°C. The residue is weighed as combined NaCl and KCl. The residue is dissolved in water and made to volume in a volumetric flask. The Cl is determined by titration (¶ 10–94) of a suitable aliquot diluted to 50 ml. Then:

$$\text{weight Na} = 3.004 \text{ (chloride)} - 1.428 \text{ (residue)} \qquad (10\text{–}25)$$

$$\text{weight K} = 2.428 \text{ (residue)} - 4.004 \text{ (chloride)} \qquad (10\text{–}26)$$

in which (chloride) and (residue) refer to the weights of Cl and combined NaCl and KCl.

10–85. Calcium Determination. An aliquot for Ca analysis is transferred to a small beaker and the Ca is determined by emission spectrophotometry (¶ 18–16). Determination of Ca (0.2 to 5 mgm) can also be made by procedures employing Versene (¶ 11–47) or oxalate (¶ 5–38).

10–86. Magnesium Determination. An aliquot for Mg analysis is transferred to a small beaker and determined by emission spectrophotometry (¶ 18–16). Determination of Mg (0.3 to 2 mgm) can also be made by procedures employing Versene (¶ 11–59) or hydroxy quinoline (¶ 5–59).

DISSOLVED CARBONATE AND BICARBONATE DETERMINATION

("Total alkalinity" of waters)

10–87. The titration of dissolved carbonate (CO_3^{--}) and bicarbonate (HCO_3^-) in waters, including soil solutions, as conventionally carried out, is often termed "total alkalinity" because it includes the usually small amounts of phosphates, borates, and silicates as well as the two species of carbonate ions. The alkalinity other than bicarbonates and carbonates in waters and soil solutions are generally small enough to be negligible, and thus the total alkalinity is virtually equivalent to the 2 dissolved carbonates. Solid carbonate is determined separately as carbonate carbon (¶ 10–121).

APPARATUS

10–88. Needed apparatus includes a 150-ml beaker, a 50-ml pipet, and a buret for standard 0.05 N H_2SO_4.

REAGENTS

10–89. Needed reagents are standardized 0.05 N H_2SO_4, phenolphthalein and methyl orange pH indicators (alternatively, brom phenol blue pH indicator may be substituted for methyl orange).

PROCEDURE[74]

10–90. To 50 ml of water sample in a 150-ml beaker, 0.15 ml of phenolphthalein indicator is added and, if a pink color develops, normal carbonate (CO_3^{--}) is present. The CO_3^{--} is titrated with 0.05 N H_2SO_4, a drop being added every 2 or 3 seconds until the pink color disappears. The buret reading in ml multiplied by 2 gives the CO_3^{--} as meq per liter, or equivalents per million parts of solution.

10–91. Bicarbonate Titration. To the solution resulting from the CO_3^{--} titration, or to the original solution if no pink color resulted, 0.1 ml of methyl orange or brom phenol blue indicator is added, and the titration is continued (without a refilling of the buret) to the first change in the methyl orange color or to the midcolor of brom phenol blue. The total buret reading is recorded. The solution is reserved for the chloride determination.

10–92. If CO_3^{--} was absent, the buret reading in ml is numerically equal to the meq of HCO_3^- per liter, or equivalents per million parts of solution. If CO_3^{--} was present, the CO_3^{--} titer in ml multiplied by 2 is subtracted from the total titer volume and the difference in ml is the meq of HCO_3^- per liter or the equivalents per million parts of solution. Blanks are run on the reagents and subtracted from the determinations.

10–93. If small amounts of CO_3^{--} are determined in the presence of large amounts of HCO_3^-, a more accurate evaluation of CO_3^{--} can be obtained by the use of the Hirsch carbonate equilibria slide rule.[75]

CHLORIDE DETERMINATION

10–94. As $AgNO_3$ solution is titrated into a chloride solution in the presence of CrO_4, only momentary formation of red Ag_2CrO_4 occurs so long as some chloride persists in the solution. When the Cl in solution is exhausted through precipitation as AgCl, the red precipitate of Ag_2CrO_4 sharply signals the end point. Alternatively, an Ag-AgCl electrode also sharply registers the change to an excess of Ag ion. Thus the $AgNO_3$ titration of chloride is the standard method, either end point measurement being satisfactory. The electrode method may be employed in the presence of soil and thus eliminates the need of extraction, if only chloride is to be determined.

---

[74] Magistad *et al.*, *Soil Sci.*, 59:65 (1945).
[75] *Ind. Eng. Chem., A.E.*, 14:943 (1942).

10–95. Needed apparatus includes a white casserole or other dish, a buret, and pipets.

REAGENTS

10–96. Needed reagents are 0.1 N H_2SO_4 and 0.1 N Na_2CO_3, phenolphthalein indicator, standard NaCl (2.923 gm per liter for 0.05 N; 1.648 gm per liter for 1 mgm Cl per ml), and the following special reagents.

10–97. Standard Silver Nitrate Solution. Exactly 8.494 gm of $AgNO_3$ is dissolved in water and diluted to 1 liter to obtain an 0.05 N solution. (Alternatively 4.791 gm per liter gives a solution each ml of which is equivalent to 1 mgm of Cl.) The $AgNO_3$ solution concentration is usually checked by titration against a standard solution of NaCl.

10–98. Potassium Chromate Indicator. Approximately 5 gm of K_2CrO_4 is dissolved in 80 ml of water, and then saturated $AgNO_3$ solution is added dropwise with stirring until a permanent red precipitate is produced. The solution is filtered, and the filtrate is diluted to 100 ml.

PROCEDURE[76]

10–99. The solution employed for the bicarbonate titration (or a fresh solution containing 5 to 25 mgm of chloride in a volume of 25 to 100 ml, obtained by dilution or evaporation; the pH is adjusted to 8.2, just colorless to phenolphthalein indicator with 0.1 N H_2SO_4 or 0.1 N Na_2CO_3 solution) is employed for the chloride titration. One ml of the chromate indicator is added and the solution is titrated with the standard $AgNO_3$ solution to the appearance of the first permanent red coloration due to precipitation of Ag_2CrO_4. A blank is titrated consisting of the same volume of chloride-free water. For a 50-ml aliquot of water, the net ml titer, after subtraction of the blank, is equal to the equivalent of Cl per million parts of solution (or equal to the mgm of Cl titrated with the alternative $AgNO_3$ standard solution).

ALTERNATIVE PROCEDURES

10–100. More than 25 mgm of Cl may be determined satisfactorily by precipitation as AgCl and weighing.[77] In order to avoid a large excess of the $AgNO_3$ precipitation reagent, a preliminary titration of the Cl is made. The pH of the solution is adjusted as in the regular procedure and a slight excess of $AgNO_3$ is added. The solution is heated to boiling, protected from light,

---

[76] Magistad et al., Soil Sci., 59:73 (1945), which is only slightly modified from Methods of Analysis, 6th ed. (Washington, D.C.: A.O.A.C., 1945), p. 632.

[77] This procedure is employed for standardization of HCl after neutralization with the $CaCO_3$, Methods of Analysis, 6th ed. (Washington, D.C.: A.O.A.C., 1945), p. 25.

and allowed to stand until the precipitate is granular. The precipitate is filtered on a Gooch crucible (previously weighed at 140° to 150°). The precipitate is washed with hot water and the filtrate is tested to verify an excess of $AgNO_3$. The AgCl is dried at 140° to 150°C and weighed.

10–101. The silver-silver chloride electrode may be substituted[78] for the chromate indicator in the $AgNO_3$ titration of Cl. The cell consisted of the following:

$$Pt, Quinhydrone, KNO_3 \parallel KNO_3 \parallel AgCl, Ag \qquad (10–27)$$
$$\text{(Sat.)} \quad \text{(Sat., in agar)} \quad \text{(In the Cl}^-\text{ solution)}$$

in which $\parallel$ represents a liquid junction and AgCl, Ag the silver-silver chloride electrode. Standardized dilute $AgNO_3$ is buretted into the soil suspension and the equivalence point is indicated when a rapid shift occurs in the potential of the cell.

SULFATE DETERMINATION

10–102. Sulfate in extracts and waters is conventionally determined gravimetrically as $BaSO_4$. The sulfate solution is made 0.1 to 0.3 N in HCl and boiled to remove carbonates, and then $BaCl_2$ is added to cause the precipitation (¶ 11–188). Because precipitation, digestion, filtration, washing, ignition, and weighing constitute a time-consuming procedure, rapid titrimetric and turbidimetric procedures have been developed. The titrimetric procedure presented here is based on the Versene chelation of the excess Ba remaining after $BaSO_4$ precipitation. The Versene indicator for Mg is employed and therefore Mg is introduced into the system, to be chelated at the end point after the Ba has been completely chelated.[79] Because an excess of barium chloride is employed, the sulphate is precipitated quantitatively, even in very low concentration. It is not necessary to remove the precipitate prior to the titration of the excess Ba, and therefore the procedure is rapid.

10–103. The sulfate range to which the method is applicable is from 5 to 200 ppm. Interferences occur with Cu, Mn, Co, and Ni, but the concentrations of these ions are generally not sufficiently high to interfere with sulfate determination in most soils and natural waters. Modifications (¶ 11–56) provide for elimination of their interference.[80]

APPARATUS

10–104. Required apparatus includes conical titration flasks, pipets, and burets.

---

[78] Best, *Trans. 4th Intern. Congr. Soil Sci.*, 3:162 (1950).

[79] Biedermann and Schwarzenbach, *Chimia*, 2:56 (1948).

[80] Diehl *et al.*, *J. Am. Water Works Assoc.*, 42:40 (1950), also provide for their elimination.

10–105. Required reagents include 0.02 N $MgCl_2$, $BaCl_2$, and Versene solutions that are standardized against a standard Ca solution (below); Eriochrome black T, 0.5 gm of the indicator with 4.5 gm of hydroxyl amine in 100 ml of methanol (¶ 11–55); and reagents for dissolved carbonate and bicarbonate (¶ 10–89) except that standard HCl is employed instead of standard H_2SO_4.

10–106. A buffer solution is required consisting of 8.25 gm of NH_4Cl and 113 ml of concentrated reagent NH_4OH in 1 liter, a concentration that should give pH 10.0 when 10 ml is added to a 50-ml aliquot of water sample.

10–107. A standard 0.02 N Ca solution is required for the standardization of the Versene, Ba, and Mg solutions. It is prepared by dissolution of 1.001 gm of dried $CaCO_3$ in a minimum of 1 : 50 HCl; the solution is boiled to expel the CO_2 and then diluted to 1 liter.

PROCEDURE[81]

10–108. The combined Ca and Mg are determined by titration with Versene (¶ 11–54). On a second aliquot, the "total alkalinity" is determined by titration with HCl (not the usual H_2SO_4 solution) (¶ 10–90). To a third aliquot, the standard HCl equivalent to the alkalinity or slightly more is added and the sample is boiled to destroy carbonates. Then a known amount (enough to exceed the sulfate) of the standard $BaCl_2$ solution is added, and the solution mixture is allowed to boil for a few seconds. Then it is cooled, 10 ml of buffer and 5 drops of Eriochrome black T indicator are added. Finally the solution is titrated with the standard Versene solution to the first end point. The first end point cannot be used as final because the accuracy is poor even when the standard solution containing some magnesium ion is employed. A small, known volume of standard Mg solution is added, and a second end point is obtained by titration with additional Versene solution. The titration is stopped at the same end point as for the original determination of Ca plus Mg.

10–109. Calculation of Results. The meq of sulfate ion may be calculated as follows:

$$\text{meq of SO}_4 = (B + \text{Ba} + \text{Mg} - T) \qquad (10\text{–}28)$$

in which B is the blank, meq of Ca + Mg in the original water; Ba is the meq of Ba added, Mg is the meq of Mg added, and T is the meq of Versene added in the total titration of the sample with Ba and Mg added.

---

[81] Slightly modified from Munger *et al.*, *Anal. Chem.*, 22:1455 (1950).

10–110. Besides the gravimetric $BaSO_4$ (¶ 10–102) and Versene titrimetric methods for sulfate, a wide variety of other methods are available. Two[82] are the benzidine hydrochloride method and titration with barium chloride in the presence of disodium tetrahydroxy quinone (THQ) indicator. The latter is limited to fairly high concentrations of sulfate because $BaSO_4$ precipitates slowly when the sulfate concentration is low. Another titrimetric method is based on precipitation of sulfate and chromate with barium. Barium chromate is added in acid solution and the excess barium is then precipitated as chromate by addition of NaOH to pH 8.3; the excess chromate, recovered in the filtrate, is titrated with thiosulfate. This titer must[83] be standardized against standard sulfate solutions. A micro method has been described[84] for sulfate in the range of 1 to 300 ugm of S. Sulphate has been determined by conductance or oscillametric[85] titration with $BaCl_2$; this is an alternative to titration with $BaCl_2$ in the presence of tetrahydroxy quinone indicator.

10–111. Turbidimetric Sulfate Determination. The determination of sulfate through the turbidity developed on precipitation as $BaSO_4$ has long been an attractive and much used method. The estimation has been refined from relatively semiquantitative procedures to satisfactory quantitative procedures. Establishment of relative freedom from interference was made by Sheen et al.[86] The procedure here given is that of Chesnin and Yien.[87] To a 20.0-gm air-dry soil sample contained in a 250-ml conical flask is added a 100-ml volume of Morgan's extraction solution (100 gm of NaOAc and 30 ml of 99.5 per cent HOAc dissolved and mixed in 500 ml of water, and the volume made to 1 liter). The suspension is shaken for one-half hour and then is filtered through Whatman's No. 42 filter paper (or centrifuged until clear). A 10- or 20-ml aliquot is transferred to a 25-ml volumetric flask. The precipitation is then carried out with 1 gm (cup measure) of sized $BaCl_2$ crystals (agate mortar ground to pass 0.5 mm and to be caught on 0.25 sieve) added to the aliquot in the flask followed by 1-minute of shaking. Then:

1. if the sulfate is below 20 ppm, one ml of 0.25 per cent gum acatia solution is added.
2. if the sulfate is between 20 and 40 ppm, 2 ml of gum acatia solution is added.

---

[82] *Standard Methods for Examination of Water and Sewage,* 9th ed. (New York: *Am. Pub. Health Assoc.,* 1946).
[83] Cantino, *Soil Sci.,* 61:361 (1946).
[84] Johnson and Nishita, *Anal. Chem.,* 24:736 (1952).
[85] Milner, *Anal. Chem.,* 24:1247 (1952).
[86] *Ind. Eng. Chem., A.E.,* 7:262 (1935).
[87] *S.S.S.A. Proc.,* 15:149 (1951).

The suspension is made to volume and shaken for 1 minute. Turbidity readings (blue filter in colorimeter) are taken between 5 and 30 minutes after the precipitation, and the sulfate is then determined by reference to a standard sulfate curve.

10–112. Exchange Column Purification of Sulfate Solutions. According to Samuelson,[88] Bahrdt[89] published a method for the rapid estimation of sulfate in natural waters. The water to be analyzed was softened in a laboratory column containing sodium zeolite. To the effluent from the column, a known amount of barium chloride was added, and the excess barium was back titrated by means of potassium palmitate. The Ca and Mg were taken up so effectively that they could not be detected in the effluent water, and therefore their interference with the palmitate method was completely removed. Present day organic resin exchangers for cations may be employed for the Bahrdt separation; his sulfate determination by difference with Ba may be completed with Versene titration or with flame emission instead of palmitate.

GYPSUM DETERMINATION FOR SOILS

10–113. The content of gypsum, $CaSO_4 \cdot 2 H_2O$, in soil is commonly estimated by the separate determinations of Ca (¶ 5–38) and SO_4 (¶ 10–102) in a water extract that is made at a sufficiently dilute soil : water ratio to permit dissolution of all the gypsum. A 1 : 5 soil : water ratio dissolves gypsum to the extent of 1.3 per cent of the soil (¶ 10–18). Extraction of the soil solution or of the saturation extract (¶ 10–27) removes $CaSO_4$ only to the extent that it normally contributes to the osmotic pressure of the soil solution in the field. The determination of total gypsum in soil is, however, an important aspect of soil soluble salt analysis. Reitemeier[90] found that 3 factors besides the solution of gypsum may influence the amount of Ca and SO_4 extracted from soil: (a) solution of Ca from sources other than gypsum, for example from $CaCO_3$; (b) exchange reactions by which the dissolved Ca replaces some ions, such as Na and Mg; and (c) the solution of SO_4 from sources other than gypsum. These errors preclude a highly accurate determination of gypsum.

10–114. Because the separate determination of Ca and SO_4 ions is a fairly lengthy procedure, a rapid conductance method for gypsum determination was developed by Bower and Huss,[91] which is given below. Those authors found good concordance of the conductance method with the de-

[88] Samuelson, *Ion Exchangers in Analytical Chemistry* (New York: John Wiley & Sons, Inc., 1953), p. 2.

[89] Bahrdt, *Z. anal. Chem.*, 70:109 (1927).

[90] *Ind. Eng. Chem., A.E.*, 15:393 (1943).

[91] *Soil Sci.*, 66:199 (1948).

termination of the separate ions, whether either Ca or SO_4 was present in excess.

APPARATUS

10–115. Needed apparatus consists of 250-ml extraction flasks and stoppers; 10-ml and 20-ml pipets; filter paper of medium porosity and a funnel; a centrifuge and conical tube of 50-ml capacity; and a conductivity cell and resistance or conductance bridge, such as described in ¶ 10–21.

REAGENTS

10–116. Needed reagents consist of water for the soil extraction and reagent grade acetone.

PROCEDURE[92]

10–117. A suitable weight of air-dry soil that has passed a 2-mm round hole sieve (10 gm of soil for each 50 ml of water extract if the gypsum content is not over 1.3 per cent) is placed in a 250-ml extraction flask and distilled water in sufficient volume is added to dissolve the gypsum present. Fifty ml of water will dissolve approximately 0.1 gm of $CaSO_4$ or 0.13 gm of $CaSO_4 \cdot 2\,H_2O$ or approximately 1.5 meq of the salt. If the gypsum content is found to approach 1.3 per cent or 15 meq per 100 gm of soil (in a 10-gm per 50-ml extraction), the determination should be repeated with a more dilute extract. Air-dry soil is used rather than oven-dry soil because oven drying converts the gypsum to $CaSO_4 \cdot 0.5\,H_2O$, which has a higher solubility in water for an indefinite period following solution.[93]

10–118. The bottle is stoppered and shaken by hand 6 times at 15-minute intervals or agitated for 30 minutes in a mechanical shaker. The suspension is filtered through a paper of medium porosity and a 20-ml aliquot of the filtered extract containing 0.1 to 0.6 meq of $CaSO_4$ is placed in a 50-ml conical centrifuge tube. To the tube is then added 20 ml of acetone, the contents of the tube are mixed, and the suspension is allowed to stand until the precipitate flocculates, usually 5 to 10 minutes. The suspension is clarified by centrifugation at 1000 times gravity (2000 rpm with a 24-cm radius) for 3 minutes. The supernatant liquid is decanted away and the tube is inverted to drain on filter paper for 5 minutes. The precipitate is then dispersed in the fresh 10-ml portion of acetone delivered from a pipet so as to wash down the walls of the tube. The centrifugation, decantation, and drainage on a filter paper is repeated as before. Finally exactly 40 ml of distilled water is added to the tube, which is stoppered and shaken until the precipitate is completely dissolved. Electrical conductance of the solution is measured by the usual procedure (¶ 10–33). The conductance is corrected to 25°C (it increases 2 per cent per degree centigrade).

[92] Essentials of the procedure are from Bower and Huss, *Soil Sci.,* 66:199 (1948).
[93] Reitemeier and Ayers, *J. Am. Chem. Soc.,* 69:2759 (1947).

10–119. The gypsum content of the solution is found by reference to a graph of the following data given by Bower and Huss from the International Critical Tables.[94]

CaSO$_4$ concentration meq/liter	Electrical conductance at 25°C millimhos/cm
1	0.121
2	0.226
5	0.500
10	0.900
20	1.584
30.5	2.205

A close approximation of the graph is provided by the relation:

$$\text{meq of CaSO}_4 \text{ per liter} = L_{\text{mmho/ cm}} \times 12.5 \qquad (10\text{–}29)$$

as in equation 10–10.

10–120. The meq of CaSO$_4 \cdot$ 2 H$_2$O in the soil is found by reference to the soil : water ratio employed in the extraction. The percentage of gypsum in the soil may be calculated from the meq of gypsum present:

$$\% \text{ CaSO}_4 \cdot 2 \text{ H}_2\text{O in soil} = \text{meq per 100 gm of soil} \times 0.0861 \quad (10\text{–}30)$$

CARBONATE CARBON DETERMINATION FOR SOILS
("Inorganic" carbon of soils)

10–121. The carbonate carbon of soils, as opposed to organic carbon (¶ 9–1), occurs as various sparingly soluble alkaline earth compounds such as CaCO$_3$ (calcite, the chief carbonate resulting from pedogenesis) and dolomite, CaCO$_3 \cdot$ MgCO$_3$, which occurs in some parent materials. Rare occurrence of pedogenic dolomite has been reported.[95] Removal of carbonate carbon has been mentioned in connection with the determination of organic carbon (¶ 9–14). Since the alkaline earth carbonates are somewhat soluble, they interfere with the determination of exchangeable cations (¶ 5–2) and also affect the composition of the extracted soil solution (¶ 10–18). Soluble carbonates and bicarbonates are determined by titration in solution (¶ 10–87). Gaseous CO$_2$ occurs as a part of the soil atmosphere, but the amount is inappreciable in terms of percentage of mineral carbonate in soils even if the content is as high as 20 per cent of the soil gases.

10–122. Carbonate carbon can be estimated for soils, as for limestone, from neutralizing equivalence (¶ 4–66). Carbonate carbon is quantitatively determined by evolution of CO$_2$ by treatment of the soil sample with acid.

---

[94] Vol. 1, pp. 231, 236.
[95] Sherman, M. S. Thesis, Univ. of Minn. (1937); Sherman and Thiel, *Bul. Geol. Soc. Am.*, 50:1535 (1939).

The CO_2 evolved is collected in standard hydroxide solution followed by back titration of the excess hydroxide. The procedure is similar to that for organic carbon (¶ 9–21), but involves essential differences. The CO_2 evolved may also be determined gasiometrically. The different mineral species of sparingly soluble carbonates are sensitively determined by X-ray diffraction analysis and polarizing microscope. Allocations between Ca and Mg forms can also be made by elemental analysis (¶ 4–74).

APPARATUS

10–123. Needed apparatus is the same as for organic carbon by wet oxidation and determination as CO_2 (¶ 9–24).

REAGENTS

10–124. Needed reagents are alcoholic phenolphthalein indicator, 0.04 per cent brom thymol blue indicator (1 ml of this to 10 ml of water in the trap, Fig. 9–3), CO_2-free water, approximately 0.5 N NaOH (20 gm per liter), approximately 1 M $BaCl_2$ (244 gm of $BaCl_2 \cdot 2\ H_2O$ per liter of CO_2-free water and adjusted to neutrality) and approximately 1 N HCl containing 5 gm of $SnCl_2 \cdot 2\ H_2O$ per 100 ml.

PROCEDURE

10–125. The soil sample is first passed through a 0.2-mm screen. A sample containing considerably less than 0.625 gm of $CaCO_3$ equivalent (10 gm of soil containing 5 per cent $CaCO_3$ or less or 0.25 gm of limestone is taken) is weighed out and transferred to the sample flask. The sample flask is then attached to the apparatus. To free the train of CO_2, a flow of CO_2-free air is sent through for 1 or 2 minutes longer than required for the brom thymol blue in the trap to turn from yellow to blue. Then 25 ml of 0.5 N NaOH is pipetted into the CO_2 absorption flask followed by 50 ml of CO_2-free water. The condenser cooling water is started, while the flow of CO_2-free air is continued. The bead tower is lowered to dip into the NaOH until the solution reaches the top of the beads and then the bead tower is raised so that no more NaOH solution enters. The air flow is regulated to about 3 to 5 bubbles per second. Next, 50 ml of 1 N HCl (with 5 per cent $SnCl_2$[96]) is added through the separatory funnel, slowly at first if the sample is high in carbonate. A small flame with a wind shield is placed under the sample flask and the suspension is slowly brought to boiling. The boiling is continued for 5 minutes longer than required for the brom thymol blue in the trap to change from yellow to blue.

10–126. The CO_2 evolved is collected in the absorption flask (Fig. 9–3)

---

[96] Inclusion of $SnCl_2$ is after *Methods of Analysis,* 7th ed. (Washington, D.C.: A.O.A.C., 1950), p. 30.

and determined by back titration with standard HCl after addition of $BaCl_2$ (¶ 9–30). The carbonate carbon is calculated as follows:

$$\text{meq of } CO_2 = (S - T) \times N \qquad (10\text{--}31)$$

in which S is the standardization blank titration, T is the back titration and N refers to the normality of the standard HCl. Also:

$$\% \ CaCO_3 = \text{meq } CO_2 \times \frac{5}{s} \qquad (10\text{--}32)$$

in which s is the sample weight in gm, and the factor 5 is derived from the meq weight of $CaCO_3$ $(100/2000) \times 100$.

ALTERNATIVE PROCEDURES

10–127. The CO_2 may be passed through a $Mg(ClO_4)_2$ bulb to remove water vapor and then be collected in a gravimetric absorption bulb and weighed instead of being titrated. In the absence of $MgCO_3$ (as magnesite or dolomite), the CO_2 can be evolved without heating (¶ 4–77) and determined gasiometrically.

QUESTIONS

1. List the principal ions that are likely to be present as soluble salts in soils.

2. Describe the procedure for direct qualitative determination of soil salinity conductometrically on a soil paste. What difficulties are involved?

3. What is the reason for conversion of the conductance readings to specific conductance?

4. Define: (a) specific conductance, (b) cell constant, (c) salt bridge, (d) millimhos/cm.

5. Why must tables generally be employed to convert resistance readings to salt content, while a proportionality factor can be used for conversion of conductance readings?

6. By what mechanism is the electric current carried through the solution portion of conductance circuit?

7. State the approximate relation between the magnitude of the wilting percentage, field capacity percentage, and saturation percentage of soil moisture.

8. What is the main influence of an excess of soluble salts in soils on growth of plants?

9. Why is the specific conductance of the soil saturation extract a more valid measurement of soil salinity than the specific conductance of an extract made with a constant soil : water ratio?

10. State the upper limit of the specific conductance (mmho/cm) of the soil saturation extract:

(a) Above which even salt tolerant crops do not thrive.

(b) Above which only a few highly salt tolerant plants survive.

(c) Above which crops tolerant of salts thrive but those nontolerant do not.

11. What is the effect of making the extraction with more and more dilute soil : water ratios on salt concentration calculated to the soil basis? Consider the several possible cases.

12. List the numerical factors for conversion of $L_{mmho/cm}$ to:
(a) meq of salt per liter
(b) equivalents per million
(c) ppm in solution
(d) osmotic pressure of solution
(e) per cent in soil

13. What evidence is there that the soil solution may be displaced from a soil by means of a solution infiltrated through a column of soil?

14. Explain the reason for sharp differentiation between bare spots and tall growth of a crop in a field affected by salinity.

15. Define the "enrichment ratio" with reference to runoff waters.

16. State the principle involved in the analytical determination in soluble salt solutions from soils of (a) bicarbonate, (b) carbonate, (c) sulfate, and (d) chloride.

11

Elemental Analysis of Mineral Colloids, Soils, Minerals, and Rocks

The elements and their combination

11–1. Elemental analysis of soils and rocks is the determination of the total amount of a mineral element present in the sample. Historically elemental analysis was developed for the analysis of rocks and minerals. Later it was used to evaluate soil fertility directly from the quantities of the elements present, but was supplanted largely by the concept of "available" nutrients—exchangeable, extractable, and equilibrium-released ions, except for the minor elements Cu, Zn, and Mo (Chapter 15). Elemental analysis of mineral colloids now is employed mainly as a means to study their crystal chemistry and their allocation to the mineral species present. Such application of soil chemical analysis is of great importance to the fundamental interpretations of the chemical processes of soil development and as a background to soil fertility interpretations.

11–2. The elements of soils and rocks are usually combined as constituents of 1 or more minerals. Because ionic oxygen is the major anion in silicates, the elemental constituents are generally reported as the percentages of oxides, so that the total approaches 100 per cent of the ignited sample weight (¶ 11–3). There is also a logical basis for reporting the analyses as the percentage of the element. The equivalent percentages of O, F, and OH can readily be included so that the analyses tend to total 100 per cent as before. The basis for reporting has no bearing on either the choice or execution of the procedures.

11–3. Ignited Weight Basis. The ignited weight basis is in some respects the most satisfactory for reporting the results of elemental analysis because the organic matter and combined water are not determined as an integral part of the elemental analysis system. Thus most of the constituents are determined in or calculated to the ignited state, and the determinations thus add up to 100 per cent within the accuracy and completeness of the elemental determinations.

11–4. Oven-Dry Weight Basis. Strictly speaking, the H_2O, $-OH$ and other constituents are integral parts of the sample and should be determined as part of the elemental analysis. The weight loss at 100°C is usually reported as adsorbed water (¶ 11–5) or $H_2O(-)$. The loss between 100°C and 800° to 1000°C is reported as organic matter and $H_2O(+)$. Frequently the losses are calculated on the 100°C weight basis, adsorbed H_2O thus being excluded from the 100 per cent total. Fluoride, sulfide, $MgCl_2$, and other salts, if present in the sample, constitute a portion of the volatile matter losses at 800° to 1000°C. Except for losses of such constituents, interconversion is readily made between the 100° and the ignited basis of reporting elemental analyses.

11–5. The analytical sample, unless derived from suspension (¶ 11–12), is often weighed out in the air-dry condition. A separate sample is taken for the determination of adsorbed water. There is no precise oven temperature or period of drying at which all of the hygroscopic water and none of the water of constitution have been driven off. The common procedure for bulk materials consists of drying a separate 3-gm sample in a dish for which a tightly fitting cover is available, at 100° to 110°C for 10 to 16 hours for removal of hygroscopic moisture; then cooling it in a desiccator for 0.5 hour and weighing. The weight after such drying is the oven-dry basis for the analysis, the basis employed for most common soil analyses.

11–6. Methods of Bringing the Sample into Solution. The usual 2 procedures for bringing the elements of sample into solution are (a) fusion in Na_2CO_3, or (b) some system of heating in acids such as with HF, $HClO_4$, H_3PO_4, and H_2SO_4. These 2 procedures are used in the analytical systems detailed in this chapter. A few minerals such as chromite and zircon do not become soluble through these treatments, and another type of fusion, such as in Na_2O_2 or $K_2S_2O_7$ (¶ 11–198) is necessary.

11–7. Systems of Elemental Analysis. Systems of elemental analysis may be divided into 4 categories:

1. Rapid micro and semimicro absorption spectrophotometric (colorimetric) systems

2. Micro and semimicro emission spectrophotometric (flame, arc, spark) systems

3. Semimicro titrimetric systems

4. Macro gravimetric systems

11–8. The 3 main factors that dictate the choice of method of analysis are accuracy, speed, and simplicity. For macro samples, conventional gravimetric and titrimetric systems[1] are usually considered to be more accurate[2] than the semimicrochemical spectrophotometric methods. For semimicro samples, spectrophotometric methods are more accurate and have the advantages of greater simplicity and rapidity. Absorption spectrophotometry (Chapter 17) has progressed sufficiently far to permit the majority of analyses to be made by that means.[3] Emission spectrophotometry (Chapter 18) with flame excitation is the easiest and most accurate for the alkali metals and is usually satisfactory for the alkaline earth metals. Analyses of difficultly separable elements having nearly the same chemical properties requires the specificity of emission spectrophotometry (Chapter 18). Micro samples, such as individual sand grains that are to be analyzed to correlate with their respective individual optical properties, or soil specimens to be employed for criminal case work also require the sensitivity of the spectrograph (¶ 18–51).

11–9. Because of the simplicity and great saving in time, a semimicrochemical spectrophotometric and titrimetric system of elemental analysis is given first for the elements Si, Al, Fe, Ti, Ca, Mg, K, and Na. A combination of several of the general types of systems conventionally employed is given as a second system. In the second (conventional) system, the more abundant constituents, such as Si and Al, are determined gravimetrically, whereas the constituents present in intermediate amounts, such as Fe (including ferrous iron separately), Ca, Mg, and K, are determined titrimetrically, and the least abundant constituents, such as Ti, Mn, and P, are determined colorimetrically. The separate determinations of ferrous iron, S, F, Zr, and Li are considered near the end of this chapter.

---

[1] Comprehensive treatises of the classical methods of elemental analysis are available; Hillebrand and Lundell, *Applied Inorganic Analysis* (with special reference to the analysis of metals, minerals, and rocks) (New York: John Wiley & Sons, Inc., 1929); Hillebrand, U.S. Geol. Surv. Bul. 700 (1919); Groves, *Silicate Analysis,* 2nd ed. (London: George Allan & Unwin Ltd., 1951); Jakob, *Chemische Analyse Der Gesteine Und Silikatischen Mineralien* (Basel, Switzerland: Verlag Birkhauser, 1952); Washington, *Manual of the Chemical Analysis of Rocks,* 3rd ed. (New York: John Wiley & Sons, Inc., 1919); Mellor, *A Treatise on Quantitative Inorganic Analysis with Special Reference to the Analysis of Clays, Silicates and Related Minerals* (London: Charles Griffin & Company, Ltd., 1913).

[2] Even with the greatest care, the accuracy of the conventional methods is not as high as often is supposed, as indicated by comparative studies by Schlecht, *Anal. Chem.,* 23:1568 (1951); Fairbairn, U.S. Geol. Surv., Cir. 980 (1951); Fairbairn and Schairer, *Am. Mineral,* 37:744 (1952).

[3] Colorimetric systems have been presented by Guthrie and Miller, *Mineralogical Mag.,* 23:405 (1933); Hecht, *Mikrochim. Acta,* 2:188 (1937), abstr. *Analyst,* 63:209; Hedin, *Colorimetric Methods For Rapid Analysis of Silicate Materials,* Proc. Swed. Cement and Concrete Res. Inst., Stockholm (1947); Shapiro and Brannock, U.S. Geol. Surv. Cir. 165 (1952); Corey and Jackson, *Anal. Chem.,* 25:624 (1953).

11–10. Methods of Checking Accuracy. Methods of checking the accuracy of silicate analysis consist of 1 or more of the following:

1. Analysis of pure chemicals (not satisfactory for the final check)

2. Addition of standard amounts to samples (test of increase in the recovery)

3. Analysis of standard samples, such as those provided by the National Bureau of Standards, and calculation of the standard deviation.

11–11. Preparation of the Soil or Rock Sample. A bulk soil or rock sample is sieved (¶ 2–58), mixed, air-dried, and quartered to a minimum of 1 kgm (¶ 2–63). In case of a rock or mineral, a hard steel mortar is used for coarse crushing. The -2 mm soil (¶ 2–60) is ground in an agate mortar[4] (¶ 2–62) and partitioned (¶ 2–66) until the final 5-gm portion is passed in its entirety through a 150-µ (100 meshes per inch) bolting cloth.

11–12. Preparation of the Mineral Colloid Sample. Minerals frequently require elaborate individual separations and purification or preconcentration in preparation for elemental analysis. Usually, from the mineral colloid suspension an aliquot is taken that contains the correct sample weight (known from drying a separate aliquot). The particles are flocculated with a minimum of HCl and thrown down by centrifugation. The sample is then washed by means of the centrifuge procedure (¶ 4–3) to remove all soluble electrolytes and exchangeable metallic cations, five times with 0.05 N HCl and twice each with 70 per cent ethanol, absolute methanol, and finally benzene (to remove oil originating from the supercentrifuge). The suspension is either transferred with methanol and water to the platinum crucible and dried for analysis, or (if prepared as a bulk sample) is transferred to a porcelain dish with benzene and dried.

11–13. Care and Use of Platinum Utensils.[5] Platinum utensils are virtually indispensable for accurate elemental analyses, but must be used with care because of their expensiveness. Platinum costs upwards of $3 per gm. An ordinary fusion crucible costs $100 or more. Platinum metal is remarkably resistant to a variety of chemicals although it is soluble to an appreciable extent (0.5 to 1 mgm per Na_2CO_3 fusion, for example) in the majority of the reagents that may "properly" be used in platinum utensils. Platinum has a melting point of about 1770°C but is appreciably volatile at 1000°C and above (about 0.1 mgm/cm²/hr at 1000°C and 1 mgm/cm²/hr at 1200°C). Corrections for volatility are made by heating the empty crucible for a similar time and weighing. Platinum density is 21.37.

---

[4] Robinson, *Soil Sci.,* 59:7 (1945).

[5] For additional information on the properties and care of platinum utensils the reader is referred to Kolthoff and Sandell, *Textbook of Quantitative Inorganic Analysis* (New York: The Macmillan Company, Inc., 1945), p. 179; and Hillebrand and Lundell, *Applied Inorganic Analysis* (New York: John Wiley & Sons, Inc., 1929), pp. 18–20, 272–273, 295.

Being too soft when pure, platinum is alloyed for stiffening, usually with a fraction of a per cent of iridium. The useful life of platinum utensils should be guarded by (a) keeping them chemically clean, (b) avoiding specific reagents in which platinum is soluble or reactive, and (c) handling them so as to keep them in good mechanical condition.

11–14. Cleaning and Burnishing Platinum Utensils. For satisfactory life, platinum utensils are kept clean and in proper mechanical condition. Cleaning should include chemical treatments as necessary to make the utensil appear clean, mechanical straightening and burnishing, and finally washing in 6 N HCl. The crucibles should be cleaned singly. The initial chemical cleaning procedure consists of:

1. Soaking in hot water and scrubbing; if not clean, then
2. Boiling in 6 N HCl for a few minutes. If still not clean, the crucible is dried, and
3. Fused with potassium pyrosulfate, $K_2S_2O_7$, the melt being poured into dry waste sand, and the residue dissolved from the crucible in warm 6 N HCl. If certain types of impurities persist, not usually the case except for crucibles that have been improperly used, the crucibles are further cleaned by
4. Fusion with Na_2CO_3, or, in some cases, digestion with a little HF to which 3 drops of H_2SO_4 have been added.

11–15. The cleaned crucible is straightened with a wood form or a smooth maple rod. It is then burnished with 0.1 to 0.5 mm rounded sea sand held on a soft cloth on the finger. (Ground powders are never used because of angularity and resulting abrasiveness.) Burnishing smooths the surface and retards the development of scale and cracks. The scale and microscopic cracks should be removed promptly because once started, they develop rapidly with further use of the utensil. Burnishing is not continued longer than necessary because there is always some abrasion of the platinum. Following burnishing, the crucible is warmed for a few minutes in 6 N HCl, rinsed with distilled water and dried in an oven, being grasped only with platinum tipped or pure nickel tongs.

11–16. Avoidance of Specific Reagents in Which Platinum is Soluble or Reactive. Although remarkably inert chemically, platinum is readily attacked, and may easily be alloyed and cracked by reactions with improper reagents added or products formed. Salient precautionary conditions are as follows:

1. Chlorine attacks platinum. Thus platinum utensils must not be digested in aqua regia, from which chlorine is liberated. Similarly, manganate liberates Cl_2 from HCl and, therefore, the manganate formed in the Na_2CO_3 fusion should be reduced by addition of ethanol or mechanically separated from the platinum before the addition of HCl. Two other halogens, free bromine and iodine, also attack platinum at ordinary temperatures. Salts of these elements should not be mixed with nitrates in acid solutions in platinum.

2. Ferric chloride in the presence of HCl attacks platinum, with the partial reduction of the iron to ferrous and the simultaneous appearance of platinum in solution. Such solutions should not be evaporated in platinum.

3. Hydroxides, oxides, peroxides, nitrites, and cyanides of the alkalies strongly attack platinum. Use of crucibles of other metals is necessary for fusions involving these fluxes. BaO also attacks platinum.

4. Reducing conditions, found in a luminous flame involving incomplete combustion or produced by contact with carbonaceous material in the absence of a good circulation of oxygen, are conducive to formation of platinum carbide. Silica and borate react with platinum under reducing conditions. However, silica and precipitated iron held in filter paper may be heated with a low, nonluminous flame with an abundant circulation of air without damage to the crucible if the paper and contents, placed in the crucible, are first oven-dried.

5. Reducing conditions may result in alloying the platinum with any easily reducible metal that is present. To be excluded from platinum are compounds of the following easily reducible elements, as well as the elements themselves: Ag, Pb, Hg, Bi, Sn, Sb, Se, and As. Free phosphorus, sulfur, and sulfides combine with platinum, and should, therefore, be excluded.

11–17. Precautions in Handling Platinum Utensils. Platinum utensils are easily damaged mechanically unless proper care is exercised. Most important precautions are as follows:

1. The utensils are handled in such a manner as to prevent deformation. Storing in cotton packing avoids denting by collision.

2. Triangles of platinum, silica-tubed wire, or pipe clay should be employed. Triangles of nichrome are fairly satisfactory for crucibles if kept scrupulously clean and dry, but are not satisfactory under large platinum dishes. Nichrome triangles have frequently been employed with a false sense of security. Iron triangles are never employed.

3. Platinum-tipped or pure nickel tongs are employed (never brass, nickel-plated, or iron tongs).

4. Before the burner is lighted, the utensils are put in place, and the mounting is checked for position with respect to the burner. Then the burner should be directed away, lighted, the flame adjusted to nonluminous, and the burner position fixed so that the platinum is well out of the green cone, which contains incompletely burned (reducing) gases.

5. Before the crucible is grasped after heating, it is allowed to cool momentarily. Stiffening of the platinum occurs as red heat is lost.

6. A porcelain plate, beaker, or asbestos pad is employed to set the platinum utensil on, never a desk top or ring stand.

11–18. As a matter of habit, the exterior of the platinum utensils should be kept chemically clean, because it frequently must be extracted by immersion in the solution, and because contaminants on the exterior may cause injury to the utensil. A good analyst always has his platinum well-shaped, bright, clean, and protected from damage and contamination. So used, the utensil will last for decades.

SEMIMICROCHEMICAL SYSTEM OF SILICATE ANALYSIS

11–19. Semimicro (0.1-gm) samples of mineral colloid, soil, mineral, or rock are analyzed for their content of the elements Si, Al, Fe, Ti, Ca, Mg, K and Na by rapid spectrophotometric techniques (¶ 11–7). Spectrophotometric determinations of Mn and of P (Chapter 7) can also be made with slight adaptations of the procedures. The principal problems in a rapid semimicrochemical system of analysis center around the chemical separations and flow sheet (¶ 11–22), rather than the spectrophotometric determinations of the individual constituents. This is true because procedures for the individual elements have become available in the field of general analytical chemistry. The separations of the constituents and the preparation of solutions free from interfering substances is the special contribution of the method.[6] The chemical determinations of the elements have been refined and adapted to fit the conditions resulting from the method employed for bringing the sample into solution and making the separations.

11–20. Extension of the Semimicrochemical System. The same elements from other sources, such as in solutions derived from differential solubility studies, may also be determined by the same procedures. Each element must be obtained in the proper concentration range in a solution free from interfering substances, and the salt concentration and pH values of the solution must be adjusted to approximately the same as in the procedure given in the semimicrochemical system.

11–21. Accuracy. The accuracy of the individual determinations in the semimicrochemical system is on the order of 1 to 3 per cent of the total amount of the constituent present. This accuracy of individual constituents permits an over-all accuracy of ±2 per cent, which is satisfactory for a majority of interpretations in which elemental analyses are applied. Although the precision is less than is ordinarily considered attainable with the conventional longer methods, the conventional methods themselves, even with the greatest care, are much less accurate than is sometimes supposed (¶ 11–8).

11–22. Flow Sheets. In general plan or flow sheet, the analytical system makes use of 2 0.1-gm samples, 1 of which is decomposed by heating with HF and $HClO_4$ (Fig. 11–1) and the other by fusion with Na_2CO_3 (Fig. 11–2). These reagents release the elements concerned from nearly all soil minerals (¶ 11–6). Two samples are necessary because it would be extremely difficult to determine Si and the alkali metals in the same sample. Separations are speeded by the use of volumetric pointed centrifuge tubes and centrifugation. The point in the flow sheet at which each element is

---

[6] Corey and Jackson, *Anal. Chem.,* 25:624 (1953); special thanks are due to Drs. L. D. Whittig and L. D. Swindale for assistance with several of the improvements included.

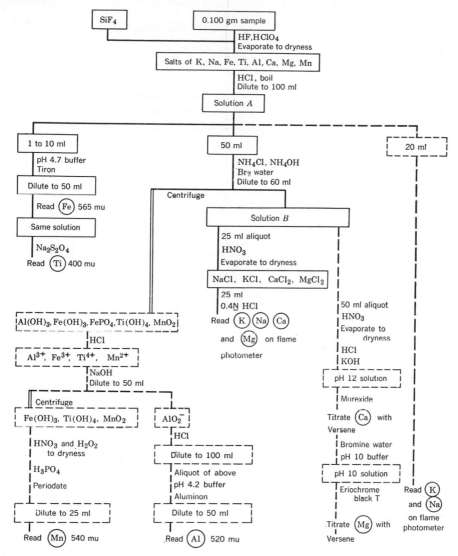

Fig. 11–1. Flow sheet for sample decomposed with HF in semimicrochemical system.

determined is indicated in a circle. Since 2 samples are employed, some of the elements may be determined in either sample. The procedures that are generally employed are shown in solid lines. Alternative procedures, which are usually employed when only 1 sample is analyzed (for fewer than 8 elements), or when the flame emission spectrophotometer is not available for Ca and/or Mg, are indicated by broken lines on the flow sheets.

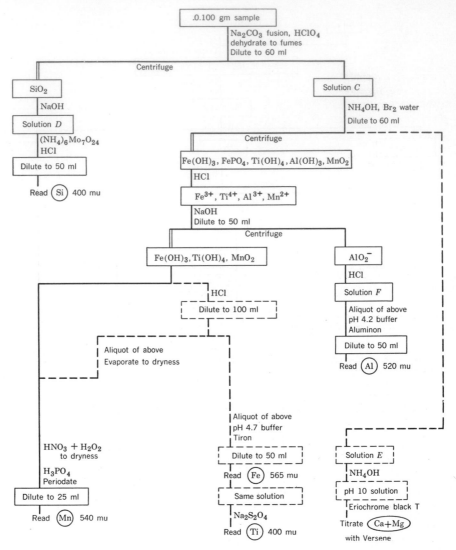

Fig. 11–2. Flow sheet for sample decomposed with Na_2CO_3 in semimicrochemical system.

11–23. The products obtained by the various procedures are enclosed in rectangular boxes. Reagents added and operations performed are listed beside the lines joining the boxes. The precipitates, indicated by double vertical lines above their boxes, are written to the left and the solutions to the right. The method of separation is shown under the horizontal line connecting each box to the rest of the flow sheet. The wave lengths refer to the light maxima employed for the respective determinations.

11–24. The sample decomposed by HF is used for the determination of K, Na, Ca, and Mg by the flame emission method. It is also used to determine Fe and Ti. Also, Ca and Mg can be determined by Versene if desired. Likewise it is possible to determine Al with this solution. The Na_2CO_3 fused sample is used for the determination of Si and Al. Also, the total of Mg plus Ca plus Mn can be determined by Versene if desired. It is also possible to determine Fe and Ti on this sample fused in Na_2CO_3. Analysis of 8 materials (4 in duplicate) for 8 elements can be accomplished in a few days, or, under ideal conditions, in 1 day.

11–25. The order of procedures adopted for greatest efficacy is as follows:

1. Decomposition of sample with HF (¶ 11–31), resulting in *Solution A* (Fig. 11–1)

2. Fusion of second sample in Na_2CO_3 (¶ 11–35), resulting in *Solutions C* and *D* (Fig. 11–2)

3. Determination of K, Na, Ca, and Mg by flame emission, on *Solution B* (¶ 11–37). [Alternatively, K and Na may be determined on *Solution A* (¶ 11–45) and Ca by flame emission or Versene (¶ 11–44) on *Solution B;* in this event, the total of Ca plus Mg is determined with Versene on *Solution B* (¶ 11–54) or *Solution E* (¶ 11–60), derived by the NH_4OH-Br separation (¶ 11–94) carried out on *Solution C.*]

4. Determination of Fe and Ti on *Solution A* (¶ 11–62)

5. Determination of Si on *Solution D* after *Solution C* is removed following $HClO_4$ dehydration (¶ 11–72)

6. Determination of Al on *Solution F* (Fig. 11–2) resulting from the NH_4OH-Br (¶ 11–94) and NaOH (¶ 11–96) separations on *Solution C*

11–26. Blanks. Blanks are carried throughout for control of impurities of reagents and contamination from glassware.

APPARATUS FOR SEMIMICROCHEMICAL SYSTEM

11–27. For analysis of 8 materials for 8 elements and for 1 blank, the following apparatus is required: 9 30-ml or larger platinum crucibles and covers; 8 500-ml nickel or platinum beakers; 11 50-ml Pyrex beakers; 9 125-ml Pyrex conical flasks; 18 50-ml volumetric flasks, 1 set of 9 to be used exclusively for the determination of Fe, Ti, and Al, and the other set for Si; 17 100-ml volumetric flasks, 1 set of 9 to be used exclusively for *Solution A* and the other 8 for *Solution F;* 8 500-ml volumetric flasks; 1 50-ml Lowy pipet (with 3-way stopcock); pipets delivering 1, 2, 3, 4, 5, and 10 ml of solution; a suction-decantation apparatus (Fig. 11–3); a photoelectric colorimeter with 400-, 520-, and 565-mu light maxima; 18 matched colorimeter tubes, 1 set of 9 tubes to be used exclusively for the determination of Fe, Ti, and Al, and the other set for Si; an electric hot plate, 200° to 225°C and sand bath; and a flame emission spectrophotometer.

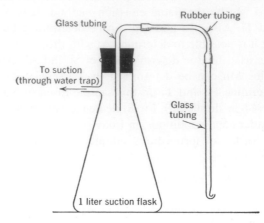

Fig. 11–3. Suction apparatus for removal of supernatant liquid.

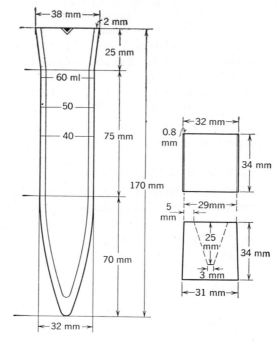

Fig. 11–4. Special 60-ml pointed centrifuge tube and special rubber cushion enclosed in brass cylinder for support during centrifugation. (After Corey and Jackson, *Anal. Chem.*, 25:624, 1953.)

11–28. An International size 2 centrifuge is employed, with 16 graduated 60-ml pointed centrifuge tubes (Fig. 11–4) and special cushions (obtained from Internation Equipment Co., Boston, Mass.). The precipitates are stirred with an air-jet stirrer consisting of a 20-cm length of 3-mm outside diameter glass tubing pulled out to a fine point on one end (filtered air is forced through this tube to mix solutions in the pointed tubes and also to dislodge precipitates from the bottom of the pointed tubes). A 2-liter Pyrex beaker is used as a hot water bath for sets of 8 pointed centrifuge tubes.

11–29. A crucible radiator is made from a 100-ml crucible of nickel, iron, or porcelain over which a silica-covered nichrome triangle is fitted to hold a platinum crucible.

REAGENTS

11–30. The acids and other reagents are analytical reagent grade. Reagents needed for the HF decomposition include 48 per cent HF, 60 per cent $HClO_4$, and 6 N HCl; and for the Na_2CO_3 fusion, anhydrous Na_2CO_3 powder. The reagents are listed separately for the determination of each element.

PROCEDURE

11–31. Decomposition of Sample with HF. A 0.1000-gm, finely ground sample that has been dried at 100°C for 2 hours (or on which a separate moisture sample has been run) is placed in a 30-ml platinum crucible. The sample is wetted with a few drops of water, then 0.5 ml of $HClO_4$ and 5 ml of 48 per cent HF are added.[7] The crucible, with the lid covering nine-tenths of the top, is placed on a sand bath at a temperature of 200° to 225°C, and the acids are evaporated to dryness. The solution must not boil vigorously or spattering may occur. The $HClO_4$ should drive off virtually all of the F, because appreciable F interferes with the Fe determination. Organic matter, which sometimes condenses onto the cover and upper sides of the crucible, is often not attacked completely by the $HClO_4$. If a dark color is present on the cover and sides, indicating organic matter, a Meker burner is directed on the sides of the crucible exterior just long enough to dispel the organic matter. A faint red heat is usually all that is necessary.

11–32. The crucible is removed from the sand bath and cooled, 5 ml of 6 N HCl is added, and the suspension is diluted to two-thirds of the vol-

---

[7] Volatilization of Ti in the absence of H_2SO_4 (¶ 11–117) was shown to be almost negligible by data of Hoffman given by Hillebrand and Lundell, *Applied Inorganic Analysis* (New York: John Wiley & Sons, Inc., 1929), p. 724, and verified by Dr. L. D. Whittig in this laboratory. Use of H_2SO_4 is abandoned because of interference with dissolution of high Ti samples and in the Na and K determination with the flame photometer.

ume of the crucible with water. The crucible is then covered and placed in the radiator described with the apparatus (¶ 11–29). The radiator crucible is then heated with a relatively low flame so that the solution boils gently without bumping. After 5 minutes of boiling, the residue should be completely dissolved[8] (¶ 11–34).

11–33. If the sample is high in Al_2O_3 or coarse-grained particles, difficulty is sometimes encountered in dissolution of the residue. If no additional sample is available, the solution is evaporated to dryness and the HF-$HClO_4$ treatment is repeated (¶ 11–31). The residue is once more treated with 6 N HCl, water, and boiling. This process is repeated until all the residue is dissolved. With some unusual types of sample, a different type of dissolution must be considered (¶ 11–6).

11–34. When the residue is completely dissolved, the solution in the crucible is transferred to a 100-ml volumetric flask, cooled, and diluted to a volume of 100 ml. (In high Ti samples, some opalescence tends to develop by Ti precipitation, but when the solution in the volumetric flask is heated for several minutes in a hot water bath, the Ti goes into solution.) This is *Solution A,* used for the determination of K, Na, Ca, and Mg by flame emission (¶ 11–37) and Fe and Ti (¶ 11–62). The K and Na determinations are run as soon as possible to minimize contamination from the glassware. If necessary, this solution may also be used for the determination of Ca (¶ 11–44) and Ca plus Mg with Versene (¶ 11–54). Also, Al may be determined, but the F must have been completely removed by fuming in $HClO_4$ (¶ 11–31) to prevent its interference (¶ 11–86).

11–35. Decomposition of Sample by Na_2CO_3 Fusion. A 0.1000-gm, finely ground sample that has been dried at 100°C for 2 hours (or for which a separate moisture sample has been run) is weighed in a 30-ml platinum crucible. Then approximately 0.75 gm of Na_2CO_3 is added, and the sample and the carbonate are thoroughly mixed by rotation of the crucible with the fingers. Approximately 0.25 gm of Na_2CO_3 is then added on top of the mixture. The crucible is placed in a slanting position on a silica-covered triangle with the lid covering about seven-tenths of the top. The low flame of a Meker burner is placed so as to heat one side of the crucible, and the heat[9] is gradually increased until the melt is liquefied. If the material is finely ground, the fusion is usually complete in 1 to 2 minutes, at which time the flux appears quiet with small curds of precipitate floating in the otherwise clear liquid, and the evolution of gas has ceased. The crucible is then grasped with nickel tongs and swirled to spread the

---

[8] Traces of organic matter not removed (¶ 11–31), appearing as dark specks in the solution, sometimes are simply ignored.

[9] Shell, *Anal. Chem.,* 26:591 (1954), recommended fusion in the electric furnace at 1200°C to avoid transfer of iron from the sample to the Pt metal, which occurs if very good oxidizing conditions are not maintained.

flux in a thin layer over the sides of the lower half of the crucible so that any silica adhering to the sides is fused. Heating is continued under full Meker flame for 2 or 3 minutes, after which the burner is removed and the crucible is swirled to spread the melt in a thin, easily dissolved layer.

11–36. The Na_2CO_3 fused sample is used for the determination of Si (¶ 11–72) and Al (¶ 11–86). Ca plus Mg may be determined with Versene (¶ 11–54). Likewise, Fe and Ti may also be determined in this sample (¶ 11–62), but their determinations are faster and more accurate in the HF decomposed sample.

POTASSIUM, SODIUM, CALCIUM, AND MAGNESIUM DETERMINATIONS
(Rapid semimicrochemical system)

11–37. The flame emission spectrophotometric determinations of K, Na, Ca, and Mg are far more rapid and better adapted to the sample size employed in this semimicrochemical system than are titrimetric, colorimetric, or gravimetric determinations. If flame emission techniques are not available, suitable alternative procedures (¶ 11–44) are adaptable to the semimicrochemical system. The NH_4OH separation is given to remove Fe, Al, and P, which interfere with the flame emission determination of Ca and Mg. If titrimetric procedures (¶ 11–46) are to be carried out for Ca and Mg, then the Br_2 separation (¶ 11–41) is included with the NH_4OH separation to remove Mn, while K and Na are determined on *Solution A* (Fig. 11–1 and ¶ 11–45).

APPARATUS

11–38. Apparatus needed for the NH_4OH or NH_4OH-Br separation includes 60-ml pointed centrifuge tubes and centrifuge, an air-jet stirrer, a hot water bath, a 125-ml conical flask, and a steam plate or electric hot plate with sand bath. A Beckman or other suitable flame emission spectrophotometer is needed for the determination (¶ 18–7).

REAGENTS

11–39. Reagents needed for the NH_4OH separation include 4 N NH_4OH, solid NH_4Cl, and concentrated HNO_3. For the NH_4OH-Br separation, saturated Br_2 water is also needed. For the determination, 0.4 N HCl and standard solutions of K, Na, Ca, and Mg in base electrolyte concentrations comparable to those of the test sample (¶ 18–15) are needed.

PROCEDURE

11–40. NH_4OH Separation. A 50-ml aliquot of *Solution A* (¶ 11–34) is placed in a 60-ml pointed centrifuge tube. Approximately 1 gm of NH_4Cl is dissolved in this solution by agitation with the air-jet stirrer, 3 drops of brom cresol purple indicator are added, the solution is warmed in a boiling water bath, and 4 N NH$_4$OH is dispensed from a buret until the full purple-violet color is reached, and then 2 ml of additional NH$_4$OH is added.

11–41. NH$_4$OH-Br Separation. To cause the precipitation of the Mn as MnO$_2$ with the R$_2$O$_3$ precipitate, 2 ml of saturated Br$_2$ water is added to oxidize the Mn. The Br$_2$ also decolorizes the indicator. If both Ca and Mg are to be determined by flame emission instead of by Versene, this paragraph may be omitted.

11–42. The tube is placed in a hot water bath for 5 minutes to flocculate the R$_2$O$_3$ (and MnO$_2$) precipitate. It is then cooled, and the volume is adjusted to exactly 60 ml. The suspension is mixed thoroughly with the air-jet stirrer, then centrifuged 5 minutes at 1800 rpm. The K, Na, Ca and Mg are in the supernatant liquid (*Solution B*).

11–43. A 25-ml aliquot of the supernatant liquid is pipetted into a 125-ml conical flask. To destroy most of the ammonium salts, the solution is evaporated to 10 ml, 10 ml of concentrated HNO$_3$ is added, and the solution is evaporated to dryness on a steam plate or an electric plate with sand bath. The residue is taken up in 25 ml of 0.4 N HCl, and the K, Na, Ca, and Mg are determined by flame emission (¶ 18–27). The *Solution A* was diluted by a factor of 5/6, hence, for K, Na, Ca, or Mg:

$$\% \text{ element} = \text{mgm of element per 100 ml} \underset{\text{(from curve)}}{} \times \frac{0.120}{\text{weight of sample, gm}}$$

$$(11–1)$$

ALTERNATIVE PROCEDURES

11–44. Calcium is most expeditiously determined by the flame emission spectrophotometer (¶ 18–16) applied to *Solution B* obtained after the NH$_4$OH separation (¶ 11–40) even when Mg cannot be because of equipment limitations. In this case, Ca plus Mg is determined with Versene (¶ 11–59) followed by subtraction of Ca determined by flame emission, to obtain Mg by difference. The Mg may also be determined by 8-hydroxy quinoline (¶ 5–59). Also, Ca may be determined in *Solution B* by Versene (¶ 11–46) or by the semimicro oxalate-cerate procedure (¶ 5–38).

11–45. The K and Na are most expeditiously determined (¶ 18–27) by a flame emission spectrophotometer, even if Ca and/or Mg cannot be (¶ 11–44) because of equipment limitations. In the complete absence of flame emission equipment, the K and Na must be determined by conventional methods (¶ 11–176) rather than by this semimicrochemical system. Approximately 20 ml of *Solution A* (¶ 11–34) is transferred to a 50-ml beaker or other suitable vessel and then K and Na are determined by flame emission (¶ 18–27). Since *Solution A* is not diluted or otherwise changed, the concentration reading from the flame emission curve gives the mgm of K or Na in the entire 100 ml of *Solution A:*

$$\% \text{ K or Na} = \text{mgm of K or Na per 100 ml} \times \frac{0.100}{\text{wt. sample, gm}}$$

(11–2)

11–46. Versene Method. The Versene (disodium dihydrogen ethylene-diamine tetra-acetic acid) titration procedure of Schwarzenbach and Biedermann[10] is employed alternatively for the Ca and Ca plus Mg determinations because its speed and simplicity are next to those of the flame emission method. Versene exhibits very strong complexing powers with various polyvalent cations. The logarithms of the equilibrium constants of some of the metal Versene complexes for the reaction $M^{n+} + Ver^{4-} \longrightarrow$ M-$Ver^{n/4}$ are as follows: Fe^{+++}, 25.1; Cu^{++}, 18.4; Ni^{++}, 18.4; Pb^{++}, 18.2; Cd^{++}, 16.5; Zn^{++}, 16.2; Co^{++}, 16.1; La^{+++}, 15.4; Fe^{++}, 14.2; Mn^{++}, 13.5; Ca^{++}, 10.59; Mg^{++}, 8.69; Sr^{++}, 8.63; Ba^{++}, 7.76; Li^{+}, 2.79; and Na^{+}, 1.66.

11–47. Calcium by Versene Titration. Any metal whose Versene complex is less dissociated than that of Ca (whose equilibrium constant is higher) will be preferentially complexed before Ca and thus will be included in the Ca titration. Interfering[11] ions include Hg (ous), Be, Cd, Sn (ous or ic), Cu, Zn, Fe (ic) and Mn (ous). The interfering ions that would be encountered in this system are Fe and Mn. The Fe is removed by the NH_4OH separation, but the Mn normally passes through. The addition of bromine water, in the NH_4OH-Br separations given, serves to remove Mn with the Fe. The removal of Mn is important for the analysis of some Latosols and many rocks. If more than 0.5 mgm of Mn is present, it makes the end point less distinct. The Mn can also be removed as carbamate (¶ 11–57), as MnO_2 by $KMnO_4$,[12] or as MnS by the addition of Na_2S to the solution and filtration, prior to titration of the Ca.

11–48. Standard Ca Solution. A 0.5005-gm portion of pure dried $CaCO_3$ is dissolved with a minimum of 0.2 N HCl. The solution is boiled to expel the CO_2 and is then diluted to 1 liter. The solution is 0.0100 N with respect to Ca.

11–49. Standard Versene Solution. A 2.0-gm portion of Versene (disodium dihydrogen ethylenediamine tetra-acetic acid, from Bersworth Chemical Co., Framingham, Mass., or Eastman Kodak) is dissolved in 900 ml of water. The normality of this solution is obtained by titration of a 25-ml portion of the standard Ca solution according to the procedure (¶ 11–

[10] *Helv. Chim. Acta,* 31:678 (1948).
[11] Cheng and Bray, *Soil Sci.,* 72:449 (1951).
[12] Ingram and Bean, *Anal. Chem.,* 25:1217 (1953).

52), and the solution is then diluted so that the normality is exactly 0.0100. A check standardization is then made.

11–50. Murexide Indicator. A 0.2-gm portion of Murexide (Eastman Kodak) is mixed with 40 gm of powdered K_2SO_4. The Murexide indicator is best added as the powder, since it is extremely susceptible to oxidation when used as a solution. The susceptibility of Murexide to oxidation also makes the Versene determination of Ca difficult on the samples derived by fusion (¶ 11–35) because of the presence of perchlorate. The sharpness of the end point is greatly reduced by large concentrations of salts, which is one reason the ammonium salts from the NH_4OH-Br separation are destroyed (¶ 11–51) before the Ca titration. Another reason for the destruction of the ammonium salts is to facilitate the solution pH being raised to 12 for the titration.

11–51. Removal of Ammonium Salts. A 50-ml aliquot (or less if necessary to contain less than 5 mgm of Ca) of *Solution B,* the supernatant liquid in the centrifuge tube after the NH_4OH-Br separation (¶ 11–41), is transferred to a 125-ml conical flask and 10 ml of HNO_3 is added. The solution is evaporated to dryness on a sand bath. If all of the visible ammonium salts are not destroyed, 5 ml of aqua regia is added, and the evaporation is repeated. The cooled residue is dissolved with 2 ml of 6 N HCl, with heating if necessary to get a clear solution, and the solution is diluted to approximately 50 ml.

11–52. Titration of Calcium. A 5-ml portion of 10 per cent KOH is added, and 0.3 gm of Murexide indicator powder is dissolved in the solution. The amount of Ca in the solution is then determined by titration with 0.0100 N Versene solution (¶ 11–49) to a purple end point. Murexide, also known as ammonium purpurate, forms an orange-red complex with Ca ions at pH 12, which is converted to a red-violet color when the Ca ions are completely complexed by Versene. The color change is gradual, making it imperative to compare the end point color with a standard. The end point can be reached from either direction, and back titration with standard Ca solution is possible and often helpful:

$$\% \ Ca = ml \ Versene \times \frac{0.0481}{weight \ of \ sample, \ gm} \qquad (11\text{--}3)$$

11–53. The solution resulting from the Ca titration with Versene (Murexide) may be used (¶ 11–59) for the titration of Mg plus Ca with Versene (Eriochrome black T indicator) instead of the same titration on *Solution E* (¶ 11–60).

11–54. Magnesium Through Versene Titration. Total Mg is most easily determined with the flame emission spectrophotometer on *Solution B* at the same time as the K, Na, and Ca determinations (¶ 11–37). In the absence of suitable equipment, the total Mg plus Ca is determined by Versene titration[13] with Eriochrome black T indicator, following the NH_4OH-Br separation; the total Ca, determined separately, is subtracted, thus giving total Mg.

11–55. The Eriochrome black T dye gives a wine-red colored complex with Mg, but changes to blue when all the Mg ions have been removed by the Versene; the titration is much more satisfactory than that with Murexide (¶ 11–52). The formation of the Mg complex is optimum at pH 10 in the presence of NH_4Cl and NH_4OH (¶ 4–13). The Ca is complexed by Versene before the Mg, and therefore the titration value gives total Mg plus Ca.

11–56. Ions which would interfere[14] (¶11–46) include: Cu, Co, and Ni, which form a red complex with the indicator (not decomposed by the Versene titration); Fe, which precipitates the dye (if the latter is added before the solution is made alkaline) and obscures the end point if present in large amounts; and Mn, which, if present as MnO_2, causes fading of the dye and an indistinct end point. In the semimicrosystem, Fe and Mn are removed by the NH_4OH-Br separation, and Cu, Co, and Ni are complexed by NaCN.

11–57. In other applications, the interference of Fe, Mn, and Cu in the Versene titration procedure for Ca plus Mg can also be removed by the carbamate separation.[15] The sample solution in a volume of 50 ml is brought to pH between 1 and 4 and then the solution is made 0.05 to 0.1 per cent with respect to carbamate (¶ 15–45). The solution is shaken, and the brownish complexes of Mn, Fe, and Cu with carbamate are formed. Then 10 to 20 ml of isomyl alcohol is added and the flask is stoppered, shaken for about 10 seconds, and then allowed to stand until the alcohol separates from the aqueous phase. The alcoholic upper layer carrying the Mn, Fe, and Cu is removed by suction through a small glass tube connected to an evacuation flask (or can be removed by means of a separatory funnel, with less convenience). The isoamyl alcohol extraction is repeated until the aqueous solution becomes colorless. The Ca and Mg remain in the aqueous solution.

11–58. Reagents needed for the Versene titration (¶ 11–59) include concentrated and 4 N NH_4OH; NH_4Cl salt; thymolphthalein and alizarin yellow indicators; 0.0100 N Versene (¶ 11–49); Eriochrome black T indicator (Eastman Kodak), prepared as 0.5 gm of the indicator with 4.5 gm of hydroxylamine hydrochloride dissolved in 100 ml of methanol; and a 2 per cent NaCN solution. The hydroxylamine keeps any traces of Mn in

[13] Gysling and Schwarzenbach, *Helv. Chim. Acta,* 32:1484 (1949); Schwarzenbach and Gysling, *Helv. Chim. Acta,* 32:1314 (1949).

[14] Cheng and Bray, *Soil Sci.,* 72:449 (1951); Conners, *J. Am. Water Works Assoc.,* 42:33 (1950); Diehl *et al., J. Am. Water Works Assoc.,* 42:40 (1950); and Betz and Noll, *J. Am. Water Works Assoc.,* 42:49 (1950).

[15] Cheng *et al., Soil Sci.,* 75:37 (1953).

divalent form and the NaCN removes interference of traces of Cu, Co, or Ni present.[16]

11–59. Mg plus Ca Titration with Versene. The Versene titration of Ca plus Mg may be carried out either on the solution left after Versene titration of Ca with Murexide (¶ 11–53) or on *Solution E* (¶ 11–60) resulting from the NH₄OH-Br separation on the Na₂CO₃ fused sample. The latter supplies nearly twice as large aliquot of the sample and is thus advantageous if the amount of Mg is small. The Murexide indicator remaining after the Ca titration with Versene on *Solution B* is destroyed by the addition of a few drops of bromine water (an excess is avoided) and the solution is then acidified to bring the Mg(OH)₂ into solution. A solution containing 1 gm of NH₄Cl is added and then sufficient NH₄OH to bring the final solution to pH 10 (above blue to thymolphthalein and yellow-orange to alizarin yellow indicators). Next, 5 drops of the Eriochrome black T indicator solution and 1 ml of 2 per cent NaCN solution are added. The solution is then titrated with 0.0100 N Versene solution to a bright blue end point. This titration is a measure of the total Mg plus Ca in the solution. To obtain the percentage of Mg in the sample, the Ca equivalent is subtracted:

$$\text{meq Mg + Ca per gm sample} = \underset{(\text{Eriochrome})}{\text{ml Versene}} \times \frac{0.024}{\text{wt. sample, gm}}$$

(11–4)

From ¶ 11–52:

$$\text{meq Ca per gm sample} = \underset{(\text{Murexide})}{\text{ml Versene}} \times \frac{0.024}{\text{wt. sample, gm}}$$

(11–5)

Then:

$$\% \text{ Mg} = \left(\frac{\text{meq Mg + Ca}}{\text{per gm sample}} - \frac{\text{meq Ca per}}{\text{gm sample}} \right) \times 1.216$$

(11–6)

The meq of Mn (in the absence of Br₂ in the NH₄OH separation) is determined separately (¶ 11–172) and subtracted as was Ca.

11–60. To titrate Mg plus Ca on *Solution E* resulting from the NH₄OH-Br separation (¶ 11–94), a 50-ml aliquot is placed in a 125-ml conical flask, and 5 ml of concentrated NH₄OH[17] is added to give pH 10. Then 5 drops of the Eriochrome black T indicator solution and 1 ml of 2 per cent

---

[16] Dr. C. V. Cole recommended making the Eriochrome black T solution 1 per cent with respect to KCN to repress the minor element interference (possibly introduced as impurities in the indicator). Diskant, *Anal. Chem.*, 24:1856 (1952), notes that Eriochrome black T indicator is stable when dissolved in di- or triethanolamine, but states that no other solvent or salts should be added.

[17] This addition of NH₄OH together with the NH₄Cl in *Solution E* are equivalent to an NH₄OH-NH₄Cl buffer solution of pH 10 (¶ 4–13) ordinarily employed with the Versene titration with Eriochrome black T of Mg, Mg plus Ca, or Ca alone (¶ 4–21).

NaCN solution are added and the solution is titrated with 0.0100 N Versene as before (¶ 11–59) from wine-red to a bright blue end point. Nearly twice as large an aliquot of Mg and Ca is obtained in *Solution E* as in *Solution B*.

11–61. The meq of Mg plus Ca is calculated:

$$\text{meq Mg + Ca per gm sample} = \text{ml Versene} \underset{\text{(Eriochrome)}}{} \times \frac{0.0144}{\text{wt. sample, gm}}$$

$$(11\text{–}7)$$

The meq of Ca per gm sample is calculated (¶ 11–52) and then the percentage of Mg (eq. 11–6). The meq of Mn (in the absence of Br_2 in the NH_4OH separation) is determined separately (¶ 11–172), and subtracted as was Ca.

IRON AND TITANIUM DETERMINATIONS

(Rapid semimicrochemical system)

11–62. The Tiron method[18] for the determination of Fe and Ti was adopted in this system because of its simplicity, speed, and freedom from interfering ions. The yellow color of Tiron (disodium 1,2-dihydroxybenzene 3,5-disulfonate) with Ti is stable over a pH range of from 4.3 to 9.6, but the purple color with Fe^{+++} varies in intensity and hue from pH 4.7 to 7 or above and therefore the pH is buffered at 4.7 for most satisfactory results. At this pH value, the Fe complex shows a light absorption maximum at 560 mu and the Ti complex shows a maximum at 380 mu. The Fe color is read first and then is destroyed by dithionite so as not to interfere with the reading of the Ti color. The color of dithionite interferes with the Ti color unless Ti is read with a 400- to 420-mu light maximum. The colors of both the Fe and Ti complexes increase with increased concentration of reagent so that a large excess of reagent is required. The color, once formed, increases slowly in intensity for 18 hours, after which it is stable almost indefinitely. The increase, however, is very slow, so that readings may be made over a considerable period of time, and 5 to 30 minutes was adopted.

11–63. Few ions interfere with the color formed by Tiron with Fe and Ti. The only other ions forming colored solutions with Tiron are VO^{++} (purple), MoO_4^{--}, OsO_4^{--}, UO_2^{++} (yellow) and Cu^{++} (greenish yellow in alkaline solution). Ag and $AuCl^-$ are reduced to the metals by the reagent. Ions which consume the reagent are Al^{+++}, Ca^{++}, Ce^{4+}, Mg^{++}, Fe^{++}, Sn^{4+}, Th^{4+}, ZrO^{++}, and WO_4^{--}. Tolerance to these ions is increased and interference is overcome by the addition of a large quantity of reagents. The only anions that interfere seriously are fluorides, which de-

---

[18] Yoe and Armstrong, *Anal. Chem.*, 19:100 (1947).

crease the color intensity when present in concentrations greater than 10 ppm, and perchlorates, which tend to increase the color of the Fe complex.

APPARATUS

11–64. Needed apparatus includes an absorption spectrophotometer with 565- and 400- (or 420-) mu light maxima; absorption tubes; 50-ml volumetric flasks; and 5-ml, 10-ml, and other pipets.

REAGENTS

11–65. Needed reagents include 3 per cent H_2O_2, sodium dithionite ($Na_2S_2O_4$, from Amend Drug and Chemical Co., New York), Tiron reagent solution prepared fresh daily by dissolution of 4 gm of Tiron (La-Motte Chemical Products Co., Towson, Md.) in 75 ml of distilled water and dilution of the solution to 100 ml, buffer solution of pH 4.7 prepared by mixing equal volumes of $1\,M$ HOAc (60 ml of glacial HOAc per liter) and $1\,M$ NaOAc (82 gm of anhydrous NaOAc per liter) and adjustment of the pH to 4.7 (glass electrode) with NaOH or HOAc, and standard Fe and Ti solutions prepared as follows.

11–66. Standard Fe Solution. A 0.0500-gm portion of pure iron wire is dissolved in 10 ml of 0.6 N HCl and 1 ml of concentrated HNO_3, and the volume is adjusted to 1 liter, so that the solution contains 50 ugm of Fe per ml. Aliquots (2, 4, 6, and 8 ml) of this solution are taken for the standard curve, and the color is developed as described in the procedure, the standard solutions being substituted for the *Solution A* aliquot. The percentage light transmission for this series of solutions is plotted against ugm of Fe per 50 ml on semilogarithmic paper. The curve follows Beer's law.

11–67. Standard Ti Solution. A standard Ti solution is prepared by fusion of 0.1668 gm of standard ignited TiO_2 in $K_2S_2O_7$ (¶ 11–113), taking up the melt with 10 ml of 6 N HCl. The solution is then made to a volume of 1 liter by dilution with 50 ml of 6 N HCl and then with water (rapid stirring). The concentration is 100 mgm of elemental Ti per liter, in 0.4 N HCl. After this solution has been thoroughly mixed, 10 ml is pipetted into a 100-ml volumetric flask and is diluted to volume with 0.4 N HCl and mixed, giving 10 ppm of Ti.

11–68. The alternative use of $TiCl_3$ for the Ti standard, which is often recommended, gives difficulties in standardization, attributed to coprecipitation[19] of SO_4 with $Ti(OH)_4$.

---

[19] In tests by Dr. L. D. Whittig, $TiCl_3$ (which characteristically hydrolyzes to some extent to yield a precipitate) was diluted with 1 N H_2SO_4, the Ti in solution oxidized with H_2O_2, and the solution filtered. An aliquot of the clear filtrate was used for precipitation of Ti with NH_4OH. The precipitate was washed free from salts with NH_4Cl, dried, and ignited over a Meker burner for 1 hour. On the basis of this gravimetric standardization, the curve made with fresh portions of the solution gave a low recovery of Ti in National Bureau of Standards samples analyzed by the procedure. It was concluded therefore that sulfate precipitated with the Ti and persisted during the ignition, giving a fictitiously high Ti standardization.

11–69. Aliquots (2, 4, 6, 8, and 10 ml) of the 10 ppm Ti standard (¶ 11–67) are taken for the standard curve, giving 20 to 100 ugm of Ti. The color is developed as described in the procedure (¶ 11–70), the standard solutions being substituted for the *Solution A* aliquot. The percentage of light transmission for this series of solutions is plotted against the ugm of Ti per 50 ml on semilogarithmic paper. The curve follows Beer's law.

PROCEDURE

11–70. A drop of 3 per cent H_2O_2 is added to the remaining portion of *Solution A* to oxidize the Fe and Ti. To develop the color, first, a 10-ml portion of pH 4.7 buffer solution is pipetted into a clean 50-ml volumetric flask. Next, the volume is adjusted to approximately 30 ml with water, and 5.0 ml of 4 per cent Tiron reagent solution is pipetted in. An aliquot that contains from 50 to 250 ugm of Fe and 10 to 100 ugm of Ti is now transferred from *Solution A* to the 50-ml volumetric flask. (A 5-ml aliquot is convenient for samples containing up to 6 per cent Fe and 1.2 per cent Ti.) The solution is diluted to the mark with distilled water and mixed, and then approximately 20 ml of this solution is transferred to a colorimeter tube. After 5 minutes, the percentage light transmission of the blue-violet color of the Fc complex is read with a 565-mu light maximum. The readings are completed within 30 minutes. Approximately 3 mgm (a bit on the end of a spatula 1 mm wide) of $Na_2S_2O_4$ is next added to this same solution in the colorimeter tube to destroy the color due to the ferric complex by reducing it to ferrous. The colorimeter tube is stoppered with a rubber stopper, and the content of the tube is mixed by gentle inversion of the tube 4 or 5 times. The percentage light transmission of the yellow Ti complex is obtained within 10 minutes after the addition of the $Na_2S_2O_4$ with the 400-mu light maximum. The concentrations of Fe and Ti (ugm/50 ml) are then obtained from the standard curves:

$$\% \text{ Fe or Ti} = \frac{\text{ugm Fe or Ti per 50 ml}}{\text{ml aliquot taken}} \times \frac{0.01}{\text{wt. sample, gm}} \qquad (11\text{–}8)$$

ALTERNATIVE PROCEDURES

11–71. Iron may also be determined by the orthophenanthroline procedure (¶ 15–13), or by the SCN color method. Cheng et al.[20] describe the determination of Fe in soil or limestone by a Versene titration at pH 2 to 3 with salicylic acid as an indicator. The color change at the end point is from purple-red to colorless or light yellow, and the procedure is similar to the Versene titration of Ca (¶ 11–47). The Tiron procedure for Fe and Ti is much more convenient for use with the semimicrochemical system.

---

[20] *Anal. Chem.*, 24:1640 (1952), 25:347 (1953).

Titanium may also be determined as the peroxided yellow color (¶ 11–155).

SILICON DETERMINATION
(Rapid semimicrochemical system)

11–72. The silicon from the Na_2CO_3 fusion (¶ 11–35) is dehydrated with $HClO_4$,[21] washed free of metallic cations with 6 N HCl, and then is brought into solution in NaOH and determined colorimetrically by the molybdosilicic yellow color method[22] (¶ 7–3). Perchloric acid dihydrate boils at 203°C and at this temperature it is a very powerful dehydrating agent. By this method, the silica dehydration takes much less time than the hydrochloric acid evaporation, and the SiO_2 obtained is much purer, practically no Fe being coprecipitated. Titanium, however, if present in fairly large amounts will tend to be coprecipitated, as will MnO_2. This does not interfere with the subsequent silicon determination. Only 1 dehydration is required to recover all but a very minute amount of the Si present. In addition, all the metal perchlorates with the exception of $KClO_4$ are freely soluble in water or dilute acid. Removal of Ca, Mg, Fe, and Ti is necessary to prevent coprecipitation with the Si. Phosphorus interferes if left in the solution with Si, but is removed in the present system in the washings employed to remove the metallic cations.

11–73. The rate of yellow color development with molybdosilicic acid increases with the concentration of Si, high concentrations attaining maximum color development in a few minutes and very low concentrations in about an hour. After the maximum color is obtained there is a slow fading. The rate of change in intensity of color is sufficiently low after 30 minutes that 5 minutes does not produce a significant change, and a reproducible curve can be obtained.

11–74. The molybdosilicic yellow color is very sensitive to pH and somewhat sensitive to salt concentration. However the large amount of molybdate added serves as an excellent buffer so that a 0.25-ml error in measurement of the 6 N HCl does not produce a significant change of pH or color intensity.

APPARATUS

11–75. Needed apparatus includes an absorption spectrophotometer with 400-mu light maximum and tubes; 60-ml pointed centrifuge tubes and centrifuge; an air-jet stirrer; a 3-way, 50-ml pipet with stopcock (Lowy); 1-liter, 500-ml, and 50-ml volumetric flasks; 250 to 500-ml Ni (G. T. Walker, Minneapolis, Minn.) or Pt beaker; an electric hot plate; a rubber policeman, pipets, and a buret.

---

[21] Willard and Cake, *J. Am. Chem. Soc.*, 42:2208 (1920).
[22] Dienert and Waldenbulcke, *Compt. rend.*, 176:1478 (1923); and Hedin, *op cit.*

11–76. Needed reagents include NaOH (pellets and 5 per cent solution), 60 per cent $HClO_4$, 6 N and 1.2 N HCl, $(NH_4)_6Mo_7O_{24} \cdot 4 H_2O$ (150 gm in 1 liter of solution in distilled water, filtered if cloudy), and the following standard Si solution.

11–77. Standard Si Solution. Clear quartz crystals are digested for an hour in concentrated HCl to remove surface impurities, then washed and ground in an agate mortar to a fine powder that will pass a 0.15-mm sieve. The powder is ignited briefly in a crucible, then cooled, placed in a vial, and tightly stoppered. A 0.1070-gm sample is placed in a platinum crucible and fused with Na_2CO_3 (¶ 11–35). The melt is dissolved in water and diluted to a volume of 1 liter in a volumetric flask. This solution contains 50 ugm of elemental Si per ml. Aliquots (1, 2, 3, 4, 5, 6, 7, 8, 9, and 10 ml) of this solution are taken for the standard curve, and the color is developed (¶ 11–78), the aliquots of standard solution being substituted for the *Solution D* aliquot. The percentage light transmission for each of these solutions is plotted against ugm of Si per 50 ml on semilogarithmic paper.

11–78. When the crucible from the Na_2CO_3 fusion (¶ 11–35) has cooled, the cover is placed on the crucible, and 8 ml of 60 per cent $HClO_4$ is added dropwise under the slightly raised lid. When effervescence has ceased, the lid and sides of the crucible are washed down with a minimum of water, and the crucible, with the lid covering three-fourths of the top, is placed in a sand bath on an electric hot plate, and the suspension is evaporated (vigorous boiling must be prevented or loss of sample may result) to fumes of $HClO_4$. When dense fumes appear, the crucible is covered, and the suspension is boiled gently for 10 minutes at a temperature a little above 200°C.

11–79. When the crucible has cooled, approximately 5 ml of distilled water is added, and the suspension is carefully mixed and heated almost to boiling to dissolve the salts that have solidified on cooling. The suspension is then transferred to a 60-ml pointed centrifuge tube, and the crucible is rinsed with a wash bottle, the washings being added to the tube. All of the silica does not have to be removed from the crucible at this time. Approximately 2 ml of 6 N HCl is added, and the suspension is diluted to exactly 60 ml with water, thoroughly mixed with the air-jet stirrer, and centrifuged at 1800 rpm for 5 minutes to throw down the silica. The suspension adhering to the air-jet stirrer is washed back into the crucible.

11–80. A 50-ml aliquot is pipetted with a Lowy pipet from the supernatant liquid in the centrifuge tube and transferred to another 60-ml pointed centrifuge tube. This is *Solution C,* which is used for the determination of Al (¶ 11–93) (and also Mg plus Ca, Fe, and Ti, if so desired). Although the pipetting operation is more easily carried out by means of a Lowy pipet, an ordinary 50-ml pipet may be used if care is exercised. The suction apparatus shown in Fig. 11–3 may be used as a source of suction.

11–81. To wash the silica in the tube, about 50 ml of 1.2 N HCl is added and stirred, and the suspension is centrifuged at 1800 rpm for 5 minutes. The supernatant liquid is then decanted by suction and subsequently discarded, since an aliquot for analysis of the solutes has already been taken.

11–82. The silica is then washed from the tube into a 250- to 500-ml nickel or platinum beaker with a stream from the wash bottle, and the silica adhering to the sides of the crucible in which the dehydration was carried out is also transferred. The silica adheres rather tightly to the crucible so that it must be loosened with a policeman and washed out with a stream from the wash bottle. The final washing of both the crucible and centrifuge tube is made with warm 5 per cent NaOH to make sure all of the SiO_2 is removed. Approximately 2.5 gm of NaOH pellets is added to the suspension in the nickel or platinum beaker, and the volume is adjusted to approximately 100 ml. The solution is then boiled for 5 minutes to dissolve the SiO_2. When cool, this solution is transferred to a 500-ml volumetric flask and diluted to the mark with distilled water. This is *Solution D,* used for the determination of Si. A slight turbidity is ignored (¶ 11–72).

11–83. A 10-ml portion of ammonium molybdate solution is placed in a 50-ml volumetric flask, and the volume is adjusted to about 30 ml with distilled water. Then 5 ml of 6 N HCl is added, and the flask is swirled to dissolve the white precipitate that forms. Finally, a *Solution D* aliquot containing 50 to 500 ugm of Si is added, and the solution is diluted to the mark with distilled water. A 5-ml aliquot of *Solution D* is desirable for samples containing from 5 to 50 per cent elemental Si. The solution is mixed well, transferred to a colorimeter tube, and allowed to stand for 30 minutes before the percentage light transmission is read with a 400-mu light maximum. Reference to the standard curve gives the ugm of Si per 50 ml:

$$\% \text{ Si} = \frac{\text{ugm Si per 50 ml}}{\text{ml in aliquot}} \times \frac{0.05}{\text{wt. sample, gm}} \tag{11-9}$$

ALTERNATIVE PROCEDURES

11–84. For Si determination in systems other than the microchemical, the pH of the solution in which the Si is to be determined should be adjusted to approximately pH 3 to insure that the buffer capacity of the system is not exceeded as a result of excess acid or alkali in the test solution. To be determined spectrophotometrically, the Si must be in true solution. Digestion of organic compounds and colloidal aluminosilicates in $HClO_4$

usually converts the Si to forms soluble in NaOH. Silica gel is appreciably soluble even in water if the solution is sufficiently dilute.

11–85. Artificial standards for Si, consisting of chromate colored solutions, have been proposed.[23] When greater sensitivity is required than is provided by the molybdosilicic yellow color, it is provided by the reduced molybdosilicic blue color methods.[24]

ALUMINUM DETERMINATION
(Rapid semimicrochemical system)

11–86. The aluminon method for Al was adopted in this system because of its sensitivity and reliability as standardized by Smith *et al.*[25] The red color of aluminon (aurin tricarboxylic acid) with Al develops slowly for a chelated compound; approximately 20 minutes are required for full color development with the free acid at pH 4.2 at room temperature. At lower pH values, the rate is still slower, and at higher pH values an intense red color of the dye itself develops although the rate of fading is also high. The solution is buffered at pH 4.2 controlled to $\pm$ 0.1 pH unit. Controlling the pH is better than raising it to 7.0 to 7.2 in an effort to cause the excess reagent to fade selectively. Under the conditions selected, no heat or stabilizers such as gum arabic are necessary. Because aluminon is highly colored, the concentration of this reagent is a critical factor influencing the color intensity of the final solution. Also, hot solutions have a lower color intensity, but ordinary fluctuations in room temperature do not produce a significant change.

11–87. Interference by both cations and anions is extensive with Al determination, and for this reason the Al is separated in practically pure form (¶ 11–88) prior to the determination. Ions that form red colors deeper than that of Al include Be, La, Ce, Zn, Tl, Y, Nd, Er. Also, Fe forms[26] a color approximately one-third as intense as Al at 520 mu. White precipitates are formed with Bi, Pb, Sb, Sn, Hg (ic), V, Ti, and Si. Interfering anions include fluosilicate, fluoride, tartrate, citrate, oxalate, malate, and borate.

11–88. The Al is separated from other ions through the NH_4OH separation followed by the NaOH separation.

APPARATUS

11–89. Needed apparatus includes an air-jet stirrer; 60-ml pointed cen-

[23] Swank and Mellon, *Ind. Eng. Chem., A.E.,* 6:348 (1934).

[24] Kahler, *Ind. Eng. Chem., A.E.,* 13:536 (1941); Carlson and Banks, *Anal. Chem.,* 24:472 (1952).

[25] *Anal. Chem.,* 21:1334 (1949).

[26] Dependent in part on the amount of Al present; Robertson, *J. Sci. Food Agr.,* 2:59 (1950), employed thioglycollic acid or hydroxylamine hydrochloride to prevent the formation of color with iron.

trifuge tubes and centrifuge; a buret for NH_4OH; a hot water bath, a 50-ml pipet (preferably with 3-way stopcock); a 125-ml conical flask; 1-liter, 500-ml, 100-ml, and 50-ml volumetric flasks; a buret for Al standard; pipets; a colorimeter with 520-mu light maximum and tubes; and pH meter.

REAGENTS

11–90. Needed reagents include 6 N HCl, 4 N and concentrated NH_4OH, 1 per cent NH_4Cl solution, saturated Br_2 water, NaOH (25 gm per 100 ml of distilled water, made up freshly for each set of determinations and used while still hot), buffer solution of pH 4.2 (60 ml of HOAc diluted to 900 ml with distilled water plus 100 ml of 10 per cent NaOH, with final adjustment to pH 4.2 as measured with the glass electrode), and aluminon and standard aluminum solutions, made up as follows.

11–91. Aluminon Reagent. Exactly 0.200 gm of aluminon (aurin tricarboxylic acid,[27] Eastman, Rochester, N.Y.) is dissolved in 100 ml of the 4.2 buffer solution, and then the solution is diluted to 500 ml with distilled water.

11–92. Standard Al Solution. Exactly 0.500 gm of electrolytically prepared metallic Al sheet or wire free from a surface coating of aluminum oxide is dissolved in 15 ml of 6 N HCl. This solution is then diluted to 1 liter. A dilute standard solution is prepared by dilution of 10 ml of the first solution to 1 liter, giving 5 ugm of Al per ml of solution. Aliquots (1, 2, 3, 4, 5, 6, 7, and 8 ml) of the dilute standard Al solution are taken for the standard curve, and the color is developed as described in the procedure, the aliquots of standard solution being substituted for the *Solution F* aliquot. The percentage light transmission for each of these solutions is plotted against ugm of Al per 50 ml on semilogarithmic paper.

PROCEDURE

11–93. Aluminum is readied for the aluminon determination through the following separations. Calcium and Mg are also obtained for the Versene titration (¶ 11–60).

11–94. The NH_4OH-Br Separation. The 50-ml portion of *Solution C* (the supernatant solution from the silica centrifugation, ¶ 11–80) has already been placed in a 60-ml pointed centrifuge tube. Next 3 drops of brom cresol purple indicator are added. The solution is heated in a boiling water bath and then concentrated NH_4OH is added until the first traces of precipitate start to form, the solution being agitated constantly with the air-jet stirrer. (Enough HCl is present to provide adequate NH_4Cl for keeping Mg in solution.) About 4 N NH_4OH is then added dropwise until the indicator turns from yellow to purple, followed by 2 ml additional NH_4OH. Then 2 ml of saturated Br_2 water is added to oxidize Mn and cause pre-

---

[27] The commercial preparation is as satisfactory as that synthesized, Smith *et al.*, *Anal. Chem.*, 21:1334 (1949).

cipitation of MnO_2. The Br_2 also decolorizes the indicator. If the Ca and Mg both are to be determined by flame emission (¶ 11–37), the Br_2 may be omitted. The tube is placed in a hot water bath for 5 minutes and cooled, and the volume is adjusted to exactly 60 ml. The suspension is mixed thoroughly with the air-jet stirrer, then centrifuged for 5 minutes at 1800 rpm. The supernatant solution contains Ca and Mg, whereas the precipitate contains the oxides of Al, Fe, Ti, and Mn. A 50-ml aliquot of the supernatant liquid is pipetted into a 125-ml conical flask, care being taken that the precipitate is not disturbed. This is *Solution E,* which is used for the Versene titration of Mg plus Ca (¶ 11–60).

11–95. Approximately 50 ml of a 1 per cent NH_4Cl solution is then added to the tube, and the precipitate is thoroughly mixed with the air-jet stirrer. The suspension is again centrifuged at 1800 rpm for 5 minutes, after which the supernatant liquid is drawn off with the suction apparatus (Fig. 11–3) and discarded.

11–96. The NaOH Separation. The precipitate is dissolved by the addition of 3 ml of hot 6 N HCl, the suspension being stirred and heated in a hot water bath to effect solution. (If the Ti content is over about 5 per cent, the Ti precipitate may be in a form that is insoluble in HCl at this stage, but this is of no consequence if Ti is run on *Solution A,* ¶ 11–70.) Next, 10 ml of hot 25 per cent NaOH solution is added with stirring, and the suspension is placed in a hot water bath for 5 minutes and then allowed to cool. It is then diluted to exactly 50 ml with distilled water and mixed with the air-jet stirrer. The stirrer is allowed to drain completely, but the adhering solution is not washed back into the tube. The suspension is centrifuged for 5 minutes at 1800 rpm.

11–97. An aliquot containing 100 to 700 ugm of Al (5 ml for sample containing 1 to 8 per cent Al) is placed in a 100-ml volumetric flask, and 3 ml of 6 N HCl is added for each 5 ml of aliquot taken. The solution is adjusted to pH 4.2 (glass electrode), made to volume with distilled water, and mixed. This is *Solution F,* used for the determination of Al (¶ 11–99).

11–98. If the Fe content is over 10 per cent, occlusion of Al on the Fe_2O_3 precipitate may be excessive. If this problem arises, the entire supernatant liquid from the NaOH separation is decanted into a 200-ml volumetric flask instead of an aliquot of it being taken. The precipitate is dissolved in 3 ml of hot 6 N HCl and the NaOH separation is repeated, the supernatant liquid being decanted into the same 200-ml volumetric flask. The NaOH separation is carried out still a third time in lieu of washing the Fe_2O_3 precipitate. The 3 decantates combined in the 200-ml volumetric flask are diluted to volume, an aliquot that contains 100 to 700 ugm of Al (20 ml for samples containing 1 to 8 per cent Al) is placed in a 100-ml flask. Then 0.45 ml of 6 N HCl is added for each ml of aliquot taken, the solution is adjusted to pH 4.2 (glass electrode), and made to volume. This (as in ¶ 11–97) is *Solution F,* used for the determination of Al (¶ 11–99).

11–99. Development of Color with Aluminon. A 10-ml portion of pH 4.2 buffer solution is placed in a 50-ml volumetric flask, and water is added to adjust the volume to about 30 ml. Exactly 10.00 ml of 0.04 per cent aluminon reagent is added, and the flask is swirled to mix the solution. Finally, a 5-ml aliquot of *Solution F* (containing 5 to 35 ugm of Al) is added, the solution is immediately diluted to the mark, and the contents are well mixed. After 25 minutes some of the solution is transferred to a colorimeter tube, and the percentage light transmission is read with a 520-mu light maximum. Reference to the standard curve gives the ugm of Al per 50 ml of colored solution:

$$\% \; Al = \frac{\text{ugm Al per 50 ml}}{\text{ml in aliquot}} \times \frac{0.12}{\text{wt. sample, gm}} \qquad (11-10)$$

CONVENTIONAL SYSTEM OF SILICATE ANALYSIS

11–100. Conventional gravimetric, titrimetric, and colorimetric procedures may be employed for Si, Al, Fe, Fe(ous), Ti, Ca, Mg, Mn, K, Na, P, and S (¶ 11–7). The accuracy of the gravimetric procedures, though not as high (¶ 11–8) as sometimes believed, is thought in most cases to be somewhat higher than the procedures employed in the semimicrochemical system given above, when adequate amounts of sample material is available. Preparation of the sample is considered in ¶ 11–11.

11–101. The Flow Sheet. The flow sheet for the conventional system is shown in Fig. 11–5. Decomposition of 1 sample by Na_2CO_3 (¶ 11–104) is employed for the analysis of the elements, Si, Al, Fe, Ti, Ca, Mg, and Mn. Separate samples are fused (¶ 11–104) for K (¶ 6–75), for P (¶ 7–131), and for S (¶ 11–188) determinations. Decomposition of the separate samples by HF is accomplished for K and Na (¶ 11–176) and for Fe(ous) (¶ 11–182). Dehydration in $HClO_4$ is employed for silica, the cupferron separation is employed for separation of Fe and Ti from Al and P, and the NH_4OH separation is employed for separation of Al and P from Ca, Mg and Mn.

APPARATUS

11–102. Apparatus needed for the Na_2CO_3 fusion consists of a 30-ml platinum crucible and cover, an analytical balance, a 10-cm glass rod, a camel's hair brush, a silica-tube triangle, a Meker burner, nickel or platinum tipped tongs, an 8-cm platinum dish or 400-ml Pyrex beaker with watch glass to fit, a 50-ml beaker, a rubber policeman, and a 15-cm glass rod with flattened end.

REAGENTS

11–103. Reagents needed for the Na_2CO_3 fusion and decomposition of the melt are anhydrous Na_2CO_3, 70 per cent $HClO_4$; and concentrated and 6 N HCl.

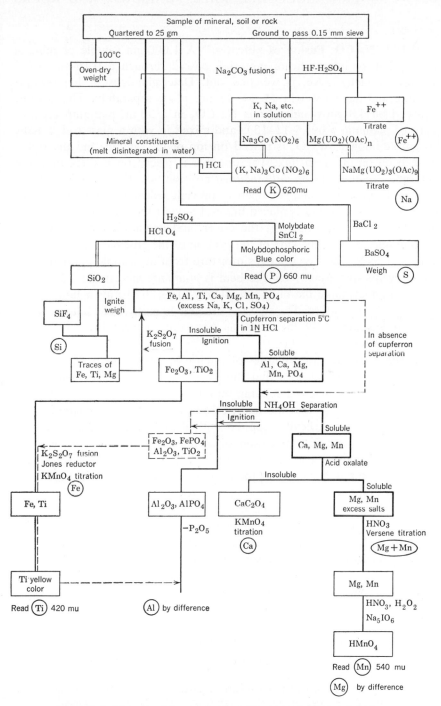

Fig. 11–5. Flow sheet for conventional system of silicate analysis.

PROCEDURE

11–104. Na$_2$CO$_3$ Fusion of Silicates.[28] A 1.000-gm sample of mineral colloid, soil, or other silicate material, passed through a 0.16-mm (100 meshes per inch) sieve, is weighed out. Determinations of hygroscopic moisture and ignited weight (¶ 11–4) are made separately. This sample is placed on 4.0 gm of anhydrous Na$_2$CO$_3$ in a 30-ml platinum crucible (care of platinum ware, ¶ 11–13), and mixed in with a glass rod. Finally 1.0 gm additional Na$_2$CO$_3$ is placed on top of the sample, and the rod is brushed off on the fresh flux. The crucible is placed on a silica tube (or nichrome) triangle in a *slightly inclined* position, and the cover is adjusted to leave the crucible about 0.1 open to prevent reducing conditions. A low flame of a Meker burner is placed under 1 side of the crucible, opposite to the side left one-tenth open by the cover, and heating is continued for 5 or 10 minutes so that the side of the bottom of the crucible takes on a dull redness. This low heating removes moisture from the sample gradually and thus prevents spattering. Now the heat is *gradually* increased so that after 5 or 10 minutes more the mass completely fuses and forms a liquid melt. The cover is kept adjusted so that the crucible is partly open but the opening is not enveloped with the flame, as that would prevent access of oxygen to the contents of the crucible.

11–105. After about 5 minutes of intense heating, bubbles of gas cease to come off, which indicates that the fusion is complete. To insure complete fusion of any material sticking on the upper sides of the crucible, the crucible is inclined so that the main fused mass covers this material, and while in this position, heat is applied until the main mass again fuses. In order to assure complete oxidation of all material, the cover is removed and the melt is heated 1 to 2 minutes more with a full flame. Then the flame is removed, and after the top of the crucible ceases to glow, the crucible is grasped with the crucible tongs and given a rotary motion to spread the contents over the sides of the lower half of the crucible, thus expediting subsequent removal and solution of the melt.

11–106. Removal of the Melt. After the crucible and contents have cooled, sufficient water is added just to cover the melt. Now gentle heat is applied to the crucible by a small flame around the sides, causing the metal to expand rapidly and thus break away from the cake inside. If the fusion has been properly made and the crucible is clean and not badly dented, the cake should loosen sufficiently to be removed, in which case it is tipped into a platinum dish or 400-ml beaker. Should the cake resist becoming free in the manner indicated so that it cannot be readily removed, the crucible with

---

[28] For an extensive discussion of the various fluxes available, interfering substances, and alternative procedures, the reader is referred to Hillebrand and Lundell, *Applied Inorganic Analysis* (New York: John Wiley & Sons, Inc., 1929), pp. 700–713.

contents is placed directly in the dish or beaker, and removal is brought about by digestion in water. If some material has spattered onto the cover, this is transferred to the beaker by means of a policeman and a little water.

11–107. Disintegration of Melt. The melt is disintegrated in 50 to 100 ml of water, with heating and the aid of a glass rod with a flattened end, and frequent stirring, the beaker being kept covered with a watch glass. For the usual silica determination and complete analysis, the solution covering the melt is acidified with 10[29] ml of concentrated HCl and 10 ml of 70 per cent $HClO_4$, and digested on the steam hot plate, with stirring from time to time. The crucible and cover are extracted with a little 6 N HCl in a separate small beaker, this solution being brought to a boil and then transferred to the main solution. The silica is determined by volatilization with HF (¶ 11–110).

ALTERNATIVE PROCEDURES

11–108. Samples that are high in oxides of manganese and iron tend to cause damage to platinum crucibles by alloying Mn and Fe with the platinum. To avoid these difficulties, Dr. G. D. Sherman pretreated the sample (prior to fusion) with aqua regia in a covered 400-ml beaker to dissolve as much of the sample as possible. The dissolved portion of the sample is decanted into a second 400-ml beaker and the residue is washed thoroughly with small portions of 6 N HCl. The residue is transferred to the platinum crucible and then dried in an oven. The residue is weighed as an estimate of quartz. The residue is then fused in Na_2CO_3 by the procedure, and the elemental analysis is made on the combined solutions resulting from the aqua regia and fusion treatments.

11–109. If the iron oxide content is low, but the manganese oxide content is high, damage to the platinum crucibles is prevented by pretreatment of the disintegrating melt with 2 ml of 50 per cent ethanol solution in 6 N HCl and allowing the manganese to be reduced prior to carrying out the procedure of removal of the cake from the crucible.

SILICA DETERMINATION[30]
(by HF volatilization and weight loss)

11–110. The silica is dehydrated in a boiling solution of $HClO_4$ and the other constituents are separated from the silica by filtration. The boiling $HClO_4$ method[31] of silica dehydration can be effected in a few minutes with-

---

[29] Or 30 ml of concentrated HCl if the $HClO_4$ is to be omitted for the alternative HCl dehydration of silica (¶ 11–118).

[30] For more detailed discussion of silica determination, the analyst is referred to Hillebrand and Lundell, *Applied Inorganic Analysis* (New York: John Wiley & Sons, Inc., 1929); Robinson, *Soil Sci.*, 59:7 (1945), U.S.D.A. Cir. 139 (1930); and Lenher and Truog, *J. Am. Chem. Soc.*, 38:1050 (1916).

[31] Willard and Cake, *J. Am. Chem. Soc.*, 42:2208 (1920).

out the necessity of the time-consuming baking of the silica necessary with the conventional HCl dehydration method (¶ 11–118). The use of perchloric acid permits elevation of the temperature to 200°C, whereas if $HClO_4$ is not present, "a temperature of 130°C must not be exceeded, as high temperatures lead to formation of basic salts with resolution of silica."[32]

APPARATUS

11–111. Needed apparatus includes a 30-ml platinum crucible and cover, glass hooks to support a 400-ml beaker cover glass, a funnel, a 100°C drying oven, a Meker burner, a silica-tube triangle, a sand bath on electric hot plate, and a fume hood to carry off $HClO_4$ fumes, preferably through a water aspirator pump (¶ 12–23).

REAGENTS

11–112. Needed reagents include 70 per cent $HClO_4$; 0.5 N HCl; retentive, ashless filter paper; 48 per cent HF; 2 N H_2SO_4; and $K_2S_2O_7$ crystals (¶ 11–113).

11–113. Preparation of Potassium Pyrosulfate. A platinum dish (or crucible) is filled nearly full of reagent grade $KHSO_4$ crystals, with care to avoid getting any crystals on the exterior or near the upper edge of the dish or crucible. The dish is placed on a silica-tube triangle, and the contents are warmed gently with a low flame from a Meker burner adjusted for a fully oxidizing flame. The water is gradually driven off, the heat being increased somewhat after most of the water has been expelled. *Precautions:* Should any of the salts spill or spatter onto the exterior of the dish, the heat is removed and the dish is cooled, washed off, and dried, after which the heating is begun again. The reaction is:

$$2\ KHSO_4 \xrightarrow[\text{(heat)}]{} K_2S_2O_7 + H_2O\uparrow \qquad (11\text{–}11)$$

The slow heating is continued for 5 minutes after active bubbling ceases. A slight bubbling (fine, nonspattering bubbles) will continue, accompanied by evolution of a small amount of smoke (SO_3), according to the following reaction:

$$K_2S_2O_7 \xrightarrow[\text{(heat)}]{} K_2SO_4 + SO_3\uparrow \qquad (11\text{–}12)$$

The objective is to obtain completion of reaction 11–11 with a minimum of reaction 11–12. This is easily accomplished if excessively rapid heating is avoided.

---

[32] Smith, *Perchloric Acid,* 4th ed., Vol. I (Columbus, Ohio: G. F. Smith Chemical Co., 1940), p. 23.

11–114. Dehydration of Silica with HClO$_4$. The solution (¶ 11–107) resulting from the Na$_2$CO$_3$ fusion and HClO$_4$ and HCl dissolution of the cake is covered with a watch glass supported on glass hooks and evaporated to dense fumes (fume hood!), the evaporation being completed on an electric or gas hot plate. The HClO$_4$ solution is gently boiled (fuming) for 15 or 20 minutes to dehydrate the silica, then cooled and diluted with 20 to 30 ml of hot water. All salts are soluble, and the silica is filtered off through a retentive ashless paper and washed with 0.5 N HCl until free of salts, about 10 or 12 washings being required. The silica contains fewer impurities than when separated by the HCl dehydration method. The filtrate is saved for the R$_2$O$_3$ separation (¶ 11–122 or 11–132). A second silica dehydration from HClO$_4$ usually is considered unnecessary because only a few tenths of a mgm of SiO$_2$ is generally recovered[33] by evaporation of the filtrate and fuming for 5 minutes in HClO$_4$. The paper and silica from the first (and second) filtration is transferred to a platinum crucible, and the crucible and contents are placed in an oven at 100°C until completely dry.

11–115. Ignition of Silica. After the silica has been dried *completely* at 100°C, the crucible containing the filter papers is placed on a silica-tube triangle and one side is heated very gently at first with a Meker burner having a small flame. *It is necessary that the paper be burned slowly* in order to prevent occlusion of carbon by silica (probably as silicon carbide). Also, the SiO$_2$ precipitate is light and fluffy and must be protected from loss by air currents. If the paper ignites, the flame is removed until the paper ceases to burn. Sparking indicates incomplete washing out of HClO$_4$. With the crucible tilted at a 45° angle, the flame is applied with just sufficient heat, first to *1 side* of the crucible and then the other, so that the crucible shows dull red only on 1 side.

11–116. After 13 to 20 minutes slow heating, when the ash has turned white on the under side, the crucible cover is placed to cover half the crucible, and the heat is increased somewhat on that side so that the carbon glows. To hasten oxidation of the last traces of carbon, it may be necessary to cool the crucible and contents and break up the crumbs and granules with a glass rod. When the carbon is completely burned and the ash is perfectly white, the crucible is blasted with the strongest flame of a Meker burner for about 10 minutes[34] during which time the crucible is about three-fourths covered and the flame is applied so that the crucible opening is not enveloped. The crucible is cooled for 10 minutes in a desiccator and

---

[33] As compared to several mgm from the second HCl dehydration, Hillebrand and Lundell, *op. cit.,* p. 723.

[34] This blasting is necessary to volatilize traces (1 to 3 mgm) of NaCl, which usually is present, according to Robinson, *Soil Sci.,* 59:8 (1945).

weighed, reheated for 5 minutes and reweighed. This process is repeated until the crucible and contents are brought to constant weight. The final weight is recorded.

11–117. Volatilization of Silica. The weight of silica is determined by volatilization weight loss:

$$SiO_2 + 4\,HF \longrightarrow \underset{(gas)}{SiF_4} + 2\,H_2O \qquad\qquad (11\text{–}13)$$

The silica is moistened with 3 ml of 2 N H_2SO_4, and then about 5 ml of 48 per cent HF is added slowly. The liquid is evaporated on a sand bath on the electric hot plate until the crucible contents are almost dry and SO_3 begins to be evolved. The crucible is cooled, 1 to 2 ml more HF is added and the crucible is rotated in an inclined position so as to dissolve any SiO_2 that may be stuck to the sides. The acid is evaporated to complete dryness on the sand bath. Then the uncovered crucible, in an inclined position, is gradually heated with a flame. The heating is finished with a fairly strong flame of a Meker burner for a few minutes. The crucible and contents are weighed, and this weight is subtracted from the previous weight to get the loss in weight of pure SiO_2. Volatilization of TiO_2:

$$TiO_2 + 4\,HF \longrightarrow \underset{(gas)}{TiF_4} + 2\,H_2O \qquad\qquad (11\text{–}14)$$

is prevented[35] when H_2SO_4 is present. The residue in the crucible is then fused with 1 gm of $K_2S_2O_7$ (or Na_2CO_3). The crucible is placed in a clean beaker and the cake is dissolved in 25 ml of N HCl, with heat. This solution is added to the filtrate from the silica separation (¶ 11–114).

ALTERNATIVE PROCEDURES

11–118. Dehydration of Silica with HCl. To the beaker containing the melt and suspended silica (¶ 11–107) is added 30 ml of concentrated HCl, and the beaker is placed on the hot plate with the cover glass supported on glass hooks. The solution is evaporated to dryness, during the process of which lumps and crusts are broken up with a glass rod with flattened end to expedite evaporation. The residue is treated with 10 ml of concentrated HCl, and the solution is covered and heated on a hot plate for 10 minutes or until the iron is in solution (*but no longer*), which is indicated by the absence of brown specks. Immediately the solution is diluted with about 15 ml of hot water, stirred up well and *without delay* filtered on an ashless filter paper (Whatman No. 40) while hot. With the aid of a policeman and a fine stream wash bottle containing hot 0.5 N HCl, all but traces of the silica are transferred onto the filter. The volume of acid used for the trans-

---

[35] McAlpine and Soule, *Qualitative Chemical Analysis* (New York: D. Van Nostrand Company, Inc., 1933), p. 385. The loss is small without H_2SO_4 (¶ 11–31).

fer is kept sufficiently small to permit a complete transfer of the solution and silica with 1 filling of the funnel. The filter and contents are washed until salts are all removed, usually requiring about 15 good washings.

11–119. In order to recover silica that is always left in solution after the first HCl dehydration, the filtrate is transferred to the original dish or beaker and evaporated to dryness again, and then the silica is dehydrated in an oven at 100°C for 2 hours.

11–120. Then 10 ml of concentrated[36] HCl is added, the beaker is covered and heated on hot plate for 5 to 10 minutes, and then immediately 15 ml of hot water is added, followed by prompt filtration on a second ashless retentive filter paper (Whatman No. 42). The filter is thoroughly washed with hot 0.5 N HCl, 12 good washings usually being sufficient. *The filtrate is saved for R_2O_3 separation.* The papers and silica from the first and second filtrations are transferred to a platinum crucible, and the crucible and contents are placed in an oven at 100°C until the papers are *completely dry*. Ignition and volatilization of the silica are carried out as given in the procedure.

11–121. The dehydration of silica from HCl is sometimes expedited by addition of methanol to the encrusted salts and evaporation, this process then being repeated twice for each dehydration step.

CUPFERRON SEPARATION OF IRON AND TITANIUM

(Precipitation of Fe, Ti, V, Zr, Sn, in 1 N HCl solution; remaining in solution are Al, Co, Ni, Mn, Ca, Mg, PO_4 and Pt)

11–122. Cupferron (nitroso-phenyl-hydroxylamine-ammonium) forms insoluble "chelate" coordination compounds[37] with iron (titanium, etc.[38]) in acid solution, forming Cp_3Fe in which Cp refers to a cupferron anion joined to Fe by one primary and one secondary valence, as follows:[39]

---

[36] Concentrated HCl used for maximum insolubility, after Lenher, Merrill, and Baldwin, *J. Am. Chem. Soc.,* 39:2630 (1917); Robinson, *Soil Sci.,* 59:8 (1945).

[37] According to Diehl, *Chem. Rev.,* 21:39 (1937), the term "chelate" was proposed by Morgan, *J. Chem. Soc.,* 117:1856 (1920), to designate those cyclic structures that arise from the union of metallic atoms with organic and inorganic molecules; it is derived from the Greek word "chela," referring to the great claw of the lobster and other crustaceans, and is applicable to these ring systems because of the caliper-like character of the associating molecule. Smith (see footnote 39) states "The formation of these rings may involve either primary or secondary valence. 'Chelate' rings may be defined to cover all 3 types, that is, rings formed by 2 primary valences, by 1 primary and 1 secondary valence, or by 2 secondary valences. Cupferron is representative of the bidentate classification of chelate rings in which there is one acidic group, and one coordinating group."

[38] For further details, the analyst is referred to Hillebrand and Lundell, *op. cit.;* and also Lundell and Hoffman, *Outlines of Methods of Chemical Analysis* (New York: John Wiley & Sons, Inc., 1938).

[39] Smith, *Cupferron and Neocupferron, their Preparation, Properties, and Analytical Applications* (Columbus, Ohio: G. F. Smith Chemical Co., 1938).

$$C_6H_5\!-\!\underset{\underset{O}{\overset{\|}{N}}}{\underset{|}{N}}\!-\!OH \quad \leftrightharpoons \quad C_6H_5\!-\!\underset{\overset{\|}{O}}{N}\!=\!N\!-\!OH \qquad (11\text{--}15)$$

Tautomeric forms of the cupferron molecule form the corresponding 2 chelate ferric iron precipitates:

$$\left[C_6H_5\!-\!\underset{N=O}{\overset{N\!-\!O}{|}} \right]_3 Fe \quad \leftrightharpoons \quad \left[C_6H_5\!-\!\underset{O\;\;O}{\overset{N=N}{\|\;\;|}} \right]_3 Fe \qquad (11\text{--}16)$$

in each of which Fe is 6-fold coordinated with oxygen.

11–123. The cupferron separation is often omitted, and the filtrate from the silica dehydration is taken directly to the ammonia separation. However, this necessitates the estimation of $Al_2O_3 + P_2O_5$ by difference.

APPARATUS

11–124. Needed apparatus consists of an ice box or bath, a rubber policeman, a filter funnel, a platinum crucible and cover, a 100°C drying oven, a Meker burner, and a silica-tube triangle.

REAGENTS

11–125. Reagents needed consist of ashless filter paper (Whatman No. 41), concentrated H_2SO_4 and HNO_3, $K_2S_2O_7$ and the following special reagents.

11–126. 6 Per Cent Cupferron. Six gm of cupferron reagent[40] is shaken in 100 ml of ice water until dissolved. Approximately 10 ml of this reagent is required per determination of 100 mgm of Fe_2O_3. This solution is stored in a refrigerator, since the cupferron decomposes in warm solution.

11–127. Filter Paper Pulp. One ashless (Whatman No. 41) filter paper (per determination) is shredded and suspended in water, and the suspension is shaken vigorously to pulp the paper.

PROCEDURE

11–128. Precipitation. To the ice cold (4°C) solution resulting from the filtration of the silica determination, combined with the residue from silica volatilization fused in $K_2S_2O_7$ or Na_2CO_3, containing Fe, Ti, etc., sufficient concentrated HCl is added to give a 1 N solution of HCl plus $HClO_4$. A little filter paper pulp (equivalent to 1 filter disc) is added to help aggregate the precipitate later. Finally the ice cold cupferron reagent is added dropwise (10 ml per 100 mgm of Fe_2O_3) until the precipitate aggregates into large clumps and the supernatant liquid is the color of the reagent, *but not reddish*. The aggregates are allowed to settle for 30 seconds, and then, to test for completeness of precipitation, a few drops additional cupferron

---

[40] Ammonium salt, as obtained from the G. F. Smith Chemical Co., Columbus, O.

reagent are added. Formation of white flashes with no further brown precipitate indicates complete precipitation.

11–129. Filtration. After the aggregates settle a few seconds, the solution is filtered through a porous (Whatman No. 41) filter paper, the sides of the beaker being policed well. The filtrate has a cloudy tan color that is due entirely to the products of decomposition of the reagent. (Presence of iron may be tested by further addition of cupferron, which should give only a temporarily white precipitate.) The precipitate is washed 5 times with cold 1 N HCl containing a little cupferron, and then 3 times in addition with ice cold water to remove most of the chlorides. The filter is then dried at 100°C.

11–130. Ignition. The precipitate, dried at 100°C, is carefully charred (as in ¶ 11–115) and finally ignited strongly to constant weight. The precipitate from clays or soils is mainly Fe_2O_3 and TiO_2. The precipitate is fused in $K_2S_2O_7$ (¶ 11–148) for the iron determination.

11–131. The *cool* filtrate from the cupferron separation is treated with 1 ml of concentrated H_2SO_4 and 10 ml of concentrated HNO_3 to remove the excess cupferron. (The mixture would be slightly explosive if the filtrate were heated before the acids were added, but is quiet if the acids are added to the cool filtrate obtained after the normal precipitation procedure.) Then the solution is placed on the steam hot plate and evaporated to dryness to evolve free Cl_2 and to oxidize and decolorize the cupferron. The mixture is finally heated on the electric hot plate to fumes to remove $HClO_4$. 3 or more HNO_3 treatments will be required. When the cupferron is destroyed, the residue is ready for the NH_4OH separation.

NH_4OH SEPARATION AND ALUMINUM DETERMINATION

(Following cupferron separation[41] of Fe and Ti, separation of Al
and PO4 from Ca, Mg, and Mn.)

11–132. The NH_4OH separation is dependent on the insolubility of the hydroxide and phosphate of Al (and Fe and Ti in the absence of the cupferron separation) at or near the neutral point, and the solubility in the presence of considerable NH_4Cl, of the hydroxides of Ca, Mg, and Mn++.

11–133. In the event the PO_4 exceeds the equivalents of Al (and Fe and Ti) present, as will always be the case in the analysis of phosphate materials, it will combine with the divalent bases, causing their precipitation, thus invalidating the separation. In this case, an excess and known amount of Al (or Fe) is added to effect the separation.

APPARATUS

11–134. Needed apparatus consists of a crude buret for dispensing 4 N NH_4OH, a platinum crucible and cover, a Meker burner, and a silica-tube triangle.

---

[41] In the absence of the cupferron separation, Fe and Ti precipitate with Al and PO4.

11–135. Needed reagents consist of concentrated HCl, 4 N NH₄OH, thymol blue and brom cresol purple indicators, filter paper (Whatman No. 41), and 0.5 per cent NH_4NO_3 washing solution (3 ml of concentrated HNO_3 per liter, to which NH_4OH is added to pH 6.4, brom cresol purple).

11–136. Precipitation of R_2O_3. Five ml of concentrated HCl is added to the H_2SO_4-HNO_3-treated residue from the cupferron separation, and the solution is then made to a volume of 250 ml (or, in the absence of the cup-ferron separation, the HCl is added to the silica filtrate combined with the $K_2S_2O_7$ solution of the residues from the silica volatilization, in a volume of about 400 ml). Next, 4 N NH_4OH is added dropwise from a buret until a drop of thymol blue indicator dropped into the solution turns from red to yellow, indicating a pH in the range of 2 to 3. Then 1 ml of brom cresol purple (BCP) indicator is added, the solution is heated to boiling, and more 4 N NH_4OH is added dropwise until pH 6.4 is reached from the acid side. (A glass electrode pH meter or methyl red may be used in lieu of BCP.)

11–137. In the presence of much iron, the indicator color may not be clearly visible. In this event, small drops of the suspension are tested on a spot plate, or a drop of BCP indicator is added from time to time and the color is observed when it first strikes the solution. The pH is not allowed to rise above the final value of 6.4 because Mn may be precipitated and will not redissolve if the pH is again dropped to 6.4. If the pH value inad-vertently exceeds 6.4, the reprecipitation later (¶ 11–139) is mandatory; otherwise it is sometimes omitted. The solution is finally brought just to the boiling point and then is set aside for the precipitate to settle, followed by prompt filtration.

11–138. Filtration. The bulk of the supernatant solution is decanted through a porous, ashless, Whatman No. 41 filter paper, the filter and pre-cipitate being washed once or twice with rinsings from the beaker with hot 0.5 per cent NH_4NO_3 solution adjusted to pH 6.4. It is not necessary to police the beaker after the first precipitation if the R_2O_3 is to be reprecipi-tated. The filtrate is saved for the determination of Ca (¶ 11–162), Mg, and Mn (¶ 11–172).

11–139. Reprecipitation of R_2O_3. In order to remove traces of man-ganese, calcium, magnesium, and other salts that contaminate the R_2O_3 precipitate, a reprecipitation is necessary. The filter paper and contents are placed into the original beaker, and about 20 ml of 6 N HCl is added. The solution is heated to boiling to dissolve the precipitate, and the filter paper is disintegrated with a glass rod. The solution is diluted with water to about 250 ml and heated to boiling. Then 1 ml BCP indicator is added and the solution brought just to pH 6.4 by adding 4 N NH_4OH, the same technique being employed as in the first precipitation. The precipitate is allowed to settle, and the solution is poured through the filter while hot. Immediately the precipitate is washed 5 times with a hot solution of 0.5 per cent NH_4NO_3 solution. The filtrates are next combined and the solution re-adjusted to pH 6.4, followed by digestion on a hot plate. If any more precipitate forms, it is caught on a third filter paper and washed 10 times. Filtrates from the ammonia separation are combined and saved for the calcium (¶ 11–162), magnesium, and manganese determinations (¶ 11–172).

11–140. Ignition. The filter paper and precipitate are placed in a weighed platinum crucible, oven-dried at 100°C and then charred carefully (as in ¶ 11–115), and finally ignited to constant weight. The ignition is completed by heating with a Meker burner for 5 to 10 minutes. Good oxidizing conditions are rigorously maintained during ignition.

11–141. Content of Al_2O_3. The net weight of the contents of the crucible, consisting of Al_2O_3 and P_2O_5 (and Fe_2O_3 and TiO_2 in the absence of the cupferron separation) is calculated. The content of P_2O_5 is subtracted (and also the content of Fe_2O_3 and TiO_2 is subtracted in the absence of the cupferron separation) from the total, and Al_2O_3 determined by difference.

IRON DETERMINATION
(Following cupferron or NH₄OH separation)

11–142. The Fe is determined in H_2SO_4 solution titrimetrically with cerate (or permanganate) after reduction in the Jones reductor (or in HCl after reduction in Walden Ag-reductor). The iron and titanium may also be determined with Tiron (¶ 11–62) or the iron by orthophenanthroline (¶ 15–6) after the $K_2S_2O_7$ fusion given here.

APPARATUS

11–143. Apparatus needed consists of 600-ml and 400-ml beakers, stirring rods, a suction flask, and a Jones reductor (prepared as follows):

11–144. Preparation of a Jones Reductor. Amalgamated zinc is prepared by treatment for about 30 seconds of approximately 300 gm of zinc granules (1 mm) with enough 1 N HCl to cover. Then 200 ml of approximately 0.2 N $HgCl_2$ solution is added followed by vigorous stirring until no more H_2 is evolved. The supernatant solution is decanted, and the amalgamated zinc is thoroughly washed with distilled water and dried on a watch glass at 100°C. The reductor column is prepared from a glass column 2 cm in diameter, with a length for the zinc of 20 cm, fitted with a glass stopcock on 1 end and a funnel on the other. A 1-cm depth of glass wool is placed in the bottom of the column, followed by 20 cm of the amalgamated zinc, and then 1 cm of glass wool.

11–145. Precautions in the Use of a Jones Reductor.

1. The zinc column is kept covered with distilled water when not in use, and with the 1 N H_2SO_4 solution (never stronger than 2.5 N) when in use. The objective is to avoid getting air into the column since this may cause low results. The amalgamated zinc corrodes and cakes if exposed at length to air.

2. Acids stronger than 10 per cent H_2SO_4 (2.5 N) are avoided. H_2SO_4 is preferred to HCl, although the latter may be employed.

3. Copper and other easily reducible metals, which may be reduced to the free metal in the reductor, are avoided.

4. Ammonium solutions render the column worthless.

5. A reductor that is newly made or has not been used for several days is treated by the passage of 100 ml of 1 N H_2SO_4 followed by 100 ml of distilled water, prior to use. This serves to remove any possible reducible substances and insures efficacy of operation.

11–146. Blank Determination on the Jones Reductor.

At the beginning of a series of determinations, a blank is run on the reductor. To do this, approximately 75 ml of 1 N H_2SO_4 is passed through the reductor at the rate of about 25 to 50 ml per minute, the stopcock being closed before the level of the liquid drops sufficiently to expose the zinc at the top. This is followed by 3 25-ml portions of distilled water. Each portion is added just before the previous portion sinks below the top surface of the zinc column. At no time is the zinc exposed to the air. When the last addition of water has reached the upper glass wool pad, and the top surface of the zinc is still covered, the stopcock is closed and the solution in the receiving flask transferred to a 400-ml beaker, and the flask is rinsed 3 times with water. The combined solution and rinsings are titrated with 0.05 N $(NH_4)_4$Ce-$(SO_4)_4$ (¶ 11–154) and orthophenanthroline indicator (or with 0.05 N $KMnO_4$). If the reductor is in good condition, the blank determination should not exceed 0.1 to 0.15 ml. This blank titration value is subtracted from the values obtained in the regular determinations.

REAGENTS

11–147.
Needed reagents consist of $K_2S_2O_7$ (¶ 11–113), NaF, 2 N and 1 N H_2SO_4, 0.05 N $(NH_4)_4$Ce$(SO_4)_4$ solution in 1 N H_2SO_4 (¶ 6–42), and orthophenanthroline indicator (or 0.05 N $KMnO_4$ instead of cerate and the indicator).

PROCEDURE

11–148. Pyrosulfate Fusion of the Oxides.
Five gm of $K_2S_2O_7$ is placed in the crucible containing the weighed precipitate of oxides of Fe and Ti (and Al and PO_4 in the absence of the cupferron separation). The mixture is fused for 1 or 2 minutes (under the fume hood) with a low flame just sufficient to bring the bottom of the crucible to faint redness and to cause

a moderate evolution of SO_3 fumes. The crucible is then allowed to cool until the melt is partially crystallized.

11–149. Then approximately 0.05 gm of NaF is added and heating is continued until all the oxides are in solution, which is indicated by the absence of solid brown or white particles in the liquid fusion. Fuming of the pyrosulfate to volatilize HF is necessary to prevent interference in the Ti determination. It usually takes 5 to 10 minutes for the fusion, but heating is not continued any longer than necessary since the crucible is attacked to some extent. After cooling, the crucible is placed (clean externally) into 40 ml of 2 N H_2SO_4 and heated until the melt dissolves. (The 2 N H_2SO_4 is sufficiently strong to maintain TiO_2 in solution.) The crucible is then removed and washed off.

11–150. The solution should be clear at this point if the fusion has been complete. However, if dark particles remain, they are filtered off on an ashless Whatman No. 42 filter paper, the filter then being dried at 100°C and ashed in a Pt crucible. The contents of the crucible are fused with 1 gm $K_2S_2O_7$ and 0.05 gm of NaF (¶ 11–148). The melt is cooled and dissolved in 2 N H_2SO_4, and this second solution is combined with the solution resulting from the first fusion.

11–151. Reduction and Titration of Iron. The H_2SO_4 solution of Fe and Ti (and Al and PO_4 in absence of cupferron separation) is now ready for reduction of the iron. The solution is stirred and then passed through the reductor (freshly washed, ¶ 11–145,5) at the rate of about 25 ml per minute. This is followed with 2 25-ml portions of 1 N H_2SO_4 and 2 25-ml portions of distilled water so as to wash out all the test solution. The top surface of the zinc is always left covered with water. The solution in the flask is transferred to a 600-ml beaker, but the total volume is held down to 400 ml to avoid the need for evaporation for the Ti determination.

11–152. The appearance of a purplish tinge in the solution indicates the presence of at least 0.10 mgm of reduced Ti per ml. Less Ti than this is reoxidized during the regular operations. To reoxidize quantities of 0.10 mgm or more, about 25 ml of distilled water is added (to carry in small amounts of oxygen), and the solution in the beaker stirred vigorously for about 6 minutes. If, at the end of this time, the color has not entirely disappeared, 25 ml more distilled water is added, and stirring is continued until the color is no longer apparent when the beaker is held over a white background, and then is continued about 2 minutes longer. This procedure does not cause reoxidation of iron.[42]

11–153. The efficacy of the reductor in reducing all of the Fe to ferrous may be tested with a few drops of KSCN added to a ml of the solution. Development of a pink or red color indicates incomplete reduction of ferric iron, but the persistence of any ferric iron is almost never found. This test

[42] Truog and Pearson, *Ind. Eng. Chem., A.E.,* 10:631 (1938).

also permits verification that Fe has remained reduced while the Ti was being oxidized. Chromium, V, and Mo are also reduced by the Jones reductor, but like Ti, are oxidized by air unless protected by collection out of contact with air.

11–154. The solution is titrated with $0.05 N$ $(NH_4)_4Ce(SO_4)_4$ to blue with orthophenanthroline (or with 0.05 N $KMnO_4$ to the first appearance of a pink color). The solution is saved for the determination of Ti. The blank titration is subtracted; then 1 ml $0.05 N$ solution $= 0.003992$ gm Fe_2O_3, or:

$$\% \text{ Fe} = \text{ml} \times N \times \frac{5.585}{\text{wt. sample, gm}} \qquad (11\text{–}17)$$

TITANIUM DETERMINATION

(Following cupferron or NH_4OH separation, spectrophotometrically after peroxidation in $2 N H_2SO_4$)

11–155. The yellow-colored compound formed when Ti is peroxidized in $2 N H_2SO_4$ has long been employed for the Ti determination.[43] The color is thought possibly to involve a complex of Ti^{6+} with SO_4^{--}. Interfering ions include V, Cr, W, Mo, and F. Also, yellow-colored ferric salts must be compensated for; Hillebrand[44] gives a correction equal to 0.2 mgm of TiO_2 peroxidized for each 100 mgm of Fe_2O_3 in 100 ml of $1.2 N H_2SO_4$. At least $1.2 N H_2SO_4$ is necessary to prevent hydrolysis of the $Ti(SO_4)_2$ to insoluble basic sulfate. Also alkali sulfate causes bleaching of the color except in the presence of a large excess of H_2SO_4. A concentration of $2 N$ H_2SO_4 is therefore employed.

APPARATUS

11–156. Needed apparatus includes an absorption spectrophotometer with 420-mu light maximum and tubes, and 500-ml and 100-ml volumetric flasks.

REAGENTS

11–157. Needed reagents include concentrated and $2 N H_2SO_4$, 30 per cent H_2O_2, and a standard Ti solution prepared as follows:

11–158. Standard Ti Solution. A standard Ti solution is prepared by fusion of 0.250 gm of ignited TiO_2 in 3 gm of $K_2S_2O_7$ (¶ 11–113) in a platinum crucible. The fusion is carried out under the fume hood, the heating being just sufficient to cause moderate evolution of SO_3 fumes. Heating is continued long enough to obtain all of the TiO_2 in solution, as indicated by a perfectly clear, quiet, fused mass. Too rapid heating, however,

---

[43] Weller, *Ber.* 15:2592 (1882); Snell and Snell, *Colorimetric Methods of Analysis,* Vol. 1 (New York: D. Van Nostrand Company, Inc., 1936).

[44] U.S. Geol. Surv. Bul. 700:160 (1919).

will convert the $K_2S_2O_7$ to K_2SO_4, which is not readily fusible. The crucible (clean externally) is placed in a beaker containing 75 ml 2 N H_2SO_4 and the mixture is warmed gently until solution is complete. The solution is transferred to a 500-ml volumetric flask and diluted to volume with 2 N H_2SO_4. This solution contains 0.5 mgm of TiO_2 per ml.

11–159. Aliquots (1, 2, 5, and 10 ml) of the Ti standard solution are pipetted into respective 100-ml volumetric flasks and diluted to 75 ml with a 2 N H_2SO_4. Next, 5 ml of 30 per cent H_2O_2 is added and the solutions are then mixed. The yellow color develops instantly. When the color has developed, each solution is made to volume with 2 N H_2SO_4 and mixed, giving 5, 10, 25, and 50 ugm of TiO_2 per ml (or 3, 6, 15, and 30 ugm of Ti) in the flasks. This series is read in the colorimeter, 2 N H_2SO_4 being used as the blank. The concentration of Ti or TiO_2 as ugm per ml is plotted on a linear scale against percentage transmission on a log scale. The curve is linear, and after having once been established, is only rechecked occasionally, with the 6 ugm of Ti per ml standard.

PROCEDURE

11–160. To the solution left after completion of the Jones reductor titration of the Fe (¶ 11–154), enough concentrated H_2SO_4 (usually about 20 ml) is added to make the solution approximately 2 N in a final volume of 500 ml, the amount of acid already present being taken into account. If the volume is less than 500, the solution is transferred to a 500-ml volumetric flask, but is *not yet* made to volume.

11–161. Development of the Ti Yellow Color. To develop the color, approximately 5 ml of 30 per cent H_2O_2 is added per 100 ml of the Ti solution at hand and the solution mixed. If the color is distinctly yellow (in range of standards), sufficient Ti concentration is present for the determination and the solution is made to volume. If too dilute, the solution is evaporated as needed to bring the Ti concentration into range. The solution is then diluted to an exact volume and mixed, the percentage transmission is read in the colorimeter with a 420-mu light maximum, and the reading is referred to the calibration curve to obtain the ugm of Ti per ml. Visual comparison may also be made to the standard by Nessler tubes. A mineral colloid or soil containing 0.5 per cent TiO_2 (common) gives 10 ugm of TiO_2 or 6 ugm of Ti per ml in a 500-ml dilution volume:

$$\% \text{ Ti} = \frac{\text{ugm per ml}}{10^4} \times \frac{\text{solution volume, ml}}{\text{wt. sample, gm}} \qquad (11\text{–}18)$$

CALCIUM DETERMINATION

(Total, in conventional silicate analysis system)

11–162. The total calcium obtained in the filtrate from the NH_4OH separation (¶ 11–138) may be determined by the oxalate procedure that follows. Through suitable standardization, total calcium may also be determined with Versene (¶ 11–46) or by the flame emission spectrophotometer (¶ 11–37).

11–163. Needed apparatus includes a 400-ml beaker, a steam hot plate, and fritted glass crucible (medium porosity) with holder and suction flask.

11–164. Needed reagents are brom phenol blue indicator, 6 N HCl, 4 N NH$_4$OH, and reagents for precipitation of calcium (¶ 5–26).

11–165. The filtrates from the NH$_4$OH separation are brought to a volume of approximately 250 ml by evaporation, but the solution is not allowed to go to dryness.[45] The solution is transferred to a 400-ml beaker, 1 ml of brom phenol blue indicator is added, and finally a little 6 N HCl is added if necessary to make the solution slightly acid. The calcium is next precipitated (¶ 5–31) in a 400-ml beaker and reprecipitated (¶ 11–166) if the amounts of calcium and particularly magnesium are large, as will be the case in the analysis of calcareous soils or dolomitic limestone. The filtrate is saved for the determination of Mg and Mn. The calcium oxalate is determined usually by titration (¶ 5–33 or 5–38) or, rarely, gravimetrically (¶ 5–37).

11–166. Reprecipitation of Calcium. Reprecipitation is necessary when the amount of magnesium is large. The precipitate of CaC$_2$O$_4$ (¶ 11–165) is redissolved with about 15 ml hot 6 N HCl and washed out of the filter with hot water, diluted to 150 ml with water and reprecipitated as in the first precipitation. The second filtrate from calcium is united with the first for the determination of Mg plus Mn (¶ 11–167).

MAGNESIUM DETERMINATION

(Total, in conventional silicate analysis system)

11–167. The procedure for Mg actually determines Mg plus Mn, but the latter is usually so small in amount as to be within the experimental error of the Mg determination. This is checked on, however, by a Mn determination (¶ 11–172). Total Mg plus Mn may be determined by titration with

---

[45] If the solution should happen to go to dryness at this point, some dark colored material becomes insoluble. If this happens, 5 ml of concentrated HNO$_3$ and 15 ml of water are added and the solution is stirred. The beaker is then covered with a watch glass supported on glass hooks, and the solution is evaporated to dryness. The residue should now be white or only slightly yellow. If not, the residue is taken up in about 3 ml of HNO$_3$ and 10 ml of HCl and evaporated to dryness again. These treatments destroy coloring matter and render other constituents easily soluble. The residue is taken up in 5 ml 6 N HCl and the solution diluted to 250 ml.

Versene (below) or as $MgNH_4PO_4$ and $MnNH_4PO_4$ (¶ 5–48). Through suitable standardization, total Mg may be determined by flame emission spectrophotometry (¶ 11–37).

APPARATUS

11–168. Needed apparatus includes a cover glass and glass hooks to raise it from the beaker, a steam hot plate, and apparatus for the titrimetric determination of Mg (¶ 11–54).

REAGENTS

11–169. Needed reagents consist of concentrated HNO_3, concentrated HCl, 4 N NH_4OH, brom thymol blue indicator, and the reagents for Mg determination (¶ 11–58).

PROCEDURE

11–170. Removal of Excess Ammonium Salts. Approximately 20 ml of concentrated HNO_3 is added to the filtrate from the calcium determination (or combined filtrates in case of reprecipitation), and the beaker is covered with a cover glass supported on glass hooks. The solution is evaporated to dryness in order to decompose the excess of ammonium salts, yielding volatile products.

Equations:

$$NH_4Cl + HNO_3 \longrightarrow NH_4NO_3 + HCl \qquad (11\text{–}19)$$

$$2\,HCl + 2\,HNO_3 \longrightarrow \underset{(\text{brown gas})}{2\,NO_2} + Cl_2 + 2\,H_2O \qquad (11\text{–}20)$$

$$NH_4NO_3 \longrightarrow \underset{(\text{colorless gas})}{N_2O} + 2\,H_2O \qquad (11\text{–}21)$$

$$3\,Cl_2 + 2\,NH_4Cl \longrightarrow 8\,HCl + N_2 \qquad (11\text{–}22)$$

$$H_2C_2O_4 + Cl_2 \longrightarrow 2\,HCl + 2\,CO_2 \qquad (11\text{–}23)$$

The treatment is repeated by adding 10 ml concentrated HNO_3 and 30 ml concentrated HCl (aqua regia) and evaporating to dryness again, and is repeated still again if considerable ammonium salts remain, which will be the case if more than the usual quantity of acid and NH_4OH were used in the NH_4OH separation.

11–171. The residue is dissolved in about 3 ml of concentrated HCl, diluted to 100 ml and neutralized with 4 N NH_4OH using brom thymol blue indicator. Then Mg (plus Mn) is determined titrimetrically with Versene (¶ 11–59). Also, Mg may be precipitated as the phosphate (¶ 5–48), and determined titrimetrically (¶ 5–52). In either case, the meq of Mn (¶ 11–61) is subtracted from the meq of Mg plus Mn titrated, and the Mg is derived by difference.

MANGANESE DETERMINATION

(Total, in conventional or rapid semimicrochemical system)

11–172. The total manganese may be determined in an aliquot of the filtrate from the NH_4OH separation (¶ 11–139, 11–40, or 11–94) or from the Ca determination (¶ 11–165), and also in the precipitate from the NH_4OH-Br separation (¶ 11–41) or NaOH separation (¶ 11–96).

11–173. Manganese may also be determined in the solution resulting from the titration of Mg plus Mn (¶ 11–171) in the conventional system, or in the solution remaining after Versene titration of Ca plus Mg plus Mn with Versene in the semimicrochemical system (¶ 11–59). Also, following a gravimetric determination as $Mg_2P_2O_7$ and $Mn_2P_2O_7$ (¶ 5–56), the ignited ash may be fused in $K_2S_2O_7$ and Mn determined in a H_3PO_4 solution of the melt.

11–174. The aqua regia treatment is given for removal of organic matter and excess ammonium salts as detailed in the Mg determination (¶ 11–170) if Mn is to be determined on an aliquot of the filtrate from either the NH_4OH separation or the Ca determination in the conventional system. This treatment is also given if Mn is to be determined on the solution remaining after titration of Ca plus Mg and Mn with Versene in the semimicrochemical system.

11–175. The Mn solution is freed of traces of organic matter, ammonium, and halides by the treatment detailed in ¶ 5–74; it is obtained in solution in H_3PO_4 and then is ready for the usual periodate determination of Mn as detailed in ¶ 5–76.

POTASSIUM AND SODIUM DETERMINATIONS

(Total, conventional system by decomposition of sample in HF)

11–176. Potassium and sodium cannot be determined on the sample fused in Na_2CO_3 earlier in this system because appreciable potassium has been introduced in the reagents during the course of the analysis, and of course sodium has been introduced in the Na_2CO_3. A separate sample is decomposed in HF, and the K and Na are subsequently determined by means of titrimetric, spectrochemical, or gravimetric methods. The following procedure details the method of decomposition of the sample in HF; it is similar to that given in the semimicrochemical system of analysis (¶ 11–31), but it is adapted to macro samples.

APPARATUS

11-177. Needed apparatus includes a 30-ml platinum crucible and cover; an electric hot plate with sand bath; a 100-ml volumetric flask; and 150-ml, 100-ml, and 50-ml beakers.

11–178. Needed reagents are 18 N H_2SO_4, 48 per cent HF solution, concentrated HNO_3, 60 per cent $HClO_4$, and 6 N HCl. In the conventional procedures for K and Na, 6 N NaOH and 6 N NH_4OH and brom cresol purple indicator are required in addition.

PROCEDURE

11–179. Decomposition of Sample in HF. A sample, of mineral colloid, soil, silicate rock, or mineral, having passed the 0.16-mm sieve (100 meshes per inch) and weighing from 0.1 to 1.0 gm, is placed in a 30-ml platinum crucible. The sample is moistened with a few drops of 18 N H_2SO_4, then 1 ml of $HClO_4$ and 5 ml of 48 per cent HF are added (the H_2SO_4 is omitted for a sample containing over 2 per cent Ti). The crucible is then about 0.7 covered and is placed on a sand bath on an electric hot plate regulated at 200° to 225°C, after which the acids are evaporated to dryness. The heating rate is regulated so that H_2SO_4 fumes are evolved, but so that the solution does not boil. Additional portions of the H_2SO_4, $HClO_4$ and HF acids are added so that a total of 3 treatments and evaporations have been given. At last, a few additional drops of H_2SO_4 are added and the mixture is fumed to drive off fluorides. Then the crucible is cooled and 5 ml of 6 N HCl is added. The suspension is diluted to 20 ml with water. The crucible is then placed in a radiator (on a triangle within a large crucible). The solution is brought to very gentle boiling with a low flame applied to the outer crucible. The residue usually goes into solution in about 5 minutes.

11–180. Analysis of the Solution. Analysis of the solution in the crucible may be made for K and Na, and in addition, for Fe, Ti, Al, Ca, Mg, and Mn if desired. The method of transfer depends on how many elements are to be determined and the determinative method to be chosen, outlined as follows:

1. For K and Na by flame emission spectrophotometer, the solution is transferred to a 100-ml volumetric flask and the determination is made directly in the HCl solution (¶ 11–45). The determinations are run as promptly as possible to minimize contamination from glassware.

2. For K determination by the cobaltinitrite precipitation method (suitable for range of 0.5 to 6 mgm of K in 5 to 10 ml, the solution in the crucible (or a known fraction of it by a prior transfer to a 100-ml volumetric flask) is transferred to a 150-ml beaker, diluted to 75 ml, heated to boiling and brought to pH 6.4 (brom cresol purple) by means of 6 N NaOH. The solution is transferred to a 100-ml (or other volume to give the proper range) volumetric flask, brought to volume at room temperature, mixed, and filtered through a dry Whatman No. 40 filter paper, with no washings and with precaution against evaporation. An aliquot of 5 or 10 ml, containing 0.5 to 6 mgm of K, is taken for precipitation of the K (¶ 6–22).

3. For Na determination by the magnesium uranyl acetate procedure (suitable for the range of 1 to 5 mgm of Na), the solution in the crucible (or a known fraction of it taken by dilution in a volumetric flask) is transferred to a 150-ml beaker, diluted to 75 ml, brought to boiling and neutralized to pH 6.4 with 6 N NH_4OH (brom cresol purple), transferred to a 100-ml volumetric flask, made to volume at room temperature, and well mixed. It is then filtered through a dry Whatman No. 40 filter paper without washing and with precaution against evaporation. An aliquot containing 1 to 5 mgm of Na is transferred to a well-weathered 100-ml beaker. Then 10 ml of aqua regia (3 HCl to 1 NHO_3) is added and the solution is evaporated to dryness to destroy ammonium salts. If much ammonium salt appears to remain, the residue is taken up to 2 ml of aqua regia and the evaporation is repeated. The Na is then determined (¶ 5–88).

ALTERNATIVE PROCEDURE

11–181. Total potassium and sodium of minerals may be determined by the classical NH_4Cl-$CaCO_3$ method of J. Lawrence Smith,[46] but it is not easy to obtain these reagents free from the alkali metals; also the method requires a relatively large sample. The sample is intimately ground into a mixture of NH_4Cl and $CaCO_3$ and heated. Finally the mixture is leached, and the filtrate is subjected to precipitation with $(NH_4)_2CO_3$, and the filtrate from this is evaporated to dryness, after which NH_4Cl is driven off by cautious heating and the NaCl and KCl weighed. The K may then be determined separately by precipitation as chloroplatinate or cobaltinitrite, the NaCl being determined by difference from the combined weight of the mixed chlorides (¶ 10–84).

FERROUS IRON DETERMINATION IN SILICATES

11–182. The determination of ferrous iron in silicates is essential for the allocation of elemental analysis to the mineral constituents. After the determination of ferrous iron, the ferric iron is determined by difference from the total iron (¶ 11–62 or 11–142).

APPARATUS

11–183. Needed apparatus includes a 30-ml or larger platinum crucible, a burner and windshield, a 400-ml beaker, platinum or nickel tongs, and a small buret. Also needed is a radiator consisting of a porcelain crucible into which the platinum crucible is suspended on a triangle.

REAGENTS

11–184. Needed reagents are 18 N H_2SO_4, 48 per cent HF, saturated H_3BO_3 solution, standard 0.025 N $(NH_4)_4Ce(SO_4)_4 \cdot 2 H_2O$ in 1 N H_2SO_4 (or standard $K_2Cr_2O_7$, or $KMnO_4$ solution). If the cerate solution is to be

---

[46] Washington, *Chemical Analysis of Rocks*, 3rd ed. (New York: John Wiley & Sons, Inc., 1919); Smith, *Am. J. Arts*, 1,3:269 (1881).

employed, 85 per cent H_3PO_4 and diphenylamine sulfonate indicator solution are needed.

11–185. A 0.1 to 0.5 gm of sample, ground to pass a 0.15-mm sieve is placed in a 30-ml platinum crucible and 1 to 2 ml of water is added to moisten the powder. Then 10 ml of 18 N H_2SO_4 is added to the crucible, the cover is placed completely over the crucible, and the solution is heated nearly to boiling with a burner, heat being applied to the radiator described with the apparatus. The crucible cover is then moved slightly to the side, and 5 ml of HF is added. The cover is replaced and the liquid is quickly heated to boiling. Gentle boiling is continued for 10 minutes, the windshield being employed to maintain steady slow heat.

11–186. While a sample is being decomposed by the HF treatment, a 400-ml beaker is half-filled with cold water and 10 ml of 18 N H_2SO_4 and 10 ml of the saturated H_3BO_3 solution are added. (The boric acid is employed for complexing F as weakly dissociated HBF_4, necessary to prevent formation of ferric fluoride complex and acceleration of ferrous oxidation in the presence of air.) By means of tongs, the crucible and cover are placed in the solution in the beaker. The solution is stirred to suspend the solid matter in the solution and then the ferrous iron is titrated with the 0.025 N standard oxidizing solution, 2 drops of "Ferroin" being added as indicator for the cerate titration (or 6 drops of diphenylamine disulfonate solution along with 10 ml of 85 per cent H_3PO_4 if $K_2Cr_2O_7$ is to be employed for the titration). If organic material is present in the sample, the end point may fade and erratic results will be obtained. After the titration the bottom of the beaker is examined for any dark particles that would indicate incomplete decomposition of the sample. If such dark particles are found, the determination is repeated with a more finely ground sample, but excessively fine grinding is avoided because ferrous iron may be oxidized as a result of the grinding.

ALTERNATIVE PROCEDURE

11–187. Maintenance of an atmosphere of CO_2 over the crucible has been[48] employed as a precautionary measure for prevention of oxidation of iron by air. However, the water vapor evolved on boiling the sample ordinarily protects against contact with oxygen and permits a satisfactory determination of ferrous iron.

---

[47] Procedure employed at this laboratory is essentially as described by Kolthoff and Sandell, *Textbook of Quantitative Inorganic Analysis,* rev. ed. (New York: The Macmillan Company, 1945), p. 746.

[48] Sarvar, *J. Am. Chem. Soc.,* 49:1472 (1927); Schollenberger, *J. Am. Chem. Soc.,* 53:96 (1931).

TOTAL SULFUR IN SOILS[49]

(Separate fusion in Na_2CO_3 and $NaNO_3$, and precipitation as $BaSO_4$)

11–188. Total sulfur determination for soils should be thought of much as the total nitrogen determination for soils. Sulfate may accumulate in soils as gypsum, $CaSO_4 \cdot 2 H_2O$, and its determination in this form has been considered (¶ 10–102) in connection with soluble salts in soils. Much of the sulfur is in organic form and slowly becomes available for crop use. The sulfur requirement of crops is relatively high, being 0.5 of the P requirement of cereals and equal to the P requirement of legumes.

APPARATUS

11–189. Needed apparatus includes a 25-ml platinum crucible, electric furnace, filter funnel, and Meker burner.

REAGENTS

11–190. Needed reagents are anhydrous Na_2CO_3, $NaNO_3$, $6 N$ HCl, 10 per cent $BaCl_2$ solution, HF, H_2SO_4 and filter paper.

PROCEDURE

11–191. Fusion. One to 2 gm of the finely ground and well-mixed soil is fused in a 25-ml platinum crucible with 5 times the weight of Na_2CO_3 and 0.2 or 0.3 gm of $NaNO_3$. The fusion is best done in an electric furnace. If gas is used for the ignition, the melt is likely to be contaminated with sulfate. To avoid the latter, the crucible is supported in platinum foil with a hole cut in it to let the crucible in for about half its height. This foil, in turn, is supported by a sheet of thin asbestos. When the flame is played on the lower part of the crucible, the upper part of the crucible is protected from the products of combustion. After fusion, the melt is thoroughly disintegrated in water on the steam bath, preferably by digestion over night. The solution is then filtered, and the silica washed. The filtrate is then made up to 150 to 175 ml if not already of this volume. Enough HCl is added to neutralize the Na_2CO_3 and to make the solution about 0.3 N HCl in excess.

11–192. Precaution. Occasionally, because of a long digestion, or too large an excess of acid, the silica remaining in the filtrate gels. One of the 2 following procedures may be used before the $BaCl_2$ is added: (a) The silica may be removed by dehydration and filtration, or (b) the silica may be filtered from the solution neutralized with NH_4OH.

11–193. Precipitation of $BaSO_4$. The solution is brought to boiling, and 10 ml of 10 per cent $BaCl_2$ is slowly added to precipitate the sulfate. The solution is allowed to stand until cool, then is passed through a small fine-porosity filter paper, and the precipitate is washed.

11–194. Ignition of $BaSO_4$. The paper is ignited at a low temperature

---

[49] Robinson, *Soil Sci.,* 59:11 (1945).

and the precipitate weighed. The ignited $BaSO_4$ is treated with a few drops of HF and H_2SO_4, cautiously ignited, and weighed again.

11–195. As the reagents used invariably contain some sulfur, blanks are carried along in the same manner as the determinations.

$$\% \text{ S} = \text{gm BaSO}_4 \times \frac{13.7}{\text{weight of sample, gm}} \qquad (11\text{–}24)$$

MISCELLANEOUS CONSTITUENTS

11–196. In the elemental analysis of soils, minerals, and rocks, interest occasionally arises in the elements zirconium, fluorine, barium, chromium, vanadium, wolfram, chlorine, and lithium.

11–197. Zirconium Determination. Because of the resistance of the mineral zircon (ZrO_2) to weathering, Zr is sometimes employed as a reference element in soil weathering. It has been proposed[50] that the determination of total zirconium is a fairly satisfactory measure of the zircon content of soil, although weathering of zircon grains has been observed.[51] Dr. L. D. Swindale found that highly podzolized horizons of certain soils contain only 25 to 80 per cent as much Zr as the parent rock, instead of showing Zr enrichment as should occur for a reference element. Soil Zr is effectively determined by X-ray fluorescence.[52] The sample is freed of organic matter with H_2O_2, dried, and ground to pass a 0.1-mm sieve (140 meshes per inch). The Zr is excited by W X-radiation and its fluorescence spectrum is obtained by a rock salt analyzer crystal. The intensity of ZrK radiation appearing at about 15.9 degrees of 2-theta is employed for quantitative estimation. The ZrO_2 content in soils and rocks is about 100 ppm, but ranges from about 10 to 800 or more ppm.

11–198. Zirconium has also been determined[53] by fusion of 15 to 25 mgm of heavy mineral residue in pyrosulfate in a transparent quartz crucible. The Zr was finally precipitated (as the phosphate), ignited, and weighed as $ZrSiO_4$, a 5-place weighing being necessary. A Na_2O_2 fusion has also been employed.[54] A series of papers has appeared on the determination of zirconium spectrophotometrically.[55]

[50] Haseman and Marshall, Mo. Agr. Exp. Sta. Res. Bul. 387, p. 68 (1945).

[51] Carroll, *J. Sed. Petrol.*, 23:106 (1953).

[52] Fluorescence analysis of Zr in metals, Mortimore and Romans, *J. Opt. Soc. Am.*, 42:673 (1952); fluorescence analysis of Zr in minerals, Carl and Campbell, *Fluorescent X-ray Spectrographic Analysis* (Atlantic City, N.J.: Am. Soc. Testing Materials Meeting, 1953).

[53] Haseman and Marshall, Mo. Agr. Exp. Sta. Res. Bul. 387, p. 68 (1945); precipitation was also employed by Willard and Hahn, *Anal. Chem.*, 21:293 (1949).

[54] Petretic, *Anal. Chem.*, 23:1183 (1951).

[55] Green, *Anal. Chem.*, 20:370 (1948); Petretic, *Anal. Chem.*, 23:1183 (1951); Kiefer and Boltz, *Anal. Chem.*, 24:542 (1952); Wengert, *Anal. Chem.*, 24:1449 (1952); Oesper *et al.*, *Anal. Chem.*, 24:1492 (1952); Klingenberg and Papucci, *Anal. Chem.*, 24:1861 (1952).

11–199. Fluoride Determination. In connection with the determination of fluoride, attention is called to the method of Rowley *et al.*[56] in which marked improvements are claimed over the classical distillation method of Willard and Winter.[57] Jeffries[58] determined F in limestone. A number of methods are offered for rapid determination of fluoride once it is in solution.[59]

11–200. Other Determinations. Barium determination[60] is important because Ba occasionally contributes to infertility of soil. The determination of chromium and vanadium,[61] and of wolfram[62] (tungsten) in soils is sometimes of interest. The chlorine in silicate rocks can be determined.[63] Lithium determination[64] is sometimes of interest in connection with rock and mineral analysis because it substitutes structurally for Mg. The separation and determination of alkali metals has been studied for silicates.[65] Separation of the alkali metals derived from insoluble silicates has been accomplished by means of ion exchange chromatography.[66]

QUESTIONS

1. When the sample weighed out in an air-dry condition for elemental analysis, how is the oven-dry basis obtained?

2. What are the limitations to interconversion between the oven-dry basis and the ignited weight basis for reporting the elemental analysis?

3. List 4 types of system for elemental analysis of soils, and briefly state the advantages and disadvantages of each.

4. Outline the steps in cleaning and burnishing platinum utensils, and make a list of the most important commonly used chemicals that attack platinum utensils.

5. What elements are determined on the sample decomposed by HF in each of the 2 systems for silicate analysis? What are the disadvantages of the determination of Mg and Al on this sample in the semimicrochemical system?

6. What elements are determined on the sample decomposed by Na_2CO_3 in

[56] *Anal. Chem.,* 25:1061 (1953).

[57] *Ind. Eng. Chem., A.E.,* 5:7 (1953); employed with rock material by Olsen, *Sci.,* 112:620 (1950).

[58] *Soil Sci.,* 71:287 (1951).

[59] Hill and Reynolds, *Anal. Chem.,* 22:448 (1950); Thrum, *Anal. Chem.,* 22:918 (1950); Willard and Horton, *Anal. Chem.,* 22:1190, 1194 (1950); Horton *et al., Anal. Chem.,* 24:548 (1952); Willard and Horton, *Anal. Chem.,* 24:862 (1952); Price and Walker, *Anal. Chem.,* 24:1593 (1952); Bumstead and Wells, *Anal. Chem.,* 24:1595 (1952); Miller and Phillips, *Anal. Chem.,* 25:172 (1953); Powell and Saylor, *Anal. Chem.,* 25:960 (1953).

[60] Robinson *et al.,* U.S.D.A. Tech. Bul. 1013 (1950).

[61] Groves, *Silicate Analysis* (London: George Allen & Unwin, Ltd., 1951).

[62] Ward, U.S. Geol. Surv., Cir. 119 (1951).

[63] Kuroda and Sandell, *Anal. Chem.,* 22:1144 (1950).

[64] White *et al., Anal. Chem.,* 23:478 (1951).

[65] Elving and Chao, *Anal. Chem.,* 21:507 (1949).

[66] Sweet, *et al., Anal. Chem.,* 24:952 (1952).

each of the 2 systems? What are the disadvantages of the determination of Fe and Ti on this sample in the semimicrochemical system?

7. State the principles utilized for determination of each of the following elements in the semimicrochemical silicate analysis system: K, Na, Ca, Mg, Fe, Ti, Si, Al.

8. What reagent is employed for the dehydration of silica prior to its separation in an acid solution?

9. State qualitatively the reactions employed for the purification of aluminum prior to its determination with aurin tricarboxylic acid.

10. What advantages may be gained by the pretreatment of a sample with aqua regia prior to the sodium carbonate fusion?

11. What are the advantages of $HClO_4$ as a silica dehydrating reagent over the HCl system of dehydration of silica?

12. List the steps by which SiO_2 is determined gravimetrically.

13. List the elements precipitated and those kept in solution by the cupferron. By the NH_4OH separation. What precautions are required to get all of the P and no Ca into the latter precipitate?

14. List the steps by which iron is determined with a Jones reductor. Why does Ti not interfere with this determination of Fe?

15. What oxidizing reagents are commonly used for the determination of calcium as the oxalate?

16. In what form is magnesium precipitated for gravimetric determinations? In what form is it weighed?

17. In what valence form does manganese react chemically in a manner similar to magnesium?

18. Why is total K or Na determined on a separate sample in the conventional system of silicate analysis?

19. Why is ferrous iron determined on a separate sample? Describe the essential features of the procedure.

20. Into what chemical combination is sulfate converted for its gravimetric determination?

21. How can zirconium of soils be determined?

12

Plant Tissue Analysis
—Mineral Constituents

The analysis of the soil by means of the plant
—HALL[1] (ROTHAMSTED)

12–1. The extraction of mineral nutrients from soil by growing crops is a unique type for soil chemical analysis. Bradfield[2] states, "The foundations of agricultural chemistry . . . had to wait the development of methods for determining the composition of plants. . . ." Plant tissue analysis aids in the characterization of soil chemical properties in terms of soil fertility and mineral nutrition of plants. *Mineral* is employed for present purposes to cover the mineral elements in plants. A wet-oxidation procedure is given which results in the conversion of the elements Na, K, Ca, Mg, Mn, Fe, P, Cu, Zn and others to proper form for analytical determination. Attention is also given to total ash, dry ashing, and sulfur, cyanide, and fluorine contents.

12–2. Chemical testing of plant tissue sap for mineral nutrient levels, while similar in objective to mineral analysis in plant ash, is entirely different in procedure and is therefore considered separately, in the next chapter. The extraction and determination of total nitrogen of plants is described in Chapter 8; of total boron, in Chapter 14; and of total molybdenum, in ¶ 15–104.

12–3. Preparation of Plant Tissue Sample. Freshly taken plant tissue is dried in air or in an oven at 60° to 80°C, in either case protected carefully from fumes that would lead to contamination. Rapid drying by forced

---

[1] *J. Agr. Sci.,* 1:65 (1905).
[2] Moulton, ed., *Liebig and after Liebig* (Washington, D.C.: Am. Assoc. Adv. Sci., 1942), p. 49.

ventilation over thin layers of tissue contained in mesh trays or bags is provided. Speed in drying helps to avoid the growth of molds or to minimize loss of weight by enzymatic action in the tissue.

12–4. All but the smaller sizes of plants and seeds must be ground, so that suitable sample sizes may be obtained for analysis. Contamination with the major elements is ordinarily negligible from grinding mills. Large samples such as corn stover or large forage samples are ground through a 30-cm diameter hammer mill (for example, Bell No. 10, 2 hp, manufactured by C. S. Bell Co., Hillsboro, Ohio), and quartered down to approximately 1-liter bulk volume. Further grinding to pass 0.3- to 0.5-mm sieve is effected by mortar and pestle, Wiley mill (Arthur H. Thomas Co., Philadelphia, Pa.), C and N mill (Christy and Norris, Ltd., Chelmsford, England), or similar apparatus.

12–5. Considerable minor element contamination is likely to occur by abrasion of materials from the grinding mill. For this reason careful study is given to this problem in relation to each element that is to be determined. Mortar grinding by hand resulted[3] in "no appreciable contamination" of Fe, Zn, Cu, B, Co, Mn, Mo, Ca, Na, Mg, P, S, or K. The minor element contamination was appreciable with the above mentioned mills and still worse with ball mills operated with various types of balls. Dr. R. G. Menzel found a specially made stainless steel screen for the Wiley mill acceptable for grinding samples for copper and zinc determinations, but contamination with iron was high.

12–6. For analysis of plant sap, and for radiochemical assay of briquetted plant tissue, the plant tissue is pressed by means of the Carver Laboratory Press (Fred S. Carver, Inc., One Chatham Road, Summit, N.J.) with suitable attachments.

12–7. Plant Tissue Sample Size for Analysis. The size of plant tissue sample needed for analysis is determined by (a) the size necessary to be representative as determined by fineness of grinding (¶ 12–4), (b) the concentration of the element in the plant, and (c) the sensitivity of the method of determination to be employed. From the first consideration, the minimum size of plant tissue sample is ordinarily about 0.2 gm, and usually not less than a 1-gm sample is taken. The plant tissue sample for analysis is kept as small as practicable to conserve time and reagents. It is more efficient to use a single sample for the determination of the several elements of interest, rather than the preparation of a separate sample for each element. Determinations of elements or radicals that are lost during the normal preparation of tissue for mineral analysis require separate samples, for example determinations of sulfur, cyanide, and fluoride.

12–8. Concentration of Mineral Elements in Crop Plant Tissue. The

---

[3] Hood *et al., Ind. Eng. Chem., A.E.,* 16:202 (1944).

concentration of each element in a given type of plant tissue varies greatly with the time of sampling and type of environment.[4] The typical (¶ 12–11) concentration range of mineral elements of several kinds of crop plant tissue (Table 12–1) are expressed as percentage or ppm of the dried tissue.

12–9. Another useful method of expression of concentration is as per 100 gm of tissue. *Concentration* of a mineral element multiplied by the crop yield gives the *content* of element per crop yield unit, representative values for which are given by Romaine[5] for field, fruit, and vegetable crops.

12–10. The sensitivity range of the method to be employed is ascertained and the size of sample is selected accordingly. For example, for P only 0.2 to 1 gm is employed. For P, K, Ca, and Mg from 2 to 5 gm is taken. For Cu and Zn, 2 to 5 gm is sufficient for polarographic determination. Up to 10, 20, or more gm may be prepared satisfactorily by the wet oxidation procedure given, when such a large sample is required.

12–11. Interpretation of Plant Tissue Analyses. The subject of interpretation of plant tissue analyses has been summarized well by Ulrich.[6] Occurrence of a characteristic content of each element in a given plant species was early recognized.[7] But the characteristic content was found to vary according to the activity of the respective element in the soil, and according to age of the tissue, cultural conditions, and climate. The plant content of a nutrient has been correlated with soil content,[8] with yield,[9] and with various nutrition values and quality factors such as carotene.

12–12. Highest yields are associated with the correct *balance* of the nutrient elements in the tissue, coupled with sufficient magnitude of the content of all nutrient elements.[10] This sufficient magnitude has been termed sufficient *"intensity* of nutrition," but may be interpreted equally well as sufficient *activity* of the respective nutrients in soil. There is a *minimum* plant content of a nutrient for any growth at all, a *low range* over which yields increase rapidly with little increase (with some elements there may be a decrease[11]) in content, an *intermediate range* over which both content and yield increase fairly rapidly ("poverty adjustment"[12]), and a high

---

[4] Beeson, U.S.D.A. Misc. Pub. 369 (1941); Lindsey *et al., Mass. Agr. Exp. Sta. Bul.* (1919); Lucas *et al., Purdue Univ. Agr. Exp. Sta. Bul.* 468 (1942).

[5] *Better Crops,* 24, 3:6 (1940).

[6] *Diagnostic Techniques for Soils and Crops* (Washington, D.C.: American Potash Institute, 1948), p. 157.

[7] Hall, *J. Agr. Sci.,* 1:65 (1905).

[8] Attoe, *J. Am. Soc. Agron.,* 38:194 (1946); Seay *et al., S.S.S.A. Proc.,* 14:245 (1950).

[9] Lundegardh, tr. Mitchell, *Leaf Analysis* (London: Hilger & Watts, Ltd., 1951).

[10] Lagatu and Maume, *Ann. ecole nat. agr. Montpellier,* 22:257 (1934); Thomas, *Plant Physiol.,* 12:571 (1937) and *Soil Sci.,* 59:353 (1945); Shear *et al., A.S.H.S. Proc.,* 47:239 (1946).

[11] Steenbjerg, *Plant and Soil,* 3:97 (1951).

[12] Macy, *Plant Physiol.,* 11:749 (1936).

TABLE 12-1

Concentration* of some mineral elements in crop plant tissue, 60° or 80°C basis

	Percentage					ppm					
	P	K	Ca	Mg	S	Fe	Mn	Cu	Zn	B	Co
Legumes											
Alfalfa	0.1 –0.5	0.5 –4.5	0.5 –4.5	0.2 –0.4	0.2	130–1000	10–120	4–15	14–110	4–30	—
Clover, red	0.2 –0.3	1.1 –3.4	1.1 –2.1	0.4 –0.7	0.2	100–1300	25–540	6–20	24–70	36	—
Lespedeza	0.1 –0.4	0.6 –2.0	0.7 –2.1	0.1 –0.4	—	100–1000	50–420	—	—	—	—
Soybean, seed	0.5 –1.1	0.8 –2.4	0.2 –0.3	0.2 –0.3	0.1 –0.2	60–570	20–280	4–12	27–80	2–29	—
Grasses											
Barley, grain	0.15–0.6	0.3 –0.8	0.02–0.1	0.07–0.2	0.08–0.3	14–350	7–38	6–41	21	2	—
Barley, straw	0.04–0.6	1.1 –2.0	—	—	0.08–0.2	—	7	—	—	—	—
Blue grass (Ky.)	0.16–0.4	1.3 –2.9	0.1 –0.4	0.2	0.1	60–430	30–220	7–14	20–90	—	—
Corn, grain	0.2 –0.8	0.2 –0.9	0.006–0.05	0.1 –0.3	0.04–0.3	25–50	5–19	4–17	20	—	—
Corn, stover	0.04–0.4	0.3 –1.9	0.1 –0.8	0.1 –0.5	0.03–0.3	160–190	50–270	2–9	5–80	—	—
Corn, leaves	0.05–0.2	0.2 –1.0	0.1 –0.9	—	—	—	—	8–17†	—	—	0.01
Oats, grain	0.15–0.5	0.3 –0.7	0.05–0.2	0.06–0.3	0.07–0.3	7–350	20–80	4–51	20	—	—
Oats, straw	0.02–0.4	0.6 –3.5	0.15–0.7	0.06–0.5	0.09–0.5	60–370	4–1660	3–54	4–200	—	—
Vegetables											
Beans, seed	0.3 –0.8	1.1 –1.6	0.07–0.3	0.1 –0.3	0.06–0.6	80–210	14–36	7–16	23–56	—	0.01
Beets, roots	0.1 –0.6	0.7 –4.1	0.09–0.4	0.01–0.5	0.12–0.2	70–280	20–100	6–27	25–69	—	—
Cabbage	0.1 –0.8	1 –9	0.4 –1.8	0.02–0.4	0.8 –1.9	11–300	5–440	3–28	—	37	0.07
Potato, tuber	0.1 –0.5	1.0 –4.0	0.02–0.1	0.05–0.2	0.06–0.4	7–360	4–94	1–26	11–14	2–16	0.06
Fruits											
Apple, leaf‡	0.1 –0.2	1 –1.5	1+	0.2	—	40–350	20–170	—	14–55	—	—
Apple, fruit	0.02–0.1	0.5 –1.4	0.02 –0.1	0.02–0.06	0.03–0.1	20–40	1–22	5–7	3–9	3–80	—
Cherry, leaf§	0.1 –0.7	0.4 –2.8	0.9 –3.0	0.4 –1.2	—	19–740	45–280	5–200	—	10–160	—
Peach, leaf§	0.1 –0.5	0.8 –2.4	1.1 –2.7	0.4 –1.4	—	40–540	17–220	4–30**	6–40	12–110	—

* Analyses rounded from compilation of Beeson, U.S.D.A. Misc. Pub. 369 (1941), except as indicated.
† Pack et al., Soil Sci., 75:433 (1945).
‡ Walrath, Vermont State Hort. Soc. Proc., 53rd meeting, p. 35 (1949).
§ Kentworthy, Proc. Am. Soc. Hort. Sci., 55:41 (1950), except as indicated.
** Zubriski, Ph.D. Thesis, University of Wisconsin, p. 85 (1950).

range over which yields increase little while the content increases rapidly ("luxury consumption"). The critical percentage[13] of a nutrient element in a plant is that "below which the yield is progressively reduced by deficiency of that nutrient and above which only moderate yield response is expected to further application of that nutrient," thus corresponding to the transition between the intermediate and high range.

TOTAL ASH CONTENT OF PLANT TISSUE

12–13. Total ash content of plant tissue is often determined as a measurement distinct from ashing for the determination of individual mineral elements. Volatilization of constituents during dry ashing is less of a problem for total ash than for elemental analysis of the ash, but volatilization error may be appreciable even for total ash as shown by Liebenthal[14] for Si.

APPARATUS

12–14. Needed apparatus consists of a porcelain or platinum crucible, a Meker burner, a 100°C oven, a muffle furnace with temperature regulator, a steam plate, and an analytical balance.

REAGENTS

12–15. Required reagents include pure olive oil and distilled water.

PROCEDURE[15]

12–16. A 3- to 5-gm (weighed to the nearest mgm) sample of the plant tissue, collected so as to be as free as possible of dust, is placed in a weighed porcelain or platinum crucible, dried at 100°C for 10 hours or overnight, and weighed. This weight is the base.

12–17. Approximately 2 ml of pure olive oil is added to the tissue and the crucible is heated slowly until smoking ceases over a Meker burner (hood) at very low flame to prevent ignition. The crucible is then placed in a (preferably cool) muffle furnace and heated to about 525°C for 45 minutes, or until the ash is nearly white.

12–18. The crucible is removed and cooled, and the ash is moistened with water from a fine-jet wash bottle to dissolve occluding salts. The ash is then dried on a steam plate and reheated in the muffle at about 525°C to constant weight (1 hour usually suffices). The crucible is cooled in a desiccator, weighed to the nearest mgm, then reheated, cooled, and weighed to check constancy of weight.

---

[13] Jackson *et al.*, *S.S.S.A. Proc.*, 12:282 (1948); Terminology Committee, *S.S.S.A. Proc.*, 15:429 (1951).

[14] *Sci.*, 114:636 (1951).

[15] The essential features of this procedure are in accord with *Methods of Analysis*, A.O.A.C., Ed. 6 (1945).

WET OXIDATION OF PLANT TISSUE

12–19. Oxidation of the organic matter of plant tissue and release of the mineral elements such as Ca, Mg, and P may be effected through either wet oxidation by means of oxidizing acids such as the HNO_3-H_2SO_4-$HClO_4$ ternary acid mixture employed in the procedure to be described herein or by dry ashing (considered in the alternative procedure, ¶ 12–32). Potassium and Na may be extracted directly from plant tissue (without oxidation of the organic matter) by means of appropriate salt solutions (¶ 18–32).

12–20. Wet oxidation with $HClO_4$ avoids the loss of K through volatilization[16] and gives a clear solution of all constituents[17] except Si, which is quantitatively dehydrated and precipitated and is removable by filtration or centrifugation. The resultant solution is ideal for analysis of both the major and minor elements. Parks et al.[18] removed the Si by HF treatment after HNO_3-$HClO_4$ digestion. It has been reported[19] that H_3PO_4 can be lost during $HClO_4$ digestion if excessive temperature (much over 200°C) is used. In the proposed procedure, recovery of phosphorus is complete up to a temperature of 230°C. Danger of explosion with perchloric acid is completely overcome by (a) predigestion with concentrated HNO_3, (b) inclusion[20] of H_2SO_4 in the $HClO_4$-HNO_3 solution used to complete the oxidation, and (c) exhaustion of the $HClO_4$ fumes through a water pump according to the arrangements in Fig. 12–1 to prevent their accumulation in the hood ventilation system.

12–21. In the $HClO_4$ procedure presented, the proportion of acid to tissue weight is carefully regulated for maximum economy of digestion and evaporation times as well as for economy of reagents.

12–22. The procedure employed departs from the usual practice of slow heating of the digestion mix containing HNO_3, H_2SO_4, and $HClO_4$ from room temperature. The mix is brought to a temperature of 180° to 200°C rapidly. The power of oxidation of the $HClO_4$ appears to increase more rapidly than the rate of evaporation, and consequently the efficiency of oxidation of the organic constituents is increased at higher temperatures. Smith[21] states that $HClO_4$ on heating yields anhydrous $HClO_4$, which further dissociates into nascent chlorine and oxygen. At a temperature of

[16] St. John and Midgley, *Ind. Eng. Chem., A.E.,* 14:301 (1942).

[17] Gieseking et al., *Ind. Eng. Chem., A.E.,* 7:185 (1935); Toth et al., *Soil Sci.,* 66:459 (1948).

[18] *Anal. Chem.,* 15:527 (1943).

[19] Snell and Snell, *Colorimetric Methods of Analysis,* Vol. 1 (New York: D. Van Nostrand Company, Inc., 1936), p. 497.

[20] Piper, *Soil and Plant Analysis* (New York: Interscience, Publishers, Inc., 1944), p. 272, emphasizes that the presence of H_2SO_4 greatly decreases the danger of explosive decomposition of perchloric acid and ammonium perchlorate at the end of the digestion.

[21] *Perchloric Acid,* 4th ed., Vol. 1 (Columbus, Ohio: G. Frederick Smith Chemical Co., 1940).

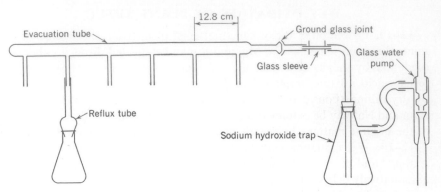

Fig. 12–1. Apparatus for wet oxidation of organic tissue in HNO_3-H_2SO_4-$HClO_4$ mixture. Special reflux tubes and manifold provide for evacuation of $HClO_4$ fumes through an NaOH trap and their discharge into the sewer line. (Apparatus developed by author and associates at the University of Wisconsin; available from Erway Glassblowing, Oregon, Wis.)

203°C, the constant boiling point of the system $HClO_4 \cdot H_2O$, the decomposition of the anhydrous $HClO_4$ appears to be complete. These nascent oxidants account for the increased oxidation efficiency at the elevated temperature employed in the digestion procedure.

APPARATUS

12–23. Needed apparatus includes 500-ml conical digestion flasks (125-ml, 250-ml, or 1-liter flasks may be used), a special digestion manifold shown in Fig. 12–1, an electric hot plate with covered element and thermostat for heating the digestion flasks (such as the Lindberg, Wilkins-Anderson, Chicago, Ill.), a sand tray to cover the electric hot plate, and burets for dispensing the digestion acids. The Kjeldahl digestion apparatus (Fig. 8–1) with disposition of fumes in water may also be employed for $HClO_4$ digestion, particularly for large samples.

REAGENTS

12–24. Needed reagents include concentrated HNO_3 and a ternary solution of three acids prepared by mixing 100 ml of concentrated HNO_3, 10 ml of concentrated H_2SO_4, and 40 ml of 60 per cent $HClO_4$ (any quantity in volume ratio of 10 : 1 : 4) and then allowing to cool before use.

PROCEDURE[22]

12–25. Precaution. Predigestion of plant tissue in HNO_3 prior to addi-

---

[22] This procedure was developed during the period from 1944 to 1950, by the author and several of his associates, including Mrs. Pauline Frink of Purdue University, Dr. B. Chatterjee, J. L. Huber, and Dr. L. D. Whittig. Drs. J. A. Kittrick and A. Kaufman also participated in the design of the aspirator; Dr. J. C. Kaudy aided in the testing of complete recovery of phosphorus after the wet oxidation procedure; and Dr. R. G. Menzel assisted in testing the procedure in connection with the recovery of Cu and Zn.

tion of $HClO_4$ is highly important to preclude danger of explosion and fire. Sixty or more per cent $HClO_4$ is *never* added directly to plant tissue without predigestion in HNO_3. Piper[23] employed a higher proportion of HNO_3 to $HClO_4$ than does the present procedure, and omitted the predigestion with HNO_3 when H_2SO_4 was included in the digest, except for oily seeds. Experience in this laboratory indicates the efficacy as well as safety of a HNO_3 predigestion followed by the combined ternary acid mixture. The digestion procedure thus designed can be carried out rapidly at an elevated temperature with complete safety and with no exceptions for various types of tissues.

12–26. Predigestion of Small Tissue Samples of 2 gm or less in HNO_3. To 2 gm or less of dried and powdered plant tissue in a 500-ml conical flask, 5 ml of concentrated HNO_3 is added for each gm of plant tissue. The flask is swirled to moisten the entire mass of tissue and then is placed on a steam plate for 30 minutes and then on the electric hot plate at 180° to 200°C as measured in a flask of glycerol standing on the hot plate. The aspirator system (Fig. 12–1) is connected to the flask to exhaust the oxides of nitrogen and to condense unreacted acid fumes. The suspension is boiled until taken nearly to dryness. This predigestion with HNO_3 requires only about 45 minutes.

12–27. Predigestion of Large Tissue Samples Over 2 gm in HNO_3. The predigestion of large samples is essentially the same as outlined in the previous paragraph with the following exceptions: (a) glass beads (8 to 10) are added to alleviate bumping, (b) with extra large samples (20 gm or more) a 1000-ml conical flask is employed, and (c) the digestion *is not placed on the hot plate,* until the preliminary action has subsided, as otherwise the sample may froth over the top of the flask. The acid is brought into contact with the tissue by thorough stirring and, if the spontaneous heating becomes excessive, it is slowed down by immersion of the flask in a water bath at 25°C. Predigestion of samples as large as 20 gm requires only about an hour.

12–28. Blank. Blank digestions (in duplicate) are run on the reagents, added in the same amounts as employed in the determinations. All steps are carried out parallel to the sample.

12–29. Digestion of samples in HNO_3-H_2SO_4-$HClO_4$. The digestion flask and contents are cooled slightly. Then an appropriate amount of the ternary mixture of acids (HNO_3-H_2SO_4-$HClO_4$) is added, consisting of 5 ml for each gm of tissue up to 2 gm of tissue and 4 ml per additional gm of tissue. Digestion is carried out at 180° to 200°C until dense white fumes of H_2SO_4 and $HClO_4$ are evolved. A brown or greenish scum of MnO_2 may appear while $HClO_4$ is present, but this redissolves in the concentrated H_2SO_4 at the end of the digestion. The digestion is continued at 180° to 200°C until the acid liquid is largely volatilized.

[23] Piper, *op. cit.*

12–30. The digestion mix rarely shows charring near the end of the digestion. Even so, there usually is sufficient $HClO_4$ remaining to oxidize the charred material completely in virtually all cases. If the acid liquid turns brown with carmelized organic matter as the volume becomes low, 5 ml more of the ternary mixture of acids is added and digestion is continued as before.

12–31. The digestion process is continued until a clear solution remains after the acids are largely volatilized. The digestion is stopped when the residues in the flask are clear and white and only slightly moist with H_2SO_4. The $HClO_4$, at this point, has been largely removed. The residue is now ready for analysis for elemental mineral constituents.

ALTERNATIVE PROCEDURES

12–32. Dry Ashing. Dry ashing (ignition) has been a popular and very satisfactory alternative to wet oxidation of plant tissue for the release of mineral elements. However, significant amounts of potassium may be volatilized at the usual ignition temperature of 550° to 600°C. Both P and K may be lost at ignition temperatures over 600°C. No phosphorus is lost by volatilization in dry ashing if the ash is alkaline but some may be lost if the ash is acid.[24] For this reason, ashing for phosphorus is generally carried out in the presence of an alcoholic solution of $Mg(NO_3)_2$ (¶ 12–34) or $Mg(OAc)_2$ the latter sometimes being preferred[25] because the former causes deflagration. If one of these salts is added, the metallic cations cannot be determined on the same ash as the phosphorus (¶ 12–34). Addition of Na_2CO_3 to the tissue serves to retain S and Cl, which are otherwise volatilized. Occasionally charring occurs with large samples with resultant incomplete ashing. Also, significant errors may occur in the determination of phosphorus and the trace elements due to a portion becoming occluded or insoluble in the ash. Dry ashing is often more time consuming than wet oxidation. Total ash content of plant tissue is occasionally desired (¶ 12–16). A technique is available[26] for ashing plant tissue in microsection for microchemical analysis.

12–33. M. Peech of Cornell University (personal communication) has devised the following simple procedure for complete ashing of plant material at low enough temperature to prevent loss of volatile mineral constituents such as K. The sample of plant material is ashed at 400° to 450°C in a muffle furnace for several hours or overnight. The sample is then cooled and treated with an excess of 1 N HNO_3, evaporated to dryness on a hot plate, and placed back in a muffle furnace at 400°C ± 10° for about 10

---

[24] Piper, *op. cit.,* p. 259.
[25] *Ibid.,* p. 268.
[26] Struckmeyer, *Am. J. Bot.,* 30:477 (1943).

minutes. The perfectly clean white ash is then cooled and taken up in appropriate acid.

12–34. Dry Ashing for Phosphorus.[27] A 0.5-gm sample of finely ground, well-mixed, dried plant material is placed in an evaporating dish of approximately 100-ml capacity. Five ml of 0.5 N $Mg(NO_3)_2$ or $Mg(OAc)_2$ and 10 ml of distilled water are added. This mixture is evaporated to dryness on a steam bath and then the dish is allowed to dry. The dish and contents are placed in a muffle and ignited at about 600°C until the residue is uniformly gray in color (30 minutes is usually sufficient time). The dish is cooled, and then 10 ml of approximately 2 N H_2SO_4 is added. The dish is rotated to bring the acid in contact with the entire ash. Then 15 ml of distilled water is added and the dish is placed on the steam bath to evaporate the suspension to a volume of less than 5 ml. The dish is removed from the steam bath and 20 ml of distilled water is added. When the dish has cooled, the sides are rubbed down with a rubber policeman and the contents are filtered into a 100-ml volumetric flask. The filter is washed and then the solution is made to volume and mixed. Aliquots of this solution are employed for the determination of phosphorus (¶ 7–22 or 7–31).

ELEMENTAL ANALYSIS OF RESIDUE FROM WET OXIDATION OF PLANT TISSUE

12–35. The analytical system for the residue from wet oxidation of plant tissue must be designed (a) to keep the silica from rehydrating and thus dispersing, (b) to keep K from precipitation as $KClO_4$, and (c) to dissolve all of the Ca, which tends to precipitate as $CaSO_4 \cdot 2 H_2O$. The digestion is carried far enough in the procedure to decrease the $HClO_4$ sufficiently to prevent $KClO_4$ precipitation in the take-up solution. Use of HCl as the solvent converts the Ca to soluble form as the chloride salt and the HCl is used at sufficient concentration to prevent the rehydration of silica.

12–36. Stock Solution of Sample (*Solution A*). The digestion flask containing the residue from the wet oxidation of plant tissue is cooled and 5 ml of concentrated HCl is added. The flask is swirled and policed and then the solution is poured into a 25- or 50-ml calibrated centrifuge tube. Five additional ml of concentrated HCl is added to the flask, and the flask is rotated to bring the HCl into contact with all the inside surfaces. This solution is decanted into the same centrifuge tube. Two additional rinsings of the flask are given with small portions of 6 N HCl, the rinsings being transferred to the tube each time. Water is not used in the transfer.

12–37. The solution in the centrifuge tube is made to the volumetric mark with 6 N HCl; the solution is then mixed with an air jet stirring rod, washing being omitted, and the tube is centrifuged for 5 minutes or until clear. The clear supernatant HCl solution is immediately decanted into a

---

[27] Bertramson, *Plant Physiol.*, 17:447 (1942).

dry flask, stoppered, and labeled *Solution A*. Washing of the silica is omitted.

12–38. The analyses of the elements present in the residue from wet oxidation of plant tissue are done by the same procedures as employed for the usual soil analyses. Interfering elements present are similar to and usually less extensive than those commonly encountered in soil analysis.

12–39. Aliquots of *Solution A* are taken for analysis. Either dilution or evaporation of an aliquot to dryness permits the control of HCl concentration, for example, prior to development of the vanadomolydophosphoric yellow color (¶ 7–56) in HNO_3. A secondary dilution is usually necessary for phosphorus determination prior to taking the final aliquot for the development of the blue color (¶ 7–26). Potassium, Na, Ca, Mg, and other metallic cations are readily determined by flame emission spectrophotometry (¶ 18–7). Potassium can be determined by the cobaltinitrite procedure (¶ 6–12), and the others by usual procedures—Ca (¶ 5–30), Mg (¶ 5–48), and Mn (¶ 5–71). Sodium is best determined by direct extraction (¶ 12–40) rather than in the wet oxidation digest, to insure freedom from contamination. Iron is readily determined as directed in ¶ 11–70, 15–13 or 7–111. Copper and zinc are readily determined polarographically (¶ 16–39) or by absorption spectrophotometry (¶ 15–47, 15–69).

ALTERNATIVE PROCEDURES

12–40. A determination of total K or Na in plant tissue or manure without the oxidation of the organic matter can be effected by direct extraction with NH_4OAc (¶ 18–32). Moreover, plant tissue samples may be formed into pellets and ignited directly in the emission spectrograph (¶ 18–58) for determination of the elements present without any form of preparation except drying and grinding. The determination of an individual element such as phosphorus is often wanted on plant material; either wet oxidation as given above or dry ashing (¶ 12–34) is satisfactory.

SULFUR CONTENT OF PLANT TISSUE

12–41. Sulfur in organic combination is volatilized[28] during the dry ashing process, and H_2SO_4 has been introduced in the wet oxidation procedure given (¶ 12–29). Thus a separate preparation must be employed for the sulfur determination in plant tissue. Sulfur contents obtained[29] by peroxide fusion methods or wet oxidation methods without H_2SO_4 were 2 to 100 times higher than obtained by the old dry ashing method. The organic sulfur content of plant tissue has been reported[30] to range from 0.1 to 0.7

---

[28] Hart and Peterson, *Wis. Agr. Exp. Sta. Res. Bul.* 14 (1911).

[29] Halverson, *J. Am. Chem. Soc.*, 41:1494 (1919).

[30] Thomas *et al., Soil Sci.*, 70:9 (1950).

per cent though total sulfur by the bomb procedure ranges on up to nearly 3 per cent.

12–42. Total sulfur analyses are usually made by ignition of the plant sample in a bomb and determination by precipitation with $BaSO_4$, but care must be employed not to air-dry samples that contain appreciable contents of volatile sulfur compounds. A bomb procedure is also given by Piper.[31] Johnson and Nishita[32] prepared plant samples by the A.O.A.C. procedure of dry ashing in the presence of $Mg(NO_3)_2$ dissolved in 95 per cent ethanol for the determination of micro quantities of sulfur by their special procedure.

CYANIDE IN PLANT TISSUE

12–43. The determination of cyanide and cyanide-producing substances in plants such as Sudan grass and sorghums is of interest to the soil chemist, for when the soil phosphorus activity is too low in the presence of adequate nitrogen, compounds that hydrolyze to form cyanide may accumulate, according to Boyd et al.[33] A brief outline of the procedure of Boyd et al. (developed by Boyd and Truog) is given herewith, because of the importance and efficacy of the procedure, although CN^- is outside of the usual determination of mineral constituents of plants. An 8-gm sample of fresh, green tissue (air-dried tissue may be employed also) of Sudan grass or sorghum, previously cut into 8-mm lengths with a razor blade or knife and mixed thoroughly, is placed in a 800-ml long neck Kjeldahl flask and then 250 ml of distilled water and 5 ml of chloroform are added. Steam is passed through this suspension of tissue to steam-distill the HCN through a condenser into a 100-ml test tube containing 5 ml of 2 per cent KOH. The delivery end of the condenser is kept below the surface of the KOH solution. Approximately 60 ml of distillate is collected and the distillation is then stopped. A 5-ml aliquot of the well-mixed distillate is pipetted into a colorimeter tube. To this 5-ml aliquot is added 5-ml of an alkaline picrate solution (50 gm of Na_2CO_3 and 5 gm of picric acid in 1000 ml of distilled water, brought nearly to boiling to obtain dissolution), the contents of the tube are mixed and digested in a boiling water bath for 5 minutes. The color is determined with a colorimeter with a 520-mu light maximum or by visual comparison to a series of standards (0.241 gm of KCN in 1000 ml of water gives 0.1 mgm of HCN per ml). The range of the method is from 5 to 500 ugm of HCN per determination.

12–44. The results are expressed as mgm of HCN per 100 gm of oven-dry tissue. Under 25 mgm is considered safe, whereas from 75 to 100 mgm is considered dangerous.

---

[31] Piper, op. cit., p. 299.
[32] Anal. Chem., 24:736 (1952).
[33] J. Am. Soc. Agron., 30:569 (1938).

FLUORIDE IN PLANT TISSUE

12–45. Fluoride determination in plant tissue is often wanted. Attention is called to the method of Rowley et al.[34] in which marked improvements are claimed over the A.O.A.C. method[35] based on the Willard and Winter[36] distillation. Remmert et al.,[37] also report determinations of fluorine in plant materials.

QUESTIONS

1. Why is it necessary to dry plant tissue samples very soon after they are taken?

2. What types of mills and mortars are available for grinding plant tissue down to suitable size for analysis and how is the choice of grinding method related to possible contamination of the sample?

3. What factors determine the size of plant tissue sample employed for analysis of the minerals present?

4. To what extent is the content of mineral elements variable in one type of tissue of a given plant species and how is this variation related to the terms "poverty adjustment," "luxury consumption," and "critical percentage"?

5. Describe the essential features of the determination of total ash of plants and give the reasons for each main step.

6. State the chief advantage of the wet oxidation method for plant tissue.

7. What is the purpose of the inclusion of H_2SO_4 with the $HClO_4$ and HNO_3 in connection with the wet oxidation of plant tissue?

8. Why is it important to exhaust the $HClO_4$ fumes through a water pump and into a sewer rather than through the usual fume hood ventilation system?

9. What is the purpose of the predigestion of plant tissue with HNO_3 prior to the addition of $HClO_4$?

10. What is the purpose of removal of virtually all of the $HClO_4$ by fuming the H_2SO_4 near the end of the digestion, and why are the quantities of acids added according to the weight of the sample?

11. Why is the temperature held down to 400°C in the Peech procedure for dry ashing, and what step of a wet oxidation system is employed for facilitation of completeness of ashing?

12. Why is $Mg(OAc)_2$ sometimes added to plant tissue prior to dry ashing?

13. Why may the elements be determined in the residue from wet oxidation of plant tissue by the same methods as employed for the usual soil analyses?

[34] *Anal. Chem.*, 25:1061 (1953).
[35] *Methods of Analysis*, 7th ed. (Washington, D.C.: A.O.A.C., 1950), p. 398.
[36] *Ind. Eng. Chem., A.E.*, 5:7 (1933).
[37] *Anal. Chem.*, 25:450 (1953).

13

Rapid Chemical Tests
of Soils and Plant Tissue

Diagnosis
—SCARSETH

13–1. Rapid chemical testing of soils and plant tissue is analogous to clinical testing and diagnosis in medicine. More elaborate analytical procedures of soil chemical analysis are simplified to be suitable for ready use by less specialized personnel in county agent offices and commercial farm service laboratories. The "diagnosis"[1] of a particular soil condition, made under the direction of a skilled agricultural agent and crop production supervisor, has become as indispensable and as widely required by farmers as that of the general practitioner in medicine.

13–2. Testing in the Field. Plant sap testing is generally carried out in the field or greenhouse, frequently with concurrent soil testing. Field tests make possible a coordinated diagnosis directly in the field by means of both plant tissue and soil tests. Reagents and apparatus for simple soil and plant tissue tests are packed into portable kits (¶ 13–78) for ready transport to the field. Although field tests are generally less accurate than laboratory tests, they are usually adequate in view of the variability of samples obtained by cursory sampling. Furthermore, testing soils and plant tissue in the field dramatizes the diagnosis for students and farmers by providing immediate answers to nutrition problems. In this way, interest is created in the soil testing service offered in central laboratories. Then systematic soil testing (¶ 13–75) in spring in preparation for preplanting applications can be developed in the normal pattern. Rapid soil tests are given below for

---

[1] Kitchen, ed., *Diagnostic Techniques of Soils and Crops* (Washington, D.C.: American Potash Institute, 1948).

aeration and porosity (¶ 13–71), for soil pH (¶ 13–87) and lime require-ment, and for readily extractable soil phosphorus (¶ 13–94), potassium, magnesium, calcium, nitrate, and ammonium. In saline soils, rapid testing of chloride, sulfate, and sodium are often important (¶ 13–109).

13–3. The basis for rapid chemical testing of plant tissue is the colori-metric determination of the levels of nitrate, phosphorus, and potassium, (sometimes magnesium and calcium,[2] manganese,[3] zinc,[4] and other ele-ments), is the sap of fresh plant tissue. Plant tissue tests, though only semi-quantitative, are highly useful as guides to interpretation of the relative supply of nutrients actually being taken up by the plant. The underlying assumption is that an adequate supply of the element is indicated by an abundance in the plant sap (¶ 13–4).

13–4. Interpretation of the Plant Tissue Tests. The presence of an abundant supply of one nutrient element in the sap may lead to a mistaken interpretation in plants when the plant growth is held back by a severe shortage of another. Use of the tests for all 3 major nutrients—nitrogen, phosphorus, and potassium—is nearly always more indicative than use of only 1. Two typical situations diagnosed by plant tissue tests are shown in Fig. 13–1. A marked response to nitrogen applied as a side-dressing was correctly predicted from the tissue tests (Fig. 13–1, A) coupled with fairly abundant growth. The need for more than 1 element (Fig. 13–1, C) can also be predicted by proper interpretation of the tissue tests and the ob-served generally retarded growth. The general appearance, size, and color of the plant are an aid in the interpretations. Leaf symptoms[5] give an ac-curate measure of severe deficiencies, but the tissue tests measure declining supplies before the visual symptoms are evident.

13–5. Tests for available phosphorus (¶ 13–94) and potassium in the soil often corroborate tissue tests for these elements but do not always do so. Factors of depth and function of rooting, controlled by soil aeration and moisture supply; root pruning through cultivation; and unusually cool tem-peratures may greatly affect the growth aside from the levels of mineral nutrient supplies in the soil. The plant roots stay in contact with the soil for long equilibrium times compared to the soil extraction times employed in soil testing. Plant roots extend to subsoil layers where available nutrients may be more abundant than in the surface soil where the soil tests are most often made. In addition, different plants have widely different capabilities for utilization of any 1 nutrient from a given soil, whereas soil testing ex-tractants are designed for general crops and are not generally standardized

---

[2] Mikkelsen and Toth (magnesium), *Agron. Jour.*, 41:379 (1941); Cheng and Bray (calcium and magnesium), *Better Crops,* 36, 1:13 (1952).

[3] Cook and Lawton, *S.S.S.A. Proc.,* 8:327 (1944).

[4] Shaw, *Soil Sci.,* 74:479 (1952).

[5] Hambridge, ed., *Hunger Signs in Crops* (Washington, D.C.: Natl. Fert. Assoc., 1941).

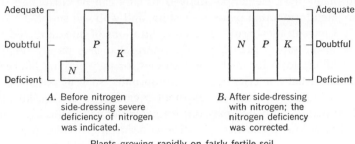

A. Before nitrogen
side-dressing severe
deficiency of nitrogen
was indicated.

B. After side-dressing
with nitrogen; the
nitrogen deficiency
was corrected.

Plants growing rapidly on fairly fertile soil.

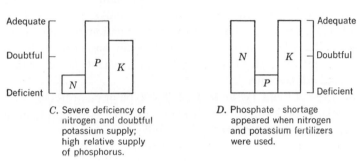

C. Severe deficiency of
nitrogen and doubtful
potassium supply;
high relative supply
of phosphorus.

D. Phosphate shortage
appeared when nitrogen
and potassium fertilizers
were used.

Plants having retarded growth on a less fertile soil.

Fig. 13–1. Plant tissue tests indicative of single (*A,B*) and multiple (*C,D*) deficiencies of nutrients. Two situations could be separated by observation of relative over-all growth rate, and fertilizer applications could be adjusted accordingly without the losses involved with inadequate fertilizer applications.

with respect to these different plant capabilities.[6] All of these factors are to some extent measured by the tissue tests, since they reflect the relative supplies of nutrients actually obtained by the plants. Like factory production, plant production depends on the raw materials (nutrients) actually conveyed to the site of manufacture (living cells), and no quantity of materials stored beyond the conveyor lines (roots) influences current production (¶ 13–81).

13–6. The laboratory analysis of plant tissue (Chapters 8, 12, 14, and 15), sometimes termed "foliar diagnosis," is similar in aim to rapid plant tissue testing in the field. The 2 systems differ in that the former determines the total content of nitrogen, phosphorus, potassium, boron, etc., but the latter determines only the currently unassimilated forms. The rapidity and on-the-spot results of field testing of tissue make the system indispensable in crop nutritional diagnosis. The total percentage of each nutrient ele-

[6] Scarseth, *Better Crops,* 27, 5:11 (1943).

ment in plants from elemental analysis usually can be correlated with the unassimilated form found by tissue testing, and with soil supply.[7]

13–7. Concentration Scale. The concentrations of unassimilated nutrient elements in the sap of plants may be interpreted in a purely relative way (high, medium, low) for each plant species, or they may be interpreted in terms of the usual numerical concentration units, such as parts per million of sap or of tissue. In either case, about 5 categories of concentration are enough to permit ready comparison; for example, very high, high, medium, low, and very low. Some tissue testing concentration scales are simplified more; for example, adequate and not adequate. Hoffer, in the Purdue University bulletin that pioneered rapid testing of plant tissue, showed the relative abundance of potassium in growing corn stalks by an inverse correlation with the colorimetric test for the accumulation of iron in the nodes (¶ 13–62). Thus the relative test for potassium was expressed in terms of the relative test for a physiologically related element; no absolute concentration standards were needed.

13–8. Type of Plant Tissue to Test. The type of plant tissue to test varies with the plant species and growth stage, as well as the preference of the operator. Hoffer employed split corn stalks; leaf, stem, and nodal slices have also been used. Juicy tissue is susceptible to mechanical maceration[8] followed by filtration, with tests on the clear sap or extract. Carbon black[9] has been employed as a filtering aid in leaf extractions.

NITRATE NITROGEN IN SAP OF PLANT TISSUE[10]

13–9. Nitrates accumulate in the sap of grass tissue roughly in proportion to the supply of soil nitrogen in relation to the rate of its utilization. The rate of utilization depends mainly on (a) the stage of growth, (b) how favorable the weather conditions are for growth, and (c) the relative supply of other nutrients. If other nutrients are in short supply, the nitrate tests may be high though the soil supply of available nitrogen may be only moderate or low (Fig. 13–1). The nitrate content of the sap varies in different parts of a plant, and it is necessary to standardize on a favorable part for the test on each species. The sensitivity of the test can be varied by choice of different parts of the plant.

13–10. When diphenylamine in H_2SO_4 is dropped on a slice of tissue, nitrate in the sap reacts to give a blue color, the intensity of which varies with the nitrate concentration. The advantages of the method are simplicity and rapidity. The disadvantages are corrosiveness of the solution

---

[7] Lundegardh, tr. Mitchell, *Leaf Analysis* (London: Hilger & Watts, Ltd., 1951).

[8] Brendler, *Sci.,* 114:61 (1951).

[9] Daniel and Turk, *Mich. Agr. Exp. Sta. Quart. Bul.* 32, 2:199 (1949).

[10] Grateful acknowledgement is extended to Dr. L. F. Marriott for his generous assistance with the sections on plant tissue and soil testing.

and the possibility that a few substances other than nitrate may give the test. The blue color develops in the presence of copper, lead, chromium, and iron, but these substances seldom cause interference in plant tissue testing.

APPARATUS

13–11. Apparatus needed includes a sharp knife, a porcelain spot plate, and a glass-stoppered dropper bottle.

REAGENTS

13–12. Needed reagents include distilled water for washing the spot plate and the diphenylamine reagent, which is prepared as follows: 1 gm of diphenylamine powder is dissolved in 100 ml of concentrated H_2SO_4. The solution is stored in a glass-stoppered bottle and the portion for use is placed in a glass-stoppered dropper bottle. The solution becomes discolored with time or with contact with the rubber bulb, and is replaced with fresh solution when this occurs. *Caution:* This reagent is corrosive.

PROCEDURE

13–13. The test is carried out somewhat differently with each crop. Procedures for corn, oats, soybeans, and grass are given as examples.

13–14. Stalk Test for Nitrate in Corn. The accumulation of nitrate is usually greatest at the base of the stalk and decreases toward the top. During the period of ear development, the nitrate utilization at the ear is so great that often a high test can be obtained just below the ear shank though a low or deficiency test can be obtained above this point. These facts should be kept in mind in the interpretation of the test results. When destruction of the stalk is not desirable, the test can be made on a thin vertical slice of nodal tissue cut with a clean sharp knife. A drop or 2 of the diphenylamine solution is placed on a freshly cut surface. The immediate development of a dark blue color indicates an abundant supply of nitrate present. A lack of blue color (brown color arising from tissue char by the acid is ignored) indicates no accumulation of nitrate, which usually is due to a nitrogen deficiency condition. Variation of intensity of the blue color ranges between these extremes, depending on the amount of nitrate present. Since the nitrate varies with height in the stalk, tests can be made at different nodes to determine the highest level at which it is present, as well as of the relative amount present. The base of the leaf midrib can also be used as the test site, the conducting tissues being cut open and the test solution being applied as indicated above. When destruction of a stalk is not a critical factor, a freshly split stalk provides a very satisfactory means of checking the amount of nitrate present from base to tassel. The test should be made on at least 6 or 8 representative stalks within the area checked so the proper interpretation of the test for a particular soil treatment can be made.

The results should also be checked against the depth of green color of the plants. These 2 criteria will usually agree except for temporary conditions affecting nitrate availability. The test usually becomes low before severe leaf symptoms of deficiency (scorching of the center of the leaf blade) appear. It has been found by C. D. Welch (N.C. Agr. Exp. Sta.) that the nitrate level is highest from about 11 A.M. to 3 P.M. This should be taken into account in the interpretation of the test.

13–15. Stem Test for Nitrate in Oats. The test for nitrate in oats is made at a node since more sap is usually present there. The plant is cut at a node and a drop of the diphenylamine solution is applied on the wet surface. The color resulting is interpreted as it was for corn.

13–16. Stem Test for Nitrate in Soybeans. The accumulation of nitrate in soybeans is greatest in the upper portion of the plant and decreases toward the base of the stem. This is the reverse of the situation found in corn, which must be considered in the interpretation of the test. In making the test, the stem is cut diagonally at the point desired and a drop or 2 of the diphenylamine solution is applied to the freshly cut surface. The color resulting is read as for corn.

13–17. Test for Nitrate in Grass Blades. A small representative sample of the grass blades to be tested is chopped finely and placed in a depression of the spot plate. A few drops of the diphenylamine solution are added and the resulting color is read as it was for corn. The test is not as clearly defined for grass blades as for stems.

13–18. Nitrate Test in Sap not Applicable to Some Plants. Legume plants, such as clover, alfalfa, and vetch, normally do not accumulate nitrates in their sap. Consequently they show a negative test, even though they fix their own nitrogen in adequate amounts directly from the air. Asparagus shoots or woody plants do not accumulate nitrate as an indication of an adequate supply, and consequently this type of test cannot be used on these plants.

ALTERNATIVE PROCEDURES

13–19. The pink powder test[11] (Fig. 13–2) for nitrate in plant sap has the advantages of a noncorrosive reagent. The white powder turns pink in the presence of nitrous acid produced by the reduction of nitrate. Manganous sulfate is employed to help prevent interference from chloride and to provide a more nearly quantitative reduction of nitrate to nitrite. The test includes both nitrate and nitrite.

13–20. The powder consists of a mixture of 4 gm of sulfanilic acid, 2 gm of alpha-naphthylamine, 10 gm of $MnSO_4 \cdot H_2O$, 2 gm of finely powdered Zn, 100 gm of $BaSO_4$, and 75 gm of citric acid. The coarse materials are ground to a fine powder before mixing, and the first 4 reagents are mixed

---

[11] Bray, *Soil Sci.,* 60:219 (1945).

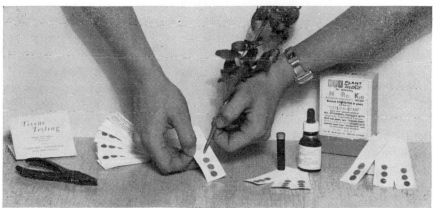

Fig. 13–2. N-P-K plant test kit by which nitrogen, phosphorus, and potassium status of plants can be determined in a few minutes and at low cost. Special filter paper color strips (lower) onto which the plant sap is squeezed eliminate filtration, glassware washing. (Available from the Urbana Laboratories, 406 N. Lincoln Ave., Urbana, Ill; Photos courtesy J. N. Bray.)

separately with a portion of the $BaSO_4$. Then all components including the remaining $BaSO_4$ and citric acid are mixed together thoroughly. Extreme care is exercised to have the room, table tops, and equipment free of nitrate and nitrite. The powder is stored in a bottle painted black since light affects the alpha-naphthylamine. A sharp knife, filter paper strips, and a small pair of pliers are needed for the test.

13–21. The test may be standardized against known amounts of nitrate. To do this a standard solution is prepared by dissolution of 0.072 gm of KNO_3 in 100 ml of distilled water. This solution contains 100 ppm of N in nitrate form. Nitrate-free filter paper is moistened with this solution or with a solution diluted by a known factor. A thin layer of the white powder is then applied, and the paper is folded over and squeezed. The intensity of the pink color after 1 minute measures the concentration of nitrate placed on the paper.

13–22. Stalk Test for Nitrate in Corn. The same principles govern the portion of the stalk to be tested by the white powder method as for the diphenylamine method (¶ 13–14). The powder test may be made in 1 of 2 ways, either on a filter paper or directly on the stalk. When the filter paper is used, a diagonal cut is made into the conductive tissues of the stalk, just deep enough to reach the plant sap, then downward a short distance so that the filter paper strip can be inserted into the cut. The paper is pressed against the fresh cut until it is wet with the sap. A small amount of the powder is sprinkled on the wet paper with a toothpick and then the paper is folded and pressed together so that the powder becomes wet. The sap is allowed to act on the powder for 1 minute so that the pink color develops fully. The intensity of the pink color is a measure of the nitrate level in the plant. When the powder remains colorless, a deficiency in plant nitrate is indicated. When the color is pink, adequate nitrates are present. When the color is dark pink to red, the plant has an excess of nitrates.

13–23. The test may also be made by sprinkling a small amount of the powder directly into the cut in the stalk and pressing it with the cut sliver so that the powder is moistened by the sap. Or, the stalk is split through the entire length for an over-all test. The color is read in the same manner as when the filter paper is used. The test may also be made at the base of the midrib of a leaf. A piece of tissue to be tested may be removed so that additional sap does not diffuse and bring more nitrate to the area tested.

13–24. Stem Test for Nitrate in Oats. Since it is often difficult to expose enough sap of an oat straw or leaf to wet the powder directly, it is most practicable to press a strip of filter paper against a node with a pair of pliers until the paper is wet with the sap. The paper often becomes stained green, but by using the side away from the node or by doubling the paper so that the chlorophyll is filtered out by the first layer of paper, a clean surface is available for application of the powder, and the pink color is not masked by the green. The color is read as in the stalk test.

13–25. Stem Test for Nitrate in Soybeans. In making the test, the stem is cut diagonally at the point desired and a small amount of the white powder is applied to the freshly cut surface. The powder must be wet with the plant sap. The color resulting after about a minute is read as it was for corn. The test may also be made by the use of filter paper strips as indicated for corn, but the different distribution of nitrate in soybeans (¶ 13–16) must be kept in mind.

13–26. Test for Nitrate in Grass. One measure of finely chopped plant material, 1 measure of the white powder, and 14 measures of distilled water are shaken together for 25 to 30 seconds and allowed to settle. The color is interpreted as for corn.

PHOSPHORUS IN SAP OF PLANT TISSUE

13–27. Phosphorus is absorbed from the soil by plants chiefly in the inorganic or phosphate form. Within the plant it is changed rapidly into organic form and utilized to produce new growth, particularly the formation of new cells. When the phosphorus supply is abundant, the plant is able to accumulate a small reserve of inorganic phosphates in the plant juices, and this gives the blue coloration in the test indicating "abundant" or "adequate" supplies. A high phosphorus test may be found in plants growing slowly because of limited supplies of nitrogen and/or potassium, the phosphorus supply being relatively more abundant. Application of the limiting element or elements will increase the growth, but phosphorus may then become the limiting factor (Fig. 13–1).

13–28. A low phosphorus test can be corroborated in conjunction with the nitrate test. Phosphorus-deficient plants usually show a high test for nitrate and a dark green color because the most limiting growth factor is phosphorus. Phosphorus-deficient plants may also show a purple coloration of the main stalk arising from high sugar accumulation because insufficient phosphorus is present to permit full conversion of the sugar formed in the leaves into growth and yield production.

13–29. When the molybdatic acid solution is dropped on filter paper wet with the plant sap (N–P–K test kit, Fig. 13–2) and this is followed by contact with a tin rod, a blue color resulting indicates that a reserve of phosphate is present. The advantages of this method are simplicity (little apparatus) and rapidity.

APPARATUS

13–30. Needed apparatus includes a sharp knife, filter paper strips, and pliers.

13–31. Needed reagents includes the acid molybdate solution ("P–K developer") and the tin rod supplied in the kit (Fig. 13–2).

PROCEDURE

13–32. The same general portion of the plant must be sampled each time for comparative work. Plants and the portions of each that may be used are as follows: corn—stalk near tassel, stalk or midrib or leaf just below the lower ear node; oats—upper stem or node; soybeans—upper part of the stem or petiole of leaf in upper part of the plant.

13–33. The surface of the tissue being tested is sliced so that a freshly cut surface is exposed. A spot on the filter paper strip is moistened with the sap by placing the paper in contact with the cut surface. In some cases it may be necessary to squeeze the paper and stem (or leaf) together gently to accomplish the wetting. A small drop of the molybdate-acid solution is applied to the wet spot, care being taken to avoid too much of the solution. The brightened end of the tin rod is immediately pressed against the spot for about 10 seconds. The color resulting is read as follows:

> No color—plant very deficient in phosphorus
> Slight blue—plant is deficient in phosphorus
> Medium blue—plant is only slightly deficient in phosphorus
> Dark blue—plant is adequately supplied with phosphorus

The test is made on 6 or 8 typical stalks in the area so that the representative level of phosphorus may be determined.

ALTERNATIVE PROCEDURES

13–34. The reaction in the Purdue test[12] is similar to that described in ¶ 13–33, with the exception that this test is carried out in a solution. The most soluble phosphates are extracted with ammonium molybdate-acid solution, and the color is developed by the addition of the stannous oxalate powder. Needed apparatus consists of a sharp knife or razor blade, ¼ teaspoon measure, rigid-toothed comb, wood block, and glass vial 11 mm in diameter and 76 mm high with a 10-ml graduation.

13–35. Needed reagents consist of stannous oxalate powder and 2 concentrations of molybdate reagent prepared as follows.

13–36. Molybdate Reagent. Eight gm of ammonium molybdate is dissolved in 200 ml of distilled water. To this solution, a mixture of 126 ml of concentrated hydrochloric acid and 74 ml of distilled water are added slowly with constant stirring. A small portion of this concentrated molybdate reagent is diluted with 4 volumes of distilled water just before use for the phosphate test. The diluted reagent may become unsuited for use

---

12 Thornton *et al., Purdue Univ. Agr. Exp. Sta. Bul.* 204 (1939).

after standing a few weeks and is checked by running a standard determination before it is used on plant material (¶ 13–42).

13–37. Test for Phosphorus in Corn. Leaf blades appear to be the best part of the corn plant to test during the early stages of growth, and are satisfactory in the later stages. Stem tissue may also be used when the plants are larger. Since tissue should be taken from at least 6 or 8 stalks to get a representative sample from an area, there is less mutilation of the plants when leaf tissue is used. The leaf just below the lower ear node has been widely used, throughout the season. If stem tissue is used, the portion selected for the test is the section just below the growing tip or below the tassel in older stalks. Tissue from several typical stalks should be combined as a representative sample for an area.

13–38. The tissue must be cut into very small uniform sections to obtain comparable results since the sap of the ruptured cells is essentially the solution tested. Uniformity of the sections also aids in the measurement of uniform quantities of tissue. To accomplish this, leaf blades with the midrib removed are superimposed one upon the other on a wood block. Then, with a rigid-toothed comb as a guide, they are cut lengthwise and crosswise with a razor blade or thin sharp knife. A similar method may be used for the stem tissue.

13–39. Next, ¼ teaspoon of the finely cut tissue is placed in a flat-bottomed glass vial. The vial is filled to the 10-ml mark with the diluted molybdate reagent, stoppered, and shaken vigorously for 1 minute. For comparable results, this time must be observed carefully, since this extraction removes only the most readily soluble phosphates. Then a fleck of stannous oxalate reagent (about the size of a pin head) is added, the solution is again shaken, and the color is observed. The resulting color may be read as follows:

Colorless or yellow—very deficient phosphorus supply
Green or bluish green—deficient phosphorus supply
Light blue—medium phosphorus supply
Medium blue—adequate phosphorus supply
Dark blue—abundant phosphorus supply

Caution: Arsenic gives the same test as available phosphorus, and therefore the test as described is not applicable for plants that have been recently sprayed or dusted with arsenic compounds.

13–40. Test for Phosphorus in Oats and Other Grasses. Similarly located leaves from each of several plants are combined and finely chopped as indicated for corn. The leaf used should be from the upper part of the plant. One-fourth teaspoon of tissue is taken for the test, and the phosphate is determined by the same procedure as for corn.

13–41. Test for Phosphorus in Soybeans. The terminal leaflet from the third node below the growing point is taken from each of 15 to 20 representative plants. The leaflets are superimposed one upon another and cut as with corn. Then ¼ teaspoon of tissue is used for the test and the phosphate determined by the same procedure as for corn.

13–42. Phosphorus Standards. A solution is made up by dissolving 0.02 gm of dicalcium phosphate $(CaHPO_4 \cdot 2 H_2O)$ or 0.016 gm of potassium dihydrogen phosphate (KH_2PO_4) in 100 ml of 0.75 N HCl. Then the procedure is followed in the usual way, the volumes of standard phosphorus solutions, being used in place of the plant tissue, as follows:

Simulated phosphorus level	Volume of standard phosphorus solution
Very deficient phosphorus supply	0.1 ml
Deficient phosphorus supply	0.2 ml
Medium phosphorus supply	0.6 ml
Adequate phosphorus supply	1.5 ml
Abundant phosphorus supply	3.0 ml

POTASSIUM IN THE SAP OF PLANT TISSUE

13–43. Nearly all of the potassium in plant tissue remains in soluble or extractable form in the plant sap. If the potassium supply is limited, its concentration in the sap declines greatly as growth continues, giving concentration differences that are easily tested. The potassium, when in deficient supply, tends to be translocated in grasses from older tissue to younger growing parts. The older grass leaves, near the base of the stem, then turn brown and die along the margins. Severe potassium deficiency causes corn ears to be poorly filled at the tip and may cause stunting of the plants. In legumes, potassium becomes deficient first in the younger leaves and white or brown necrotic spots appear between the veins. In soybeans, for example, the lower leaves are nearly always higher in potassium than the upper leaves.

13–44. The test for potassium in the sap of plant tissue is carried out with filter paper test strips,[13] or in a suspension of finely cut tissue. Sap samples may be collected on filter papers in the field, dried and the tests performed later on a routine basis in the laboratory[14] by means of the dipicrylamine reagent.[15] Test papers may be prepared with the dipicrylamine dried on test spots.[16]

APPARATUS

13–45. Needed apparatus consists of a sharp knife and pliers.

---

[13] Hoffer, *Better Crops,* 29, 4:9 (1945).
[14] Richer, *Better Crops,* 31, 1:26 (1947).
[15] Poluektoff, *Mikrochemie,* 14:265 (1933–1934).
[16] Melsted, *Better Crops,* 34, 1:26 (1950).

13–46. Needed reagents consist of the prepared test papers from the N–P–K test kit (Fig. 13–2) and the acid molybdate P–K developer of the kit, or the prepared reagents described below.

13–47. In lieu of the P–K developer, the potassium test can be completed with 0.5 N HCl.

13–48. The test papers may be prepared according to the Melsted[17] procedure. *Solution A* is prepared by dissolution of 0.60 gm of dipicrylamine (hexanitrodiphenylamine) and 0.60 gm of Na_2CO_3 in 16 ml of distilled water, the mixture being stirred and brought to a boil to hasten solution. The mixture is then cooled and filtered through a small filter paper, and the filter is washed with distilled water. The filtrate is made up to a volume of 25 ml. For convenience, the mixture may be filtered and washed directly into a 25-ml graduate.

13–49. *Solution B* is prepared by dilution of 8 ml of *Solution A* to 25 ml with distilled water in a 25-ml graduate.

13–50. *Solution C* is prepared by dilution of 10 ml of *Solution B* to 15 ml with distilled water in a 25-ml graduate.

13–51. Preparation of the Test Papers. Whatman No. 1 filter paper is cut into approximately 2×7 cm strips. At 1 end of the filter paper, a small drop of *Solution A* is placed to form a test paper spot. Then about 1 cm from this spot, a small drop of *Solution B* is placed. Finally, about 1 cm from the second spot, a small drop of *Solution C* is placed. The papers are allowed to dry in the open air or in a drying oven for 3 to 5 minutes at 85°C. When dry, the test spots should vary in color from a deep orange color for the first (*Solution A*) spot to a light orange color for the last (*Solution C*) spot. It is recommended that the prepared papers be used within a year to insure good results. Calibration:

Spot on paper	Sensitivity, ppm of K in solution
Solution A	750–1000
Solution B	2000 or more
Solution C	3000 or more

13–52. The same general portion of the plant must be sampled each time for comparative results. The portion suggested for use in this test is indicated for some of the crop plants as follows: corn—the base of the midrib of the leaf at ear level or the stalk at about the same point; oats—a node near the middle or upper part of the plant; soybeans—the enlarged base of the petiole on a leaf from the top of the plant; grass—leaves.

---

[17] *Better Crops,* 34, 1:26 (1950).

13–53. For corn, the test paper is placed along the midrib of the leaf. One jaw of the pliers is placed on 1 of the test spots and the other underneath the midrib. The jaws are squeezed together gently until the plant sap wets the spot. The procedure is repeated for each of the other 2 spots on different portions of the same midrib. The sap is allowed to react with the test spots for about 30 seconds or more. Then the spots are wet with one or more drops of the P–K developer (or 0.5 N HCl). The test is positive if the reddish-orange or brownish color persists on the test spot area. The test is negative if the spot turns a lemon-yellow color. The test may be read as follows:

1. If all spots turn lemon yellow, the plants are very deficient in potassium and show definite potash deficiency symptoms.

2. If the end spot (1000 ppm) tests a solid orange but the others are yellow, the plants are usually deficient in potassium and would probably respond to potassium treatment.

3. If the first 2 spots test a solid orange, the potassium is usually adequate for field crops, such as corn, small grain, soybeans, pasture, etc.

4. If all spots test orange, the potassium is in abundant supply.

13–54. The test was developed to give a definite reading at the concentrations indicated. Therefore, as the concentration of potassium in solution approaches the indicated levels, weak tests are obtained. Likewise, a strong test indicates a stronger concentration than needed for a positive test. Thus some range in interpretation is provided by the intensity of the color of the test spots.

13–55. The test should be made on 6 or 8 typical stalks in the area so that the representative level of potassium may be determined.

ALTERNATIVE PROCEDURE

13–56. The Purdue test[18] for potassium involves precipitation with cobaltinitrite and estimation of turbidity. Needed apparatus consists of a sharp knife or razor blade, a ½ teaspoon measure, a rigid tooth comb, a wood block, glass vials 11 mm in diameter and 76 mm high with a 10-ml graduation. Needed reagents consist of the concentrated cobaltinitrite[19] reagent prepared by dissolution of 5 gm of $Na_3Co(NO_2)_6$ and 30 gm of $NaNO_2$ in 80 ml of distilled water. Then 5 ml of glacial HOAc is added, and the volume made to 100 ml. The solution is allowed to stand for several days. Shortly before tests are to be performed a dilute reagent is prepared by the addition of 5 ml of the concentrated reagent just prepared to a solution of 15 gm of $NaNO_2$ in 100 ml of distilled water, and the pH is ad-

---

[18] Thornton *et al., Purdue Univ. Agr. Exp. Sta. Bul.* 204 (1939).

[19] The Co content of commercial preparations varies considerably and this test is based on the "Baker's Analyzed" product. The cobaltinitrite concentration is an important factor in determining the sensitivity of the test.

justed to 5.0 with HOAc. Other reagents needed are anhydrous isopropyl alcohol and 95 per cent ethanol. When ethanol for use as a reagent is difficult to obtain, a mixture of 60 parts anhydrous methanol, 40 parts isopropyl alcohol, and 5 parts of distilled may be substituted. If this mixture turns turbid, it is filtered. Denatured alcohol is not satisfactory.

13–57. Tests for Potassium in Corn. The base of the leaf, near the ear node or middle of the stalk is most appropriate for the potassium test. The tissue is first cut into very small uniform sections. To accomplish this, leaf blades are superimposed upon one another on a wood block and cut lengthwise and crosswise with the blade, a rigid tooth comb being used as a guide.

13–58. Next, ½ teaspoon of finely cut tissue is measured into a glass vial. Then 10 ml of the dilute cobaltinitrite reagent is added and the vial is shaken vigorously for 1 minute. Finally, 5 ml of the 95 per cent ethanol is added and the suspension is mixed. The yellow coloration of the solution is approximately constant and is disregarded. The degree of turbidity formed is an indication of the potassium content:

Only a trace of turbidity	Deficient potassium supply
Medium turbidity	Doubtful potassium supply
Very high turbidity	Adequate potassium supply

13–59. Potassium Standards. A standard potassium solution is made by dissolution of 1 gm of KCl in 100 ml of 15 per cent $NaNO_2$ solution. Then the procedure is followed in the usual way, with the following volumes of this solution being employed instead of the plant tissue:

Simulated potassium level	Volume of standard potassium solution
Deficient potassium supply	0.2 ml
Doubtful potassium supply	0.4 ml
Adequate potassium supply	1.0 ml

13–60. Potassium may be tested in small grains such as wheat, oats, barley, and rye by obtaining tissue at the base of the leaf in the middle of the main stem. The tissue from alfalfa, clover, and soybeans is taken from the main stem.

13–61. In a modification for peach tree leaves,[20] 1 teaspoon of finely cut green tissue taken in mid season, ⅛ teaspoon of DARCO G60 activated carbon, and 10 ml of 15 per cent $NaNO_2$ having pH adjusted to 5.0, are placed in the vial and the suspension is shaken for 1 minute, then filtered. Next, 2.5 ml of the filtrate is placed in a clean vial. The temperature is held near 20°C (68° ± 3°F) during the precipitation to follow. First, 5 ml of the dilute cobaltinitrite solution (¶ 13–56) is thoroughly mixed with the

---

[20] Garrard, *Better Crops,* 34, 6:17 (1950).

solution in the vial. Then 2.5 ml of 95 per cent ethanol is run down the side of the tube to obtain a layer on top. This layer is allowed to stand for 1 minute to start precipitation. Finally, the alcohol is mixed in slowly with a rotary motion, and 3 minutes are then allowed before the estimation of turbidity (¶ 13–58). The equivalent for a medium test is approximately 1 to 1.5 per cent K in the tissue.

13–62. Iron accumulates in the nodes of corn stalks when the plant is potassium deficient (¶ 13–7). Iron concentration was shown[21] to be inversely related to total K in the leaf, nodal, and internodal tissue. The test is made by splitting the stalk and applying a few drops of 10 per cent aqueous KSCN solution to the nodal area, followed by a drop or two of 6 N HCl. A red color (detecting iron accumulation) denotes K deficiency.

QUICK SOIL AERATION TESTS

13–63. Oxygen activity in soil is difficult to measure directly, but the valence of soluble iron ions reflects it, and these ions may be determined easily.[22] The proportion of ferric to ferrous reflects the intensity of oxygen supply.

13–64. The direct determination of oxygen activity or oxidation potential with the platinum electrode is a somewhat longer test, but it is also adaptable to rapid field determination with portable apparatus. The same dynamic intensity factor of soil oxygen activity is measured by Hoffer test for ferric and ferrous iron, given here.

13–65. Functions of Soil Oxygen. A few plants, such as rice, cranberries, weeping willows, and cypress, are able to live with extremely low activities of soil oxygen because they can utilize oxygen absorbed in the aboveground portions and translocate it to the roots.[23] In contrast, a high activity of soil oxygen is required for the satisfactory growth of most agricultural crops including corn, oats, wheat, and alfalfa. Roots of these plants require free soil oxygen for respiration and resultant liberation of energy used in the uptake of water and nutrient ions.[24] Oxygen activity affects the utilization of ammonium[25] by roots and bears on the effect of the balance between the activities of the various nutrients in the media.[26] Uptake of applied nitrogen, phosphorus, and potassium is more efficacious in the presence of adequate activity of soil oxygen.[27] Decomposition of organic

[21] Hoffer, *Purdue Agr. Exp. Sta. Bul.* 298 (1930); Hoffer and Trost, *J. Am. Soc. Agron.*, 15, 8:323 (1923).

[22] Hoffer, *Better Crops*, 29, 1:6 (1945); 29, 2:19 (1945).

[23] Cannon, *Carnegie Inst. Wash. Pub.* 368 (1925).

[24] Hoagland and Broyer, *Plant Physiol.*, 11:471 (1936).

[25] Arnon, *Soil Sci.*, 44:91 (1937).

[26] Shive, *Soil Sci.*, 51:445 (1941).

[27] Lawton, *S.S.S.A. Proc.*, 10:263 (1946).

residues in soils and release of mineral constituents for crop use requires an abundance of soil oxygen.

APPARATUS

13–66. Needed apparatus consists of a spade for the excavation of the soil and 3 glass-stoppered dropper bottles.

REAGENTS

13–67. Needed reagents include filter paper, 7 to 10 cm in diameter; 1.2 N HCl (concentrated HCl diluted with 4 parts of water); and the following special reagents.

13–68. Potassium Thiocyanate. Ten gm of KCNS is dissolved in 100 ml of distilled water.

13–69. Potassium Ferricyanide. One-half gm of $K_3Fe(CN)_6$ is dissolved in 100 ml of distilled water.

13–70. Each of the 3 solutions is placed in a separate dropper bottle, to be ready for quick service.

PROCEDURE[28]

13–71. The soil tests for ferric and ferrous iron must be made within 20 or 30 seconds on samples from freshly exposed soil surfaces. The aeration and attendant chemical reactions change very rapidly. A hole 30- to 50-cm deep is spaded in the area to be tested. The test is carried out at 10-, 20-, 30-, and possibly 40-cm depths. The test on a sample from one depth is carried out on a freshly taken sample before sampling at the next depth.

13–72. To make the test, a filter paper is creased along the diameter (Fig. 13–3, I). Two soil samples (each consisting of a pinch of soil) are placed on opposite ends of the paper. Two drops of the HCl are added to each of the soil samples. The paper is then folded over and squeezed tightly so that the liquid comes through the paper. To the wet areas on the outside of the paper 1 drop of the KCNS solution is added to the left wet area, and one drop of the $K_3Fe(CN)_6$ solution is added to the right wet area (Fig. 13–3, II). Appearance of a red area from the KCNS treated area indicates ferric iron (good oxygen supply). Appearance of a blue color from the $K_3Fe(CN)_6$ treated area indicates ferrous iron (poor oxygen supply). A faint red color, or none at all, generally is found when a blue color appears. The results are recorded at once. If both ferric and ferrous iron tests are obtained, the oxygen deficiency is usually not severe.

13–73. The test is then repeated for other soil depths. The importance of making the test very quickly can be demonstrated by permitting additional soil samples to be exposed to the air for a few minutes, particularly in sunlight, and then repeating the test. A negative ferric iron test soon

---

[28] Hoffer, *Better Crops,* 29, 1:6 (1945).

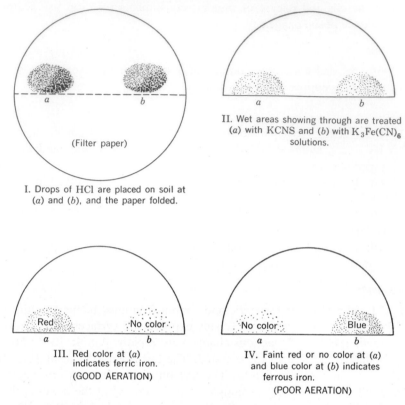

I. Drops of HCl are placed on soil at (a) and (b), and the paper folded.

(Filter paper)

II. Wet areas showing through are treated (a) with KCNS and (b) with $K_3Fe(CN)_6$ solutions.

III. Red color at (a) indicates ferric iron. (GOOD AERATION)

Red   No color

IV. Faint red or no color at (a) and blue color at (b) indicates ferrous iron. (POOR AERATION)

No color   Blue

Fig. 13–3. Chemical tests for ferric and ferrous iron in soils, indicative of oxygen supply. (After Hoffer, *Better Crops with Plant Food,* 29, 1:6, 1945.)

becomes a positive one and shows the rapidity of oxidation once the soil is exposed. Interesting information on the oxygen distribution in soils can be noted by making the test for ferric iron in the channels formed by penetrating roots of previous crops such as alfalfa or ragweed. Also, the depth of aeration over tile drains as compared to other areas is of interest. Compaction at the plow sole can be noted by tests at that depth and above and below it. The deficiency of oxygen is most likely to occur during years of adequate rainfall, except in soils that have been adequately maintained by the growth of deep-rooted crops.

ALTERNATIVE PROCEDURE

13–74. Hoffer Chalk Test. Hoffer has also proposed a test for soil porosity that gives an indication of oxygen supply. A suspension is prepared of 10 ml of dry powdered precipitated $CaCO_3$ in 50 ml of water. This suspension is shaken well just before each use. A core sample of soil is taken by means of the open faced sampling tube (¶ 2–33). The face of the core is shaved off with a knife with care not to compress the surface, and then drops of the $CaCO_3$ suspension are placed at different depths along the core. If the $CaCO_3$ particles penetrate into the soil and disappear from the surface, coarse porosity and satisfactory aeration is indicated. If, on the other hand, the white particles remain on the surface of the core, fine porosity and poor oxygen supply are indicated.

SOIL TESTING SYSTEMS

13–75. Soil testing refers to chemical tests[29] that can be made rapidly and with low cost per determination, as contrasted to conventional methods of soil chemical analysis, which are more accurate but more time consuming and expensive. Soil testing covers both rapid analysis in the field (¶ 13–2) and in the laboratory. Testing for soil aeration, being entirely a field test (not adaptable to laboratory samples) and closely allied to plant tissue testing for field diagnosis, has been given above (¶ 13–71).

13–76. Function of Soil Testing. Soil testing serves as a basis for advice to individual farmers about particular fields (¶ 13–1), as contrasted to the conventional more elaborate methods that serve not only for calibration of the rapid soil tests but also for the determination of general principles about soil types on the basis of which recommendations of general applicability are formulated. Soil tests are often designed for general use (¶ 13–5) without special calibrations for either particular crops or particular soils. Dr. C. E. Kellogg, in personal conversations with the author, has emphasized the need for standardization of soil tests according to soil types as well as according to crops. It is believed that soil-testing practice must eventually be refined to this point.

13–77. Mass Handling in Soil Testing. Because of the greater rapidity of rapid microchemical soil testing procedures than the conventional "long methods," they are generally used for soil testing on a mass scale in central soil-testing laboratories. Convenient mass-handling techniques have been described in the literature.[30] Multiple apparatus for shaking, filtration, pipetting, etc. are aids to mass handling. Time and motion studies assist in the achievement of high efficiency. A system of rapid microchemical soil tests designed for a precision approaching that of conventional "long methods" has been described.[31]

13–78. Soil-testing Kits. A number of commercial soil-testing kits[32] are

---

[29] Comparable to the spot tests of chemistry, Fiegl, tr. J. W. Matthews, *Spot Tests* (New York: Nordeman Publishing Company, Inc., 1937); B.D.H., *Reagents for Spot Tests* (London: British Drug Houses, 1936).

[30] Constable and Miles, *J. Am. Soc. Agron.*, 33:623 (1941).

[31] Peech, *Ind. Eng. Chem., A.E.,* 13:436 (1941); Peech and English, *Soil Sci.,* 57:167 (1944); Peech *et al.,* U.S.D.A. Cir. 757 (1947).

[32] A comparison of various systems was made by Anderson and Noble, U.S.D.A. Misc. Pub. 259 (1947).

available, complete with reagents and apparatus for making certain soil tests in the field. As examples, the Purdue kit is supplied by Purdue University, Lafayette, Ind.; the Hellige-Truog kit is supplied by Hellige, Inc., 3718 Northern Blvd., Long Island City 1, New York; the Morgan type kit is supplied by LaMotte Chemical Products, Towson, Md.; and the Spurway type kit is supplied by the Edwards Laboratory, Cleveland 11, Ohio.

13–79. Attendant Factors in Interpretation of Soil Tests. Soil tests in themselves, and apart from knowledge of the field conditions and other attendant circumstances, do not provide certain knowledge of proper soil management recommendations (¶ 13–5). The photometer reading cannot be transmitted to the farmer without the intermediary of human judgement —balancing the test against attendant circumstances. What are the most important attendant circumstances? The interpreter of the soil test must know the soil type and the climatic zone in which it is located. He must consider the topography of the soil, the type of drainage, the depth and aeration of the soil, and whether the subsoil is a potential source of nutrients.[33] The history of liming and fertilization must be known, since this provides a clue to the yield level to be expected. The yield history permits comparison to yields on similar soils and aids in establishing the amount and analysis of fertilizer to be used. For the immediate recommendation, the crop to be grown in the following year must be known. In this respect, the different rooting habits and the differing abilities of various crop plants to extract nutrient elements from the soil must be considered.[34] With all these factors in mind, a practical soil treatment may be formulated, assuming average moisture and temperature conditions.

13–80. Sampling Soils for Soil Chemical Testing.[35] The procedure for sampling a farm field for soil testing (details in ¶ 2–49) consists of compositing thin slices of soil through the plow layer from 10 to 20 places distributed throughout each uniform portion of the field. One such composite sample is taken for each 5 to 10 acres. Upland, middle, and bottom lands are sampled separately. Unusual soil spots such as those near gates, under stacks of manure, from dead furrows, or along field boundaries are avoided. The following information should be supplied with the sample:

1. Sample number . . . . Date . . . .
2. Field number . . . . County . . . .
3. Crop to be grown . . . .
4. Will the field be manured for next crop? . . . .
5. Yield of crop last year . . . .

---

[33] Truog, *S.S.S.A. Proc.,* 1:135 (1937).
[34] Drake *et al., S.S.S.A. Proc.,* 4:201 (1940).
[35] Reed, *Better Crops,* 37, 8:13 (1953).

6. Field is upland . . . . , bottomland . . . . , marsh . . . .

7. When field was last limed . . . . Amount per acre . . . .

8. Kind and amount of commercial fertilizer used . . . .

9. Name and address . . . .

13–81. Extractants for Soil Testing. Soil extractants to be employed for testing have been selected generally to simulate plant feeding (Morgan,[36] Spurway[37]) or to extract all or a proportional part of the available form or forms of the element being tested (Bray,[38] Truog[39]). Although the results from the 2 types of extractants may differ greatly, as in the phosphorus test, they may be so related that a factor may be employed to convert from one system to the other.[40] In any case, the results of a test must be correlated with crop response to applications of the element.

13–82. The extractant must not contain ions that would interfere with the analysis to be made. Use of a single extractant for several elements decreases the time required for several tests. Since no 1 extractant is suitable for all soils or all elements, various solutions have been used. These extractants fall generally into 4 types, as follows:

1. The strong mineral acid type, e.g., $0.3 N$ HCl (Truog as given by Nelson et al.[41])

2. The highly buffered weakly ionized acid type, e.g., 10 per cent NaOAc in 3 per cent HOAc buffered at pH 4.8 (Morgan).

3. The fairly concentrated solution of a neutral salt, e.g., $3 N$ NaNO$_3$ (Bray).[42]

4. The solutions with a solvent action of the same order as water, e.g., $0.025 N$ HOAc (Spurway).

Many different extractants are being employed within any region due to development by various independent workers. Some standardization would be desirable.

13–83. Nutrients elements are extracted from both sandy and fine-textured soils for testing by means of minitaure electrodialysis cells in the New Jersey Experiment Station testing laboratory.[43]

---

[36] Lunt et al., The Morgan Soil Testing System, Conn. Agr. Exp. Sta. Bul. 541 (1950).

[37] Spurway and Lawton, Mich. Agr. Exp. Sta. Tech. Bul. 132 (4th Rev.) (1949).

[38] Bray, Soil Sci., 66:83–89 (1948).

[39] Truog, S.S.S.A. Proc., 1:135 (1937).

[40] Peech, S.S.S.A. Proc., 10:245 (1946).

[41] Nelson et al., Soil Testing in the United States (Beltsville, Md.: Natl. Soil and Fert. Res. Committee, U.S.D.A. Soils Div., 1951).

[42] Bray, Diagnostic Technics for Soils and Crops, Ch. 2 (Washington, D.C.: American Potash Institute, 1948).

[43] Purvis, Better Crops, 37, 3:19 (1953).

PROCEDURE

13–84. Because soil-testing procedures are still individualistic with each experiment station, appropriately detailed in respective bulletins, no particular system of procedures is to be given here. As summarized in Table 13–1, the various soil testing systems vary considerably in the extractants, soil to extractant ratios, and methods of extraction; but many of the different systems are similar in type of analytical determination. The present objective is to illustrate representative analytical determinations that are employed by various laboratories.

13–85. The determinations considered are soil pH, phosphorus, potassium, nitrogen and organic matter, calcium, and magnesium. Soil testing for the minor elements is becoming increasingly important, but thus far the methods are mainly the usual analytical determinations; for example, for manganese (¶ 15–27) and boron (¶ 14–40). Tests for copper, zinc, and molybdenum have not been developed intensively beyond the determination of the total quantities (Chapter 15).

13–86. The measurement of the turbidity or color developed in soil tests is generally by photoelectric absorption photometers (¶ 17–21) or by printed color charts. The preparation of permanent plastic[44] standards is an aid to permanence, inexpensiveness, and mobility of the soil testing equipment.

13–87. The Soil pH Test. Perhaps the most important of all rapid soil tests is the soil pH test (¶ 13–90). The soil pH indicates much about the interpretation of the other soil tests, since the availability of P, Ca, Mg, Fe, Mn, and B are greatly affected by soil pH. An acid soil test, coupled with a knowledge of the crop to be grown and the soil type, permits a recommendation of the quantity of ground limestone needed (¶ 13–88). Soil areas testing alkaline need different management.

13–88. For intensive agriculture, including rotations with lime-loving legumes, the soil is limed to bring the pH value to the range of 6.5 or slightly higher. The following is a guide:

Soil pH value	Tons of ground limestone per acre to bring pH value to 6.5 (approximate guide)	
	Sands and sandy loams	Silt loams, clay loams, mucks
4.0	6	9
4.5	5	7
5.0	4	5
5.5	2	3
6.0	1	2
6.5	0	0

---

[44] Lynd and Turk, *J. Am. Soc. Agron.,* 40:940 (1948); *S.S.S.A. Proc.,* 15:152 (1951).

TABLE 13–1

General character of several soil testing systems

	Wisconsin (Truog)	Indiana† (Ohlrogge)	Michigan§ (Spurway)	Connecticut** (Morgan)	Illinois†† (Bray)	Cornell‡‡ (Peech)	Missouri§§ (Graham)
Wt. of soil used, gm	3*	P—2.5 K—5.0	2.5	5	P—1 K—5	10	P—1 K—5
Soil : extractant ratio	3 : 7*	P—1 : 2 K—1 : 4	1 : 4	1 : 2	P—1 : 7 K—1 : 2	1 : 5	P—1 : 7 K—1 : 2
Extractant	0.3 N HCl*	P—$(NH_4)_2MoO_4$ + 0.75 N HCl K—$Na_3Co(NO_2)_6$ + HOAc + $NaNO_2$	0.025 N HOAc (active) 0.13 N HCl (reserve)	10% NaAc in 3% HOAc	P—0.03 N NH_4F in 0.1 N HCl K—3 N $NaNO_3$	Morgan	Bray
pH of extractant	0.5	P—5.04	3.3 (active) 0.9 (reserve)	4.8	P—1.0 K—7.0	4.8	P—1.0 K—7.0
K test	Turbidimetric		Sodium cobaltinitrite				
PO_4 test	Molybdenum† blue color from formation of molybdophosphoric acid in acid solution with subsequent reduction with stannous ion or organic reducing solution.						
Ca test	Oxalate†	—	Oxalate	Oxalate	Oxalate	Stearate	Oleate
Mg test	Titan yellow†	—	Titan yellow	Thiazole yellow	Titan yellow	Titan yellow	Thiazole yellow
Cl test	$AgNO_3$† (special extractant)	—	$AgNO_3$ (active)	$AgNO_3$	$AgNO_3$	—	—
SO_4 test	$BaCl_2$†	—	$BaCl_2$	$BaCl_2$	$BaCl_2$	—	—

* Nelson et al., Soil Testing in the United States (Beltsville, Md : Natl. Soil and Fert. Res. Committee, U.S.D.A. Soils Div., 1951).
† Hellige, Long Island City, N.Y., Bul. 690 (1936).
‡ Ohlrogge, Purdue Univ. Agr. Exp. Sta. Bul. 584 (1952).
§ Spurway and Lawton, Mich. Agr. Exp. Sta. Tech. Bul. 132 (4th Rev.) (1949).
** Lunt et al., Conn. Agr. Exp. Sta. Bul. 541 (1950).
†† Bray, Ill. Agr. Exp. Sta. Mimeo. Circ. AG 878 (1940); AG 1028 (1942) for change in P test.
‡‡ Peech and English, Soil Sci., 57:167–195 (1944).
§§ Graham, Mo. Agr. Exp. Sta. Circ. 345 (1950).

The amount of change of soil pH with quantity of limestone applied depends on the soil type, particularly its exchange capacity and pH titration curve, but these factors are usually worked out in each laboratory in relation to the important local soil types. The lime requirement of a soil can also be determined by the more elaborate quantitative methods (¶ 4–64).

13–89. The pH preferences of various crops are outlined in Fig. 13–4. Some conditions require a limited application of lime. For example, soils below pH 5.0 to be planted to turfs that are to be watered extensively, should receive only a light dressing of 500 pounds of finely ground limestone per acre at seeding. The lime in the water will gradually bring the soil pH values up (often to too high values) and therefore heavy liming is avoided. For excessively acid potato soils (those showing manganese toxicity), a limited amount (500 to 1000 pounds per acre) of a finely ground limestone is applied.

13–90. The determination of soil pH for soil testing purposes may be by the usual glass electrode techniques (¶ 3–17) or by any of a number of systems of colorimetric pH indicators. The glass electrode is used in nearly all[46] soil testing laboratories for the determination of soil pH even on a mass production scale, because of its accuracy and because the determination can be made in the laboratory as rapidly as, or more rapidly than by colorimetric methods. The equilibrium pH methods for lime requirement (¶ 4–61) are as rapid as a simple pH measurement, and take into account the buffer capacity of the soil.

13–91. Colorimetric indicators are most useful for field testing kits and are also used in some soil testing laboratories. They give approximate but satisfactory results when properly used. The Purdue system uses 3 separate indicators, brom cresol green, chlor phenol red, and brom thymol blue, to cover the usual range of soil pH. Other systems, such as the Morgan,[47] use a mixture of the indicators brom cresol green, brom cresol purple, and cresol red (0.025 per cent each in water) to cover the pH range of 4 to 8. A similar mixed indicator (0.05 per cent brom cresol green, 0.10 per cent brom cresol purple, and 0.02 per cent cresol red in 40 per cent by volume of ethanol in water) has been used in the author's laboratory. Three drops of the indicator are placed in a white spot plate. Just enough air-dry soil is then sprinkled onto the indicator to remain rather wet with the indicator. After stirring with a spatula for a minute, the soil is moved with the spatula and the color is read against the white spotplate background. The following colors denote the soil pH:

---

[46] Nelson *et al., op. cit.*

[47] *Conn. Agr. Exp. Sta. Bul.* 392 (1937); Lunt *et al.,* Conn. Agr. Exp. Sta. Bul. 541 (1950).

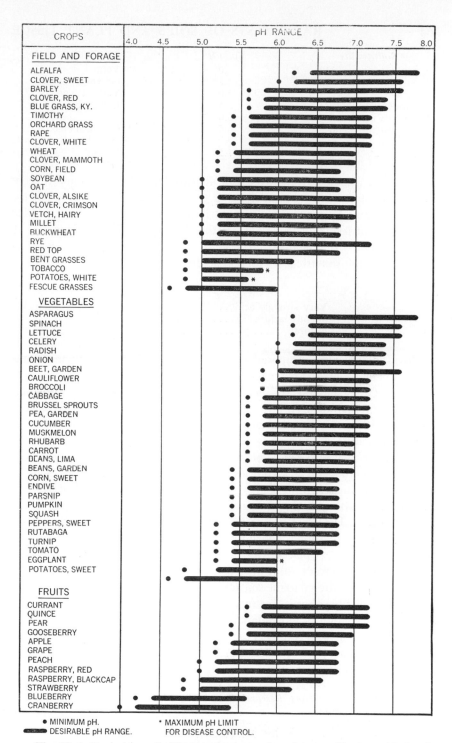

Fig. 13–4. Desirable soil pH range for a number of crops. (Courtesy National Plant Food Institute, Washington, D.C., arranged by Morgan, *Fert. Rev.*, 12, 2:7, 1937.)

Soil Acidity	Soil pH	Indicator Color
Very strongly acid	4.0	Yellow
Strongly acid	4.5	Greenish yellow
Acid	5.0	Yellowish green
Moderately acid	5.5	Light green
Slightly acid	6.0	Bluish green
Very slightly acid	6.5	Greenish blue
Neutral	7.0	Dark blue
Alkaline	7.5	Purple

The soil may also be covered over with neutral, ignited, and ground reagent grade precipitated $BaSO_4$ powder, so as to mask the soil and bring out the indicator color. A special 3-component indicator and ground and purified barite mineral for colorimetric pH testing is sold by Hellige, Inc., 3718 Northern Blvd., Long Island City, N.Y.

13–92. A colorimetric test[48] for soil acidity with a range of:

	Indicator color
Very strongly acid	Bright red
Slightly acid	Yellow
Neutral	Green

employs an indicator composed of 0.08 per cent Na-brom thymol blue, 0.04 per cent Na-methyl red, and 0.02 per cent methyl orange.

13–93. Other methods for measuring soil acidity include the thiocyanate test[49] and the sulfide test.[50] In the thiocyanate test, a 4 per cent KSCN solution in 95 per cent ethanol is shaken with an equal volume of field-moist (fairly dry) soil in a glass vial. On standing 10 minutes, acid mineral soils develop a pink to red color depending on the degree of acidity. Soils of pH 6.5 or above give a colorless solution. In the sulfide test, 9 ml of soil is placed in a 300-ml conical flask, 0.8 ml of a mixture of $BaCl_2 \cdot 2 H_2O\text{-}ZnS$ (both neutral and intimately ground together in the proportion 10 of $BaCl_2 \cdot 2 H_2O$ to 1 of ZnS by weight) is added, followed by 100 ml of water. The suspension is boiled for 1 minute then a moistened paper containing $Pb(OAc)_2$, is placed over the flask. Acid soil causes the liberation of H_2S which blackens the $Pb(OAc)_2$ paper. The degree of blackening with PbS is proportional to the soil acidity.

13–94. Soil Phosphorus Testing. The soil phosphorus test generally involves the formation of molybdophosphoric acid in acid solution with subsequent reduction with stannous ion (or organic reducing solution) to give molybdenum blue (¶ 7–4). The Purdue[51] phosphorus test is given as an example of this test.

---

[48] Yagi, H., *Agr. and Hort. Research Sta.,* 25:39 (1950); kindly demonstrated for the author by S. Aomine.

[49] Linsley and Bauer, *Ill. Agr. Exp. Sta. Cir.* 346 (1941).

[50] Truog, *Wis. Agr. Exp. Sta. Bul.* 312 (1920).

[51] Ohlrogge, *Purdue Agr. Exp. Sta. Bul.* 584 (1952).

13–95. A glass vial graduated at 10 ml is filled to the mark with molybdate reagent (¶ 13–36). One-half level teaspoon of soil (¼ teaspoon for greenhouse and garden soils) is added, and the vial is shaken vigorously for 1 minute. The solution is filtered into a funnel tube. To 5 ml of the filtrate is added about 1 cubic mm of dry powdered stannous chloride or stannous oxalate. The solution is mixed by rotation of the funnel tube, and the color produced is observed by comparison with the Phosphate Test Chart. More of the stannous chloride or oxalate is added to make certain that enough has been used. If the color becomes more intense, the latter reading is used. The range of the test is from a dark blue (abundant phosphorus) to colorless or a light yellow (low phosphorus supply). The test does not give reliable results on alkaline soils.

13–96. The most common tests for soil phosphorus involve the dilute acid extractable phosphorus, which is chiefly in calcium phosphate form. Other tests involve the extraction with solutions containing fluoride (¶ 7–82), in order to include some phosphorus forms other than the acid extractable. Testing for soil phosphorus is made difficult because in soils that are not acid, the acid soluble form may not be available. In other soils the fluoride extractable and easily oxidized organic forms of soil phosphorus may make substantial contributions to the phosphorus available to crops in a single season.

13–97. Soil Potassium Testing. The turbidimetric potassium cobaltinitrite test is used extensively. The results are affected by temperature, time of precipitation, particle size, and crystal form. A recent modification of this test is designed to reduce the effect of temperature.[52]

13–98. The Purdue potassium test is described as an example of this type of method. A glass vial graduated at 10 ml is filled to the mark with the sodium cobaltinitrite reagent (¶ 13–56). One level teaspoon of air-dried soil (½ teaspoonful for mucks, greenhouse and garden soils) is added, and the vial is shaken vigorously for 1 minute. The solution is filtered into a funnel tube. To 5 ml of the filtrate is added 2.5 ml of anhydrous isopropyl alcohol with the pipet, and the 2 solutions are mixed. After 3 minutes, the turbidity of the solution is compared with the standard potassium chart. The range of the test is from a clear solution (deficient supply) to a very turbid, dense precipitate (abundant supply).

13–99. Soil potassium tests ordinarily aim to measure the exchangeable potassium. Maintenance of a high level of exchangeable potassium is highly desirable for assurance of high yields. Acid extraction measures some potassium in addition to the exchangeable (¶ 6–83). The soil potassium that becomes available to a crop in a given year includes not only the exchangeable but a certain amount of the potassium released by current weathering.

[52] Olson, *S.S.S.A. Proc.,* 17:20 (1953).

In some soils and for some crops the potassium released by weathering is rather important. Substantial amounts of available potassium are supplied by some subsoils, whereas by others little is supplied. These variables may need consideration in the interpretation of the soil potassium test.

13–100. Soil Nitrogen and Organic Matter Testing. Protracted efforts have been made to measure the rate of nitrogen release (¶ 8–69) through biological nitrification.[53] In addition, considerable attention has been given in various countries to the partial oxidation of organic matter based on ammonia released in terms of available nitrogen. The design of a useful test for available nitrogen is very difficult because of the effect of climatic factors on the release of soil nitrogen. The climatic effect is greater on nitrogen release than on the availability of such elements as P or K. Also, chemical tests do not correlate well with biotic N release from fresh organic matter residues in soils because of C : N effects. Many laboratories therefore simply determine the organic matter content with the rapid chromic acid method (¶ 9–57) applied on a mass production basis, instead of attempting a direct estimation of the N released from the oxidizable organic fraction. A knowledge of the total organic matter content of soil aids materially the making of soil management recommendations. The immediately preceding cropping history must be taken into account *in addition to* any of the chemical tests.

13–101. Rapid tests for nitrate, ammonium, and nitrite nitrogen may also be made. They are generally of less value than the other tests, except that abnormally high or low results may be indicative. The level of these 3 forms of nitrogen in the soil is dependent on the soil, cropping, and climatic conditions prevailing immediately prior to the test.

13–102. Nitrates may be determined rapidly with brucine or diphenylamine. In the Morgan system[54] with diphenylamine, 1 drop of soil extract is placed on a spot plate, and 4 drops of the reagent (0.05 gm of diphenylamine in 25 ml concentrated H_2SO_4) are added. After 2 minutes the mixture is stirred and the intensity of the resulting blue color is determined with comparison to the color chart.

13–103. The active ammonium test as given by Spurway and Lawton[55] involves the addition of 1 drop of Nessler's solution to 3 drops of soil extract (Table 13–1) on a test plate. The color develops rapidly. If a brown precipitate forms, the soil extract is diluted and the test repeated.

13–104. The Morgan method is given as an example of nitrite nitrogen determination. Ten drops of soil extract (Table 13–1) are placed on a spot plate. One drop of nitrite reagent (1 gm of sulphanilic acid is dissolved by

[53] Russel *et al., Soil Sci.,* 19:381 (1925).

[54] Lunt *et al., The Morgan Soil Testing System,* Conn. Agr. Exp. Sta. Bul. 541 (1950).

[55] *Mich. Agr. Exp Sta. Tech. Bul.* 132 (4th Rev.) (1949).

heating in 100 ml of a saturated solution of NH_4Cl, then 1.5 gm of phenol is added followed by thorough mixing), 1 drop of $6 N$ HCl, and 4 drops of 15 per cent NaOH are added. The mixture is stirred, and let stand 1 minute. The resulting color ranges from yellowish orange for very high nitrite test, to a trace of yellowish tint for very low test.

13–105. Soil Calcium Testing. Calcium in soil testing is usually estimated turbidimetrically as the oxalate. This procedure is subject to errors due to different pH levels, presence of organic matter, and interfering ions. Calcium may also be determined as the stearate in the presence of citrate (Cornell)[56] or as the oleate (Missouri).[57] In the Michigan[58] system, 2 drops of ammonium oxalate (5 gm in 100 ml of distilled water) are added to 1 ml of soil extract in a small tube and mixed by shaking. A white precipitate indicates calcium, and the amount is determined by comparison to a turbidity chart.

13–106. The soil calcium test is generally high if the soil pH is properly adjusted. Ordinarily, therefore, the soil pH test obviates the need for testing soil calcium.

13–107. Soil Magnesium Testing. Magnesium in soil testing is usually determined by the titan yellow or thiazole yellow procedure. This involves the precipitation of $Mg(OH)_2$, which absorbs the dye to form a magnesium lake. In the Michigan[59] system, 1 drop of titan yellow solution (0.15 gm of titan yellow dye dissolved in a mixture of 90 ml of either ethyl or isopropyl alcohol, and 10 ml distilled water) is added to 1 ml of soil extract in a small tube and mixed by shaking. To this mixture is added 1 drop of 5 per cent NaOH solution and this is followed by thorough shaking. The magnesium test colors range from light orange to peach red, with a yellow color indicating no magnesium. In other procedures (Peech, Graham), a protective colloid (starch) is introduced to disperse the precipitate and intensify the color. Calcium and aluminum are added in a compensating solution to produce their maximum intensity of color, since their presence in varying amounts causes erratic results.

13–108. Soil magnesium levels are usually satisfactory if dolomitic limestone has been employed for adjustment of the soil pH. However, if calcic limestones are prevalent as a source of liming material in a locality, soil magnesium testing is essential, independently of soil pH testing.

13–109. Chloride, Sulfate and Sodium Testing. In saline and alkali soils the testing of soil chloride, sulfate, and sodium becomes important. The determination of soil chloride and sulfate is especially important also in connection with saline soils in commercial greenhouses where heavy fertili-

---

[56] Peech and English, *Soil Sci.,* 57:167 (1944).
[57] Graham, *Mo. Agr. Exp. Sta. Cir.* 345 (1950).
[58] Spurway and Lawton, *Mich. Agr. Exp. Sta. Tech. Bul.* 132 (1949).
[59] Spurway and Lawton, *Mich. Agr. Exp. Sta. Tech. Bul.* 132 (1949).

zation has been practiced. Tests for these constituents have been given (chloride, ¶ 10–94; sulfate, ¶ 10–102; and sodium, ¶ 5–81).

13–110. Biotic Soil Tests. Since the crop relation to soil is ultimately a biotic one, the most basic calibration of chemical soil tests must be with biotic tests. To make possible testing on an extensive scale, small-scale biotic systems have been devised as contrasted with the field plot test. The most noted of the small-scale biotic tests are the Mitscherlich[60] pot test and the Neubauer seedling cup.[61] The pot method for soil cultures has been described in detail.[62] Yield equations derived from field tests or pot tests can be projected into the quantity of nutrient elements evidently "available" from the untreated soil itself, and data are thereby provided for calibration of chemical soil tests. In general, biotic methods themselves do not fulfill the definition of soil testing (¶ 13–75) because of not being rapid and low in cost. They are even more costly than conventional long methods of soil chemical analysis, and thus must be employed strategically in calibration of soil tests.

QUESTIONS

1. Discuss the analogy in function between the soil testing laboratory and clinical testing and diagnosis in medicine.

2. What is the underlying assumption that forms the basis for rapid chemical testing of the sap of plant tissue as a means of diagnosing adequacy of plant nutrient supply?

3. Explain how a mistaken interpretation of plant sap tests might be made of abundance of 1 nutrient element in the soil supply when the growth of the plant is held back by a severe shortage of another nutrient element.

4. Explain what is indicated when the diphenylamine test gives a strong blue color on a slice of nodal corn tissue. Is the blue diphenylamine test obtained in such tissue as clover and asparagus? Explain.

5. Explain the principle and advantages of the pink powder test for nitrate in the sap of plants.

6. Summarize briefly the different procedures for testing for phosphorus in plant sap.

7. Summarize briefly the different procedures for testing for potassium in the sap of plants.

8. Why is it possible to determine the instantaneous oxygen activity of a soil by field colorimetric tests for ferric and ferrous iron in the HCl extract of the soil?

9. Why may the rapid imbibition of suspended chalk particles in a soil column surface be used as a measure of good soil aeration?

---

[60] Hoover and Norman, *Soil Sci.,* 53:329 (1942).

[61] Thornton, *Purdue Univ. Agr. Exp. Sta. Bul.* 399 (1935); McGeorge, *Soil Sci.,* 58:389 (1944).

[62] MacIntire and Winterberg, *Soil Sci.,* 62:33 (1946).

10. Why do soil tests not automatically provide specific recommendations for soil management without the intermediary of human judgment?

11. What 2 general types of soil pH tests are employed? Why is it that soil testing for calcium and magnesium is seldom practiced in routine?

12. What difficulties are presented in the extraction of "available" soil phosphorus?

13. What difficulties are presented in the extraction of "available" soil potassium?

14. Why is the determination of "available" soil nitrogen especially difficult?

15. Under what circumstances may analysis for chlorides, sulfates, and sodium be of interest in soil testing?

16. Discuss the relationship of biotic tests to soil chemical tests.

Boron Determinations
for Soils and Plant Tissue

. . . plants will not make growth without boron any more than . . . without phosphorus or potassium which they require in considerable amounts.

—TRUOG[1]

14–1. Of the 4 elements essential to plants that occur in soils principally as anions (N, P, S, and B), the one plants need in the smallest quantities is boron. (However, as will be pointed out in Chapter 15, molybdenum in soils is most available in anion form, and this element is needed by plants in still smaller quantity.) Like soil nitrogen and sulfur compounds, soil boron compounds of highest availability are in water soluble form. Hot water soluble soil boron was found[2] to be correlated with the boron content of red beet leaves, and such extraction appeared to be a better measure of available soil boron than acid soluble boron or total boron. Analyses for water soluble, acid soluble, and total boron for a large number of representative soils are published.[3]

14–2. The amount of water soluble boron in cultivated soils appears to be influenced more by the soil pH than any other factor, but is influenced also by the soil organic matter content, mineral colloid content, age of the soil, and by the type of irrigation water that has been employed. Significant positive correlation of water soluble boron was found[4] with soil pH values

---

[1] Statement before Wisconsin Canner's School, March 13, 1940.
[2] Berger and Truog, *J. Am. Soc. Agron.,* 32:297 (1940); Berger, *Adv. Agron.,* 1:321 (1949).
[3] Whetstone *et al.,* U.S.D.A. Tech. Bul. 797 (1942).
[4] Berger and Truog, *S.S.S.A. Proc.,* 10:113 (1946).

from pH 4.7 to 6.7, and negative correlation between pH 7.1 and 8.1. Although over-liming is known[5] to accentuate boron deficiency in accord with these findings, it has been shown[6] that the fixation of boron in water insoluble form is caused by the rise in pH independent of the presence of high activity of calcium ion. Acidification releases the boron fixed in the presence of high ^-OH activity.

14–3. Increasing the organic matter content in soil increases the water soluble boron, although a soil of higher organic matter content fixed more as the pH was raised.[6] This indicates that the organic matter is in active equilibrium with water soluble boron. Since a soil of pH value of near neutrality holds boron better than an acid soil, the low level of water soluble boron in old, acid, leached soils is explained. Fixation at pH values of 8 to 10 did not exceed 15 to 40 per cent of the water soluble boron, thus indicating that boron seldom will become deficient in alkaline soils, and may even become toxic in alkaline soils.

14–4. The condensation of the borate radical into long chains in the presence of calcium, increasing hydroxyl activity, and low moisture has been pointed out[7] as a possible mechanism for making boron less available under some circumstances. Marked decrease in boron availability under conditions of low soil moisture has been observed extensively. The behavior of boron in soils has been studied indirectly in simplified chemical systems involving pure chemicals[8] and soil organic matter[9] by observation of precipitation and solubility. Entry of boron into the structure of calcium silicates and calcium aluminosilicates was indicated. The magnitude of boron retention by humus systems and the chemical reactions between boron and dihydroxy organic compounds suggests[10] that soluble soil boron is fixed by diols such as of uronic acid of soil organic matter.

14–5. There are rather narrow limits between adequate amounts and toxic amounts of boron in soils. Boron toxicity has been a problem in connection with soils irrigated with waters[11] containing over 1 to 3 ppm of B, and the value for excellent irrigation water should be below 0.3 to 0.6 ppm (¶ 10–80). Boron toxicity occurred in soils fertilized with potash carrying a high boron content.[12] Toxicity resulted from use of boron in manure to repress fly larvae.[13]

14–6. Methods for Boron Determination. Boron in soils and plants can be determined titrimetrically (¶ 14–52) in macro and semimicro amounts,

[5] Naftel, *J. Am. Soc. Agron.,* 29:761 (1937).
[6] Olson and Berger, *S.S.S.A. Proc.,* 11:216 (1947).
[7] Colwell and Cummings, *Soil Sci.,* 57:37 (1944).
[8] Parks and Shaw, *S.S.S.A. Proc.,* 6:219 (1941).
[9] Drake *et al., J. Am. Soc. Agron.,* 33:454 (1941).
[10] Parks and White, *S.S.S.A. Proc.,* 16:298 (1952).
[11] Wilcox, U.S.D.A. Cir. 784 (1948).
[12] Conners and Fergus, *Ind. Agr. Exp. Sta. Bul.* 239 (1920).
[13] Cook and Wilson, *J. Agr. Res.,* 13:451 (1918).

and colorimetrically or spectroscopically (Chapter 18) in micro amounts. Biological assay of available soil boron also has been perfected.[14] Colorimetric methods have a distinct advantage for the determination of the micro amounts of boron of the order of 0.5 to 7 ugm, which are frequently derived from convenient sample weights of soils or plants. Both the curcumin (¶ 14–7) and the quinalizarin (¶ 14–17) colorimetric methods are adapted for either visual or photometric evaluation of the color. Because the chemical separations are easier, the colorimetric determinations are generally more convenient than the titrimetric method, even when the amount of boron is not a factor. The methods based on anthraquinones,[15] such as the quinalizarin and caramine[16] methods, all have their colors developed in concentrated H_2SO_4 and therefore temperature change causes great variation in colorimetric readings.

BORON DETERMINATION
(Colorimetrically with curcumin)

14–7. The curcumin procedure for boron has the advantages over the anthraquinone procedures of having a less corrosive solvent than concentrated H_2SO_4, nonsensitivity to small changes of temperature in the solution to be read, and a sharp spectral separation between the reagent color (absorption slight at 500 mu and higher), and the boron-dependent color (rosecyanine, 550 mu maximum absorption). The boron-dependent color develops from curcumin, extracted from its crude vegetable source, tumeric.[17] The formation of rosecyanine takes place in proportion to the B present, but requires the presence of 0.2 gm of oxalic acid. This amount of oxalic acid is not soluble in the aqueous $HCl-H_2C_2O_4$ solution ordinarily recommended except as a supersaturated solution or a suspension. In the improved[18] procedure detailed here, the combined curcumin-$H_2C_2O_4$ reagent in 95 per cent ethanol provides the required oxalic acid and the advantages of a single combined reagent. Colored lakes develop with curcumin in alkaline solution in the presence of Be, Al, Fe, or Mg, and therefore an acid medium must be maintained during color development. The presence of $H_2C_2O_4$ maintains sufficient acidity for the color development if the solution containing the boron is slightly acid, thus eliminating the need for addition of concentrated HCl in the procedure.

14–8. Nitrate interferes in the acid solution if there is over 20 ugm of N as nitrate in the 1-ml aliquot taken for analysis. Nitrates can be eliminated from the test solution by evaporation of an aliquot (to which suffi-

---

[14] Colwell, *Soil Sci.*, 62:43 (1946).
[15] Ellis *et al.*, *Anal. Chem.*, 21:1345 (1949).
[16] Hatcher and Wilcox, *Anal. Chem.*, 22:567 (1950).
[17] Naftel, *Ind. Eng. Chem.*, *A.E.*, 11:407 (1939).
[18] Dible *et al.*, *Anal. Chem.*, 26:418 (1954).

cient saturated water solution of $Ca(OH)_2$ has been added to make it alkaline[19]) and gentle ignition; the ash is taken up in 0.05 N HCl. According to Feigl,[20] Fe, Mo, Ti, and Zr interfere also, if present in unusual amounts (over about 300 ppm) in the boron solution to be analyzed.

APPARATUS

14–9. Needed are a photoelectric colorimeter with 540- or 550-mu light maximum for most sensitive range (0.2 to 1.5 ugm of B) and 580- or 600-mu light maximum for a less sensitive range (1 to 7 ugm of B); standardized colorimeter tubes; a boron-free glass beaker, 250-ml; pipets, 1-ml, 4-ml, 25-ml, and 50-ml; volumetric flasks, 1-liter, 500-ml, series of 50-ml; and a drying oven or bath, regulated at 55 ± 3°C.

REAGENTS

14–10. Ethanol, 95 per cent, A.R., is needed, redistilled if necessary to make it boron-free.

14–11. Curcumin-Oxalic Acid Reagent.[21] 0.04 gm of finely ground curcumin (Eastman Kodak No. 1179) and 5.0 gm of $H_2C_2O_4 \cdot 2 H_2O$ are dissolved in 100 ml of boron-free 95 per cent ethanol. This solution is stored in an amber bottle in a cool dark place. Because of the slow decomposition of curcumin, this reagent is made up fresh every few days. This may be extended to a week or more by storage in a refrigerator without undue exposure at room temperature.

14–12. Boron Standard Solution. A stock boric acid solution is prepared by dissolving 0.572 gm of dried reagent grade H_3BO_3 in 1 liter of distilled water, giving a 100 ugm of B per ml standard. A dilute stock solution is prepared by pipetting 50 ml of the first stock solution into a 500-ml volumetric flask and diluting it to volume with distilled water, giving a 10 ugm of B per ml standard. The dilute stock solution is employed for making up a series of standards, in 50-ml volumetric flasks, for the calibration curves, in accordance with Table 14–1.

PROCEDURE[22]

14–13. A 1-ml aliquot of slightly acid aqueous solution, containing 0.2 to 5 ugm of boron is transferred to a 250-ml boron-free glass beaker. (The same 1-ml pipet is employed to transfer standard and test solutions, and therefore no special volumetric calibration is needed; however, the 1-ml constant volume is critical.) Then 4 ml of the curcumin-oxalic acid solu-

[19] Gooch, *Am. Chem. J.*, 9:23 (1887).

[20] Tr. J. W. Matthews, *Spot Tests* (New York: Nordemann Publishing Company, Inc., 1937), p. 211.

[21] Dible *et al.*, *Anal. Chem.*, 26:418 (1954).

[22] Dible *et al.*, *Anal. Chem.*, 26:418 (1954).

TABLE 14–1

Appropriate concentration ranges of boron standard solutions
for curcumin and quinalizarin methods

Solution number	Volume of stock* solution diluted to 50 ml (ml)	Concentration obtained when diluted to 50 ml† (ugm of B/ml)	Concentration range and steps			
			Curcumin method		Quinalizarin method	
			540-mu light	580- to 600-mu light	Visual	Color-imeter
Blank	0.0	0.0	0.0	0.0	0.0	0.0
1	1.0	0.2	0.2	—	0.2	—
2	2.0	0.4	0.4	—	0.4	—
3	2.5	0.5	0.5	—	0.5	0.5
4	3.0	0.6	0.6	—	0.6	—
5	4.0	0.8	0.8	—	0.8	—
6	5.0	1.0	1.0	1.0	1.0	1.0
7	7.5	1.5	1.5	1.5	1.5	1.5
8	10.0	2.0	—	2.0	2.0	2.0
9	12.5	2.5	—	2.5	2.5	2.5
10	15.0	3.0	—	3.0	—	3.0
11	17.5	3.5	—	—	—	3.5
12	20.0	4.0	—	4.0	—	4.0
13	22.5	4.5	—	—	—	4.5
14	25.0	5.0	—	5.0	—	5.0
15	27.5	5.5	—	—	—	5.5
16	30.0	6.0	—	6.0	—	6.0
17	35.0	7.0	—	7.0	—	7.0

* Stock solution containing 10 ugm of B per ml.
† The ugm of B per determination, since 1 ml is taken. The ugm of B per ml of final solution is 1/11 these values, but all concentrations specified in procedures herein refer to the concentration in the 1-ml volume taken for analysis, not the final concentration.

tion is added and the 2 solutions are mixed by rotating the beaker. Finally, the solution is evaporated to dryness in an oven (or in a bath) regulated[23] at $55 \pm 3°C$, and the residue is baked at this temperature for 15 minutes to insure dryness. The colored substance, rosecyanine, is developed during the evaporation and drying.

14–14. The beaker containing the dried residue is cooled to room temperature. Then 25 ml of 95 per cent ethanol is added, the residue is triturated to extract the color, and the solution is filtered through a Whatman No. 2 filter paper directly into the colorimeter tube. (Slight boron contamination from the paper is not a factor here since the color-forming step is past.)

14–15. The color is read with a 540-mu light maximum within 2 hours,

---

[23] Naftel, *Ind. Eng. Chem.*, *A.E.*, 11:407 (1939); Hafford, Ph.D. thesis, Univ. Wis. (1942).

since rosecyanine gradually hydrolyzes to curcumin; this is noticeable after 2 hours. If the percentage transmission is too low (less than 25 to 30 per cent), indicating over 1.5 ugm of B, the solution is immediately reread with a 580- or 600-mu light maximum. Reference is made to the calibration curve corresponding to the light maximum employed for the determination, and the ugm of B contained in the 1-ml aliquot is thus determined.

ALTERNATIVE PROCEDURES

14–16. When an insufficient amount of boron is obtained in a 1-ml aliquot, the solution can be concentrated by evaporation after being made alkaline with $Ca(OH)_2$ solution,[24] and then dissolved in a small volume of HCl of sufficient strength to give a slightly acid solution.

BORON DETERMINATION
(Colorimetrically with quinalizarin)

14–17. The quinalizarin procedure is suitable for the determination of 0.2 to 8 ugm of B in the final aliquot. Careful regulation of the H_2SO_4 concentration in the final solution to 89 per cent has been considered necessary for reproducible color development. This is accomplished by obtaining the B in 1 ml of aqueous solution and subsequently adding 10 ml of the reagent in 98 per cent H_2SO_4. The intensity of coloration of quinalizarin is sensitive not only to H_2SO_4 concentration but also to temperature changes. The blue coloration of the quinalizarin-boric acid complex increases with decreasing temperature and increasing acid concentration, up to about 90 per cent. This is attributed[25] to increasing the distortion of the molecule rather than increasing the completeness of the reaction. The color may be read visually (0.2 to 2.5 ugm of B) or by means of a photoelectric colorimeter (0.5 to 8 ugm of B). Sensitivity of the quinalizarin method to H_2SO_4 concentration is greatly decreased[26] by increasing the quinalizarin concentration to 45 mgm per liter (instead of the 25 mgm generally employed[27]). Ordinary concentrated H_2SO_4 (96 ± 1 per cent) can then be substituted for the 98 per cent H_2SO_4 without appreciably decreasing the sensitivity of the method; and 2.5 ugm of F per ml of test solution does not interfere with the boron determination.

APPARATUS

14–18. Needed apparatus consists of stoppered 20 × 100 mm shell vials for visual comparison or colorimeter tubes and photoelectric colorimeter

---

[24] Gooch, *Am. Chem. J.,* 9:23 (1887).
[25] Berger and Truog, *Soil Sci.,* 57:30 (1944).
[26] MacDougall and Biggs, *Anal. Chem.,* 24:566 (1952).
[27] Olson and Berger, *S.S.S.A. Proc.,* 11:216 (1947).

equipped with 620-mu light maximum, a 1-ml pipet, and a dispenser for the quinalizarin-H$_2$SO$_4$ solution (Fig. 14–1).

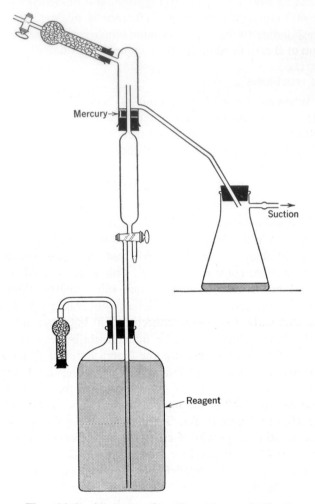

Fig. 14–1. Apparatus for dispensing quinalizarin-H$_2$SO$_4$ solution with protection from moisture of air. The volume of the reagent is exactly reproducible, though not necessarily exactly 10 ml. (After MacDougall and Biggs, *Anal. Chem.,* 24:566, 1952.)

14–19. The glassware must be boron-free, such as Kavalier or Corning 728. Ordinary soft glass may be used for most of the reagents. Borosilicate glassware such as Pyrex is not used. All glassware is weathered in strong HCl prior to use.

14–20. Standardization of Colorimeter Tubes. In the standardization of colorimeter tubes, a large number of clean, unscratched (preferably new) tubes made of boron-free glass is taken for preliminary testing. To each tube, 10 to 15 ml of the quinalizarin-sulfuric acid solution (¶ 14–27) is added. The tubes and contents are allowed to stand at room temperature for at least 1 hour to insure uniform temperatures and absence of air bubbles. The outside of each tube is wiped clean with a cloth dampened slightly with distilled water, and then polished with a clean, dry, lint-free towel. With a 620-mu light maximum in the colorimeter, the first tube is inserted in it and the galvanometer is adjusted to give a reading of between 60 and 100 per cent transmission. The first tube is rotated to give a reading not subject to small changes in the orientation of the tube, and this orientation is marked on the tube. Each successive tube is placed in the colorimeter and rotated to a position insensitive to rotation, the galvanometer is read to the nearest 0.25 per cent transmission, and the results are recorded. Between each successive tube reading the colorimeter is adjusted to read exactly the same as with the first tube observed.

14–21. A working set of tubes that agree within 1 or 2 per cent transmission is selected. This selected set of tubes is rechecked (¶ 14–20), and the tube representing the mode of the readings is selected as the primary standard. The other tubes are then reread against the primary standard tube, and the deviations from the standard in percentage transmission are recorded respectively for each tube. The deviation for each tube is applied as a correction each time it is used for a determination.

14–22. The high refractive index of the concentrated sulfuric acid solution magnifies the effect of scratches on the tubes. Care therefore must be taken *not to scratch the tubes in any way*. In cleaning the tubes, the sulfuric acid is poured out and the tubes are rinsed out with distilled water. A brush is not used in the cleaning process. Occasional restandardization of the tubes (¶ 14–21) is made as a precaution.

REAGENTS

14–23. Needed reagents consist of brom phenol blue indicator, standard boron solution (¶ 14–12) and the following 2 reagents.

14–24. Sulfuric Acid, 98 $\pm$ 0.5 Per Cent. A 454-gm (1-pound) bottle of Merck reagent grade fuming H_2SO_4 is added to 978 gm of Grasselli 95 per cent (concentrated) H_2SO_4 contained in a soft glass bottle. The solutions are thoroughly mixed by rotation of the bottle. The concentration is determined by weighing about 2 gm of the acid into a covered weighing bottle, pouring the acid into a 400-ml beaker containing about 200 ml of boiled and cooled water, the bottle and cover being quickly immersed. The acid is titrated with 1 N NaOH with brom phenol blue as an indicator. Both hydrogens are replaced:

$$\% \ H_2SO_4 = \text{meq NaOH} \times \frac{4.9}{s} \tag{14-1}$$

in which s is the gm of H_2SO_4 taken.

14–25. The quantities of the 2 acids taken may with practice be selected so that the mixture comes out 98 per cent each time. Proportionately more fuming or 95 per cent H_2SO_4 is added as needed to bring the concentration to 98 ± 0.5, and the titration is then repeated. If the acid concentration is much outside this range, the quinalizarin color development is not a maximum (¶ 14–17).

14–26. Quinalizarin-Sulfuric Acid Solution. For *visual* measurement, 5 mgm of quinalizarin is dissolved per liter of 98 per cent H_2SO_4 (prepared above). The reagent is stored in a boron-free glass bottle under a dry atmosphere. Incoming air is passed through an anhydrous $CaCl_2$ tube (Fig. 14–1).

14–27. For *photoelectric colorimeter* measurement, 25 mgm of quinalizarin is dissolved per liter of 98 per cent H_2SO_4, and stored as in the preceding paragraph.

PROCEDURE[28]

14–28. Visual Comparison. One ml of the standard or test solution (Table 14–1) is placed in the 20 × 100 mm soft glass vial, with care to measure exactly the 1 ml with the same pipet for all standards and test samples. Then exactly 10 ml of the 98 per cent sulfuric acid solution containing 5 mgm of quinalizarin per liter is added. The vial is stoppered immediately and the contents mixed by whirling gently, with care not to allow any of the acid solution to come in contact with the rubber stopper.

14–29. The concentration in the test sample is determined by direct comparison to the series of tubes containing 0.0 to 2.5 ugm of B (Table 14–1). In making the comparisons, the stoppers are removed so that the solutions can be viewed from the top.

14–30. The acid solutions are somewhat hygroscopic, and therefore become diluted by moisture in the atmosphere when the tubes are opened for comparisons. New color standards must be made up from time to time depending on how frequently the tubes are opened.

14–31. Colorimeter Comparison. Exactly 1 ml of the standard or test solution (Table 14–1) is transferred to a tube by means of the same 1-ml

[28] Berger and Truog, *Ind. Eng. Chem., A.E.,* 11:540 (1939); McHargue and Hodgkiss, *J.A.O.A.C.,* 25:311 (1942); Berger and Truog, *Soil Sci.,* 57:25 (1944); Olson and Berger, *S.S.S.A. Proc.,* 11:216 (1947). Dr. R. V. Olson of Kansas State College generously assisted with the preparation of this section.

pipet. Then exactly 10 ml of the 98 per cent sulfuric acid solution containing 25 mgm of quinalizarin per liter is added to each colorimeter tube. The tube is stoppered immediately and the contents is mixed by whirling the tube gently. Care is taken not to allow any of the acid solution to come in contact with the rubber stopper. The tubes are allowed to come to room temperature by standing for at least 2 hours. The outsides of the tubes are cleaned with a cloth moistened in distilled water followed by polishing with a dry lint-free towel.

14–32. The blank (0.0 ugm of B) is placed in the colorimeter with 620-mu light maximum, and the colorimeter is adjusted to give 100 per cent light transmission. The percentage transmission is read for all of the other tubes to the nearest 0.25 per cent transmission. Then the readings are corrected with the corresponding tube correction (¶ 14–21). Duplicates should agree within 0.5 per cent transmission.

14–33. The Standard Curve. Since the room temperature variation causes a shift in the standard curve, 1 of the standard boron solutions (containing 1.0 to 1.5 ugm of B) is saved and designated the "standard tube" for correcting the curve to the original temperature for each set of determinations. The "standard tube" is placed in the colorimeter at the beginning of each set of determinations of test solutions and the percentage transmission is adjusted to read the same as was obtained in making up the standard curve, thus correcting the entire curve to the temperature of the test solutions. The percentage transmission readings are plotted against ugm of B. The color is stable except for the effect of moisture absorbed from the air.

14–34. The calibration curve obtained varies slightly with changes in the amounts of sulfuric acid and quinalizarin in the solutions so that it is necessary to make a new curve each time a new 98 per cent sulfuric acid-quinalizarin solution is prepared.

WATER SOLUBLE BORON IN SOILS

14–35. The range of water soluble boron in mineral soils of the humid region is generally from 0.2 to 1.5 ppm, and ranges on up to 2 or more ppm in muck soils and down to 0.2 in fairly fertile sandy soils. Soils of the semiarid regions may fall in the same ranges but occasionally contain 10 to 40 ppm or more. The water soluble boron is considered to be the form immediately "available" to plants. The boron extracted in a 1 : 2 soil : water ratio is given as the common procedure; that extracted by leaching is given in the alternative procedure. The analytical determination may be either by the curcumin (¶ 14–13) or quinalizarin (¶ 14–28) procedure.

14–36. The level of water soluble boron may vary greatly over short distances in the field. Sampling at the time a growing crop such as alfalfa is on the field permits observations of areas of acute boron deficiency.

Separate soil samples are drawn from suspected deficient areas and compared to areas on which normal growth occurs.

14–37. Nitrates are generally below interfering levels of 40 pp2m in soil samples taken in the spring before nitrification has begun or taken under a growing crop. Fallowed or incubated soils may develop sufficient amounts of nitrate to cause interference and nitrate must be removed (¶ 14–43).

APPARATUS

14–38. Needed in addition to apparatus for the colorimetric determination are a torsion balance, 125-ml boiling flasks (boron-free glass) fitted with a 1-hole stopper and condenser, 100-ml centrifuge tubes and centrifuge, a 20-ml pipet, 9-cm porcelain evaporating dishes, small glass funnels, and 9-cm filter paper (boron-free, E and D or Whatman No. 2).

REAGENTS

14–39. Reagents needed include distilled water and $1 \ N \ CaCl_2$ for extraction for the curcumin determinative procedure, unless soil nitrates exceed 20 ppm. In the latter case, additional reagents needed include approximately $0.1 \ N$ HCl and saturated $Ca(OH)_2$ (protected from CO_2). In preparation for the quinalizarin determinative procedure, $0.36 \ N \ H_2SO_4$ is needed instead of $0.1 \ N$ HCl.

PROCEDURE[29]

14–40. Equilibrium Extraction. To a 20-gm sample of air-dried and sieved soil placed in a 125-ml boiling flask, a 40-ml volume of distilled water is added, and a reflux condenser is attached. (Five or 10 gm or other weight of soil sample may be taken, so long as the soil : water ratio is kept at 1 : 2.) The suspension is boiled for 5 minutes and allowed to cool, and the condenser is disconnected.

14–41. A blank is determined by placing 40 ml of water in the extraction flask and boiling for 5 minutes as in the soil extraction. This solution is carried through all steps in the subsequent procedure.

14–42. The soil suspension is transferred to a centrifuge tube, 2 or 4 drops (not to exceed 5 drops) of a $1 \ N$ solution of $CaCl_2$ is added, and the suspension is centrifuged for 5 to 10 minutes. In lieu of centrifuging, the $CaCl_2$-treated suspension may be filtered.

14–43. For the curcumin determinative procedure, 1 ml of the clear supernatant liquid is taken directly for the test (¶ 14–13) unless soil nitrates exceed 20 ppm, in which case the solution must be made alkaline, evaporated to dryness, and ignited as in the quinalizarin procedure.

14–44. For the quinalizarin determinative procedure, a 20-ml aliquot of

---

[29] Essential features are of the procedure of Berger and Truog, *Soil Sci.,* 57:32 (1944).

the clear supernatant solution is transferred by means of a pipet to a porcelain evaporating dish, 2 ml of saturated $Ca(OH)_2$ solution is added, and the entire solution is evaporated to dryness on a steam hot plate. It is essential that the extract be alkaline before evaporation so that, if the soil is extremely acid or has had acid treatments, the H_3BO_3 will not volatilize. If the acid treatments have been such as to exceed the 2 ml of $Ca(OH)_2$ solution, more of the latter is added to insure alkalinity.

14–45. The residue is ignited gently to destroy nitrates and all organic matter. It is then cooled and 5 ml of approximately $0.36\ N\ H_2SO_4$ is employed if the quinalizarin procedure is to be employed (¶ 14–28). Five ml of $0.1\ N$ HCl is added if the curcumin procedure is to be employed (¶ 14–13). The residue is triturated thoroughly with a policeman to dissolve all soluble matter. The solution is filtered through a 9-cm filter paper on a small funnel. A 1-ml aliquot of the clear filtrate is taken for color development.

14–46. Calculation of Results. The ppm of water soluble B in soil is calculated from the ugm of B in solution, minus the blank, by means of the following equation:

$$\text{ppm of water soluble B in soil} = \text{ugm B in 1 ml of solution tested}$$
$$\times \frac{40\ \text{ml extractant}}{20\ \text{gm soil}}$$
$$\times \frac{1}{\text{ml extractant represented in test}}$$
$$(14\text{--}2)$$

ALTERNATIVE PROCEDURES

14–47. Extraction with a more dilute soil : water ratio, such as $1:5$,[30] causes an increase in the B extracted, in contrast to the behavior of simple water soluble anions such as nitrate (¶ 14–1). An equilibrium apparently exists between the soil boron and the water solution (¶ 14–2, 14–49).

14–48. In a continuous leaching procedure,[31] the soil sample is placed in a soxlet thimble supported in the neck of a Kjeldahl type flask made of boron-free glass. Boiling the solution in the flask drives steam into a condenser in the top of the flask that drops the water into the thimble. Leaching for 6 hours results in extraction of as much boron as 12 or 24 hours, indicating completeness of extraction.

14–49. The boron extracted by continuous leaching, L, is related to the equilibrium extracted boron, E (¶ 14–40),

$$E = 0.24\ L + 0.01 \qquad (14\text{--}3)$$

A correlation coefficient of 0.94 was noted. The quantity L is not particu-

[30] Haas, *Soil Sci.*, 58:123 (1944).
[31] McClung, *S.S.S.A. Proc.*, 15:268 (1951).

larly dependent on the quantity of soil in ratio to solvent, and decreases by an amount equal to the boron removed by cropping ($r = 0.89$). As long as 3 months may be required for re-establishment of the equilibrium level of boron after it has been lowered by cropping (as measured by the continuous leaching method). The continuous leaching method may offer a more absolute measure of the quantity of boron available to plants than an equilibrium extraction, although the latter can be equally well calibrated for crop responses to boron.

14–50. Water soluble boron has also been extracted[32] with a 1 : 1.5 soil : water ratio and boiling for 15 minutes; followed by filtration and 3 successive similar extractions with a 1 : 1 soil : water ratio. Approximately 60 per cent of the boron extracted was obtained in the first of the 4 equilibrium extractions, compared to equilibrium extractable boron of 24 per cent of that extracted by continuous leaching (¶ 14–49).

ACID SOLUBLE BORON[33]

14–51. Treatment of the soil with 85 per cent H_3PO_4 extracts the boron present in the organic colloids and precipitated forms, but excludes that in tourmaline (3.5 per cent B) and other resistant borosilicate minerals. Other acids, such as HCl and H_2SO_4, are less satisfactory. The acid soluble boron averages 17 ppm for 203 soils and is a small fraction of the total for stony mineral soils, approximately half for many fine-textured mineral soils, and a large fraction of the total for soils that are high in mineral and organic colloids.

14–52. The titration (¶ 14–58) of H_3BO_3 requires 0.1 to 2 mgm of B. It is based on the formation of a complex between boric acid and mannite that permits titration of the first hydrogen of boric acid with a standard hydroxide solution. Interfering substances include other weak acids, 4-valent germanium, and hexavalent tellurium,[34] all of which are removed by steam distillation of H_3BO_3 as the methyl ester (¶ 14–56) or are ordinarily rare in the preparations from soils or plants.

APPARATUS

14–53. Needed are a round-bottom 500-ml extraction flask with short neck (all glassware should be boron-free), 250-ml beaker, a platinum dish, alcohol "steam" distillation apparatus, a buret, and a pH meter.

REAGENTS

14–54. Reagents needed include 85 per cent H_3PO_4, boron-free anhydrous methanol, 2 N and 0.1 N HCl, 0.5 N, 0.2 N and 0.02 N NaOH

---

[32] Whetstone *et al.*, U.S.D.A. Tech. Bul. 797 (1942).
[33] Whetstone *et al.*, U.S.D.A. Tech. Bul. 797 (1942).
[34] Eaton and Wilcox, U.S.D.A. Tech. Bul. 696 (1939).

(carbonate-free, the latter standardized), saturated $Ca(OH)_2$, neutral mannite, and brom thymol blue indicator.

14–55. Extraction. A 50-gm sample of air-dry soil that has passed a 2-mm sieve, is placed in a 500-ml short necked, round bottom, flask. Then 75 to 100 ml of 85 per cent H_3PO_4 is added, the amount of acid depending upon the composition of the soil. Sandy soils require less than soils high in bases and carbonate. The soil and acid are thoroughly mixed and heated on a steam bath overnight. Any lumps are disintegrated by means of a stirring rod, and the mixture is cooled. A blank is run on the reagents.

14–56. Distillation. Fifty to 100 ml of anhydrous methanol is added to the cooled digest, the flask is then connected to the distillation set up, and the mixture is agitated. The anhydrous alcohol in the still reservoir should be boiling when the digestion flask is connected to prevent the soil mixture from stopping up the inlet tube. The methyl borate is "steam-distilled" (with alcohol vapors from the reservoir) until about 500 ml of distillate has been collected. During the major portion of the distillation, the volume of the mixture in the digestion flask is kept constant by regulating the burners. Toward the end the volume may be somewhat decreased.

14–57. Ignition. The distillate is made just alkaline to brom thymol blue with 0.2 N NaOII solution, and then 2 ml of saturated $Ca(OH)_2$ is added. The methanol is then distilled off and recovered. The aqueous residue is transferred to a platinum dish, evaporated to dryness, and gently ignited to destroy the organic matter.

14 58. Titration. The residue is taken up in water and transferred to a 250-ml beaker or conical flask, the dish being rinsed with a few drops of 2 N HCl. The solution is diluted to 150 ml, 2 or 3 drops of 1 per cent brom thymol blue indicator solution are added, and the solution is acidified with 2 N HCl. The solution is then boiled to expel CO_2 and more acid is added as necessary to maintain slight acidity. The flask is then cooled by immersion in cold water. The solution is titrated, brom thymol blue indicator or a glass electrode pH meter being employed. To perform the titration, the solution is adjusted to a definite pH that is near neutrality with 0.5 N NaOH (carbonate-free), 0.1 N HCl, and finally with 0.02 N NaOH. Then 5 gm of neutral mannite is added, and the solution is titrated with standard 0.02 N NaOH to exactly the initial pH. The NaOH is standardized against known amounts of H_3BO_3 in the same manner.

ALTERNATIVE PROCEDURE

14–59. Colorimetric Determination. The residue from evaporation of the distillate may be dissolved and a small aliquot used for colorimetric de-

---

[35] Whetstone *et al.,* U.S.D.A. Tech. Bul. 797 (1942).

termination of boron by means of the curcumin (¶ 14–13) or quinalizarin (¶ 14–28).

TOTAL BORON IN SOILS

14–60. The total boron content of 118 soils averaged[36] 30 ppm. The concentration in igneous rocks averaged[37] 10 ppm, and in sea water,[38] 4.5 ppm. The total boron in soils ranged from 4 to 98 ppm, and fine-textured humid soils analyzed about 30 to 60 ppm. Sandy soils often have as low as 2 to 6 ppm. Of the total, that portion that is strong acid insoluble is attributable to tourmaline (¶ 14–51).

APPARATUS

14–61. Needed apparatus includes an analytical balance, a platinum crucible, a 250-ml beaker and glass cover (boron-free glassware throughout), a 500-ml volumetric flask, 100-ml centrifuge tubes and centrifuge, a 600-ml beaker, a rubber policeman, a platinum dish, a funnel, 9-cm boron-free filter paper, and a 500-ml graduated cylinder.

REAGENTS

14–62. Needed reagents include anhydrous Na_2CO_3, approximately 4 N H_2SO_4 (50 ml of concentrated H_2SO_4 to 400 ml of water), 0.1 N HCl (curcumin procedure), and boron-free ethanol or methanol (redistilled in boron-free glassware, if necessary). For the quinalizarin procedure, approximately 0.36 N H_2SO_4 is employed instead of 0.1 N HCl.

PROCEDURE[39]

14–63. Fusion. A 0.5-gm sample of a soil that has passed a 0.16-mm (100 meshes per inch) sieve is placed in a platinum crucible. Then 3 gm of anhydrous Na_2CO_3 is placed in the crucible and mixed with the sample with a glass rod. The mixture is fused over a Meker burner until the reaction is complete, and then the crucible is cooled and placed in a 250-ml beaker containing about 50-ml of distilled water. The beaker is covered with a glass, and 4 N H_2SO_4 is added from time to time (about 14 ml of 4 N H_2SO_4 is required) until the melt has disintegrated and the solution has a pH of 6.5 or below (tested with brom thymol blue employed as an external indicator). The melt is triturated from time to time with a rubber policeman to hasten the disintegration.

14–64. With each set of determinations a duplicate set of blanks is run

---

[36] Whetstone, *et al.,* U.S.D.A. Tech. Bul. 797 (1942).

[37] Clarke and Washington, U.S. Geol. Surv., Prof. Paper 127 (1924).

[38] Moberg and Harding, *Sci.,* 77:510 (1933).

[39] Fusion and separation after Berger and Truog, *Soil Sci.,* 57:25 (1944), as slightly modified by Dible *et al., Anal. Chem.,* 26:418 (1954).

by the addition of all reagents except the soil, the same procedure being carried out as with the soil. The blank is employed for the 100 per cent transmission setting to find the ugm of B found for the soil.

14–65. The resulting suspension is transferred to a 500-ml volumetric flask, the beaker and crucible being washed several times with distilled water and the washings being added to the flask. The total volume of the solution should not exceed 150 ml. Then methanol or ethanol is added to the flask to make a volume of nearly 500 ml and the contents are mixed thoroughly. Flecks of Na_2CO_3 are added with mixing until the solution is slightly alkaline. Then the solution is brought to full volume with alcohol. During this time the excess of Na_2SO_4 is thrown out of solution. The suspension is centrifuged (or filtered) until the supernatant liquid is clear.

14–66. A 400-ml aliquot of the clear supernatant solution is placed in a 600-ml beaker and 100 ml of distilled water is added to prevent subsequent precipitation. The solution is evaporated to a small volume, then transferred to a platinum dish and finally evaporated to dryness and ignited carefully. The dish and residue are cooled and then 5 ml of 0.1 N HCl (5 ml of 0.36 N H_2SO_4 for the quinalizarin procedure, ¶ 14–28) is added and the residue triturated thoroughly with a policeman. This solution is then filtered and a 1-ml aliquot is taken for the boron determination with curcumin (¶ 14–13).

14–67. Calculation of Results. The ppm of total boron in soil is determined as follows:

$$\text{ppm B in soil} = \text{ugm B per ml in solution tested} \times 12.5 \quad (14\text{–}4)$$

when the factor 12.5 represents:

$$\frac{5 \text{ ml final solution}}{0.5 \text{ gm soil}} \times \frac{500 \text{ ml volume}}{400 \text{ ml evaporated}}$$

TOTAL BORON IN PLANTS

14–68. The range of boron contents of plants is wide, but 4 to 10 ppm can be taken as typical for cereals such as oats, 20 to 50 ppm for legumes such as alfalfa, and 20 to 100 for crops such as turnips and beets. The content in plants that are deficient in boron varies widely with the plant part and the species. A content of 8 ppm has been shown[40] to be the content in the apical portion of boron-deficient alfalfa plants, whereas the lower part of the plant contained 30 ppm. This result emphasizes the need for care in systematic sampling of plant parts for boron analysis, since boron is not very mobile in the plant. A content of 28 to 30 ppm has been reported to the critical content in red clover.[41] In the following procedure

---

[40] Dible and Berger, *S.S.S.A. Proc.*, 16:60 (1952).
[41] Tucker and Smith, *S.S.S.A. Proc.*, 16:252 (1952).

the plant is ground and ashed, the boron in the ash is extracted with dilute acid, and finally the boric acid is separated by a filtration step without distillation.

APPARATUS

14–69. Needed apparatus for the ashing and extraction consists of a 9-cm porcelain evaporating dish, a flame or muffle furnace, 10-ml and 1-ml pipet, a rubber policeman, a small centrifuge tube and centrifuge or a funnel, and 9-cm filter paper. A Christy mill is employed for the tissue grinding.

REAGENTS

14–70. Reagents needed for the extraction and preparation of plant tissue for the analysis include 0.1 N HCl (0.36 N H_2SO_4 for quinalizarin procedure) and solid $Ca(OH)_2$ for use with seed tissue.

PROCEDURE[42]

14–71. Ignition. A 0.50-gm sample of oven-dry and finely ground plant tissue is placed in a porcelain evaporating dish. Vegetative tissue ordinarily contains enough bases to prevent loss of B on ignition;[43] for seeds, particularly oily seeds, a little base such as $Ca(OH)_2$ may be added. The tissue is ignited gently to a white or gray ash, over an open flame or in a muffle furnace at 550°C.

14–72. Extraction. The dish and contents are cooled and then 10.0 ml of 0.1 N HCl (or approximately 0.36 N H_2SO_4 for the quinalizarin procedure) is pipetted into the dish, and the residue is triturated with a policeman. After the suspension is filtered or centrifuged until clear, it is ready for the boron determination. An aliquot of 1.0 ml is taken for either the curcumin or quinalizarin procedure (¶ 14–13 or 14–28).

14–73. With each set of determinations, 2 reagent duplicate blanks are carried throughout the procedure, and the ugm found in the blank is subtracted from that found in the sample.

14–74. Calculation of Results. The content of boron in the plant tissue is obtained as follows:

$$\text{ppm B in plant tissue} = \text{ugm B in 1 ml solution tested} \times 20 \quad (14\text{–}5)$$

in which the factor 20 arises from 10 ml solution/0.5 gm sample.

ALTERNATIVE PROCEDURES

14–75. A plant tissue sample of 10 to 15 gm may be treated[44] with 75 ml

---

[42] Dible *et al., Anal. Chem.,* 26:418 (1954).
[43] Berger and Truog, *Ind. Eng. Chem., A. E.,* 11:540 (1939), *Soil Sci.,* 57:25 (1944); McHargue and Hodgkiss, *J.A.O.A.C.,* 24:518 (1941).
[44] Whetstone *et al.,* U.S.D.A. Tech. Bul. 797 (1942).

of H_3PO_4 and the H_3BO_3 immediately distilled from the mixture as for acid soluble boron (¶ 14–55). Also, the plant tissue may be ashed followed by determination by titration.[45]

14–76. Boron has been determined[46] on fresh strips of plant tissue without the necessity for ashing. The direct determination was preferred because of noted losses of boron on ignition of organic materials at temperatures as low as 100°C, possibly as volatile esters in organic constituents of the plants, and also because of the boron contamination noted even in the double acid washed filter paper. The procedure was to cut 5-cm strips from leaves and to determine the color by addition of the curcumin directly to the strips. Results were reported as ugm of B per 10 cm² of leaf tissue.

QUESTIONS

1. What 4 elements essential to plants normally occur in soils as anions?

2. Which of these anions occurs in soils largely in water soluble form?

3. Of which of these anions can the water soluble form be correlated very closely with plant response?

4. State the relationship of boron availability in a given soil to hydroxyl ion activity adjusted with NaOH.

5. Because of the reversion of boron compounds to water insoluble forms in alkaline pH ranges, is boron likely to be deficient in alkaline soils?

6. List the chief methods by which boron has been determined commonly.

7. Name the 2 most commonly used colorimetric methods for boron.

8. What is the principle utilized in obtaining 2 concentration ranges in the curcumin method for boron determination?

9. What are the effects of sulfuric acid concentration and temperature on the blue color intensity of the quinalizarin-boric acid molecule?

10. What is the purpose of the addition of $Ca(OH)_2$ before evaporation of the boron solution derived from acid extraction of plant ash or from the fusion analysis?

11. State the quantitative relation between equilibrium-extracted water soluble boron from soils (1 : 2 soil : water ratio) to the water extractable boron obtained by continuous leaching.

12. State the general concentration ranges of boron in soils in (a) water soluble form, (b) acid soluble form, (c) total.

13. How can the content of the mineral tourmaline of soils be estimated by boron analysis?

14. What is the normal boron content as ppm of tissue of different classes of plants?

---

[45] Wilcox, *Ind. Eng. Chem., A.E.,* 12:341 (1940).
[46] Winsor, *Anal. Chem.,* 20:176 (1948).

15

Iron, Manganese, Copper, Zinc, Molybdenum, and Cobalt Determinations

More minor elements are found to be essential to plants as methods are refined.

—A TREND IN MINOR ELEMENT CHEMISTRY

15–1. The elements needed by plants only in trace amounts—*minor elements* in amounts but not in importance—are iron, manganese, copper, zinc, molybdenum, cobalt (considered here), and boron (considered in Chapter 14). Sometimes magnesium, sodium[1] (Chapters 5 and 11), and sulfur (Chapters 10 and 11) are also considered to be minor elements. Cobalt is unlikely to be deficient enough in soils to affect plant growth, but it is important in animal feeds, which are supplied with it by plant uptake from soils. For this reason the soil chemist is sometimes called on for soil and plant analyses for cobalt (¶ 15–115).

15–2. The 6 elements, Fe, Mn, Cu, Zn, Mo, and Co, when added to soils in various moderately soluble compounds, tend to revert largely to forms of much lower solubility and availability than common exchangeable cations such as calcium and magnesium (Chapter 5). The extent and rapidity of this conversion depends upon the soil pH. Increasing soil acidity favors higher activity of all of them except Mo, which becomes less active, possibly by precipitation as the extremely insoluble MoS_2 (molybdenite) and MoO_3. Increasing soil pH, particularly above pH 7, favors their conversion to oxides, hydroxides, and silicates, in which form the activity of all but Mo

---

[1] Volk, *J. Am. Soc. Agron.*, 37:821 (1945).

decreases toward the point of deficiency in plants. Molybdenum appears to go over to anionic molybdate form of sufficient activity to be adequately available or even toxic.

15–3. The chemistry of soil availability of these 6 elements largely remains to be worked out. The water soluble and exchangeable forms are, of course, assumed to be readily available. But other soil forms are of sufficient activity to be important in the nutrition of crop plants. Thus dilute acid soluble and easily reducible iron and manganese are determined. Total and strong acid soluble copper, zinc, and cobalt appear to be related to availability of these elements in soils. Total molybdenum has been determined as a measure of the adequacy of supply of this element in soils.

15–4. The chief methods for the determination of these elements are spectrochemical and polarographic. Of the spectrochemical methods, the absorption spectrophotometric methods are considered in this chapter, whereas the emission spectrophotometric and spectrographic methods are considered in Chapter 18. The polarographic method is considered in Chapter 16.

15–5. First the chemical *determination* is described for an element and then consideration is given various methods for *extraction* of the element from soil. Procedures for extraction from plant tissue are given in Chapter 12. A systematic procedure for 12 nutritionally important elements in plant tissue including the 6 involved in this chapter has been described.[2]

IRON DETERMINATION
(Colorimetrically as *o*-phenanthroline red ferrous complex[3])

15–6. Procedures are given here for iron (in soils) that is exchangeable, readily soluble in dilute acids, or easily reducible. Iron determination by orthophenanthroline, as described here, is a sensitive and fitting method for the small amounts likely to be extracted for these analyses or from plants (¶ 12–19). That extracted from soils is readily determined with SCN (¶ 13–71, 13–93). The larger amounts of total elemental Fe are readily determined by reduction with amalgamated zinc (¶ 11–142) or, when Ti is to be determined also, with Tiron (¶ 11–62).

15–7. The iron is determined by reduction to ferrous with hydroxylamine hydrochloride, and formation of a ferrous complex of orthophenanthroline, a chelate ring compound of intense red color. A slightly acidic reaction must be used, since some cations will interfere in the alkaline ranges because of precipitation of their hydroxides. No common soil anions interfere except orthophosphate through precipitation of Ca and Fe. Twenty ppm of

---

[2] Parks *et al.*, *Ind. Eng. Chem.*, *A.E.*, 15:527 (1943).

[3] Saywell and Cunningham, *Ind. Eng. Chem.*, *A.E.*, 9:67 (1937); Fortune and Mellon, *Ind. Eng. Chem.*, *A.E.*, 10:60 (1938).

P_2O_5 from $(NH_4)_2HPO_4$ caused an error[4] of 1.4 per cent, but this quantity is not commonly encountered with the amount of iron determined in soil or plant extractions.

15–8. Needed apparatus includes a colorimeter with 490-mu light maximum, colorimeter tubes with a 20-ml calibration mark, pipets for taking aliquots, 1-liter and 100-ml volumetric flasks, and a pH meter or an indicator spot plate.

15–9. Needed reagents include dilute HCl and NH_4OH, 2,4-dinitrophenal indicator, and the following special reagents.

15–10. Orthophenanthroline, 1.5 Per Cent in 95 Per Cent Ethanol. To 100 ml of 95 per cent ethanol is added 1.5 gm of the white crystalline orthophenanthroline, and the solution is stirred until the crystals are dissolved. (This reagent should not be confused with the oxidation reduction indicator "Ferroin," which is the ferrous complex of orthophenanthroline, sometimes termed "orthophenathroline" in laboratory practice.)

15–11. Hydroxylamine Hydrochloride, 10 Per Cent. Ten gm of hydroxylamine hydrochloride is dissolved in 100 ml of distilled water.

15–12. Standard Iron Solution. A piece of pure iron wire weighing approximately 0.10 gm, or 0.7023 gm of $Fe(NH_4)_2(SO_4)_2 \cdot 6 H_2O$, is weighed out. The iron wire is dissolved in 20 ml of 0.6 N HCl with warming if necessary; or the salt is solved in water and 20 ml of 0.6 N HCl added. The solution in either case is transferred to a liter volumetric flask and diluted to volume with water. This solution contains 100 ppm Fe. From this solution, a second solution is prepared containing 10 ppm Fe by dilution of 10 ml to 100 with water. Aliquots (0.5, 1, 2, 3, 4, 6 ml) are then taken for the Fe calibration curve (¶ 15–13), giving 5 to 60 ugm of iron.

15–13. An aliquot of iron in dilute HCl solution (standard or test solution) containing from 5 to 60 ugm of Fe is placed in the colorimeter tube graduated at 20 ml and diluted to about 5 or 6 ml. The pH of the test solution is adjusted to pH 1.5 to 2.7 with dilute HCl or NH_4OH (the standards fall in a suitable range[5] of pH 1.08 to 3.1 without adjustment). A pH meter can be applied to a separate aliquot, or a test can be made with 2,4-dinitrophenol (yellow above pH 2.7) on an indicator spot plate of a

---

[4] Hummel and Willard, *Ind. Eng. Chem., A.E.,* 10:13 (1938). These authors employed 1 per cent hydroquinone solution buffered in NaOAc-HOAc of pH 4.5 for reduction of the iron, in a solution of pH 3 to 4 to avoid precipitation of calcium phosphate with occlusion of iron.

[5] Range limits determined by I. Hashimoto in the author's laboratory (1957).

small drop carried on a glass rod. Next, 2 ml of 10 per cent hydroxylamine hydrochloride and 1 ml of 1.5 per cent orthophenanthroline solution are added. The solution is made up to volume with distilled water, and read in the colorimeter with light of 490 mu maximum. The color reaches maximum strength immediately and is stable for months.

15–14. The concentration of iron in solution is read from the calibration curve drawn from the readings of the standard iron solutions.

EXCHANGEABLE FERROUS IRON[6]

15–15. Exchangeable ferrous iron is not completely extracted from soils by neutral ammonium acetate in the usual procedure for exchangeable cations because it oxidizes during the time for ordinary extraction and the ferric ions are largely precipitated. A separate extraction of the soil sample is therefore carried out for the determination of exchangeable ferrous iron.

APPARATUS

15–16. Needed apparatus includes a 11-cm Buchner funnel, a 1000-ml suction flask and rubber adapter for the funnel, 11-cm Whatman No. 5 filter paper, an aspirator pump, and a 500-ml conical extraction flask. The filter funnel and paper are set in readiness before the extraction is begun.

REAGENTS

15–17. Needed reagents include neutral, 1 N NH_4OAc solution, 400 ml per extraction.

PROCEDURE

15–18. From a freshly taken soil sample, field-moisture condition unchanged (moisture determined later on separate sample), a 25-gm sample is quickly weighed out, placed in a 500-ml conical flask, and 250 ml of neutral 1 N NH_4OAc solution added. The suspension is shaken vigorously for 20 to 30 seconds and filtered quickly on the previously prepared Buchner funnel fitted with Whatman No. 5 filter paper. Three successive 50 ml portions of NH_4OAc solution are employed for further extraction of the soil. To avoid oxidation of ferrous iron, the entire extraction is completed in 5 minutes or less.[7] Walkley[8] noted that the ferrous iron was rather completely oxidized in soils during the operation of air-drying for 1 or 2 days, even those which had been highly reduced (smelled strongly of H_2S). This observation was made in connection with the interference of ferrous iron

---

[6] Procedure for exchangeable ferrous iron kindly suppled by Dr. G. D. Sherman, Hawaiian Agr. Exp. Station, Honolulu, Hawaii, by personal communication.

[7] Oxidation of the ferrous iron can amount to 20 per cent in 15 minutes, and to 80 per cent in 60 minutes.

[8] *Soil Sci.*, 63:261 (1947).

with chromic acid titration of soil organic matter (¶ 9–40). The ferrous iron determination must be carried out on the field-moist soil immediately following the collection of the samples.

15–19. The filtrate, containing exchangeable ferrous iron, is freed of NH_4OAc by evaporation (oxidation of the iron of no consequence here) on a steam hot plate. The last traces of organic matter are removed by treatment of the residue with 10 ml of aqua regia, and then the solution is again brought to dryness. The iron is taken into solution in 1 ml of 1 N HCl followed by water to give the correct dilution for the iron determination (¶ 15–13).

ALTERNATIVE PROCEDURES

15–20. Sherman added 20 ml of concentrated HCl to the filtrate, and evaporated it to a small volume, then added a few ml of 8 N HNO_3 to oxidize the organic matter, and evaporated to a water clear solution of small volume. This procedure is suitable for use on an electric hot plate, on which the evaporation to dryness is likely to cause spattering.

15–21. Paddick[9] tested alkaline soils for available iron by a 1-minute extraction with thioglycolic acid. Morgan[10] described a rapid approximate soil test for ferrous iron. A rapid qualitative test for ferrous iron in soils is given in ¶ 13–71.

COMBINED EXCHANGEABLE FERROUS AND FERRIC IRON AND DILUTE ACID SOLUBLE IRON

15–22. Exchangeable iron exists in soils as (a) ferrous, Fe^{++} and (b) $[Fe(OH)n]^{(3-n)+}$. Although the ferrous iron can be extracted by a rapid procedure with NH_4OAc, the ferric iron is only partially extracted even though replaced from the exchange charges by NH_4^+, because some of it precipitates. Rather large amounts of iron and aluminum are sometimes extracted from acid soils by neutral NH_4OAc. Extraction with NH_4OAc at a pH value of 3 keeps all of the ferric iron in solution, and has been applied successfully in ferric exchange studies with aluminous clays.[11] However, in soils and ferruginous clays, some nonexchangeable iron is extracted. This dilute acid soluble iron may be of significance to its plant availability.

APPARATUS

15–23. Needed apparatus includes a 11-cm Buchner funnel, a 1000-ml suction flask and rubber adapter for the funnel, an aspirator pump, and Whatman No. 5 filter paper.

9 *S.S.S.A. Proc.*, 13:197 (1949).
10 *Conn. Agr. Exp. Sta. Bul.* 372:457 (1935).
11 Bower and Truog, *S.S.S.A. Proc.*, 5:86 (1941).

15–24. Needed reagents include 1 N NH_4OAc, of pH 3.0, made from approximately neutral NH_4OAc by the addition of concentrated HCl.

15–25. A 25-gm sample of soil is extracted as for exchangeable ferrous iron (¶ 15–18) except that the NH_4OAc of pH 3 is employed. The same speed of extraction is maintained to avoid undue contact of the acid extractant with the soil.

15–26. Centrifuge tubes and centrifuge may advantageously be substituted for the Buchner funnel filtration for studies of ferric iron as an exchangeable cation in clays.

SOLUBLE, EXCHANGEABLE, AND EASILY REDUCIBLE MANGANESE OF SOILS

15–27. The extraction of water soluble and easily reducible manganese are the chief concern here, but the exchangeable Mn^{++} is also extracted in the system described. The analytical *determination* of Mn as MnO_4^- with periodate has been outlined in connection with the exchangeable metallic cations (¶ 5–74). Extraction of the total Mn in soils (¶ 11–172) and plants (¶ 12–19) has been given.

15–28. There is an equilibrium of manganous and manganic forms of manganese in soils, and this is related to availability of manganese to plants; the exchangeable (divalent) form was considered to be the best index of plant availability.[12] *Easily* reducible manganese oxides are distinguished by the test from those in which the Mn is rather inert and unavailable. Easily reducible manganic oxides may involve mixtures of Mn valences from 2 to 4. The equilibrium system may be represented:

$$\text{Water sol. } Mn^{++} \rightleftharpoons \text{Exchangeable } Mn^{++} \rightleftharpoons \text{Colloidal hydrated } MnO_{1 \text{ to } 2} \rightleftharpoons \text{Inert } MnO_2$$
$$(15\text{–}1)$$

15–29. Strongly acid soils that contain 25 ppm or less of easily reducible Mn are likely to become manganese deficient when limed.[13] Individual soils vary greatly as to the limits in ppm of Mn under which the manganese will become deficient.[14] Some acid Kentucky soils with only 3 to 10 ppm of easily reducible manganese showed[15] over-liming injury (manganese de-

[12] Piper, *J. Agr. Sci.,* 21:762 (1931).
[13] Leeper, *Proc. Roy. Soc. Victoria,* 47(II):225 (1935).
[14] Leeper, *Soil Sci.,* 63:79 (1947).
[15] Sherman *et al., Soil Sci.,* 54:253 (1942).

ficiency), but clay soils having over 10 ppm of easily reducible manganese did not show over-liming injury. Acid organic soils frequently are low in total manganese owing to continual leaching of the manganese under conditions favoring its conversion to Mn^{++}. Manganese deficiency, although not present in the acid condition, is likely to develop when this type of soil is limed.

15–30. Acid soils that contain less than 10 to 25 ppm of easily reducible manganese will generally not supply plants with sufficient manganese for normal growth. Highly acid soils which are low in manganese sometimes show manganese toxicity if large amounts are applied, because the process of oxidation of added manganese to manganic form is slow. Productive neutral or alkaline soils usually contain 100 or more ppm of easily reducible manganese. Alkaline soils[16] should have at least 3 ppm of exchangeable Mn^{++} in addition to 100 ppm of easily reducible manganese to be free of deficiency. The mechanisms of retention of Mn by soil colloids have been examined.[17]

15–31. The total Mn in soils ranges[18] generally from 10 to 2000 or more ppm, of which 0.3 to less than 0.1 is easily reducible. In Hawaiian soils,[19] the total Mn is sometimes 1 to 4 per cent.

15–32. The Sample. The soil sample should be freshly taken from the field, because air-drying (or heating) of the sample may increase the exchangeable Mn by a large amount (4 ppm raised to 80 ppm[20]). Drying releases Mn^{++} from the MnO_{1to2} complex as water is removed.[21] A separate portion of the sample is taken for moisture determination.

APPARATUS

15–33. Needed apparatus consists of 500-ml conical extraction flask, a shaking machine, a Buchner funnel, a suction flask, an asbestos and Gooch crucible and holder, a 400-ml beaker, and a steam hot plate.

REAGENTS

15–34. Needed reagents consist of distilled water, filter paper to fit Buchner funnel, 1 N NH_4OAc of pH 7, 30 per cent H_2O_2, concentrated HNO_3, and 1 N NH_4OAc of pH 7 to which 0.2 gm of hydroquinone has been added to each 100 ml.

---

[16] Sherman and Harmer, *S.S.S.A. Proc.*, 7:398 (1943).

[17] Hemstock and Low, *Soil Sci.*, 76:331 (1953).

[18] Leeper, *Soil Sci.*, 63:79 (1947).

[19] Fujimoto and Sherman, *Soil Sci.*, 66:131 (1948).

[20] Sherman and Harmer, *S.S.S.A. Proc.*, 7:398 (1943).

[21] Fujimoto and Sherman, *S.S.S.A. Proc.*, 10:107 (1946).

EXTRACTION PROCEDURES[22]

15–35. Water Soluble Manganese. To 25 gm of soil in a 500-ml conical flask, 250 ml of distilled water is added and the flask is stoppered tightly. The suspension is shaken by a machine for 30 minutes. Then the mixture is filtered through a Buchner funnel and, if the filtrate is not clear, re-filtered through a layer of acid-washed asbestos in a Gooch crucible. The filtrate is evaporated to dryness, the organic matter is destroyed, and the manganese is determined as described in ¶ 5–74. The soil and asbestos filter are returned to the 500-ml conical flask.

15–36. Exchangeable Manganese. The determination of exchangeable manganese has been described (¶ 5–71) in connection with the NH_4OAc procedure for exchangeable cations. However, if easily reducible manganese is to be determined, the exchangeable Mn is generally determined also on the same sample.

15–37. To the 25-gm soil sample from which the water soluble Mn has been removed, 250 ml of N NH_4OAc of pH 7 is added. The flask is stoppered and shaken in the machine for 30 minutes and then allowed to stand at least 6 hours with frequent shaking. The soil mixture is next filtered through a Buchner funnel, and the filtrate is evaporated to dryness on the steam hot plate. The excess ammonium acetate is destroyed by moistening the residue with water and reevaporating it to dryness. Then the residue is treated with 30 per cent H_2O_2 and HNO_3, and the Mn is determined (¶ 5–74). The use of H_2SO_4 is avoided at this point because of the possibility of formation of $CaSO_4$ with soils high in calcium. The soil sample is returned to the original flask for the determination of easily reducible manganic compounds.

15–38. Easily Reducible Manganese. To the original 25 gm of soil, 250 ml of N NH_4OAc solution containing 0.2 per cent of hydroquinone is added. The suspension is shaken at frequent intervals for 6 hours to insure completeness of equilibrium, and then is filtered on a Buchner funnel. To the filtrate, 10 ml of concentrated HNO_3 is added, the filtrate is evaporated to dryness on the steam hot plate, and the Mn is determined (¶ 5–74). It is essential that all of the hydroquinone be destroyed.

ALTERNATIVE PROCEDURES

15–39. Extraction of manganic manganese with an 0.05 per cent water solution of quinol with 1 hour of contact was suggested by Jones and Leeper[23] as being more selective than quinol in NH_4OAc for the extrac-

---

[22] Extraction procedures of Leeper, *Proc. Roy. Soc. Victoria,* 47(II):225 (1935), as modified and described by Sherman *et al., Soil Sci.,* 54:253 (1942), and Sherman and Harmer, *S.S.S.A. Proc.,* 7:398 (1943).

[23] *Sci.,* 11:463 (1950).

tion of easily reducible manganese. The solution $1\,N$ NH_4OAc-quinol (0.05 per cent quinol) extracted considerable manganese from hausmannite (having a formula $MnO_{1.35}$), a compound that did not correct the manganese deficiency of oats. The water-quinol solution extracted little from this compound, but it did extract 0.2 to 0.6 times as much manganic manganese from a number of higher oxides of manganese as the ammonium acetate-quinol solution extracted.

15–40. Extraction of a quantity of available manganese with $0.2\,N$ HOAc was suggested by McCool.[24] A rapid test for Mn in soils and plants is available (¶ 13–3).

COPPER DETERMINATION[25]
(Colorimetrically as carbamate)

15–41. The reaction of sodium diethyldithiocarbamate ("carbamate") with copper gives the copper salt of diethyldithiocarbamic acid, which has a golden brown color. Formation of this compound is one of the most sensitive methods for copper determination and is unaffected by pH over the range of 5.7 to 9.2. As little as 0.01 ugm of Cu per ml may be detected, and the range for quantitative determination without concentration in an organic solvent is 10 to 70 ugm in 25 ml of solution, or 1 to 10 ugm in 10 ml of isoamyl acetate extractant.

15–42. Interfering substances are few in the procedure given. Ni and Co give high positive interferences when amounts of the order of 10 ugm are present with 10 ugm of Cu, and thus ordinarily do not interfere with the Cu determination on soils and plants. Bi interferes and accompanies Cu through the dithizone preliminary separation (¶ 16–34) if that is employed; however, it would seldom interfere with soil and plant analysis. Bi-carbamate is not decolorized by a KCN solution[26] as is Cu-carbamate, and the presence of Bi can therefore be established and corrected for in terms of its Cu color equivalent after a KCN treatment of the final solution. A medium alkaline with NH_4OH is used in this procedure to precipitate Fe^{+++} and Al^{+++}, which would interfere, and to convert the copper to the soluble cupric-ammonia complex ion form. Interference by traces of Fe^{+++} and Zn remaining is prevented by the presence of NH_4Cl and other conditions of the procedure.

APPARATUS

15–43. Needed apparatus consists of a photoelectric colorimeter with 440-mu light maximum and colorimeter tubes; a 125-ml conical flask;

24 *Boyce Thompson Inst. Contrib.,* 6:147 (1934).

25 After Callan and Henderson, *Analyst,* 54:650 (1929). The method has been employed by Sherman and McHargue, *J.A.O.A.C.,* 25:510 (1942), Holmes, *Soil Sci.,* 56:359 (1943) and others. J. A. Kittrick employed the method in this laboratory and worked out many details of the procedure given.

26 Hibbard, *Hilgardia,* 13:1 (1940).

volumetric flasks, 1-liter, 500-ml, 200-ml, set of 25-ml; a centrifuge and centrifuge tubes with 15-ml volume calibration, a buret, and pipets to take necessary aliquots. For the most sensitive procedure, a 150-ml separatory funnel is required. In addition to usual cleaning, all glassware is rinsed twice with 0.5 N HCl, twice with tap water to remove the HCl, and finally twice with redistilled water. Care is used to avoid contamination from stoppers, tubing, and other sources.

REAGENTS

15–44. Reagents needed consist of redistilled water (Pyrex still; stored in Pyrex bottle), litmus paper, concentrated NH_4OH, 0.5 N HCl (415 ml of concentrated HCl diluted to 10 liters with distilled water), and 25 per cent NH_4Cl solution (25 gm per 100 ml). Isoamyl acetate and 15 per cent citric acid in water are required for the procedure of highest sensitivity.

15–45. Carbamate Reagent, 2 Per Cent. Two gm of sodium diethyldithiocarbamate (obtained from Eastman Kodak Co., Rochester, N.Y.) is dissolved in about 100 ml of redistilled H_2O, and the solution is filtered through a coarse quantitative paper into a 200-ml volumetric flask. The solution is diluted to volume with redistilled water and mixed. Stored in a brown bottle in a cool, dark place, this reagent keeps for several months.

15–46. Standard Copper Solution. Exactly 0.500 gm of pure metallic copper (preferably Bureau of Standards copper) is dissolved in 15 ml of 3 N HNO$_3$ at room temperature in a covered 125-ml conical flask. When the solution has cooled, 1 ml of concentrated H_2SO_4 is added and the solution is evaporated cautiously to SO$_3$ fumes. The solution is cooled again, diluted with 10 to 15 ml of redistilled water, and again evaporated to SO$_3$ fumes. Finally, when cooled, the solution is transferred to a 1-liter volumetric flask and made up to volume with redistilled water. This stock solution contains 0.50 mgm of copper per ml. A more dilute standard solution containing 10 ugm per ml is prepared by diluting 10 ml of this stock solution to 500 ml. A series of aliquots (1,2,3,4,5, and 6 ml) is taken of the 10 ugm per ml standard solution for the standard curve, and the color is developed as described in the procedure.

PROCEDURE

15–47. A 10 ml or smaller volume of solution of Cu (25 ugm or more) in HCl, obtained from extraction from soil (¶ 15–64) or plants (¶ 12–39), usually without dithizone purification (¶ 16–34), is placed in a volumetric centrifuge tube. Then 5 ml of 25 per cent NH_4Cl solution is added, followed by concentrated NH_4OH from a buret with stirring (air jet held under the solution surface) until the solution is neutral to litmus and then 3 ml in excess. The solution is diluted to 15 ml with redistilled water, mixed, and centrifuged at about 2000 rpm for 5 minutes.

15–48. From the supernatant liquid a suitable aliquot containing from 10 to 60 ugm of Cu is transferred to a 25-ml volumetric flask, 5 ml concentrated NH_4OH is added, and the solution is diluted to about 22 ml with redistilled water. Then 1 ml of 1 per cent carbamate is added from a pipet or buret, and the solution is diluted to volume with redistilled water and mixed.

15–49. After 15 minutes the color is read in the colorimeter with the 440-mu light maximum. The color is stable for at least 1 hour, after which it slowly decreases in intensity. Reference to the standard curve gives ugm Cu per ml of solution (ppm in solution).

ALTERNATIVE PROCEDURES

15–50. Isoamyl Acetate Extraction[27] for Greater Sensitivity. To a 150-ml separatory funnel, 5 ml of 15 per cent citric acid solution and an aliquot of the copper solution containing 1 to 10 ugm of Cu are added. Then concentrated NH_4OH is added dropwise to neutral with litmus and then 2 drops in excess are added. Next 1 ml of the 1 per cent carbamate solution is added and the solution is made to approximately 50 ml with water. Finally, 10 ml of isoamyl acetate is added, the funnel is tightly stoppered, and the suspension is vigorously shaken for 1 minute each of 4 times at intervals of 1 or 2 minutes. The 2 liquids are allowed to separate during a period of 20 to 30 minutes, and the aqueous layer is slowly drained off. The colored isoamyl acetate layer is then drained into a dry colorimeter tube (centrifuged if necessary to clear) and the color is determined with a 440-mu light maximum.

15–51. Refinements of the carbamate method are available.[28] Copper, in low amounts and with great freedom from interference, can be determined[29] by 2,9-dimethyl-1,10-phenanthroline ("Neocuproine," G. F. Smith Chemical Co., Columbus, O.) with a 457-mu light maximum. The copper is reduced with hydroxylamine sulfate, and the color is extracted with *n*-hexyl alcohol. A similar reagent, 2,9-dimethyl-4,7-diphenyl-1,10-phenanthroline, is also specific for Cu.[30]

TOTAL COPPER AND ZINC EXTRACTION FROM SOILS

15–52. The total copper in temperate and tropical soils ranges[31] generally from 5 to 40 ppm but falls to 1 or 2 ppm in copper deficient soils and

---

[27] Details of this procedure were kindly supplied by J. A. Asleson from his M.S. Thesis, Univ. of Wis. (1947).

[28] Cheng and Bray, *Anal. Chem.*, 25:655 (1953); Chilton, *Anal. Chem.*, 25:1274 (1953).

[29] Smith and McCurdy, *Anal. Chem.*, 24:371 (1952); Gahler, *Anal. Chem.*, 26: 577 (1954).

[30] Smith and Wilkins, *Anal. Chem.*, 25:510 (1953).

[31] Holmes, *Soil Sci.*, 56:359 (1943); Stenberg and Eckman, *Nord. JordbrForsk.*, 4–6:689 (1948); Vermaat and Vander Bie, *Plant and Soil*, 2:257 (1950).

may rise to 100 ppm or more in some soils. Total zinc of soils falls in the same range. Decomposition of soils with HF (with a few drops of H_2SO_4) was found by R. G. Menzel to yield up to 50 per cent more copper and zinc than decomposition of the soils in $HClO_4$ (¶ 15–57). Much of the copper in some soils may be in organic combinations[32] and be completely released by $HClO_4$, whereas in other soils much of the copper may be in silicates that resist $HClO_4$ decomposition.

APPARATUS

15–53. Needed apparatus consists of a platinum crucible, a small agate mortar, a 250-ml Pyrex beaker, an electric hot plate and sand bath, a rubber policeman, and an analytical balance.

REAGENTS

15–54. Needed reagents consist of redistilled water, 48 per cent HF, concentrated H_2SO_4, concentrated HNO_3, and a ternary acid mixture consisting of 10 ml of concentrated HNO_3, 1 ml of concentrated H_2SO_4, and 4 ml of 60 per cent $HClO_4$.

PROCEDURE[33]

15–55. One gm of air-dry soil sample, finely ground in an agate mortar, is weighed and transferred to a platinum crucible. The soil is moistened with water and 3 drops of concentrated H_2SO_4. Then two successive 5-ml portions of HF are evaporated from the sample on the sand bath at 180°C to volatilize the SiO_2. The crucible with the sample is placed in a 250-ml beaker with 10 ml of concentrated HNO_3, and then covered with redistilled water. The residue of the sample is loosened by heating the solution, and is washed into the beaker with redistilled water, with the aid of a rubber policeman. The solution is evaporated to dryness and the organic matter oxidation is completed by digestion with 10 ml of ternary acid mixture at 200°C. No brown color from organic matter must be left if a good dithizone separation is to be obtained. The residue, including a small amount of H_2SO_4 that moistens the residue after the ternary liquid digestion, is taken up in 10 ml of redistilled water. Not enough Pt is dissolved at the low temperatures employed to interfere with the Cu carbamate determination. (Pt in solution would interfere, and interfering amounts are dissolved from a Pt crucible by dry ashing[34] at 450°C or above or in the Na_2CO_3 fusion.[35]

---

[32] Lucas, *Soil Sci.,* 51:461 (1948).
[33] After Menzel and Jackson, *Anal. Chem.,* 23:1861 (1951).
[34] Bailey and McHargue, *Plant Physiol.,* 20:79 (1945).
[35] J. A. Asleson, private communication (Aug. 1952).

15–56. The total copper and zinc in soil is determined by means of a usual semimicroanalytical procedure either colorimetrically (¶ 15–41 for copper, ¶ 15–69 for zinc) or polarographically after dithizone separation (¶ 16–34).

EXTRACTABLE COPPER IN SOILS

15–57. The soil copper extractable in various reagents (¶ 15–65) varies from nearly all of it (1 to 100 ppm of soil) in $HClO_4$ to a very small fraction of it in neutral NH_4OAc. Release of nearly all of the soil copper (and zinc, cobalt, lead, etc.) by $HClO_4$ digestion has been reported.[36] Tests of the insoluble residue generally showed only traces of copper remaining in the residue (compare HF release, ¶ 15–52). Copper in minerals that would not be decomposed by $HClO_4$ might be considered of no significance to soils.

15–58. The $HClO_4$ extractable Cu in soils was used[37] as a measure of the "potentially available" Cu in organic soils. The copper content of plants increased from 2 to 5 ppm with increasing soil content of $HClO_4$ extractable Cu from 1 to 8 ppm; the content of copper in plants increased only to around 7 ppm as the extractable copper content increased on up to 100 ppm.

15–59. Uptake of copper (and zinc) by plants from montmorillonite was proportional to the degree of saturation from 0 to 0.1 per cent but was less than proportional above this degree.[38] That copper is held in soil by other than the usual cation exchange forces has been shown by several studies.[39] Even extremely insoluble compounds show some availability of copper.[40]

15–60. The $HClO_4$ treatment brings about oxidation of the organic matter and extraction of the metallic cations from most minerals as soluble perchlorates, with concurrent dehydration and precipitation of free SiO_2. J. A. Kittrick of this laboratory found that when the decomposition is carried out in the presence of a small quantity of H_2SO_4, the $HClO_4$ can be boiled off and the higher-boiling H_2SO_4 keeps the residue from baking as a crust on the digestion vessel, and holds the cations as readily dissolved sulfates.

APPARATUS

15–61. The $HClO_4$ digestion of soil has been carried out in a wide-

---

36 Holmes, *Soil Sci.*, 59:77 (1945).

37 Lundblad *et al.*, *Plant and Soil*, 1:277 (1949).

38 Epstein and Stout, *Soil Sci.*, 72:47 (1951).

39 Bower and Truog, *S.S.S.A. Proc.*, 5:86 (1941); Lucas, *Soil Sci.*, 66:119 (1948); Menzel and Jackson, *Trans. 4th Intern. Congr. Soil Sci.*, 1:125 (1950), *S.S.S.A. Proc.*, 15:122 (1951); DeMumbrum and Jackson, *Soil Sci.*, 81:353 (1956), *S.S.S.A. Proc.*, 20:334 (1956).

40 Steenbjerg, *Physiologia Plantarum*, 4:677 (1951).

mouthed conical flask[41] covered with a special conical cover glass arranged to drop the refluxed $HClO_4$ at the center of the bottom of the flask. J. A. Kittrick found that the $HClO_4$ digestion of soil could conveniently be carried out in Pyrex digestion tubes placed in a 4-liter beaker bath containing H_3PO_4, as illustrated in Fig. 15–1. The $HClO_4$ fumes are carried off by

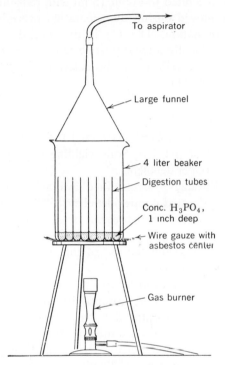

To aspirator

Large funnel

4 liter beaker

Digestion tubes

Conc. H_3PO_4, 1 inch deep

Wire gauze with asbestos center

Gas burner

Fig. 15–1. Digestion bath for decomposition of soil in $HClO_4$ for release of copper. (After Dr. J. A. Kittrick.)

means of a glass funnel collector through tubing attached to an aspirator pump.

REAGENTS

15–62. The needed reagents employed are redistilled water and an acid mixture consisting of 100 ml of 60 per cent $HClO_4$ mixed with 10 ml of concentrated H_2SO_4. This mixture is termed the 10 : 1 digestion mix.

PROCEDURE

15–63. To a 2.000 gm soil sample (up to 5 gm for sands and other soils low in Cu) placed in the digestion tube, 10 ml of the 10 : 1 digestion mix-

---

[41] Holmes, *Soil Sci.,* 59:77 (1945).

ture is added. Several such tubes are slowly heated in the H_3PO_4 bath until the $HClO_4$ is boiled off and only 1 ml or so of H_2SO_4 is left. If the samples do not digest to a clear white residue, a few more ml of the 10 : 1 mixture is added and the digestion is continued.

15–64. When the tubes have cooled, they are removed from the bath and the digested sample is diluted to about 15 ml with redistilled water. The insoluble residue is removed during the separation procedure at the first of the analytical determination. The Cu is determined colorimetrically (¶ 15–47) or polarographically after dithizone separation (¶ 16–34). The Zn released by this same procedure can be determined by the usual Zn procedures (¶ 15–69 or 16–34).

ALTERNATIVE PROCEDURES

15–65. Steenbjerg and Boken[42] extracted 0.1 to 0.3 ppm of Cu from fertile soils with HCl of pH 2.0. Soils yielding less than this amount of copper were usually copper deficient.

15–66. Antipov-Karataev[43] determined available copper by extraction with 0.5 N HNO_3, and noted copper deficiency if the available copper was less than 50 per cent of the total present, or if the total was less than 18 ppm.

15–67. Eriksson[44] suggested the use of the stable complex, $CuP_2O_7^{--}$ for the extraction of available copper. He states that all copper sorbed on clay minerals should be removed by this treatment as well as that organically bound by oxygen and amine groups. Wiklander[45] extracted soil with an equal weight of hydrogen-saturated ion exchange resin, the soil being washed away while the resin was retained on the cloth filter. The resin was then extracted with 2 N HCl to release the Cu and Zn. Small amounts of these elements added to soils were effectively removed by this extraction even after the soils had been dried.

15–68. Many workers, including Dr. J. A. Asleson in this laboratory (1951) have extracted soil Cu in N NH_4OAc. Soil copper extracted by *Aspergillus niger* can also be assayed[46] in 0.1 to 1 ugm amounts either by mycelium weights or spore coloration.

ZINC DETERMINATION

(Colorimetrically as dithizonate)

15–69. The acid form of diphenylthiocarbazone (dithizone) is soluble in CCl_4 whereas the ammonium salt is soluble in water containing a slight

---

[42] *Tids. Planteavl*, 52:375 (1948).
[43] *Pedology*, 1947:652 (1947).
[44] *Ann. Roy. Agr. Coll. Sweden*, 16:72 (1949).
[45] *Ann. Roy. Agr. Coll. Sweden*, 16:670 (1949).
[46] Dole, *Soil Sci.*, 73:135 (1952).

excess of NH_4OH. Dithizone forms complexes with Zn, Cu, Co, and Ni, which can be extracted from a water solution into CCl_4 at pH values between 8 and 10.[47] In the present procedure, Cu, Ni, Co, and Pb are held in carbamate complex form in the aqueous layer whereas the Zn is separated into the CCl_4 layer at pH 8.8.

15–70. The interference by Ni is not wholly removed, but is satisfactorily eliminated for soil and plant analyses. The range of zinc that can be determined is from 1 to 25 ugm.

15–71. The analytical procedure given here can be adapted to total zinc of soils (¶ 15–52) or plants (¶ 12–39) and to the various types of extractable zinc from soils (¶ 15–83).

APPARATUS

15–72. Needed apparatus consist of 125-ml pear-shaped separatory funnels, 4-liter separatory funnels; a mechanical vertical shaker (Fig. 15–2), a colorimeter with 535- and 620-light maxima; colorimeter tubes; volumetric flasks, 1-liter and 25-ml; and pipets including 1 of 5-ml volume.

REAGENTS

15–73. Needed reagents include zinc-free distilled water prepared by redistillation in a Pyrex still or passage through an ion exchange column; 1 N HCl, prepared by distillation of approximately 6 N HCl in a Pyrex still, and dilution of the condensate to 1 $N;$ 1 N NH_4OH prepared by distillation of concentrated NH_4OH into zinc-free water in a Pyrex container packed in ice (or by collection of anhydrous NH_3 in a Pyrex container of zinc-free water); ACS purity CCl_4 (or redistilled S-free CCl_4, stored in the dark); thymol blue indicator; and the following special reagents.

15–74. Carbamate Solution, 0.2 Per Cent. A 0.2 per cent solution is prepared by dissolving 0.2 gm of sodium diethyldithiocarbamate (Eastman Kodak Co.) in 100-ml of zinc-free water. This solution keeps satisfactorily in a brown bottle, if kept in a cool, dark place.

15–75. Dithizone Solution in CCl_4, 0.01 Per Cent. Into a 4-liter separatory funnel, 0.2 gm of diphenylthiocarbazone (Eastman Kodak Co.) and 1 liter of CCl_4 are placed, and the solid brought into solution by frequent agitation for about 15 minutes. To this solution, 2 liters of zinc-free 0.02 N NH_4OH is added and the mixture is shaken to transfer the dithizone to the aqueous phase. The CCl_4 (light green color) is discarded and the aqueous phase is rinsed with several 100-ml portions of CCl_4. Then 500 ml of CCl_4 and 50 ml of zinc-free 1 N HCl are added. The mixture is shaken to transfer the dithizone to the CCl_4 layer, and then the CCl_4-dithizone

---

[47] The formula for dithizone is given in ¶ 16–34. Further details of the condition for formation of complexes with various elements is given by Welcher, *Organic Analytical Reagents,* Vol. 3 (New York: D. Van Nostrand Company, Inc., 1947).

Fig. 15–2. Vertical shaker for separatory funnels. (Photo courtesy Dr. R. S. Holmes. Details of construction are given by Holmes and Mullins, *Soil Sci.,* 69:233, 1950.)

phase is diluted to 2 liters. The solution is stored in a glass-stoppered Pyrex bottle, in a refrigerator.

15–76. Ammonium Citrate, 0.4 M. To 90 gm of ammonium citrate, enough water is added to make 1 liter. To this solution, enough zinc-free concentrated NH_4OH is added to bring the pH to 8.5. The zinc impurities are removed by extraction with portions of dithizone in CCl_4 in a large separatory funnel until the latter reagent no longer changes color, and then with portions of CCl_4 until the citrate solution is free from dithizone color.

15–77. Standard Zinc Solution. Exactly 0.1 gm of pure zinc is dissolved in 50 ml of 0.02 N H_2SO_4, and diluted to 1 liter to give a 100 ugm/ml concentration of Zn. A secondary dilution of 10 ml to 500 ml gives a 2 ugm/ml working standard.

PROCEDURE[48]

15–78. A solution containing 5 to 20 ugm of zinc in 30 to 40 ml of 0.02 N HCl is placed in a 125-ml separatory funnel. Fifty ml of ammonium citrate buffer and 3 ml of carbamate are added and the solution pH is adjusted to 8.5 to 8.8 with redistilled NH_4OH or HCl (thymol blue indicator). Exactly 10 ml of dithizone reagent in CCl_4 is added. The mixture is shaken for 5 minutes. The CCl_4 phase is transferred to another separatory funnel, 25 ml of 0.01 N NH_4OH is added to the CCl_4 phase, and the mixture is shaken again for 3 minutes to extract the excess dithizone into the aqueous phase.

15–79. A 5-ml aliquot of the organic phase is taken with a pipet and diluted with CCl_4 to 25 ml. The solution thus obtained is mixed and transferred to a colorimeter tube, and the light transmission is measured at a 535- (or 540-) mu light maximum. The amount of zinc present is determined by reference to a standard curve prepared in an identical manner with known amounts of zinc. All equipment may be satisfactorily cleaned with either CCl_4 or water if it is restricted to this analysis.

ALTERNATIVE PROCEDURES

15–80. R. G. Menzel found that the distribution of excess dithizone between aqueous and CCl_4 layers is markedly affected by the solution pH and other conditions, and that to measure its color was better than to attempt to hold its amount constant. The test solution is read at 540-mu against air as 100 per cent transmission (L_{540}). Then the optical density (L_{620}) of the excess dithizone is determined at 620-mu (at which wave length zinc dithizonate does not have absorption) against air as 100 per cent transmission. The zinc dithizone optical density (L_{Zn}) is found, for the Evelyn Colorimeter, by the equation:

$$L_{Zn} = L_{540} - 0.345 (L_{620}) + 0.084 \qquad (15\text{-}2)$$

Since the excess dithizone has 0.345 times as much optical density at 540

[48] Cowlings and Miller, *Ind. Eng. Chem., A.E.*, 13:145 (1941); Holmes, *Soil Sci.*, 59:77 (1945); Sandell, *Colorimetric Determination of Traces of Metals*, 2nd Ed. (New York: Interscience Publishers, Inc., 1950), p. 628; Shirley, *J.A.O.A.C.*, 31:285 (1948); *J.A.O.A.C.*, 32:276 (1949); Shaw and Dean, *Soil Sci.*, 73:343 (1952); Dr. R. G. Menzel, personal communication.

mu as it has at 620 mu, the optical density of zinc dithizonate alone is obtained by the equation. The constant term arises from the fact that the CCl_4 blank would read over 100 per cent transmission against the air reading as 100 per cent.

15–81. Some off color of the dithizone extraction may be obtained occasionally with soil or plant extracts, but ordinarily has little effect on the final reading. It can be eliminated by returning the zinc from CCl_4 to fresh ammonium citrate-carbamate reagent through the addition of HCl to 0.02 N concentration, and re-extraction of the Zn with fresh dithizone reagent by repetition of the procedure.

15–82. More elaborate means of chemical separation of zinc have been employed by several groups of investigators.[49] A field method is available.[50]

DITHIZONE EXTRACTABLE SOIL ZINC

15–83. The method of Shaw and Dean[51] given here for extraction of zinc from soils in dithizone was shown to be fairly promising for extraction of a fraction of the soil zinc that can be correlated with that which is relatively available to plants. The interpretation of the results depends in part upon a correlation with the soil pH. For soils below pH 6.5, zinc deficiency seems to be correlated with 0.5 ppm or less of zinc extracted. For zinc deficient soils above pH 6.5, the dithizone extractable zinc may extend to 2.5 ppm. A dithizone extractable zinc content of above 0.5 ppm seems to be correlated with nondeficiency of zinc for soils of pH between 5 and 6.5. Dithizone extractable zinc may extend to 5 and 17 ppm in acid soils high in available zinc.

APPARATUS

15–84. Apparatus needed consists of 125-ml pear-shaped separatory funnels, mechanical vertical shaker (Fig. 15–2), 60-ml conical centrifuge tubes and centrifuge, and a 10-ml pipet.

REAGENTS

15–85. Reagents needed include redistilled water, HCl, CCl_4, and dithizone in CCl_4 (¶ 15–75) and the following.

15–86. NH₄OAc Buffer, 1 M. Seventy-seven gm of c.p. NH_4OAc is dissolved in enough redistilled water to make a final volume of 1 liter. The pH is adjusted to 7 with zinc-free NH_4OH. The buffer is purified in a large separatory funnel with dithizone and CCl_4, the organic phase being discarded until it no longer changes color. The dithizone that has become dissolved in the aqueous phase is removed by repeated extraction with CCl_4.

[49] Parks *et al.*, *Ind. Eng. Chem., A.E.*, 15:528 (1943); Holmes, *Soil Sci.*, 59:77 (1945).

[50] Reichen and Lakin, U.S. Geol. Surv. Cir. 41 (1949).

[51] *Soil Sci.*, 73:346 (1952).

PROCEDURE[52]

15–87. Soil Samples. Since the quantities of zinc to be determined are very small, the soil samples are collected and prepared with the usual care recommended for minor element work. The soils are air-dried, crushed with a wooden pestle, and passed through a zinc-free 1-mm sieve (18 meshes per inch). The sieve is made of iron wire or any zinc-free wire commercially available. The samples are stored in cardboard ice cream containers. Cleansing tissues generally have been sufficiently free of zinc to be useful for such operations as wiping out weighing pans.

15–88. Extraction. To extract the dithizone extractable zinc from soils, 25 ml of 1 N NH_4OAc and 25 ml of dithizone-CCl_4 solution are pipetted into a 125-ml pear-shaped separatory funnel. Then 2.5 gm of soil is added. The separatory funnel is firmly stoppered and shaken on a mechanical vertical shaker (Fig. 15–2) for 1 hour. The separatory funnel is then placed on the stand and the soil-CCl_4 suspension is drained into a 60-ml conical centrifuge tube. While the suspension is centrifuged to develop a continuous CCl_4 phase, the original separatory funnel is rinsed with water.

15–89. A 10-ml aliquot of the CCl_4 solution containing the zinc is removed by means of a pipet, care being exercised to locate the tip of the pipet in the CCl_4 phase. Air is expelled from the tip as it passes through the aqueous and soil layers and the tip is kept away from the walls of the tube where soil and water may be contacted. A mark on the pipet greatly facilitates its placement at the proper depth in the centrifuge tube. The pipet is withdrawn and the adhering soil and water are washed from the tip with a wash bottle, the volume is adjusted to the mark, and the tip is rinsed again. The 10-ml aliquot is added to the cleaned separatory funnel from which it originally came, and 50 ml of 0.02 N HCl is added. The mixture is agitated for 3 minutes on the shaker to cause the extraction of the zinc from the CCl_4 phase into the HCl phase. The CCl_4 phase, which contains interfering elements and some oxidized dithizone, is discarded. The aqueous phase is rinsed twice with CCl_4 with agitation by hand. The zinc so extracted may be determined by the standard methods, colorimetrically as the dithizonate (¶ 15–69) or polarographically (¶ 16–34).

ALTERNATIVE PROCEDURES

15–90. Many types of extraction of soil zinc have been studied. As with copper, the $HClO_4$ extractable zinc represents the majority of the zinc present[53] and may be obtained by the same procedure as $HClO_4$ extractable copper (¶ 15–57).

15–91. Wear and Sommer[54] extracted the available zinc from soils by

[52] Shaw and Dean, *Soil Sci.,* 73:342 (1952).
[53] Holmes, *Soil Sci.,* 59:77 (1945).
[54] *S.S.S.A. Proc.,* 12:143 (1948).

means of 0.1 N HCl and claimed good correlations between this type of extractable zinc and zinc deficiency on a number of Alabama soils.

15–92. Hibbard[55] recommended extraction of soil zinc with 1 N KCl acidified to pH 3.2 with HOAc. Lyman and Dean[56] used NH_4OAc of pH 4.6, and noted that pineapples were likely to show zinc deficiency on soils that yielded less than 1 ppm of Zn in this reagent. Bergh[57] recommended 0.1 N $MgSO_4$ of such acidity that the final pH of the extracted solution was the same as the original soil pH. Soils yielding less than 5 ppm of zinc in this solution, were considered likely to be zinc deficient. Thorne *et al.*[58] used KCl-HOAc at pH 3.2.

MOLYBDENUM DETERMINATION

(Colorimetrically by thiocyanate orange-red color)

15--93. Determination of Mo in soils and plants has been carried out by various improvements in the method based on the thiocyanate-colored complex, developed through reduction with acetone,[59] ascorbic acid,[60] or chlorostannous acid.[61] Spectographic and polarographic methods are also known.[62] Alkaline separation of Mo from many interfering ions as employed by Robinson and intensification and stabilization of the color have made possible the elimination of need for extraction of the chromogen with organic solvents for the range of 1 to 75 ugm of Mo. The method is suitable for determination of Mo extracted from soils or plants. Any rhenium (Re) is included with Mo by the method, but ion exchange separation of these two elements has been reported.[63]

APPARATUS

15–94. Needed apparatus includes a colorimeter with 470-mu light maximum (the light absorption maximum is 470 mu, although from 420- to 525-mu light maxima have been used by various workers with resulting much lower sensitivity), colorimeter tubes, volumetric flasks (1-liter, 25-ml), and pipets.

REAGENTS

15–95. Needed reagents include 10 per cent potassium thiocyanate (10 gm of KSCN dissolved in 100 ml of water), acetone (reagent grade), HCl (concentrated, specific gravity 1.18 to 1.19), and the Mo standard.

---

[55] *Hilgardia,* 13:1 (1940).
[56] *Soil Sci.,* 54:315 (1942).
[57] *K. Norske Vidensk. Selskabs, Skrifter,* 1945, No. 3 (1948).
[58] *Soil Sci.,* 54:463 (1942).
[59] Ellis and Olson, *Anal. Chem.,* 22:328 (1950).
[60] Robinson, *Soil Sci.,* 66:317 (1948).
[61] Barshad, *Anal. Chem.,* 21:1148 (1949).
[62] Nichols and Rogers, *Ind. Eng. Chem., A.E.,* 16:137 (1944)
[63] Fisher and Meloche, *Anal. Chem.,* 24:1100 (1952).

15–96. Molybdenum Standard. Exactly 0.1840 gm of ammonium molybdate, $(NH_4)_6Mo_7O_{24} \cdot 4 H_2O$, is dissolved in 900 ml of water and the solution is diluted to exactly 1 liter, giving 100 ppm of Mo. A 5-ppm Mo standard is prepared by dilution of 50 ml to 1000. Aliquots of this solution (0.5, 1, 2, 5, and 10 ml) are taken for the standard curve, the color being developed as for the test solution in the procedure. The above gives the optimum range of 2.5 to 50 ugm in 25-ml volume of colored solution, or 0.1 to 2.0 ppm Mo. A 1-ppm Mo standard is employed to extend the range down to 1 ugm of Mo, and a 15-ppm Mo standard is employed for 75 ugm of Mo (3.0 ppm Mo) to cover the maximum range of 1 to 75 ugm of Mo.

PROCEDURE[64]

15–97. Preparation of Test Solution. The test or standard solution is prepared to contain 2.5 to 50 ugm (1 to 75 ugm permissible) of Mo in 10 ml of water, to 15 HCl, or H_2SO_4 solution. The solution should contain no actively oxidizing acids, such as HNO_3 or $HClO_4$, and if present they are removed by evaporation. In the extraction procedure (¶ 15–104), the Mo is oxidized to hexavalent state and iron is removed by the Na_2CO_3-water slurry separation. If some other test solution contains more than the equivalent of 100 ppm of Fe in the 25-ml final volume, the iron is precipitated and removed by the NH_4OH separation, since more than this amount causes a fine precipitate in the final Mo test solution.

15–98. Development of the Amber Color. The standard or test solution of Mo (¶ 15–97) is placed in a 25-ml volumetric flask. Enough HCl must be present or be added to make the final 25-ml of solution 1.2 to 4 N with respect to nonoxidizing acids (3 ml of concentrated HCl is added for water solutions); the HCl has already been added in the solutions taken from the silica separation procedure (¶ 15–112). Then 1.5 ml of 10 per cent KSCN solution and 8 ml of acetone are added and the solution is made to volume and mixed. The solution in the flask is digested in a 60° to 70°C water bath for an hour, or longer if necessary for disappearance of the red $Fe(SCN)_3$ color. (The color of the standards develops in 20 minutes, but

[64] Adapted here to increased sensitivity by use of 470-mu filter and smaller volumes, from Ellis and Olson, *Anal. Chem.,* 22:328 (1950). These authors obtained a more intense color by acetone reduction than by chlorostannous reduction. Their calibration curve with 420-mu light is nonlinear; their reported range of 5 to 1000 ugm of Mo resulted in reported transmissions of 96 to 1 per cent respectively, which is considerably beyond the optimum range. The range of 1 to 75 ugm of Mo employed here gives transmissions of 97 to 18 per cent, but the percentage transmission can be decreased enough for the determination of 0.15 to 15 ugm of Mo by extraction of the color in organic solvents (¶ 15–101) and by use of a 5-cm absorption cell, as reported by Parks *et al., Ind. Eng. Chem., A.E.,* 15:528 (1943). Appreciation is expressed to Drs. Roscoe Ellis, H. G. Raj, and H. H. Hull for help with testing at the University of Wisconsin the modifications of the original procedure incorporated here.

interfering red Fe(SCN)$_3$ color of soil extracts may not be gone for 1 to 3 or more hours. The color remains satisfactory if heating is continued as long as 2 or 4 hours.) The solution is then cooled to room temperature and mixed. It is examined for traces of turbidity. If they are present, a portion of the solution is centrifuged (or filtered through Whatman No. 42 filter paper). The color is read at once in a colorimeter with 470-mu light maximum.

15–99. The ugm of Mo present is obtained by means of a standard curve. The Mo content of the reagents is taken into account through blank determinations carried through all of the steps of the preparatory procedures.

ALTERNATIVE PROCEDURES

15–100. Intensification of the thiocyanate color with chlorostannous reduction has been reported as resulting from the presence of ferric[65] and nitrate ions, but these additions are apparently unnecessary when acetone reduction is employed. In 1 procedure,[66] 3 or 4 drops of 0.01 N FeCl$_3$ are added per determination. The color is developed with freshly prepared chlorostannous acid (SnCl$_2$ · 2 H$_2$O in 1.2 N HCl) in sufficient quantity to cause the loss of ferric thiocyanate color and maximum development of molybdic thiocyanate color, but a large excess of reductant is not permissible. Tests of increments of chlorostannous acid are suggested for the particular system to be employed. The intensification by nitrate is attributed to more efficient conversion of the Mo to hexavalent state prior to color development. In another procedure,[67] 1 mgm of Fe is added as a ferric solution to each determination for color intensification. In another,[68] 3 drops of 0.01 N FeCl$_3$, 1 ml of 5 N NaNO$_3$, and 6 ml of 10 per cent SnCl$_2$ · 2 H$_2$O in 1.2 N HCl are added to each Mo determination.

15–101. Extraction of Colored Mo Solution in Organic Solvents. As a means of increasing the sensitivity of the method, and so decreasing the required size of sample when the Mo content is low, the Mo color developed with SnCl$_2$ has been extracted in organic solvents. A solution heavier than water,[69] which is a considerable advantage, consists of CCl$_4$ and isoamyl alcohol mixed in equal volumes. Silicone stopcock grease was employed on the separatory funnels and the color read at 470 mu. The Mo thiocyanate color has been extracted with peroxide-free isopropyl ether.[70]

[65] Nichols and Rogers, *Ind. Eng. Chem., A.E.,* 16:137 (1944).

[66] Barshad, *Anal. Chem.,* 21:1148 (1949).

[67] Fujimoto and Sherman, *Agron. Jour.,* 43:425 (1951).

[68] Sarthou, Ph.D. Thesis, Univ. Wis. (1951).

[69] Arkley and Johnson, *Anal. Chem.,* 26:572 (1954).

[70] Reichen and Ward, U S. Geol. Surv. Cir. 124 (1951); Purvis and Peterson, *Soil Sci.,* 81:223 (1956).

To detect peroxides, 5 ml of isopropyl alcohol was shaken vigorously with 5 ml of acidified aqueous solution of KI. If the KI solution does not remain practically colorless, enough peroxides are indicated to make the ether unsatisfactory.

15–102. Fujimoto and Sherman[71] placed a 50-ml aliquot of the Mo test solution in a 125-ml separatory funnel and then added 1 ml of 10 per cent ammonium citrate, 3 ml of 10 per cent NH_4SCN, and 3 ml of 10 per cent $SnCl_2 \cdot 2 H_2O$ in 2 N HCl, followed by shaking. The colored complex then was extracted in 6 ml of normal butyl alcohol by vigorous shaking for 1 minute. Since butyl alcohol is partially soluble in water, the initial 6 ml decreased to about 4 ml. The aqueous layer was drained into a beaker and kept for further extraction. The butyl alcohol phase was slowly run into a 10-ml calibrated centrifuge tube. The aqueous portion was returned to the separatory funnel, 4 ml of fresh butyl alcohol added, and the extraction repeated. For the third extraction, only 2 ml of butyl alcohol was used. The combined alcohol extract was diluted to 10.0 ml with butyl alcohol and shaken vigorously. The small amount of aqueous solution, which unavoidably drained with the alcohol, disappeared when the solution was diluted to 10 ml with alcohol and shaken. The occasional turbidity of the alcohol solution was removed by a few minutes of centrifugation. The clear supernatant solution was transferred to the comparator tube and allowed to stand for 10 minutes and then the percentage transmission was measured spectrophotometrically. The standard solutions were evaporated and subjected to fusion and other treatments similar to the samples.

15–103. Molybdenum of plants[72] and soils[73] has been determined by the green-colored molybdenum-dithiol complex. Determination of Cu and Mo in the one dithiol system has an advantage because of the interrelationship of these 2 elements in animal nutrition. The lengthy separations involved has led to preference[74] for the thiocyanate method for Mo in some laboratories.

TOTAL MOLYBDENUM IN SOILS AND PLANTS

(Na_2CO_3 fusion and alkaline separation)

15–104. The total molybdenum content of soils for parts of North and South America and Asia range from 1 to 10 ppm, but extend in some soils to 20 and even to 30 or more ppm. Liming a soil containing 32 ppm of Mo resulted[75] in the production of legume vegetation containing over 10 ppm

---

[71] *Agron. Jour.,* 43:425 (1951).

[72] Piper and Beckwith, *J. Soc. Chem. Ind.,* 67:374 (1948); *Proc. Specialists Conf. in Agr. Australia,* 1949:144 (1951); Dick and Bingley, *Australian J. Exp. Biol. Med. Sci.,* 25:193 (1947).

[73] Williams, *J. Sci. Food Agr.,* 6:104 (1955).

[74] Purvis and Peterson, *Soil Sci.,* 81:223 (1956).

[75] Robinson *et al., Soil Sci.,* 72:267 (1951).

of Mo, the content at and above which toxicity to cattle begins. The Mo content of various plants ranged from 0.1 to 47 ppm. However, plants in Hawaii ranged[76] mainly below 1 ppm in spite of unusually high soil content of Mo (¶ 15–113). Soil Mo becomes tightly associated[77] with free iron oxides and then has an extremely low availability. Barshad[78] reported as much as 200 ppm of Mo in some alfalfa in California, and Cunningham and Hogan[79] reported an increase from 3 ppm Mo in pasture plants to 100 ppm Mo, as a result of the application of 150 gm of ammonium molybdate or 82 gm of Mo per hectare (0.15 and 0.08 pounds per acre, respectively) of acid peat.

APPARATUS

15–105. Needed apparatus consists of a platinum dish (plants) or 35-ml crucible (soils), an electric furnace or Meker burner, 100-ml and 25-ml graduated cylinders, a 250-ml beaker, a centrifuge and 25-ml volumetric centrifuge tube, a filter funnel and Whatman No. 40 paper, a 100-ml volumetric flask, and pipets.

REAGENTS

15–106. Needed reagents are anhydrous Na_2CO_3 (Mo-free or low in Mo, such as Baker's, Phillipsburg, N.J.), 3 per cent of ethanol in water, and concentrated and 3 N HCl.

PROCEDURE

15–107. Soil or the ash of plant tissue is fused in Na_2CO_3 to effect solution of molybdate as the sodium salt and to separate much of the interfering substances as insolubles in the water extract. The platinum ware is cleaned by alternate fusions in Na_2CO_3 and $KHSO_4$ followed by digestion in dilute HCl until the Mo blank is reproducible and fairly low.

15–108. Ashing and Fusion of Plant Tissue.[80] One to 10 gm of dried plant tissue is ashed in a platinum dish in an electric furnace at 500°C. The ash is then fused in 2 gm of anhydrous Na_2CO_3 (of low Mo content as determined in preliminary tests) at 1000°C in an electric furnace or over a Meker burner. Care is taken to bring all of the ash into contact with the flux for a complete fusion. The melt is treated as for soils (¶ 15–111).

15–109. Fusion of Soils.[81] A 2-gm sample of soil, ground to pass 0.25 mm openings (60 meshes per inch) of silk bolting cloth, is transferred to a 35-ml platinum crucible containing about one gm of anhydrous Na_2CO_3.

[76] Fujimoto and Sherman, *Agron. Jour.*, 43:424 (1951).
[77] Robinson and Edgington, *Soil Sci.*, 77:237 (1954).
[78] *Soil Sci.*, 66:187 (1948).
[79] *New Zealand J. Sci. Tech.*, A 31:(1)39 (1949).
[80] Robinson and Edgington, *Soil Sci.*, 77:237 (1954).
[81] Robinson *et al.*, *Soil Sci.*, 72:267 (1951).

Six gm more of Na_2CO_3 is mixed with the soil by stirring with a glass rod, the latter being brushed off afterwards, to return adhering particles to the crucible. The heating is carried only to about 500°C to burn off the soil organic matter during the first 5 or 10 minutes, in an oxidizing atmosphere, to avoid the possibility of Mo loss,[82] before the charge is actually fused.

15–110. The crucible is partially covered and the temperature is gradually raised to 950° to 1050°C in an electric furnace or with the full heat of a Meker burner, for 15 to 20 minutes or until fusion is complete, the flux being swirled to mix at intervals after it becomes molten. When bubbles cease to rise and the melt is quiet, the crucible is rotated to spread the melt on the sides as it sets into a cake. (Precautions in handling platinum are described in ¶ 11–13).

15–111. Extraction of Mo from Cake. When the crucible or dish, containing the Na_2CO_3 cake from soil or plant-ash fusion, has cooled, it is inverted over a 250-ml beaker and the cake is dropped from the platinum container as the latter is gently rolled between the thumb and fingers. If the cake does not become detached, the crucible is placed in the beaker. The cake is disintegrated in 100 ml of water (containing 2 per cent by volume of ethanol to reduce the manganate[83] and avoid attack of the platinum ware if the crucible has been placed in the beaker). The disintegration of the cake is hastened by trituration with a rubber policeman on a glass rod and warming on a steam hot plate for a period of several hours. The volume or the resulting slurry suspension, in which the particles have been thoroughly disintegrated, is measured in a graduated cylinder and filtered through a dry Whatman No. 40 filter paper into a 250-ml beaker. The volume of the undiluted filtrate is measured and all (or an aliquot) is taken for the Mo determination. (In lieu of filtering, the suspension may be clarified by centrifugation.) The Mo remains soluble as sodium molybdate while Fe, Ti, Ca, Mg, and many other ions remain in the precipitate.[84] The filtrate should be perfectly clear.

15–112. Removal of Silica. The clear filtrate solution is acidified with HCl (2 ml of concentrated HCl per gm Na_2CO_3 contained) and is evaporated to dryness. The residue is taken up in exactly (pipet) 20 ml of 3 N HCl (in lieu of HCl addition in the color development, ¶ 15–98). The suspension is briefly warmed on a steam plate while being triturated thoroughly. It is then transferred to a 25-ml centrifuge tube and centrifuged to throw down the silica and undissolved salt. As large an aliquot as possible (but not over 15 ml) of the clear supernatant solution is taken for the Mo

[82] Robinson, *Soil Sci.,* 66:318 (1948); Fujimoto and Sherman, *Agron. Jour.,* 43: 425 (1951).

[83] Fujimoto and Sherman, *Agron. Jour.,* 43:425 (1951).

[84] Hillebrand and Lundell, *Applied Inorganic Analysis* (New York: John Wiley and Sons, Inc., 1929); Sandell, *op. cit.,* p. 462; Robinson and Edgington, *Soil Sci.,* 72: 267 (1951).

analysis (¶ 15–97). If the amount of Mo is too low, the use of more sample is preferable to substitution of washing of a filter in either of the two separations.

15–113. With plant ash low in silica, silica does not need to be removed from the filtrate of the second separation[85] (¶ 15–112). Direct HCl extraction of Mo from the plant ash obtained in a porcelain dish has been employed.[86] A procedure for extraction of Mo from plants by wet oxidation in HNO_3, $HClO_4$, and H_2SO_4 has been employed.[87] But for thiocyanate color stability, the strongly oxidizing acids must be removed. Strong acids have been employed to extract the Mo from the Na_2CO_3 fusion of soils, but this sacrifices the alkaline slurry separation obtained after the Na_2CO_3 fusion (¶ 15–111). Reported[88] Mo contents of Hawaiian soils ranged from 9 to 74 ppm with strong acid extraction, while only 1.8 to 18.6 ppm were found[89] for the same soils when the alkaline separation (¶ 15–111) was employed, and the lower values were confirmed by spectrographic analysis. Field methods have been reported for Mo in plants[90] and rocks and soils[91] that are suitable for biogeochemical prospecting.

15–114. One proposed[92] method for available soil Mo involves extraction of the soil with acid ammonium oxalate solution buffered at pH 3.3.

COBALT DETERMINATION

15–115. Two micro methods have found wide use for the determination of cobalt in the small quantities available for analysis from convenient sizes of plant, animal, and soil samples. Both are based on a chromogen developed by cobalt with the "o-nitroso-R" type salts,[93] with 550-mu light maximum[94] giving a Beer's Law relationship. This type of salt was first prepared, and later made readily available through an easy process of synthesis, by Baudisch and coworkers.[95] Determination of cobalt by o-nitro-

---

[85] Robinson et al., Soil Sci., 72:269 (1951).

[86] Barshad, Anal. Chem., 21:1149 (1949).

[87] Parks et al., Ind. Eng. Chem., A.E., 15:527 (1943); Piper and Beckwith, Proc. Specialists Conf. in Agr. Australia (1951).

[88] Fujimoto and Sherman, Agron. Jour., 43:425 (1951); Bartrand, Compt. rend., 211:406 (1940).

[89] Robinson and Alexander, Soil Sci., 75:287 (1953).

[90] Reichen and Ward, U.S. Geol. Surv. Cir. 124 (1951).

[91] Ward, Anal. Chem., 23:788 (1951).

[92] Grigg, New Zealand J. Sci. Tech., A34:405 (1953), Analyst, 78:470 (1953); Purvis and Peterson, Soil Sci., 81:223 (1956).

[93] Sandell, op. cit., p. 287.

[94] Cooper and Mattern, Anal. Chem., 24:574 (1952); Claassen and Westerveld, Rec. trav. chim., 67:720 (1948); Haywood and Wood, J. Soc. Chem. Ind., 62:37 (1943).

[95] Ber., 45:1164 (1912), 48:1660 (1915); Sci., 92:336 (1940); J. Am. Chem. Soc., 63:622 (1941).

sophenol has been described by Cronheim,[96] and by *o*-nitrosocresol by Ellis and Thompson.[97] The latter method has given more consistent results and, in spite of the dithizone separation involved, is essentially a simpler method, according to K. C. Beeson.[98] It has been employed for the determination of total Co in soils by Holmes.[99] A colorimetric field method for cobalt has been described by Almond and Bloom.[100] No details of the micro procedures are given here.

15–116. Determination of larger quantities of cobalt (0.1 to 10 mgm Co) has been described in connection with potassium determination by the cobaltinitrite procedure (¶ 6–27). It can also be determined as $K_3Co(NO_2)_6 \cdot 1.5 H_2O$ (¶ 6–61).

QUESTIONS

1. State why the extraction and availability of the elements Fe, Mn, Cu, Zn, Mo, and Co cannot be treated in the same way as that of metallic cations that are strong base formers?

2. What is the relation of iron valence to *o*-phenanthroline color formation? How can the orthophenanthroline compound be employed as an oxidation-reduction indicator?

3. Why must the extraction of ferrous iron from soils be carried out very rapidly?

4. Why cannot exchangeable ferric iron of soils be extracted in neutral NH_4OAc?

5. Why is a reducing agent employed in the extraction of available manganese from soils?

6. Why may manganese deficiency be induced in a soil, which did not previously show deficiency, by the application of ground limestone?

7. Why is the color intensified by isoamyl acetate extraction of the copper carbamate?

8. What principle is employed in the separation of zinc as dithizonate from elements that would interfere with its determination as the dithizone compound?

9. List several types of extractions employed for fractions of soil copper and of soil zinc that may be correlated with availability.

10. Discuss the valence relations of molybdenum determination as the thiocyanate.

11. Into what chemical form is the molybdenum converted during the alkaline slurry separation?

12. Why is cobalt determination in plant materials and soils important to the soil chemist?

[96] *Ind. Eng. Chem., A.E.,* 14:445 (1942).
[97] *Ind. Eng. Chem., A.E.,* 17:254 (1945).
[98] Private communication.
[99] *Soil Sci.,* 59:77 (1945).
[100] U.S. Geol. Surv. Cir. 125 (1951).

16

Polarographic Analysis
for Soils and Plant Tissue

*Voltammetric[1] determination of substances which are reducible
or oxidizable at the dropping mercury electrode*

16–1. The minor nutrient elements, Cu, Zn, Fe, Mn, Co, and Mo, from soils and plants are readily determined voltammetrically ("polarographically") with a dropping mercury electrode. Though highly effective colorimetric methods are available for most of these elements (Chapter 15), the polarographic method of analysis is the most effective for several of them, especially Zn. It has been employed for Mn obtained in cation exchange capacity measurement (¶ 4–31). Procedures are given (¶ 16–34) for dithizone separation of Cu and Zn from solutions derived from soils (¶ 15–52, 15–83) or plant tissue (¶ 12–39), and for determination of Cu, Zn, and Mn.

16–2. Organic compounds that are reduced or oxidized at the dropping mercury electrode at characteristic potentials can be determined. Possibilities exist for many applications to soils and plant systems. For example, the voltage recorded[2] on a polarograph attached between a plant stem and a solution bathing the roots was equal to the ionization potential ($E\frac{1}{2}$) of the ion supplied in the solution. Also, the polarogram of a soil varies with pH and exchangeable cation.[3]

16–3. Basic Principles. Polarographic analysis is based on the fact that both qualitative and quantitative analyses can be made from the voltage-

---

[1] Kolthoff and Jordan, *Anal. Chem.*, 25:1833 (1953).

[2] Breazeale and McGeorge, *Soil Sci.*, 75:443 (1953).

[3] Puri, *Soils, their Physics and Chemistry* (New York: Reinhold Publishing Corporation, 1949), p. 141.

current curve obtained when an electro reducible or electro oxidizable element or compound in solution is electrolyzed with an increasing voltage on the electrodes (EMF). The analysis is thus essentially a *voltammetric* determination. The voltage measured is the polarization voltage, recorded graphically, hence the name *polarograph*.[4]

16-4. The voltage is applied between a small, readily polarized electrode (dropping Hg) and a large, nonpolarized electrode (and calomel cell-KCl junction) separated by an indifferent *supporting electrolyte* (Fig. 16–1).

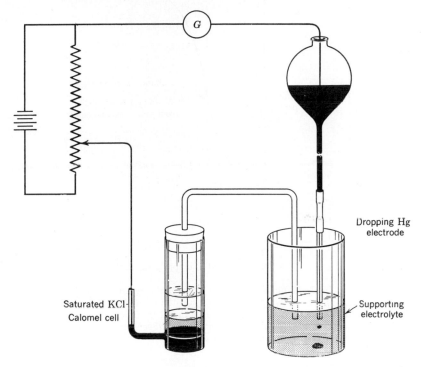

Fig. 16–1. Schematic arrangement of apparatus for polarographic analysis. (After Menzel and Jackson, *Anal. Chem.,* 23:1861, 1951.)

The technique is distinguishable from amperometric, conductometric, electrophoretic and electrodialysis determinations by its dependence on the oxidation or reduction potential of the constituent. It has similarities to the

---

[4] Heyrovsky, *Chem. Listy,* 16:256 (1922); automatic recording, Heyrovsky and Shikata, *Rec. trav. chim.,* 44:496 (1925); Heyrovsky, *Polarographie* (Ann Arbor, Mich.: J. W. Edwards, 1947); Kolthoff and Lingane, *Polarography,* 2nd ed. (New York: Interscience Publishers, Inc., 1952); Muller, *The Polarographic Method of Analysis,* 2nd ed. (Easton, Pa.: Chemical Education Publishing Co., 1951).

graded cathode potential method[5] of separation of metals by electrodeposition.

16–5. The characteristic current-voltage curve obtained is called the *polarogram* (Fig. 16–2). At low potentials, the curve shows only a small

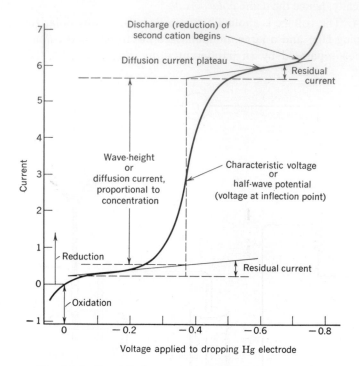

Fig. 16–2. General character of the polarogram or voltammetric curve of a single reducible substance. An ionic, atomic, or molecular species or organic functional group can be identified qualitatively by the *characteristic voltage,* and determined quantitatively by the *wave height.*

"residual current" and only a slight rise in current with increasing EMF. The EMF has not yet become sufficiently high to cause the main electrode reaction to occur. Only a small current, due to cathodic capacitance effects or possibly to minute traces of other materials, is flowing.

16–6. Diffusion Current. As the EMF increases further there is a sudden sharp rise in the current flow, followed by a leveling off at a new and higher current (Fig. 16–2). The rise in current indicates that an EMF has been reached that is great enough to produce the electrode reaction with the consequent increase in current passage. As soon as the electrode reaction be-

---

[5] Diehl, *Electrochemical Analysis with Graded Cathode Potential* (Columbus, Ohio: G. F. Smith Chemical Co., 1948).

gins, the solute involved in the reaction becomes exhausted in the vicinity of the small electrode, producing a condition of concentration polarization at the electrode.

16–7. The supply of solute at the electrode is renewed only by kinetic diffusion from the body of the solution, since movement of solute to the electrode and the influence of the potential gradient between the electrodes has been reduced to a negligible quantity by the addition of an excess of a "supporting" electrolyte that does not enter into the electrode reaction. This means that the resistance of the solution is low and thus provides a very low potential gradient, $E = IR$.

16–8. The solute diffusion rate is proportional to the difference in concentration of solute at the electrode and in the body of the solution. Since the concentration at the electrode is zero, the rate of diffusion is directly proportional to the concentration in the body of the solution. When the "diffusion current" has risen to the value corresponding to the rate of arrival of solute at the electrode by diffusion, it levels off and remains constant even though the EMF continues to rise. Since the rise in current is proportional to the rate of diffusion of solute, it is also proportional to the concentration of solute in the body of the solution, and this concentration may be determined by measuring the height of the current rise or "step" (wave height) through the application of the necessary instrumental factors.

16–9. The Ilkovic equation for diffusion current (i_d) is

$$i_d = 605\ n\ CD^{1/2}m^{2/3}t^{1/6} \tag{16–1}$$

in which n is the number of electrons involved in the electrode reaction, C is the concentration of the reduced or oxidized ion, D is the diffusion coefficient, m is mass of Hg flowing per second from the capillary, and t is the number of seconds required for a drop to form. It will be seen that for a given capillary and reacting substance, the current will be proportional to the concentration of the reduced or oxidized substance. The usual range of concentration is from 10^{-3} to 10^{-5} molar.

16–10. Sometimes a substance being determined causes a maximum in the diffusion current just after its decomposition potential is reached and then drops back to its normal current. The production of this maximum may result from adsorption on the dropping mercury. The production of maxima may be suppressed by the addition of a suitable organic reagent such as gelatin or fuchsin. Gelatin also helps to stabilize the viscosity of the solution through a series of test samples.

16–11. The voltage may shift from (+) to (−) within the course of a single wave step (Fig. 16–2).

16–12. The Characteristic Voltage or Half-Wave Potential. The midpoint or inflection point of the current rise (Fig. 16–2) occurs at an EMF that is the constant for and characteristic of a particular solute under closely prescribed conditions of environment, such as supporting electrolytes, reference electrode, or Hg drop size. The EMF corresponding to the midpoint of the step is known as the "half-wave potential" and serves for qualitative identification of the solute being oxidized or reduced. Each solute species tends to exhibit its own characteristic oxidation or reduction potential, and is not reduced until that potential is reached.

16–13. Supporting Electrolyte. A method for a specific ion species consists of a supporting electrolyte solution with suitable complexing agents to permit each solute species to be reduced or oxidized at a potential that is well separated (about 0.2 volt) from the potentials at which other species are reduced or oxidized. Dissolved oxygen must be removed from the polarographic sample before analysis, since, if present in the supporting electrolyte, it would be reduced at a more negative potential than the elements being determined, and thus would interfere. The supporting electrolyte solution composition can be rather heterogeneous as to other solutes present. But the accuracy falls off somewhat with increase in solute concentration much over 0.1 M, because of the increase in "residual current" not attributable to the reduction of ions of interest (Fig. 16–2). Sometimes the separation cannot be made by selection of supporting electrolyte composition, in which case the separation must be made by conventional chemical methods prior to the instrumental analysis.

16–14. The Dropping Mercury Electrode. The dropping mercury electrode consists of a very fine glass capillary through which mercury is passing at such a rate that it will produce falling drops at a constant rate (every 2 to 5 seconds). This mercury drop has proved to be the most suitable small, readily polarized electrode. No electrode of more general scope has been developed, although many other small metallic electrodes have been tested. The dropping mercury electrode is peculiarly suited to polarography because of the following properties: (a) it gives complete polarization rapidly, (b) it presents a continuously renewed electrode surface, and (c) it gives a high hydrogen "over-voltage."

16-15. At any fixed EMF, the current through the dropping mercury electrode oscillates regularly over a small range because the growth and detachment of mercury drops causes consequent variation in the electrode area. Thus the recorded polarographic step is oscillatory in character rather than even. The various methods of measuring step height automatically compensate for these oscillations. The amplitude of the oscillations can be varied by capacitive damping.

16–16. The rate of flow of the Hg is controlled by the capillary size together with the height of the Hg column. The Hg height is arranged to be variable and is often scale mounted.

COPPER AND ZINC DETERMINATION

(Polarographically in sulfite-ammonia supporting electrolyte)

16–17. Copper and zinc derived from soils or plants (¶ 16–40) can be determined in a solution 0.10 molar in NH_4OH and 0.25 molar in Na_2SO_3 by means of a single polarogram.[6] In this supporting electrolyte, the reduction reactions and half-wave potentials are:

$$Cu(NH_3)_2{}^+ + e^- = Cu(Hg) + 2\,NH_3(H_2O) \qquad (16\text{–}2)$$
$$E_{\frac{1}{2}} = -0.50 \text{ volts}$$

$$Zn(NH_3)_4{}^{++} + 2e^- = Zn(Hg) + 4\,NH_3(H_2O) \qquad (16\text{–}3)$$
$$E_{\frac{1}{2}} = -1.23 \text{ volts}$$

The diffusion current is proportional to the concentration of Cu or Zn up to about 10 millimoles per liter. As little as 0.05 millimoles per liter of Cu can be determined within ± 10 per cent. The accuracy is higher with Zn or with larger amounts of Cu.

16–18. Ferric ion interferes with the polarographic determination of Cu and Zn because it is reduced at a more positive potential. Therefore, Cu, Zn, Co, and Ni are extracted from plant tissue digests by the dithizone separation procedure (¶ 16–34). Cobalt is reduced at nearly the same potential as Zn; however, the content[7] of Co in plants is usually less than 1 ppm compared to 20 to 40 ppm of Zn commonly present. Thus Co rarely influences the Zn determination by more than 2 per cent and can be neglected except with plants of low Zn content. When the Co content is sufficiently great to cause significant error, it can be determined colorimetrically (¶ 15–115), and the equivalent Co wave height then can be deducted[8] from the Zn plus Co wave height. The wave for Ni is at −0.9 volt, well separated from the Cu and Zn waves, and Ni was determined polarographically along with Cu and Zn in analysis of iron pyrites samples. A polarographic accuracy of better than ± 10 per cent for Ni determination in plants would be difficult to attain consistently, as Ni often occurs in lesser concentrations than Cu.

APPARATUS

16–19. Needed apparatus includes a recording polarograph, dropping mercury electrode, saturated calomel half-cell, 2 × 7 cm sample vials, and 50-ml conical flasks. In addition to the usual cleaning, all glassware is rinsed twice with 0.5 N HCl and twice with redistilled water.

---

6 Menzel and Jackson, *Anal. Chem.,* 23:1861 (1951).
7 Beeson, U.S.D.A. Misc. Pub. 369 (1941).
8 Cooper and Mattern, *Anal. Chem.,* 24:574 (1952).

16–20. Several kinds of commercial polarographic (or voltammetric[9]) apparatus record the diffusion current on photographic film or by pen on chart paper (examples, Fig. 16–3 and 16–4). To do this, an electric motor

Fig. 16–3. Sargent's Model XII photographic recording Polarograph. (Photo courtesy E. H. Sargent & Co., Chicago, Ill.)

drives a voltage divider and the recorder synchronously. The applied voltage range can be set to extend from a positive or negative value through zero to a value of the opposite sign (Fig. 16–2), with a total range of up to about 4.5 volts. The current (¶ 16–6) passing through the dropping mercury electrode is measured by a sensitive galvanometer, the sensitivity of which is adjusted with a variable shunt. A manually operated polarograph (example, Fig. 16–5) is less expensive and is suitable for an analysis in which only 1 substance is to be determined and the step shape is approxi-

---

[9] Voltammetric (¶ 16–3) apparatus is sold under copyrighted names such as "Polarograph" (E. H. Sargent & Co.), "Electro-Chemograph" (Leeds & Northrup Co., and "Elecdropode" (Fisher Scientific Co.).

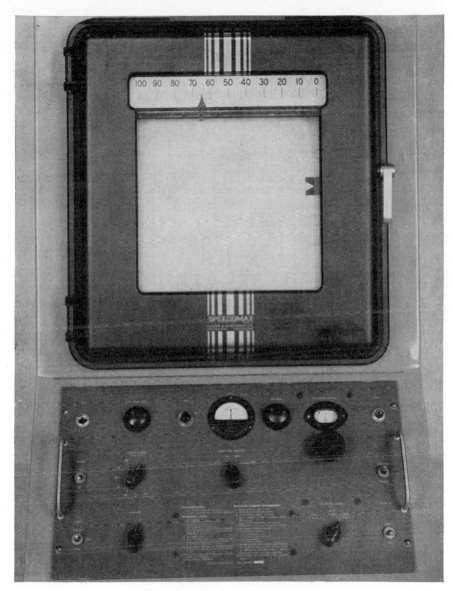

Fig. 16–4. Leeds and Northrup pen-recording Electro-Chemograph. (Photo courtesy Leeds & Northrup Co., Philadelphia, Pa.)

mately a pure form. The latter is characteristic of reversible reactions involved with simple ions in fairly high concentrations. The step height can be measured as the difference between 2 points, 1 on the residual current plateau and 1 on the diffusion current plateau (Fig. 16–2).

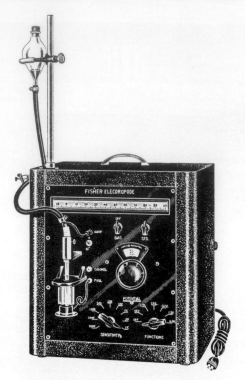

Fig. 16–5. Fisher's manually operated Elecdropode. (Photo courtesy Fisher Scientific Co., Pittsburgh, Pa.)

REAGENTS

16–21. Needed reagents include purified distilled water (distilled water run through an exchange resin column or redistilled in Pyrex glass apparatus), 0.1 per cent gelatin (0.1 gm of gelatin is dissolved with gentle heating in 100 ml of redistilled water), and the supporting electrolyte solution.

16–22. Supporting Electrolyte Solution. For supporting electrolyte enough for 1 set of 12 determinations, 2.1 gm of Na_2SO_3 is dissolved in 66 ml of 0.1 N NH_4OH obtained by dilution of distilled NH_4OH with redistilled water. Because NH_3 is volatile and SO_3^{--} is oxidizable, the solution is freshly prepared each day.

PROCEDURE

16–23. To the dry sample residue from the dithizone separation procedure (¶ 16–41) exactly 5 ml of supporting electrolyte solution and 1 drop of gelatin solution are added. For samples known to be very low in copper, as little as 2 ml of supporting electrolyte may be added. One hour, with occasional gentle swirling of the flask, is enough to dissolve the copper and zinc. The solution is then poured into a dry sample vial.

16–24. The mercury column above the capillary is previously adjusted to a height that gives a drop time of about 4 seconds in the supporting electrolyte with no applied potential. If the capillary is clean, the drop time remains constant for a given height. The sample vial is placed in position with the dropping mercury as 1 electrode and a KCl-agar bridge leading to a calomel half-cell as the other electrode (Fig. 16–1). Recording of the polarogram is begun with an applied potential of −0.2 volt on the dropping mercury electrode. The Cu half wave potential is approximately −0.5 volt. When the potential reaches −0.8 volt, it may be desirable to reduce the sensitivity in order to record the Zn wave. The Zn half-wave potential is approximately −1.2 volt. The recording of the polarogram is stopped when the potential reaches −1.5 volts. The temperature of the solution is measured.

16–25. On the polarogram (photographic print, developed and dried, or pen-recorded polarogram), the diffusion current wave height is measured (Fig. 16–2). If the temperature of the polarographic solution was not 25°C, a correction of 2 per cent per degree difference is made, the correction being added if the temperature was lower and subtracted if it was higher than 25°C. The relation between the diffusion current wave height and the concentration of copper or zinc is determined by the use of standard samples.

ALTERNATIVE PROCEDURES

16–26. The sulfite-chloride supporting electrolyte (¶ 16–32) can also be used for copper and zinc determination. The half-wave potentials for reduction of copper and zinc are −0.3 and −1.0 volts, respectively. However, the more negative reduction potential obtained for copper in the sulfite-ammonia supporting electrolyte allows a more accurate estimate of low concentrations of copper.

16–27. The polarograph has been applied to zinc analysis of soils and plants after precipitation of iron,[10] for zinc after concentration by dithizone extraction[11] (¶ 16–34), for copper,[12] and for several elements simultaneously after the separation of silica.[13] Different supporting electrolytes have been used by each investigator. Trace elements have also been preconcentrated by ion exchange.[14]

[10] Cummings and Reed, *S.S.S.A. Proc.,* 5:167 (1941).
[11] Stout *et al., Coll. Czech. Chem. Comm.,* 10:129 (1938); Walkley, *Australian J. Exp. Biol. Med. Sci.,* 20:139 (1942).
[12] Cranston and Thompson, *Ind. Eng. Chem.,* A.E., 18:323 (1946).
[13] Zak, *Biedermanns Zentr.,* B. *Tierernähr.,* 14:301 (1942).
[14] Riches, *Nature,* 158:96 (1946).

MANGANESE DETERMINATION
(Polarographically in sulfite-chloride supporting electrolyte)

16–28. Manganese can be determined in a solution 0.25 molar in Na_2SO_3 and 0.10 molar in NaCl. In this supporting electrolyte the reduction reaction and half-wave potential are:

$$Mn^{++} + 2e^- = Mn \text{ (Hg)} \qquad (16\text{–}4)$$
$$E_{\frac{1}{2}} = -1.5 \text{ volts}$$

Standard samples with manganese concentrations ranging from 0.01 to 0.1 millimoles per liter are determined within ± 5 per cent in the presence of similar concentrations of copper and zinc.

16–29. Manganese is not extracted with Cu and Zn by the dithizone-CCl_4 separation procedure (¶ 16–34). Manganese is more abundant in plant material than copper and zinc and its wave occurs after those of copper and zinc at a suitable potential of −1.5 volts in the sulfite-ammonia supporting electrolyte (¶ 16–22). Manganese, copper, and zinc of soils and plants could be determined on a single polarogram if the separation procedure were modified to include manganese and still exclude iron. A disadvantage for Mn determination arises because the diffusion current for Mn in the sulfite-ammonia supporting electrolyte is abnormally low, 1.69 microamperes per millimole of concentration. The low diffusion current may arise from the repression of manganese solubility. The solubility product of $Mn(OH)_2$ is exceeded and the ammonia concentration may be too low to form a soluble manganous amine ion. In a supporting electrolyte consisting of sodium sulfite alone or sulfite and chloride (¶ 16–32), the diffusion current for millimolar Mn is about 4 microamperes and gives a satisfactory determination (¶ 16–33).

APPARATUS

16–30. Needed apparatus includes a recording polarograph, a dropping mercury electrode, a saturated calomel half-cell, 2 × 7 cm sample vials, and 50-ml conical flasks. In addition to the usual cleaning, all glassware is rinsed twice with 0.5 N HCl and twice with redistilled water.

REAGENTS

16–31. Needed reagents include redistilled water (distilled water is redistilled in the Pyrex glass apparatus), 0.1 per cent gelatin (0.1 gm of gelatin is dissolved with gentle heating in 100 ml of redistilled water), and the supporting electrolyte solution.

16–32. Supporting Electrolyte Solution. 2.1 gm of Na_2SO_3 and 0.39 gm of NaCl are dissolved in 66 ml of redistilled water. The solution is freshly prepared each day.

PROCEDURE

16–33. The procedure for polarographic determination of manganese is the same as that for copper and zinc, with appropriate substitution of reagents and voltages in recording the polarogram.

COPPER AND ZINC SEPARATION FROM RESIDUE OF WET OXIDATION OF PLANT TISSUE[15]
(Dithizone separation)

16–34. Diphenylthiocarbazone (dithizone) forms complex with most transition metals according to the general reaction:

$$n\,S = C \underset{\substack{N-N-\bigcirc\\H\ \ H}}{\overset{N=N-\bigcirc}{\Big\langle}} + M^{n+} \longrightarrow \left[S = C \underset{\substack{N-N^-\bigcirc\\H}}{\overset{N=N-\bigcirc}{\Big\langle}} \right]_n M + n\,H^+$$

(16–5)

These complexes are to be quantitatively extracted from water solution into CCl_4. The pH range for stable complex formation varies somewhat with the different metals. Thus, Cu, Zn, Co, and Ni are extracted at pH values from 8 to 10. Ferrous ion is extracted at pH values from 6 to 7 and Mn is reported to be extracted at pH 11.[16]

APPARATUS

16–35. Needed apparatus includes a 1-liter separatory funnel, 125-ml separatory funnels, and 500-ml and 50-ml conical flasks.

REAGENTS

16–36. Needed reagents include thymol blue indicator, dithizone (diphenylthiocarbazone, Eastman Kodak Co., Rochester, N.Y.), redistilled water (distilled water is redistilled in Pyrex glass apparatus), 6 N HCl (redistilled in Pyrex apparatus), 4 N NH_4OH (NH_3 absorbed in redistilled water cooled in an ice salt bath), and the following.

16–37. Ammonium Citrate Buffer. This buffer is made by adding 50 ml of 10 per cent citric acid solution to 200 ml of 4 N NH_4OH.

16–38. Distilled CCl_4. Technical grade or used CCl_4 is purified by washing successively with 20 per cent H_2SO_4, 20 per cent NaOH, and distilled water. The washed product is distilled over Na_2CO_3 in Pyrex glass apparatus.

PROCEDURE

16–39. Three hundred ml of ammonium citrate buffer, 10 ml of redistilled CCl_4, and 0.1 gm of dithizone are shaken together vigorously for 1 minute in a 1-liter separatory funnel. The buffer solution becomes red, ow-

[15] Menzel and Jackson, *Anal. Chem.*, 23:1861 (1951).
[16] An extensive discussion of dithizone reactions will be found in Welcher, *Organic Analytical Reagents*, Vol. 3 (New York: D. Van Nostrand Company, Inc., 1947).

ing to the solubility of ammonium dithizonate in water. Copper and zinc impurities from the reagents are removed by drawing the CCl₄ layer out of the funnel. The buffer solution is extracted once more by shaking for 1 minute with 10 ml of redistilled CCl₄, which then has a clear green color, due entirely to the solubility of dithizone in carbon tetrachloride.

16–40. Twenty-five ml of purified buffer solution containing dithizone, and 5 ml of redistilled CCl₄ are placed in a 125-ml separatory funnel. The plant tissue digest (¶ 12–39) or soil extract (¶ 15–52, 15–57, 15–83) is transferred to the separatory funnel with 2 washings of the flask with redistilled water. The separatory funnel is shaken for 1 minute to bring most of the copper and zinc into the CCl₄ layer. If the pH of the aqueous phase is not between 9 and 10, as indicated by thymol blue indicator on a spot plate, it is adjusted with distilled HCl or distilled NH₄OH. The funnel is again shaken for 1 minute and the carbon tetrachloride phase is withdrawn into a 50-ml conical flask. None of the silica that collects between the layers must enter the stopcock bore. Two 2-ml washings with redistilled CCl₄ usually suffice to remove all the copper and zinc, as indicated by the clear green color of the CCl₄ layer in the last washing.

16–41. The carbon tetrachloride extract is evaporated to dryness. The dithizone is oxidized by digesting the residue in the conical flask with 2 ml of ternary acid mixture (¶ 12–24) at 300°C on an electric hot plate for 2 hours. Finally the sides of the conical flask are heated briefly and cautiously above a Meker burner to remove the last traces of sulfuric acid. The Cu and Zn in the residue is ready for the polarographic analysis (¶ 16–23).

QUESTIONS

1. State the basis for qualitative analysis by means of the polarograph.

2. State the basis for quantitative analysis by means of the polarograph.

3. Define the following: (a) supporting electrolyte, (b) residual current, (c) diffusion current plateau.

4. Draw a typical voltammetric curve such as obtained with the polarograph when the step shape approximates pure form; label the diagram as to residual current, half-wave potential, diffusion current plateau; and indicate the wave height.

5. List the 3 general types of voltammetric instruments that are available commercially. (Operating types rather than commercial makes are wanted.)

6. What is the purpose of the addition of gelatin to the supporting electrolyte?

7. List the half-wave potentials for Cu and Zn in the NH_4OH-Na_2SO_3 supporting electrolyte.

8. Under what conditions can Cu, Zn, and Mn be determined in a single solution and recorded on a single polarogram?

9. Outline the typical procedure employed for the dithizone separation of Cu, Zn, etc. from iron. Why is the separation necessary?

17

Absorption Spectrophotometry

> . . . a systematic property of the material containing the con-
> stituent, such as color . . . light absorptive capacity . . .
>
> —MELLON[1]

17–1. Absorption spectra have been observed by man since earliest times, through visual color in rainbows, stones, waters, plants, and animals. White light changes to colored light when some wave lengths have been absorbed, and substances from which such light is passing are said to be *colored*. Precisely speaking, the substance shows "light absorptive capacity," and the actual color is dependent on the quality of light incident on the material. Certain wave lengths are preferentially absorbed, but the color *seen* is that characteristic of the wave lengths *not* absorbed. Thus, the *hue* of color seen will vary according to the spectrum of the incident light.

17–2. Basic Principles. Energy of atoms and interatomic bonds in crystals, in solvated ions in solution, in radicals, or in molecules is subject to changes in level by absorption of light energy. Light absorption of a general character merely heats up the absorbing material without coloration. But usually a given absorbing mechanism favors absorption of light in specific short wave length bands; and the resulting variation in light intensity as a function of wave length is an absorption spectrum. Absorption spectrophotometry began by visual estimates of intensity and hue of light transmitted by a sample. Quantitative measurement of color began with comparison of standard and test solutions in tubes of the same size and shape. Flat bottoms and parallel sides incorporated in Nessler tubes permitted accurate comparisons of different thickness of solution reciprocally with dif-

---

[1] *Colorimetry for Chemists* (Columbus, Ohio: G. F. Smith Chemical Co., 1945), p. iii.

ferent concentrations. Addition of lenses to bring the view of the two tubes together gave the visual colorimeter.[2]

17–3. *Colorimetry* concerns the absorption of visible light, usually by a solution. *Absorption spectrophotometry*[3] (also *absorption spectroscopy*[4]) concerns radiation absorption by solid or solution in the visible, ultraviolet, and infrared wave length ranges of electromagnetic radiation. Absorption spectrophotometry performs 2 distinct functions: (a) radiation absorption is measured as a function of *concentration* at a given narrow wave length band (¶ 17–19) and (b) the radiation absorption is measured as a function of *wave length* (narrow band increments), for a given constant quantity of sample, to obtain the absorption spectrum (¶ 17–44). *Emission spectrophotometry* (also *emission spectroscopy*) refers to measurement of the quality of spectrum and quantity of radiation *emitted* by the sample constituents (Chapter 18). Taken together, the emission and absorption techniques are the basis of *spectrochemical* methods. There is no sharp boundary between the 2 techniques, because radiation absorption effects accompany emission. Also, fluorescent emission sometimes occurs when radiation is absorbed in solutions or in crystals—the basis of *fluorescence analysis.*

17–4. Spectral Sensitivity of Human Vision. Human vision detects electromagnetic wave lengths extending from about 400 mu to about 730 mu, the range of "visible" radiation. The spectral colors defined by human vision have wave length range in mu as follows:

violet—400 to 450	green—500 to 570	orange—590 to 620
blue—450 to 500	yellow—570 to 590	red—620 to 730

Eye sensitivity in the extremes of the visible range vary considerably in different individuals. The human eye has its maximum sensitivity to green at 540 mu (520 to 600), responding to as little as 4 or 5 quanta of light.[5]

17–5. Photocell Sensitivity to Wave Length. Each type of photocell has its wave length band of maximum sensitivity (Fig. 17–1). The photronic cell (also termed rectifier, barrier layer, or photogalvanic cell) has a sensitivity similar to human vision, and is suitable for measurement of the wave lengths emitted by the incandescent wolfram (W) filaments used in ordinary light bulbs. The photronic cell gives sufficient current to be registered directly on the galvanometer without amplification. Because of this, and

---

[2] Snell and Snell, *Colorimetric Methods of Analysis,* Vol. I (New York: D. Van Nostrand Company, Inc., 1936).

[3] Hiskey and Young, *Anal. Chem.,* 23:1196 (1951); Mellon, *Anal. Chem.,* 23:2 (1951); Rosenbaum, *Anal. Chem.,* 23:12 (1951); Stillman, *Am. Soc. Test. Mat. Bul.,* 125:17 (1943).

[4] Mellon, *Analytical Absorption Spectroscopy* (New York: John Wiley & Sons, Inc., 1950).

[5] Hecht, *Am. Scientist,* 32:159 (1944).

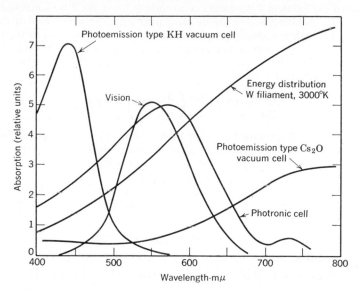

Fig. 17–1. Relative response of photoelectric cells and the human eye compared to energy distribution of wolfram (W) filament emission. (After Withrow, *et al., Ind. Eng. Chem., A. E.,* 8:214, 1936.)

since no cathode heating power is required, maximum simplicity in instrument design is possible. Typical potassium hydride (KH) vacuum tube photocells are most sensitive in the shorter wave lengths of the violet and ultraviolet spectrum. The Cs_2O type vacuum tube cell has maximum sensitivity for red and infrared wave lengths. Choice of photocell type is influenced by the absorption spectrum of the colored constituent to be determined (¶ 17–6).

17–6. Sensitivity Dependent on Wave Length of Incident Light. The color or wave length band of incident light used for a colorimetric determination is selected to coincide with that most absorbed by the test solution. The greatest sensitivity is thus obtained because the determination of concentration is based on the *change* in light intensity that results from light passage through the colored solution. Little or no change occurs in intensity of wave lengths other than those specifically absorbed.

17–7. *Example.* Consider that 90 per cent of the incident light is of wave lengths that are not absorbed, and that only 10 per cent of the incident light is of wave lengths that are absorbed. Further, let it be supposed that the concentration of the colored solution is such as to absorb 25 per cent of the incident light of the wave lengths appropriate to be absorbed. Then the transmitted light intensity is 90 per cent plus ¾ × 10, or 97.5 per cent. Little sensitivity of measurement could be expected in this case, since only 2.5 per cent of the incident light would be absorbed. Next, let it be supposed that a light filter is interposed in the incident light which removes 8/9 of the light of wave length not absorbed by the solution, and transmits all of the light of wave length appropriate for absorption by the solution. The incident intensity is raised by a factor of (100/20) through instrument settings. Then the transmitted light is:

$$\frac{100}{20} \times 10 + \frac{100}{20}\left(\frac{3}{4} \times 10\right) = 87.5\%$$

The relative absorption has been increased to 12.5 per cent, a 5-fold increase in sensitivity. Removal of all of the wave lengths not absorbed by the solution would result in absorption of 25 per cent of the incident light and transmission of only 75 per cent giving a 10-fold increase in sensitivity. This example points out how the sensitivity is increased by the use of incident light rich in precisely the wave lengths most efficiently absorbed by the solution.

17–8. Selection of Wave Length Band. The light absorption band of some colored solutions is narrow enough to permit the incident light wave length band to be kept within both boundaries (Fig. 17–2). The light ab-

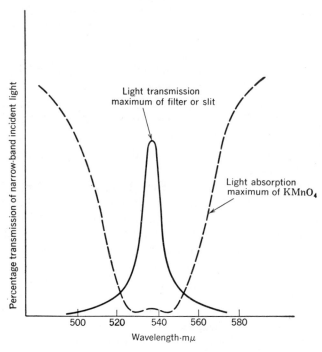

Fig. 17–2. The light maximum of the incident beam selected for a colorimetric measurement should coincide with the absorption maximum of the colored solution being measured.

sorption by other colored solutions cuts off the portion of the spectrum below a given wave length (Fig. 17-3). For the latter, the incident light

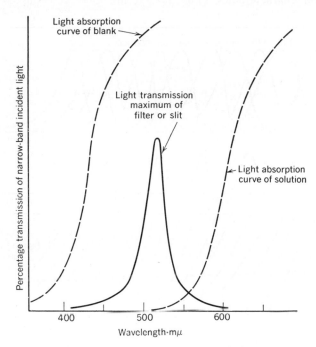

Fig. 17-3. Light maximum of the incident beam selected to coincide with the absorption maximum of the colored solution, but at maximum transmission of the blank.

wave length band is kept below the steep rise in the absorption curve of the test solution, but above the strongly absorbed wave lengths of the blank. The appropriate light absorption wave length bands for most colorimetric procedures are available in the literature but can be determined or re-checked by the analyst (¶ 17-44). Some examples are 535 mu for $HMnO_4$ (¶ 5 69), 620 mu for cobalt hydrocarbonate green (¶ 6-31), and 660 mu for molybdophosphoric blue (¶ 7-4). It is frequently possible to obtain more than one range in sensitivity of a colorimetric method by selection of a succession of incident light maxima which progressively encroaches on the rising portion of the absorption curve of the solution, as for vanado-molybdophosphoric yellow (¶ 7-61). Nonlinearity often accompanies the less sensitive calibration curves in such a series.

17-9. Obtaining the Wave Length Band. The appropriate light wave length band is obtained either (a) by passage of the light through light filters or (b) by slits to cut off a segment of a light spectrum arrayed by means of a prism (¶ 17–46) or grating (¶ 17–47). Light filters are generally made by superpositioning 2 or more glass plates of selected spectral transmission characteristics (Fig. 17–4), much as coloring over yellow

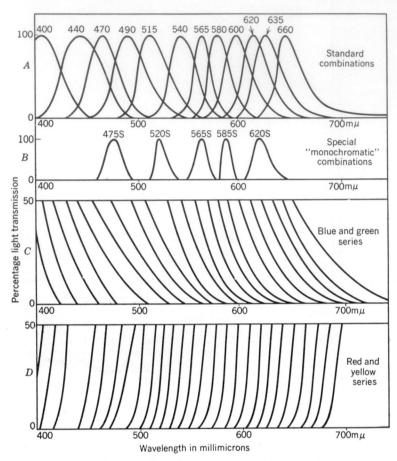

Fig. 17–4. Glass light filter characteristics. *A,* percentage light transmission of a number of filters available with the Evelyn colorimeter, each relative to the maximum transmission and weighted for photocell and lamp characteristics. *B,* special narrow band filter series. *C, D,* percentage transmission of a number of component glasses utilized in light filter construction. (From *Bulletin 460,* Rubicon Co., Philadelphia, Pa.)

crayon with blue or mixing yellow paint with blue gives green. Since the spectral bands provided by light filters advance through the spectrum in discrete increments, a light filter instrument is sometimes termed an "abridged" absorption spectrophotometer. Narrow wave bands of 20 mu or less have been obtained by interference in 1 colorimeter (Baush & Lomb, Rochester, N.Y.). Special narrow wave filters of 7- to 15-mu width with high percentage transmissions are available (Baird Associates, Cambridge, Mass.).

17–10. Percentage of Light Transmission. The fraction of the incident light of intensity, I_0, which is transmitted by the solution is termed transmission, T, defined:

$$T = \frac{I}{I_0} \tag{17-1}$$

in which I is the light intensity after passage through the solution. Percentage transmission is $100\ I/I_0$. In any spectrophotometer in which the nature of the photoelectric circuit is such that the current, G, flowing through the galvanometer is directly proportional to the light, I, striking the photocell, G/G_0, may be substituted for I/I_0. G_0 is the galvanometer reading of the blank solution. It is apparent that the transmittance or T scale of such absorption spectrophotometers is simply the usual linear galvanometer scale.

17–11. When the percentage of light transmitted or absorbed is plotted against the concentration, a curve results (Fig. 17–5). Evidently, the per-

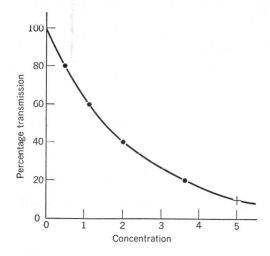

Fig. 17–5. Percentage light transmission plotted against concentration on linear graph paper, illustrating nonlinearity of the relationship.

centage of light transmitted or absorbed is *not* proportional to concentration. A quantitative insight into the relationship of light absorption to concentration (Beer's law) is desirable.

17–12. Beer's Law. Beer's law states that equal successive increments, *dc,* of concentration of a true solution containing a colored constituent absorb equal fractions, $-dI/I$, of the incident light. (Lambert's law states the same proposition for "increments of thickness" of the solution.) The light intensity decreases as the concentration increases, thus the negative sign:

$$\frac{-dI}{I} = kdc \qquad (17\text{--}2)$$

Summing up by integration all the small changes of intensity corresponding to increments of concentration,

$$\int kdc = \int \frac{-dI}{I} \qquad (17\text{--}3)$$

which on performance of the integration, becomes,

$$kc = -\ln I + A \qquad (17\text{--}4)$$

in which A is a constant. At zero concentration, that is, when $c = 0$ and $I = I_0$,

$$A = \ln I_0 \qquad (17\text{--}5)$$

Thus, in general, substituting (17–5) in (17–4),

$$kc = -\ln I + \ln I_0 \qquad (17\text{--}6)$$

Or, in the form of Beer's law,

$$c = \frac{1}{k} \ln \frac{I_0}{I} = \frac{1}{k_1} \log_{10} \frac{I_0}{I} \qquad (17\text{--}7)$$

17–13. Optical Density. The optical density, D, of a solution (or solid) is defined as:

$$D = \log_{10} \frac{I_0}{I} = \log_{10} \frac{1}{T} \qquad (17\text{--}8)$$

and, from equation 17–7, is proportional to concentration:

$$D = k_1 c \qquad (17\text{--}9)$$

when Beer's law applies (Fig. 17–6).

17–14. In reviewing older literature, it is sometimes desirable to calculate optical density from different solution depths or volumes in Nessler tubes. The equation used in matching Nessler tubes:

$$\frac{\text{ml (std)}}{\text{ml (test)}} = \frac{\text{conc (test)}}{\text{conc (std)}} \qquad (17\text{--}10)$$

resolves itself into:

$$\frac{\text{ml (std)}}{\text{ml (test)}} = k_2 c \qquad (17\text{--}11)$$

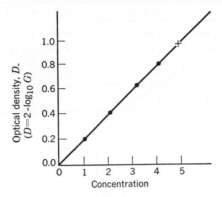

Fig. 17–6. Optical density plotted against concentration, both on linear scales. A straight line indicates conformity to Beer's law.

in which c is the concentration of the test solution and k_2 is a proportionality constant (reciprocal to constant standard concentration). Then from equations 17–9 and 17–11, D is proportional to the ratio $\dfrac{\text{ml (std)}}{\text{ml (test)}}$.

17–15. Extinction Coefficient. Optical density per unit of concentration and per unit thickness is the *extinction coefficient*. Color producing capacity of a given chromogen (color producing constituent) is important in the evaluation of sensitivity of methods. It is quantitatively expressed in the extinction coefficient, k:

$$k = \frac{1}{cx} \log_{10} \frac{I_0}{I_x} \qquad (17\text{–}12)$$

in which x is cm thickness of solution through which the light, I_x, passes, and c is the concentration in gm per liter. Optical density per mole per liter per cm of thickness is the *molar extinction coefficient, E:*

$$E = Mk = \frac{M}{cx} \log_{10} \frac{I_0}{I_x} \qquad (17\text{–}13)$$

in which M is the molar weight in gm.

17–16. Linearity of Calibration Curves. When the percentage transmission is plotted on a logarithmic scale against concentration (normality, mgm per liter, ppm, etc.) on a linear scale (Fig. 17–7), points lying on a straight line indicate conformity to Beer's law (eq. 17–7). The point (+) in Figs. 17–5, 17–6, and 17–7 are the same point. Such a semilogarithmic plot substitutes for mathematical or instrumental conversion to optical density in testing for adherence to Beer's law.

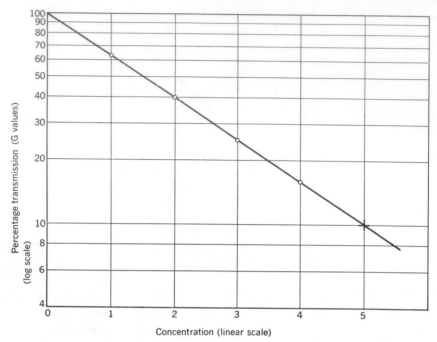

Fig. 17–7. Percentage of light transmission plotted against concentration on semi-logarithmic paper. A straight line indicates conformity to Beer's law.

17–17. Plotting to obtain linear calibration curves is a distinct advantage. Data points that are at variance with the trend and the general reproducibility of a colorimetric method can be judged. It is to be noted, however, that nonlinearity of the calibration curve does not hinder graphic determination of concentrations of test solutions or use of a colorimetric method that does not obey Beer's law (¶ 17–20).

17–18. If the structure of the colored ions or of the colored nonelectrolytes in the dissolved state does not change with a change in concentration, Beer's law will usually hold over a wide range of concentrations. However, deviations from Beer's law are likely to occur in solutions whose color is dependent upon dissociation phenomena, complex formation, and suspensions of precipitates. The color may then depend upon the concentration of the reactants, temperature of preparation, time of standing, and the presence of other electrolytes in addition to the concentration of the light absorbing substance under analysis.

CONCENTRATION DETERMINATION BY ABSORPTION SPECTROPHOTOMETRY

17–19. The concentration of a sample component that gives color is measured by the height of a given light absorption peak of the sample relative to that of a standard. The wave length position of the characteristic absorption peak must be known (¶ 17–8) or determined (¶ 17–44) before the simpler routine analytical determination of concentration can be made. But once an absorption peak suitable for the analysis has been determined for a given colored compound, it seldom has to be repeated, even though many modifications of analytical procedure may be made concerning preconcentration, purification, color development, and other steps in the colorimetric method.

17–20. Colorimetric procedures are most efficacious when the color (a) is highly specific for the element to be determined, (b) is intense per unit of concentration, (c) is stable, (d) is developed rapidly at room temperature, (e) is developed in the same solvent as the reagents and does not require extraction with an organic solvent, and (f) is not affected by excess of reagents or changes of pH. Knowledge of the origin of the colored constituent is helpful in procedure design. The color of solutions frequently arises from oxidation, reduction, formation of a complex ion, or coupling with a large molecule. Color of crystals has been correlated[6] with structure and the presence of mixed valences of the same element.

APPARATUS

17–21. Needed apparatus consists of a photoelectric absorption spectrophotometer with spectral control either with light filters or with prisms or gratings, and cells or tubes of appropriate dimensions and light transmission character to hold the test and standard solutions.

17–22. Several kinds of commercial absorption spectrophotometers are available. Representative of the glass filter instruments is the Evelyn[7] photoelectric colorimeter (Fig. 17–8) which is used extensively in soils laboratories. The popularity of the instrument is attributable to its simplicity and accuracy. The glass filters (¶ 17–9) give a perfectly reproducible incident light of sufficiently narrow wave band (20- to 60-mu width) for high sensitivity. The more generally used macro section of the instrument requires 6 to 10 ml of solution and is 5- to 20-fold more sensitive than visual colorimeters. A micro section, requiring 0.15 to 1.1 ml, provides a 40-fold increase in sensitivity. Great stability of light source is attained by use of a 6-volt storage battery to operate a small bulb about the size of a pocket flashlight bulb, at much less than its rated voltage. A photronic cell (¶ 17–5) is used. Light filtration is effected prior to incidence on the solution (Fig. 17–9), heating of the solution thus being avoided. The instrument is designed to use standardized test tubes approximately 2 cm in diameter for holding the colored solutions.

---

[6] Weyl, *J. Phys. Colloid Chem.*, 55:512 (1951).
[7] Evelyn, *J. Biol. Chem.*, 115:63 (1936).

Fig. 17–8. Evelyn photoelectric colorimeter, a precision light filter absorption spectrophotometer. The galvanometer reads percentage transmission on a linear scale directly from current output of photronic cell without amplification. (Courtesy Minneapolis-Honeywell Regulator Co., Rubicon Instruments, Philadelphia, Pa.)

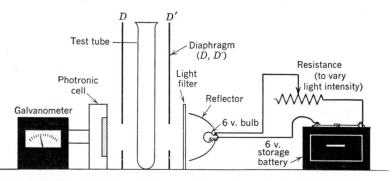

Fig. 17–9. Diagram of Evelyn colorimeter, illustrating typical components of the light filter type of absorption spectrophotometer. Special features include light filtration prior to incidence on the test solution, low energy light source, test tube comparator cell, and direct reading photronic cell, requiring no amplification.

Fig. 17–10. Coleman Junior absorption spectrophotometer, used for colorimetric determinations in many soil testing laboratories. A replica grating gives a continuous series of wavelength bands from 400 to 700 mu (Fig. 17–14). (Photo courtesy Coleman Instruments, Inc., Maywood, Ill.)

17–23. Grating or prism type spectrophotometers (¶ 17–46, 17–47) are also used for concentration determination (example, Fig. 17–10). Care is required in reproducibly setting the wave length band for the determination of a given constituent.

17–24. Double-beam absorption spectrophotometers provide for comparison of the light coming simultaneously through the standard and test sample. They are advantageous when the light source intensity is variable. The voltage corresponding to the difference in light intensity between the standard and test sample is balanced out (galvanometer null point) and translated by scale calibration of the potentiometer into percentage transmission or optical density. Galvanometer null-point reading may also be built into single-beam instruments, and virtually always is used in vacuum photocell instruments.

17–25. Standard Solutions. A series of standard concentrations of the constituent to be determined is prepared, and the color is formed according to the appropriate analytical procedure. All of the reagents included for soil extraction should be included in the standard series.

17–26. A blank solution is prepared exactly the same way as in the procedure, including extraction solution and all other reagents and conditions. A slight color may appear because of impurities in the reagents.

17–27. A series of dichromate (440-mu maximum) or permanganate (535- or 540-mu maximum) solutions of appropriate color intensity range may be prepared by dilution of a standard solution. The permanganate is diluted as in the manganese procedure (¶ 5–68) and the dichromate with distilled water. The proper concentration range is determined to give 4 to 6 well-distributed transmission readings between 20 and 95 per cent, beginning with 0.05 N solutions (oxidation-reduction normality).

PROCEDURE

17–28. Operation of Evelyn Colorimeter. A suitable light filter (¶ 17–9) is placed in position in the slot at the left of the coarse adjustment knob. The filter holder is pushed down (a) until a catch and notch are felt to become engaged in order to bring the lower filter in position, or (b) until it will go no further, to bring the upper filter into position. Next, the bakelite diaphragm tube is pulled up until the first encircling line appears above the panel, and then it is rotated until the number 10 faces the operator and an engaging pin is felt to arrest the tube. *Caution:* the diaphragm tube in the photometer must be kept carefully in place as indicated by its arrest by the engaging pin. Even slight displacement will greatly change the observed readings. The galvanometer lamp switch is turned on, and then the galvanometer is adjusted to give a zero reading by turning the lever on top of the box and by sliding the frosted glass galvanometer scale. The colorimeter lamp is turned on and allowed to warm up for 5 minutes.

17–29. Operation of the Beckman Absorption Spectrophotometer as a Colorimeter. The Beckman (Fig. 17–11) light source and instrument switches are turned on and the instrument is allowed to warm up for a period of 10 to 20 minutes. During this time the dark current adjustment is kept at zero, with the light shutter closed. When it becomes unchanging, warm-up is complete. In the meantime, the wave length selection (¶ 17–8) is made and the slit-width is adjusted to the appropriate value, usually as narrow as possible within limits of sensitivity of the method. A sensitivity control gives a 10-fold range in sensitivity.

17–30. Calibration of Test Tube Absorption Cells. The absorption cells must be accurately paired optically, either by the manufacturer or by the analyst. Ordinarily the analyst makes his own selections and pairing of test tubes if this type of absorption cell is employed. To do this, the test tubes that fit the instrument are cleaned in warm chromic acid cleaning solution, but cleaning with a brush is avoided because of the likelihood of producing scratches. The tubes are half filled with distilled water or the solution to be analyzed (the latter is particularly important with solutions of high refractive index, ¶ 14–22). The same light wave length band is used as will be used in the determination. With the tube in place in the instrument, the settings are adjusted so that the reading of the first tube falls at 100 per cent transmission. The tube orientation is adjusted for the most stable reading and the orientation is marked. Successive tubes are placed in the instrument and a set selected which give readings within ± 0.5 per cent of the average. Alternatively, 2 accurately paired tubes (1 for reference and 1 for test solution) may be selected to give the same light transmission at all orientations. With solutions of high refractive index (¶ 14–21), each tube of a set is numbered and its deviation from the mean is recorded as a correction.

17–31. It will be noted that the transmission reading of the Evelyn colorimeter is lower without a tube (air-reading) than with the tube in place in it. The reason is that the cylindrical tube acts as a condenser lens and increases the amount of light that passes from the light source through the diaphragms to the photocell. The air reading or "center setting" is noted and kept constant by rotating the rheostats as required. This is equivalent to maintaining the standard tube reading at 100. Changes in filament and circuit temperatures at first cause a drift from the standard adjustment of 100, which is easily corrected in this manner.

17–32. The Blank Setting. The blank (¶ 17–26) is placed in position for light transmission and the percentage transmission is adjusted to 100 per cent by means of the light intensity controls ("sensitivity" on the Beckman). When the light transmission cannot be brought to 100 per cent in the usual range, a "brighter" setting may be switched in (spreading the 0 to 10 per cent section of the scale to 0 to 100 per cent for the Beckman). If the blank setting still cannot be brought to 100, the attained transmission percentage with the blank can simply be recorded (¶ 17–43). The "center setting" (¶ 17–31) of the Evelyn colorimeter is recorded.

17–33. Standard Solutions. Each standard solution tube or cell is polished externally and inserted (after check of both zero point and 100 per cent transmission reading if much time has elapsed after the original adjustments) and the percentage transmission is observed to the nearest 0.25 per cent, recorded (Table 17–1), and plotted as a calibration curve (¶ 17–16 and 17–35).

17–34. Test Solutions. The same procedure is followed for the test solutions as for the standard solutions. Greater accuracy[8] is assured if the read-

---

[8] Ayres, *Anal. Chem.*, 21:652 (1949).

ings of the test solutions are kept between 20 and 80 per cent transmission (a 37 per cent transmission gives the lowest error). The concentrations are maintained in the optimum range by suitable aliquot and dilution volumes. The total volume of test solution is recorded. (The solution volume in the Evelyn tubes may be decreased to 6 ml if the "6" mark on the Bakelite diaphragm is turned toward the operator and raised to engage the pin. Tube selection and calibration curve must be repeated, ¶ 17–33.)

TABLE 17–1

Record form for absorption spectrophotometric measurement of concentration

Solution No.	Aliquot volume diluted to ____ml	% Transmission or galvanometer reading	Conc of solution*	Quantity of constituent determined (Vol × conc)	Sample weight represented	Conc in sample
0	ml (blank)	100.0	0.0	0.0	0.0	—
1	. . . .	. . . .	. . . .	. . . .	. . . . . .	. . . . .
2	. . . .	. . . .	. . . .	. . . .	. . . . . .	. . . . .
3	. . . .	. . . .	. . . .	. . . .	. . . . . .	. . . . .
4	. . . .	. . . .	. . . .	. . . .	. . . . . .	. . . . .
5	. . . .	. . . .	. . . .	. . . .	. . . . . .	. . . . .
6	. . . .	. . . .	. . . .	. . . .	. . . . . .	. . . . .
7	. . . .	. . . .	. . . .	. . . .	. . . . . .	. . . . .
8	. . . .	. . . .	. . . .	. . . .	. . . . . .	. . . . .
9	. . . .	. . . .	. . . .	. . . .	. . . . . .	. . . . .
10	. . . .	. . . .	. . . .	. . . .	. . . . . .	. . . . .

* Taken of standard or from calibration curve of test sample.

17–35. Interpretation of Results. Concentration is determined from percentage transmission readings (Table 17–1) through a calibration curve (Fig. 17–7). The concentration may be expressed as normality, gm per liter, ppm, or other convenient units. *Quantity* of constituent determined is the product: *Concentration × Volume.*

17–36. Concentration can also be calculated (¶ 17–13) from optical density, D, by proportion:

$$\text{Conc, test sample} = \frac{D, \text{ test sample}}{D, \text{ standard}} \times \text{Conc, standard} \quad (17\text{–}14)$$

Since the blank was set at 100 per cent transmission, from equation 17–7, optical density, D, is given:

$$D = \log \frac{100}{G} = \log 100 - \log G = 2 - \log G \quad (17\text{–}15)$$

The value of D is often replaced by L, giving $L = 2 - \log G$. Tables of optical densities $(L = 2 - \log G)$ for various percentage transmission values are available. Values may also be calculated from ordinary log tables. Some instruments have optical density scales, as well as percentage transmission scales, so that optical density values can be read directly and plotted. The optical density is converted to concentration by equation 17–14.

17–37. Before leaving the Evelyn colorimeter at the end of work, the following are checked:

1. The lamp switches are turned off.

2. A light filter is always left in position for use (a protection against excessive illumination reaching the photocell when the operation is resumed).

3. The coarse rheostat is turned to the left (to lower the intensity to guard against excess illumination if a less dense filter is next used).

17–38. Excess drift of the Evelyn galvanometer usually indicates either that the battery needs recharging or that it has been over-charged. Overcharging can be corrected by shorting the battery for a few seconds and then allowing the lamp to run for 20 minutes. Unsteadiness of the rheostat settings usually can be corrected by wiping the rheostat coils with a soft cloth and smearing a light dressing of Vaseline along the region of contact.

17–39. Polychromogen Systems. Polychromogen (more than 1 color source) systems are of 3 types. The simplest is monochromatic, with the reagent blank carrying a certain amount of color of the same hue as that derived from the test sample. Justification for setting the colored blank at 100 per cent transmission to eliminate the effect of the blank comes from the fact that optical densities are additive, that is:

$$D \text{ (test)} = D - D \text{ (blank)} \qquad (17\text{–}16)$$

in which D (or L, ¶ 17–36) is the optical density of the test sample if read against a colorless blank not containing any analytical impurities. Or, in terms of galvanometer readings,

$$D(\text{test}) = \log \frac{G_0}{G} - \log \frac{G_0}{G(\text{blank})} \qquad (17\text{–}17)$$

in which G values correspond to the reading of each colored solution against a clear solution blank. This simplifies to:

$$D(\text{test}) = \log \frac{G(\text{blank})}{G} \qquad (17\text{–}18)$$

which is the mathematical equivalent of reading the test sample against the colored analytical blank; and the latter, simpler procedure is thus established as fundamental.

17–40. The second case is polychromatic, in which the reagent blank has an invariable color different from that of the principal chromogen in the test sample. This effect is cancelled by maintaining the blank color constant in the test sample as a "background" color, and minimizing its effect by using a filter system (¶ 17–8) that is designed to maximize absorption by the principal chromogen and minimize absorption by the extraneous chromogen of the blank.

17–41. The third case is polychromatic, in which the reagent color varies with the amount of the test element and its light absorption cannot be completely separated by selection of the incident light wave length maximum. This type of system is analyzed by direct use of a calibration curve, which is inevitably nonlinear. Bicolor system analysis, for example, by measurements at 2 wave length maxima, has also been effectively used (¶ 15–80) with suitable equations or nomographs.[9]

ALTERNATIVE PROCEDURES

17–42. Nessler tubes may be used to compare the intensity of the color of the test sample to that of the standard. To do this, 20 ml of the standard solution is placed in 1 Nessler tube, and then increments of the test solution are added to the second Nessler tube until the color densities appear equal when viewed from top to bottom. The 2 tubes are held adjacent to one another in one hand, and viewed toward a white background (creased filter paper) by indirect outdoor light. The crease is oriented to divide the center field of view of each tube. The volume of the test sample required is recorded and then the process is repeated 4 or 5 times, the readings being averaged. Then:

$$\text{Conc test sample} = \frac{\text{ml standard}}{\text{ml test sample (av.)}} \times \text{Conc standard}$$

$$(17\text{--}19)$$

17–43. When a blank reading of 100 cannot be obtained by the full setting of rheostats (¶ 17–32), it is possible to set the blank at 50 (or 80) and to multiply the galvanometer readings by 2 (or 1.25) before application of the optical density $(L = 2 - \log G)$ table (¶ 17–36). Since with the blank at 100, $L = \log (100/G)$, with the blank at 50 (or 80),

$$\log \frac{50}{G} = \log \frac{100}{2G} \quad \text{or} \quad \log \frac{80}{G} = \frac{100}{1.25G} \qquad (17\text{--}20)$$

Thus, the $2G$ (or $1.25G$) value for the test solution is entered in the optical density $(L\text{-}G)$ table as though it was the G value observed.

ABSORPTION SPECTRUM DETERMINATION

17–44. The absorption spectrum of the specimen is yielded by determination of the amount of radiation absorption by a solution or solid as a function of the wave length of incident light (by narrow band increments)

[9] Kitson, *Anal. Chem.*, 22:664 (1950); Knudson *et al.*, *Ind. Eng. Chem.*, *A.E.*, 12:715 (1940); Kozelka and Klochesky, *Ind. Eng. Chem.*, *A.E.*, 13:484 (1941); Venning *et al.*, *J. Biol. Chem.*, 120:225 (1937).

over a wide range of wave lengths. The components (bonds, molecules, ions) of the specimen are identified qualitatively by the *positions* of the spectral absorption peaks, in the visible, ultraviolet, and infrared regions. The quantity of each component is estimated by the *relative height* of the characteristic absorption peaks (¶ 17–19).

APPARATUS

17–45. Needed apparatus includes a prism or grating absorption spectrophotometer equipped with absorption cells of transmittancy suitable for the spectral regions to be investigated. Glass cells are used for the visible

Fig. 17–11. Beckman quartz prism absorption spectrophotometer, model DU. Percentage transmission and optical density scales read with galvanometer at null. (Photo courtesy Arthur Thomas Co., Philadelphia, Pa., and Scientific Instruments Division, Beckman Instruments, Inc., Fullerton, Calif.)

region, quartz cells for ultraviolet, and KBr or NaCl "sandwich" cells for the infrared region. Automatically recording infrared absorption spectrophotometers are manufactured by Baird (Cambridge, Mass.), Perkin-Elmer (Norwalk, Conn.), and Beckman (Fullerton, Calif.).

17–46. The Beckman[10] DU absorption spectrophotometer (Fig. 17–11) is suitable for near ultraviolet, visible, and near infrared spectra up to 2000 mu, and is used extensively in soils laboratories. The usual 4-compartment solution holder has a 1-cm optical length of Corex or quartz, but 2-, 5-, and 10-cm cells are available and are used, with an interchangeable cell housing, when needed to increase the sensitivity of colorimetric methods. This instrument well illustrates the principles of the prism type instrument (Fig. 17–12). A 6-volt storage battery and 25-watt W-filament lamp are employed as the light source for absorption down to 320 mu, and a stabilized 110-volt A.C. hydrogen discharge lamp is used for ultraviolet absorption below 320 mu. An image of the light source A is focused by the condensing mirror B and diagonal mirror C, on the entrance slit at D. The entrance slit is the lower of 2 slits placed vertically over each other. The light fall-

---

[10] Cary and Beckman, *J. Opt. Soc. Am.,* 31:682 (1941); variability treated by Castor, *Anal. Chem.,* 23:1229 (1951).

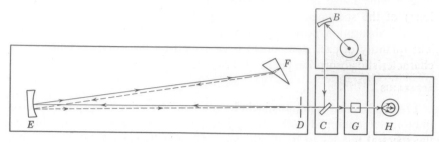

Fig. 17–12. Diagram of Beckman spectrophotometer. (Courtesy Scientific Instruments Division, Beckman Instruments, Inc., Fullerton, Calif.)

ing on the collimating mirror E is rendered parallel and reflected toward the quartz prism F. The back surface of the prism is aluminized so that light refracted at the first surface is reflected back through the prism, undergoing further refraction as it emerges from the prism (Littrow prism principle). The collimating mirror E focuses the spectrum in the plane of the exit (upper) slit at D. Variation of the prism position by means of the wave length selector knob setting determines the wave length band which passes out of the slit, through the absorption cell G to the sealed, desiccated phototube compartment at H. One vacuum tube photocell (¶ 17–5) is the cesium oxide type (for 600 to 1000 mu) and the other is a blue-ultraviolet sensitive type (for 200 to 625 mu). A sliding rod brings either phototube into position and simultaneously switches the electrical connections. A switch coupled to the phototube aperture shutter permits the dark current of the phototube to be checked at any time without changing any control setting or removing the cells. The 200- to 2000-mu wave length scale is 1 meter long, and light wave length bands as narrow as 0.1 to 1 mu can be defined by the slits. As with glass prisms generally, the extent of angular dispersion of light is a function of the wave length. Attachments are available for emission spectrophotometry (¶ 18–12), the flame unit replacing the light source at A.

17–47. The Coleman replica grating absorption spectrophotometers are also widely used in soil analysis. The Universal model (Fig. 17–13) gives light wave length maxima from 320 to 800 mu (Fig. 17–10). As is true of spectral gratings generally, the extent of angular dispersion is the same for all wave lengths. Cells of 0.5-, 1-, 2-, 3.5-, 4-, and 5-cm optical length are available. A stabilized power source that operates on a 110-volt A.C. supply is employed for energizing the lamp run at 8 volts. A photronic cell (¶ 17–5) is used for registration, on direct reading scales, of transmission percentage or optical density (Fig. 17–14).

17–48. A rapid-scanning absorption spectrophotometer that projects the

Fig. 17–13. Coleman replica grating absorption spectrophotometer, Universal model. (Photo courtesy Coleman Instruments, Inc., Maywood, Ill.)

absorption spectrogram on an oscilloscope (60 times per second) is offered by the American Optical Co., Buffalo, New York. Permanent records are made with an oscilloscope camera.

REAGENTS

17–49. Absorption spectra can be made with any standard colored solution such as $KMnO_4$ (¶ 5–68) or $K_2Cr_2O_7$.

PROCEDURE

17–50. The light absorption curve of $KMnO_4$ or $K_2Cr_2O_7$ is prepared either with a prism or grating instrument (or approximated with a series of light filters) to determine which incident light color gives the greatest sensi-

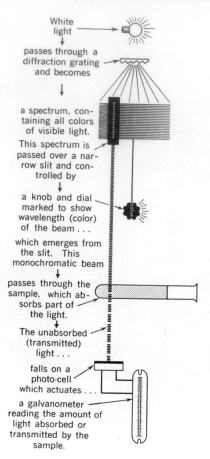

White
light →

passes through a
diffraction grating
and becomes

a spectrum, con-
taining all colors
of visible light.

This spectrum is
passed over a nar-
row slit and con-
trolled by

a knob and dial
marked to show
wavelength (color)
of the beam . . .

which emerges from
the slit. This
monochromatic beam

passes through the
sample, which ab-
sorbs part of
the light.

The unabsorbed
(transmitted)
light . . .

falls on a
photo-cell
which actuates . . .

a galvanometer
reading the amount of
light absorbed or
transmitted by the
sample.

Fig. 17–14. Operating principles of the Coleman replica grating absorption spectrophotometer. (After *Waco Catalyst,* 9:10, 1952, Wilkins-Anderson Co., Chicago, Ill.)

tivity. For advance work, the infrared absorption[11] of a specimen such as clay may be determined.

17–51. The specimen is first checked for proper concentration range to give at least 20 per cent but not much over 30 per cent transmission at the greatest absorption maximum or transmission minimum. To do this the procedure given in the following paragraphs is run through rapidly and approximately. Then the procedure is repeated in detail after the instrument sensitivity, slit width, and specimen concentration have been adjusted. The appropriate photocell and light source are employed for the spectral region in which measurements are being made.

[11] Hunt *et al., Anal. Chem.,* 22:1478 (1950).

17–52. The transmission percentage is observed at a wave length maximum near one end of the spectrum against the blank as 100 per cent transmission. The wave length band is advanced by an increment and the transmission percentage determined again, the blank being reset at 100 per cent transmission at this wave length setting. Increments are taken through the entire spectral region of interest. The size of increment taken is chosen according to the refinement desired.

17–53. Interpretation of Results. Absorption spectra of solutions are fre·quently made to select a suitable wave length maximum for the determination of concentration (¶ 17–19). These are most effectively recorded and interpreted as a plot of transmission percentage or optical density against wave length.

17–54. Characterization of solutions and solids is effected by the positions of the absorption maxima, and components are determined quantitatively by the relative heights of the absorption maxima compared to those of the standards. Separations of components previous to absorption measurement may aid the characterization. In the characterization of organic and mineral colloids, the interpretation is based on comparison of the absorption spectrophotometric pattern with that of standard colloidal substances. Methods for this type of analysis have many details yet to be worked out, but enough research work has been carried out[12] to show the promise of the methods for distinguishing molecular and crystalline species not fully differentiated by other techniques. For example, the absorption maximum for water is at a longer wave length than that for hydroxyl, and these 2 can thus be distinguished in crystalline materials.

QUESTIONS

1. What procedure is followed to determine the correct light wave length band for a given colorimetric procedure?

2. State Beer's law.

3. Describe the absorption spectrophotometric procedure followed to determine whether Beer's law applies to a solution.

4. Does nonlinearity of the optical density-concentration graph necessarily prove nonobeyance of Beer's law for a given solution under all circumstances?

5. Describe the procedure for measurement of a colored constituent concentration, when it is initially known that Beer's law is not obeyed.

6. Given a ml of test solution that matched a known volume and concentration of standard solution in Nessler tubes, derive the equation for expressing the data as optical density.

7. How is the absorption spectrum determined?

8. In what ways are absorption spectra useful?

---

[12] Hunt *et al.*, *Anal Chem.*, 22:1478 (1950); Adler *et al.*, *Preliminary Reports Reference Clay Minerals*, Am. Pet. Inst. Res. Proj. 49, No. 8 (1951); Keller and Pickett, *Am. J. Sci.*, 248:264 (1950); Gore, *Anal. Chem.*, 23:7 (1951); Launer, *Am Mineral*, 37:764 (1952).

18

Emission Spectrophotometry

. . . no doubt that this [method of analysis] is one of the most powerful now available for investigating the natural universe.
— HARRISON, LORD, AND LOOFBOUROW[1]

18–1. Emission spectra have been observed by man from earliest times through visual detection of colors in fire. Flame tests used in qualitative analysis utilize easily excited atomic spectra. For example, the bright yellow flame of sodium is familiar to the analyst. Use of a colored glass to screen out the sodium flame color permits a search for the reddish flame of potassium. Instruments have been developed for precise determinations of many elements through their emission spectra excited in various ways.

18–2. Basic Principles. When atoms, ions, or their groupings are subjected to some form of energy excitation, as in a flame or in an electric arc or spark, an *emission* spectrum results. Energy is first absorbed (¶ 17–2) by electron shifts to positions more distant from the atomic nucleus. As the electrons regain or partially regain their stable or reference state, the previously absorbed energy is re-emitted as electromagnetic radiations, the wave lengths of which correspond to the quantity of energy involved in the respective electron shifts, in accordance with quantum theory. Thus:

$$\triangle E = E_2 - E_1 = hf \tag{18–1}$$

in which $\triangle E$ is the change in energy level, between initial E_1 and final E_2 states, h is Planck's constant, and f is the wave frequency of light. One electron shift, yielding a given quantity of energy, results in the production of a given emission maximum or line in the spectrum. For each element there is a tremendous number of possible shifts and corresponding spectral maxima or lines. *Band* spectra generally originate from molecules

---

[1] *Practical Spectroscopy* (Englewood Cliffs, N.J.: Prentice-Hall, Inc., 1948), p. 1.

452

or incandescent polyatomic gases and vapors that are cool enough not to be totally dissociated. For example, band spectra are produced by $O-H$, H_2, and $C-H$ bonds.

18–3. When excitation of an element has occurred, the subsequent emission of energy does not necessarily have to occur by shift directly to the stable state, but may first occur by shift to some intermediate level followed by a secondary shift to the stable state, giving 2 emission maxima. The greater the level of excitation, the greater the number of electron shifts and energy levels involved, and the more complex the spectrum produced. If the excitation is at an extremely high level, the emission becomes a *continuous* spectrum, because the number of emission phenomena is so great as to leave no finite gaps.

18–4. *Emission spectrophotometry* or *emission spectroscopy*[2] (¶ 17–3) is chemical analysis by measurement of spectral line intensity. Emission spectra may best be visualized as a plot of intensity of radiation as a function of wave length. The spectrum useful for analysis extends from 2000 to 100,000 A (Fig. 18–1). Instruments used for emission spectrophotometric analysis consist of 3 discrete component systems: (a) sample excitation system (the *source*), (b) radiation dispersion system (prism, grating), and (c) radiation measurement system (photography, photocell). The conventional *spectrograph* employs high temperature excitation in an electric arc or spark and records a spectrum through a wide range of wave lengths on a photographic plate or film. The *flame emission spectrophotometer* employs a relatively low temperature excitation and measures with a photocell the emission intensity in a selected wave length range, corresponding to a given element.

18–5. Emission spectrophotometry is an absolute *qualitative* method, in as much as each particular element has its own spectrum, specific for that atomic species. As a qualitative technique it is far more specific than most precipitation tests for a single ionic species. Emission spectrophotometry is a comparative or empirical *quantitative* method, the quantity of emission being compared, for a given instrumental set-up, with a known quantity of the element to be determined. It is thus analogous to colorimetric methods of absorption spectrophotometry (Chapter 17).

18–6. One of the advantages of emission spectrophotometric analysis lies in the economy of time when large numbers of soil or plant analyses are to be made on a routine basis. (If only a few or one determination is to be made, the conventional chemical methods are faster.) The sensitivity of the

---

[2] Brode, *Chemical Spectroscopy,* 2nd ed. (New York: John Wiley & Sons, Inc., 1947); Sawyer, *Experimental Spectroscopy* (Englewood Cliffs, N.J.: Prentice-Hall, Inc., 1946); Candler, in *Practical Spectroscopy* (London: Hilger & Watts, 1949); Thompson, *A Course of Chemical Spectroscopy* (Oxford: Clarendon Press, 1938); Gerlach and Schweitzer, *Foundations and Methods of Chemical Analysis by the Emission Spectrum* (London: Hilger & Watts, Ltd., 1929).

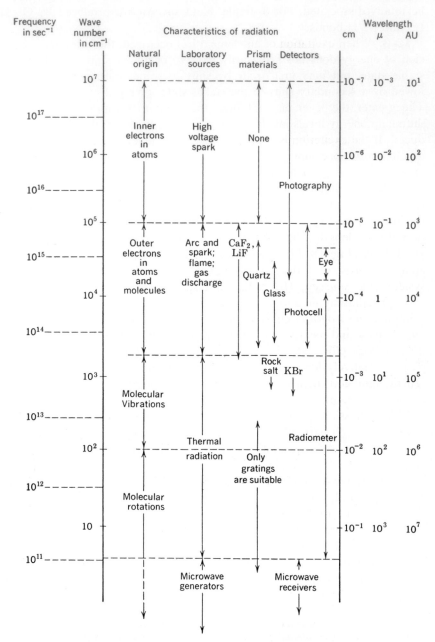

Fig. 18–1. Emission spectral regions and instrumental conditions for excitation and detection. (From Harrison *et al., Practical Spectroscopy,* Englewood Cliffs, N.J.: Prentice-Hall, Inc., 1948, p. 3.)

spectral method to both macro and micro amounts of 60 to 70 elements makes it ideally suited to refined and comprehensive analysis of soils in relation to the growing list of soil elements that are important to the growth of plants.

DETERMINATIONS WITH FLAME EMISSION SPECTROPHOTOMETER

18–7. In 1910, Klemperer[3] began flame emission spectrophotometry by matching oxyacetylene flame colors produced when various solutions were sprayed into the flame, a split field spectroscopic eye-piece being used for comparison of standard and test solutions. The method was made more quantitative by the combination of the flame excitation with the prism system for the light dispersion, photographic recording, and spectral line intensity determination by a photocell densitometer.[4] Determinations of K, Na, Ca, Fe, Mn, Sr, Tl, Cu, Ag, and later many other elements (¶ 18–34) were effected.

18–8. Spraying of the sample solution into a flame is used in various forms in modern commercial instruments. A wide variety of elements can be determined (Table 18–1). The elements K, Na, Ca, and Mg, extracted from soil, rocks, runoff, plants, or residues can easily and quickly be determined by a flame emission spectrophotometer. Elements such as Ba and Cu derived from cation exchange capacity measurements can also be determined. The appropriate concentration range, which varies with the element and with the instrument, must be considered in a particular procedure (¶ 18–16).

18–9. Accuracy. Most manufacturers of flame emission spectrophotometers claim an accuracy of 1 to 3 per cent in the analysis of K, Na, Ca, Mg, and other elements, in solutions of chemically pure salts in suitable concentrations. Variations in spray and flame production such as those caused by variation in solution viscosity or pressure can be diminished greatly by the use of an internal standard (¶ 18–33). Error arises also by the nonreproducibility or incomplete isolation of the characteristic spectral line of the element to be determined.

18–10. Interference in the determination of an element may be caused by (a) the enhancement of background intensity by extraneous cations, or (b) decrease in cation emission intensity by certain anions through formation of high melting point or high boiling point compounds in the flame.[5] Such interferences cause some loss of accuracy with unpurified soil and

---

[3] According to Mitchell, *Spectrochim. Acta,* 4:62 (1950).

[4] Lundegardh, *Die quantitative Spectralanalyse de Elemente* (Jena: Fischer, Ed. 1, 1929; Ed. 2, 1934), *Z. Phys.,* 66:109 (1930); *Leaf Analysis,* tr. Mitchell (London: Hilger & Watts, Ltd., 1951), p. 115.

[5] Margoshes and Vallee, *Anal. Chem.,* 28:180 (1956).

TABLE 18–1

Wave lengths and relative intensities of flame spectra, determined with the Beckman flame spectrophotometer†

Element	Wave length, mu	Relative* intensity	Element	Wave length, mu	Relative* intensity	Element	Wave length, mu	Relative* intensity
Co	238.9	—	Pd	363.5	1.5	Gd	461.4	—
Hg	253.6	0.15	Pb	364	0.1	Y	464.4	—
Au	267.6	1.5	Pb	368.5	0.2	Y	467.5	5
Pb	283.3	0.1	Rh	369.1	—	B	473	—
Mg	285.2	10	Rh	369.6	—	Y	486.0	—
In	303.9	—	Mg	370.8	10	B	495	10
Cu	324.8	50	Fe	372.0	7	Mn	510	10
In	325.6	—	Ru	372.7	3	Ba	520	20
Cd	326.1	0.15	Fe	373.6	10	B	521	15
Sn	326.2	0.2	Tl	377.6	80	Tl	535.0	—
Cu	327.4	20	Mg	383	8	Mn	541	30
Ag	328.1	7	Fe	386.0	7	B	548	20
Na	330.2	7	Ga	403.3	—	Ba	550	20
Rh	332.3	—	Mn	403.4	100	Ca	556	200
Sn	333	0.2	K	404.6	7	Mn	561	70
Ag	338.3	50	Pb	405.8	0.3	La	563	—
Rh	339.7	—	In	410.2	—	Na	589.3	10,000
Ni	341.5	3	Ga	417.2	—	Ca	603.5	100
Rh	343.5	—	Rb	420.2	3	Ca	626	300
B	345	0.3	Ca	422.7	—	Ca	650	100
Ni	349.3	2	La	438.4	100	Li	670.8	2,000
Co	350.2	20	La	443.3	—	La	714	—
Ni	352.5	6	Rh	449.2	—	La	745	—
Co	352.7	20	Gd	451.4	—	K	767	2,000
Rh	352.8	—	Sn	452.5	0.1	La	798	—
Cr	357.9	70	B	454	2	Ba	850	50
Rh	358.3	—	Cs	455.5	0.7	Cs	852	1,000
Rh	359.6	—	Sr	460.7	150	La	860	—

* Relative intensity of an element at a given wave length is equal to 100 divided by the number of parts per million of the element necessary to give a photometric response equal to 0.5 per cent of the flame background.

† Instruction manual 193-B, Table 2, courtesy Beckman Instruments Inc., Fullerton, Calif.

456

plant extracts, which is not noted with chemically pure solutions of the element to be determined. They can best be eliminated by chemical separations since they are not susceptible to correction by the internal standard method. In practice, a variability of 3 to 8 per cent of some elements determined is expected and is usually acceptable in rapid analysis for fertility diagnosis.

APPARATUS

18–11. A flame emission spectrophotometer and suitable flasks and beakers to hold the sample are required.

18–12. The Beckman model DU (Fig. 18–2) is an efficient and popular

Fig. 18–2. Beckman quartz prism single-beam spectrophotometer equipped with flame emission source, model DU. Percentage transmission and optical density scales read these properties of the spectral line with the galvanometer at null. (Photo courtesy Arthur H. Thomas Co., Philadelphia, Pa., by permission of Scientific Instruments Division, Beckman Instruments, Inc., Fullerton, Calif.)

single-beam flame emission spectrophotometer. The spectrophotometer portion of this instrument is also used for absorption spectrophotometry (¶ 17–46). A photomultiplier increases the sensitivity. A special "bucking circuit"[6] has been developed to give greatly increased sensitivity (0–2 ppm of Mg and 0–5 ppm of Mn). The flame attachment to this instrument con-

---

[6] E. C. Boycks and V. V. Meloche, Chemistry Department, University of Wisconsin.

sists of 2 parts, the oxygen and fuel (acetylene or hydrogen) regulation system, and the burner and sample introduction system. Coarse pressure adjustments are made at the respective supply tanks and the finer adjustments are made at the pressure regulation system of the flame attachment. The burner and sample sprayer ("atomizer") functions are combined into a single small assembly. The sample is introduced through a capillary tube, the oxygen from a chamber concentric with the capillary, and the fuel from another chamber concentric with both the capillary and the oxygen chamber. The oxygen serves both for combustion of the fuel and for dispersion of the sample solution through a venturi effect. The fuel, oxygen, and sample spray come together and burn immediately above the burner. Special cooling of the burner is not necessary. Constancy of sample and standard solution characteristics and operating conditions are highly essential, as with any single beam instrument.

18–13. The Perkin-Elmer Model 52C can be operated as a double beam or single beam flame emission spectrophotometer (Fig. 18–3). In the double beam type of operation, an internal standard element, commonly

Fig. 18–3. Perkin-Elmer prism double-beam flame spectrophotometer, model 52C. (Photo courtesy Perkin-Elmer Corp., Norwalk, Conn.)

lithium, is placed in both the standard and test samples (¶ 18–33). Spectral dispersion is by a prism system. The elements K, Na, and Ca, and, with modifications, Mg can be determined. The sample is introduced from a dropping funnel into a sprayer. The spray is fed through a chamber that has a provision for elimination of any condensed liquid and finally into the bottom of a Meker type burner.

18–14. Multichannel[7] flame emission spectrophotometers are feasible, as used by Lundegardh (¶ 18–7) or better, through combination with a battery of photocell recorders (¶ 18–55) set to record several wave bands simultaneously.

REAGENTS

18–15. A series of stock solutions containing, respectively, 1000 ppm of K, Na, Ca and Mg are prepared as follows: for K, 1.907 gm of KCl is dissolved in 1 liter of water; for Na, 2.541 gm of NaCl is dissolved in 1 liter of water; for Ca, 2.500 gm of clear calcite ($CaCO_3$) is dissolved in 10 ml of N HCl, and the solution is boiled to expel CO_2 and then diluted with water to 1 liter; and Mg, 1.000 gm of metallic Mg foil is dissolved in 10 ml of N HCl, and the solution is diluted with water to 1 liter. The blank, containing all salts that will be present in the analytical determination, except the element to be determined, is called the *base electrolyte solution.* The base electrolyte solution must be exactly the *same in the standard and the test samples,* to provide the same interferences and viscosity effects. Dilutions are made to give 40 ppm of K, 40 ppm of Na, 50 ppm of Ca, and 60 ppm of Mg in 1 N NH$_4$OAc, 0.4 N HCl, or other base electrolyte solution. More dilute standard solutions are made if the bucking circuit (¶ 18–12) is employed to increase the sensitivity. A 10 to 20 ppm standard is used for the 100 per cent transmission setting when the content of cation in the test solution is less than this (for example, if K or Na is less than 2 per cent in the total elemental analysis). Serial dilutions with base electrolyte solution are made of each of the standards. The appropriate kind of extraction solution for soil or ash is suggested in individual procedures. The use of Li as an internal standard, is considered below (¶ 18–33).

PROCEDURE[8]

18–16. An inexperienced person must always obtain instructions from an experienced operator of the flame emission spectrophotometer. He should also carefully study the bulletin for a particular instrument, furnished by the manufacturer.

18–17. The regular (almost weekly) replacement of the desiccant in the

---

[7] Vallee and Margoshes, *Anal. Chem.,* 28:175 (1956).

[8] Appreciation is extended to Dr. L. D. Swindale for assistance with the writing of portions of this procedure.

Beckman flame emission spectrophotometer is highly important. The instrument is allowed to warm up (¶ 17–29) for a period of 10 to 15 minutes prior to putting it in operation. The selector switch is set to 0.1. It is important to select the correct photoelectric cell and load resistor (suggestions in Table 18–2) and to allow them to warm up at the same time as the rest of the instrument. The determination of K[9] or other elements requiring the red-sensitive photoelectric cell (those elements whose major flame emission line or band occurs between 600 and 1000 mu, Table 18–1) is carried out first because this cell takes a considerable time to stabilize, whereas the blue-sensitive cell reaches its operative condition in a few seconds and no delay is experienced when the changeover is made. During the warm-up period, the various standard solutions and sample solutions are poured into 5-ml beakers and a suitable record sheet is drawn up. When a steady dark current is obtained the instrument is ready for the analysis.

18–18. Acetylene or hydrogen fuel gas is employed, burned with tank oxygen. Acetylene is cheaper and is completely satisfactory for Na, K, and Ca determinations. For Mg, acetylene gives a bent calibration curve instead of the desired straight line obtainable with hydrogen. Acetylene gives more sensitivity at low Mg concentrations, and less sensitivity at high Mg concentrations than hydrogen. Also, acetylene gives a hotter flame and less interference of Ca with Mg and of P with Ca.

18–19. The burner is lighted in accordance with the manufacturers instructions. The oxygen is first adjusted to about half the operating pressure at the pressure regulator on the emission spectrophotometer attachment. Following this, the fuel gas is turned up slightly, at which time the burner is lighted from the bottom. The pressure of oxygen and of fuel are then adjusted to give a hot oxidizing flame. Optimum operating conditions vary from burner to burner and some experimentation is necessary to obtain proper settings for the lowest flame background with the highest setting of the sensitivity control and the smallest slit width. A reducing flame and deposition of carbon on the burner should be avoided.

18–20. The most concentrated standard is put into the instrument with the proper wave length selected and the transmission dial set at 100. The sensitivity control and the slit width are varied to balance the galvanometer needle at null-point. Standards of intermediate concentrations are then put into the burner and their transmission percentage is obtained. From these readings the calibration curve is drawn. Finally, solutions derived from soils or plants are run through the spraying procedure, the percentage transmission is observed, and the concentration is determined by reference to the calibration curve. The most concentrated standard is run through from

---

[9] The photomultiplier attachment, used at full sensitivity, makes possible the advantage of K determination with the blue-sensitive cell. Rich, *Agron. Jour.*, 48:430 (1956).

TABLE 18–2

**Conditions with Beckman flame emission spectrophotometer for determination
of several cations excited in oxygen-acetylene flame**

	K	Na	Ca	Mg	Ba	Cu
Working range, ppm	0–100	0–50	0–200	0–200	200–500	5–50
Selector switch	0.1	0.1	0.1	0.1	0.1	0.1
Phototube color sensitivity	Red	Blue	Blue	Blue	Red	Blue
Phototube load resistor position	3	2	2	2	3	2
Photomultiplier sensitivity	—	Full or 3	Full or 3	Full	—	Full
Zero suppression	1	1	1	1	1	1
Wave length,* mu	770	590	554	285	873	325
Slit width, mm	0.1	0.01	0.02	0.06	0.25	0.06
Oxygen pressure, p.s.i.	10	10	10	8	8	7
Acetylene pressure, p.s.i.	7	7	7	8.5	8.5	8.5

* Selection for midrange of the line or band is made by dialing for the maximum response near the wave length specified.

time to time to insure that the operating conditions are constant. If a change in operating conditions is indicated by a change in the transmission percentage of the standard solution, the sensitivity or slit width must be altered slightly until the original operating conditions are restored. If the test element concentration exceeds that of the most concentrated standard, the test solution may be diluted with the base elecrolyte solution (¶ 18–15). Greatest accuracy is generally obtained if the test samples are kept in the range of 20 to 100 per cent of the standard curve range.

18–21. Cation Exchange Capacity by the Flame Emission Method. The flame emission technique is a rapid and sensitive method for the determination of the cation exchange capacity of soil or clay (¶ 4–6). Measurement with K, Na, Ca, Ba, Cu, Mn and other ions all have been adapted to the flame emission determination. The use of Ca or K is recommended (¶ 4–9). The saving in time over titrimetric, colorimetric, or gravimetric determinations is considerable. In each case, the cation exchange determination consists (¶ 4–16) of saturation of the exchange charges with 1 of the above cations, removal of the excess soluble salt by leaching with alcohol, and then displacement of the exchangeable cation by means of a solution of a second saturating cation. Ammonium acetate is a satisfactory displacement solution because flame emission determinations can be carried out directly in this solution (¶ 18–16). Other solutions can be used for displacement, but interferences and viscosity effects may be considerable.

18–22. Low sensitivity of the instrument (Table 18–2) to Ba and interference by Ca in the Ba determination detracts from the exchange capacity determinations with Ba. Sufficiently concentrated solutions can usually be obtained by using appropriate soil-to-solution ratios. One procedure[10] with Ba consisted of leaching 2.5 gm of soil on a 7-cm conical funnel consecutively (in 10-ml increments) with 50 ml of 0.1 N HCl (to remove Ca interference with the flame emission method, since 10 ppm of Ca responded as 400 ppm of Ba), 50 ml of $BaCl_2$ solution buffered to pH 8.1 with triethanolamine, 50 ml of $BaCl_2$ solution, 100 ml of distilled water, and 90 ml of neutral 1 N NH_4OAc. The NH_4OAc extract was caught in 100-ml volumetric flask containing sufficient LiCl solution to make 25 ppm Li in the final volume. The Ba was determined by means of the Perkin-Elmer model 52C flame emission spectrophotometer.

18–23. Dr. L. E. DeMumbrum in this laboratory determined exchanged Cu (Table 18–2) with the Beckman instrument (¶ 18–16), obtaining a precision of 1 per cent. When the hydrogen burner was used instead of acetylene, concentrations below 5 ppm could be obtained with 1 per cent precision.

18–24. Exchangeable K, Na, Ca, and Mg of Soils. The NH_4OAc extract of many soils contains low enough concentrations of interfering ions such as phosphate, Al, and Fe to obviate the need for chemical separations. The standards are made up in 1 N NH_4OAc as the base electrolyte and the exchangeable cations of soil are determined (¶ 18–16) directly in the extract. A higher soil : extractant ratio and smaller increments of extractant than usual (¶ 5–11) are generally employed in the NH_4OAc leaching in order to give sufficiently high concentrations of cations for direct excitation in the solution without preconcentration. Preconcentration may also be readily accomplished. The exchangeable cations have also been determined[11] directly in a 0.05 N HCl extract. Systems of chemical purification of the extract to remove interfering ions have been described.[12]

18–25. The effect of variability of surface tension on the feeding rate of the capillary which supplies the fog to the burner (Perkin-Elmer flame emission spectrophotometer operated without an internal standard) was

---

[10] Pratt and Holowaychuk, *S.S.S.A. Proc.*, 18:365 (1954), adapted to flame emission from Mehlich, *Soil Sci.*, 66:429 (1948).

[11] Rich, *S.S.S.A. Proc.*, 16:51 (1952).

[12] Fieldes *et al.*, *Soil Sci.*, 72:219 (1951); Toth and Prince, *Soil Sci.*, 67:439 (1949).

overcome[13] by the use of an extraction solution for K and Na that was
0.2 N with respect to $Mg(OAc)_2$ as well as 2 N with respect to NH_4OAc.
From 15 to 30 gm of soil was extracted with 50 ml of extraction solution
for 0.5 hour. Filtration was effected in a small Buchner funnel followed by
leaching with 3 successive 15-ml portions of the extraction solution. Finally the suction flask was rinsed with 5 ml of the extraction solution, and
the solution was brought to 100-ml volume in a graduated cylinder. The
pH of this solution after passage through soils of pH values between 4.9
and 7.7 did not cause the solution pH to vary beyond 6.6 to 7.2 a pH range
within which the photometer readings checked to within 1 per cent.
Elimination of the interference of large amounts of Ca with the Na determination with a filter instrument was effected[14] by inclusion of 0.5 gm
of $(NH_4)_2C_2O_4$ in with the soil extracted. This interference does not occur
with a prism instrument.

18–26. Exchangeable K in Runoff Waters. By means of a graduated
beaker (¶ 10–64), 100 ml of well-mixed runoff suspension is measured out
and transferred to a 500-ml conical flask. Then 100 ml of extraction solution which is 4 N with respect to NH_4OAc and 0.4 N with respect to
$Mg(OAc)_2$ is added. The mixture is shaken for 0.5 of an hour and 25 to
35 ml of solution is filtered into a 50-ml beaker. The exchangeable K is determined (¶ 18–16) with the flame emission spectrophotometer. A 0 to 5
ppm K standard is usually employed; occasionally a 0 to 10 ppm K standard is required. Then:

$$\text{ppai} = \text{ppm K} \times 2 \times 0.227 \times \text{correction factor} \qquad (18\text{--}2)$$

in which ppai is the pounds of K per acre inch of runoff, and the correction
factor is given by equation 10–20. Also:

$$\text{pp2ms} = \frac{\text{ppai of K}}{\text{ppai of solids}} \times 2{,}000{,}000 \qquad (18\text{--}3)$$

in which pp2ms refers to the parts of K per 2 million of solids in runoff.

18–27. Total K, Na, Ca, and Mg of Minerals, Clays, Soils, or Rocks.
The K, Na, Ca, and Mg are determined in the order listed, with the Beckman flame emission spectrophotometer. The sample is decomposed in HF
(¶ 11–31), and ions which interfere are removed by the NH_4OH separation (¶ 11–40). The resulting *Solution B* is treated to remove ammonium
salts (¶ 11–43) and taken up in 0.4 N HCl for the determination by flame
emission (¶ 18–16). The HCl solution is advantageous for the determination of Mg, and is excellent for the other cations also. Phosphate and Al,

[13] Attoe and Truog, *S.S.S.A. Proc.,* 11:221 (1947). Myers *et al., S.S.S.A. Proc.,*
12:127 (1948) destroyed the NH_4OAc and determined the Na and K in 0.1 N HNO_3.
[14] Seay *et al., Soil Sci.,* 71:83 (1951).

which interfere with Ca determination at 554 mu, are removed by the NH$_4$OH separation. A calibration curve is prepared for each element in 0.4 N HCl base electrolyte solution (¶ 18–15). The concentration of each element is expressed as mgm per 100 ml of solution (¶ 11–43, eq. 11–1). The 40 ppm standards for K and Na are 4 mgm of K or Na per 100 ml.

18–28. It is advisable to determine the cations as soon as possible after they are brought into solution in order to keep contamination with Na from glassware as low as possible. Blanks should be run with every set of determinations.

18–29. No ions that interfere with K or Na determinations are likely to be present in *Solution A* (¶ 11–45) derived from soils or clays. These 2 ions are therefore determined (¶ 18–16) on *Solution A* when Ca and Mg are determined by methods other than flame emission (¶ 11–44).

18–30. For total K, Na, and Ca, a 1-gm mineral sample was decomposed[15] in 15 ml of HClO$_4$ and 10 ml of 47 per cent HF evaporated in a Pt dish (2 or 3 evaporations were sometimes necessary). Treatment was given with HClO$_4$ alone at the end to expel F from CaF$_2$. Then the K, Na, and Ca were determined with a Perkin-Elmer model 52 instrument.

18–31. Total K of clays can also be determined by decomposition of the sample by Na$_2$CO$_3$ fusion, take-up of the melt in HCl (¶ 6–75), removal of the bulk of silica and R$_2$O$_3$ with the NH$_4$OH separation, and determination by flame emission after dilution of the solution with equal volume of 4 N NH$_4$OAc-0.4 N Mg(OAc)$_2$ to approximate the composition of the extraction solution for exchangeable cations (¶ 18–25).

18–32. K, Na, Ca, and Mg of Plants and Organic Residues. The K and Na can be extracted directly from plant tissue with 2 N NH$_4$OAc-0.2 N Mg(OAc)$_2$ (¶ 18–25) with the same recoveries of these 2 elements found as by ashing the plant tissue.[16] Extraction of the K and Na of organic residues gives that organically bound and the exchangeable forms of K and Na but appropriately excludes that in the extraneous mineral particles. A 0.5-gm sample of ground and dried organic material is extracted for 1 hour with 100 ml of 2 N NH$_4$OAc-0.2 N Mg(OAc)$_2$ solution, the suspension is filtered, and the concentrations of K and Na are then determined (¶ 18–16). The Ca and Mg of plant tissue or organic residues are rendered soluble by oxidation of the organic matter (¶ 12–25) dissolved in 0.4 N HCl, and determined (¶ 18–16). The Cu of plant tissue has been determined similarly.[17]

---

[15] Knight *et al., Anal. Chem.,* 23:1704 (1951).

[16] Attoe, *S.S.S.A. Proc.,* 12:131 (1948). Myers *et al., S.S.S.A. Proc.,* 12:127 (1948), ashed plant tissue at 475° to 500°C and took up the residue in 0.1 N HCl for K and Na determination by flame emission.

[17] Massey, *Anal. Chem.,* 29:365 (1957).

18–33. Use of Internal Standard. Lithium is employed for an internal standard for the determination of K, Na, Ca, and Mg with the Perkin-Elmer model 52C flame emission spectrophotometer (¶ 18–13). Two optical systems pick up the emission simultaneously 1 having a wave length setting for Li at 671 mu, the other for a critical wave length maximum for the test element (for example, 589 mu for Na or 767 mu for K). The Li emission is balanced against that of the test element, thus measuring the ratio of Li concentration to that of the test element. Variations of emission intensity caused by changes in solution acidity and viscosity, flame temperature, and pressure changes are thus cancelled out. With K, from 25[18] to 200 ppm of Li is employed for the 0 to 20 and 0 to 100 ppm K standard curve and 0 to 10 ppm Na standard curve. A stock solution containing 1000 ppm of Li is prepared by dissolution of 9.93 gm of oven-dry $LiNO_3$ per liter of distilled water. This stock is further diluted (1 to 5 for 200 ppm Li) in the standards. With Ca, a 100 ppm Li concentration has been employed[19] for 0 to 480 ppm Ca standard curve. With Mg, a 25 ppm Li standard is employed[20] with the 0 to 1000 ppm Mg standard curve.

18–34. The Lundegardh type (¶ 18–7) of flame emission spectrograph has been employed[21] for the determination of a number of elements in soils and plants. In a modification,[22] 5 gm of soil is extracted with 200 ml of N NH_4OAc, leached through in the usual way (¶ 5–11) to remove exchangeable cations. The leachate is made up to 250 ml, and a 50-ml aliquot is diluted to 250 ml (or more if the soil contains over 8 meq of Ca per 100 gm) for Ca determination. The remainder of the leachate is evaporated to dryness and the organic matter is removed by means of H_2O_2. The solution is made up to 50 ml, and then all other cations are determined on that solution. The following concentrations in the standard stock solution, expressed as moles per liter, were employed for exchangeable cation determinations for soils: Ca, 0.25; Mg, 5.0; K, 5.0; Na, 10.0; Li, 0.25; Sr, 0.10; Mn, 0.25; and Fe^{+++}, 5.0. This stock solution is diluted for each photographic plate by factors of 1, 2, 5, 10, and 20.

QUALITATIVE ANALYSIS WITH ARC OR SPARK EMISSION SPECTROGRAPH

18–35. Qualitative analysis by the emission technique may best be thought of in two distinct categories: (a) search for a specific element, and

---

[18] Toth, *Soil Sci.*, 67:439 (1949).
[19] Jones and Hoover, *S.S.S.A. Proc.*, 14:96 (1950).
[20] Tucker and Smith, *S.S.S.A. Proc.*, 16:252 (1952).
[21] Mitchell, Comm. Bur. Soil Sci. Tech. Com. 44, Harpenden, Herts., England (1948).
[22] Ells and Marshall, *S.S.S.A. Proc.*, 4:131 (1940).

(b) identification of spectral lines originating from an unknown element. Theoretically, all elements can be identified by emission spectra; however, some of the nonmetals are difficult to excite because of high ionization potentials. Related to qualitative analysis is the comparison of samples as to possible *identity of source,* through comparison of the spectrographic patterns in a comparator. This technique applies the "fingerprint" matching approach; identification of the different spectral lines with elements is not required, nor need the amounts be determined.

APPARATUS

18–36. Needed apparatus includes a spectrograph (¶ 18–37), equipment for shaping the electrodes, an agate mortar for grinding the soil sample, a master spectrogram, and a comparator-densitometer (¶ 18–48). Equipment may be obtained from: Applied Research Laboratories, Glendale, Calif.; Jarrel-Ash Co., Boston, Mass.; Baird Associates, Cambridge, Mass.; and Bausch & Lomb Optical Co., Rochester, N.Y.

18–37. Emission spectrophotometers that use a high energy source for excitation are generally known as "spectrographs." A spectrograph consists of 3 principal components, the A.C. or D.C. arc or A.C. spark excitation source (several types may be combined in a "multisource" unit), grating or prism for spectral dispersion (¶ 18–38), and recording components (usually photographic, but sometimes by photocell, ¶ 18–55).

18–38. In the grating spectrograph, a concave grating, entrance slit, and recording device (photographic film or photocell) are placed on the circumference of the Rowland circle (Fig. 18–4). The diameter of the circle is

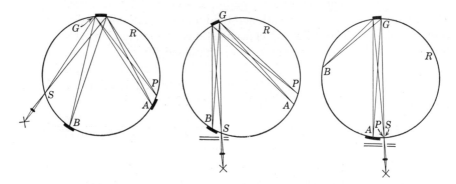

Fig. 18–4. Principle of the Rowland Circle and the optics of the grating spectrograph. *R,* the Rowland Circle; *S,* entrance slit; *G,* diffraction grating; *P,* principal focus, white light; *A, B,* spectral distribution of images of slit, dispersed linearly about the circumference of the circle. Left diagram, Paschen mounting in which recorders are placed at *A* and *B.* Middle and right diagrams, Eagle mounting, in which movement of the grating brings different portions of the spectrum into position near the entrance slit. (From *Better Analysis,* No. 2, p. 3, Cambridge, Mass.: Baird Associates, Inc., 1950.)

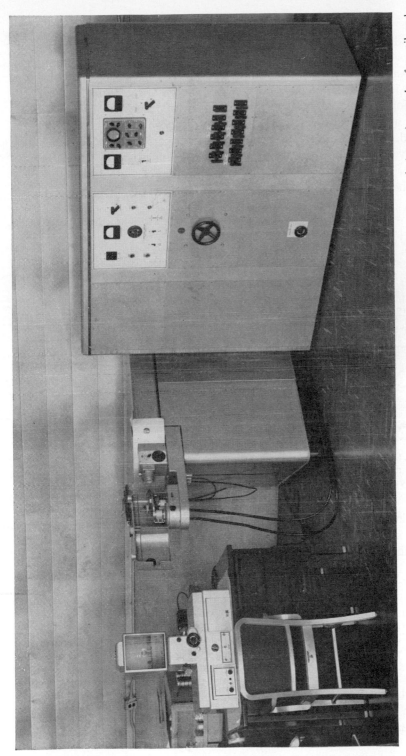

Fig. 18–5. Spectrographic laboratory equipped with the ARL 1.5-meter Paschen-mounted grating spectrograph (center), popular for soil and plant analysis. Photographic recording is on 35-mm film, covering about 2500 A in one exposure and 16 exposures in one 38-cm length of film. Right, multisource excitation unit. Left, projection comparator-densitometer. (Photo courtesy Applied Research Laboratories, Glendale, Calif.)

the radius of curvature of the grating. Grating systems give an angular dispersion that is approximately the same for all wave lengths, in contrast to prism systems (¶ 18–39) which give angular dispersion, the degree of which is a function of the wave length. The grating type of instrument is superior to most prism type instruments with respect to spectral range, linear aperture, resolving power, relative dispersion, and the fact that the second order is usable. The gratings effect dispersion of emitted radiation of wave lengths of about 1800 to 21,000 A (one-half, one-third, etc. of this for higher order spectra). Either the position of the photographic plate (Paschen mounting, Fig. 18–5) or the position of the grating (Eagle

Fig. 18–6. Baird 3-meter grating spectrograph equipped with Eagle mounting (stands against wall, needing no access to back) and photographic plate recording. (Photo courtesy Baird Associates, Cambridge, Mass.)

mounting, Fig. 18–6) must be varied for different wave length ranges of radiation. The greater the number of grating lines per cm, the greater the linear dispersion.

Kind and size	Grating lines per cm	Dispersion, A per mm		Mounting
		1st order	2nd order	
ARL 1.5m	9600	6.9	3.5	Paschen
ARL 2m	9600	5.2	3.4	Paschen
ARL 2m	14400	2.6	1.7	Paschen
Baird, 3m	5900	5.5	—	Eagle

The Paschen mounting provides for equal dispersion of a given wave length interval regardless of its position in the spectrogram, thus facilitating comparison to a master film in the comparator-densitometer. In the Eagle mounting, both the grating and the photographic plates are rotated slightly so that they remain on the Rowland circle, and the focus remains sharp. The Eagle mounting gives a more compact instrument (Fig. 18–4), but involves a different linear dispersion for different grating positions.

18–39. In the prism spectrograph (Fig. 18–7) the spectral radiation is dispersed by the Littrow-type quartz prism (one-half of a 90° prism with the cut surface silvered, Fig. 18–8). The optical system will be recognized as being of the same general arrangement as the quartz spectrophotometer (Fig. 17–12), reemphasizing the parallelism between absorption and emission spectrophotometry. Normally, 3 photographic plates, each 10 inches long and of different emulsion characteristics, are used to cover the spectral

Fig. 18–7. Bausch & Lomb, Littrow prism spectrograph and illuminating unit. The usable spectrum, extending from 2100 to 8000 A with full resolving power, is recorded photographically. (Photo courtesy Bausch & Lomb Optical Co., Rochester, N.Y.)

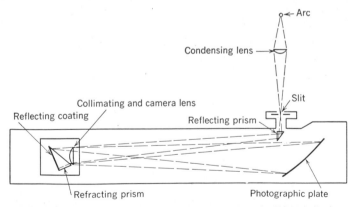

Fig. 18–8. Optical system of Bausch & Lomb, Littrow prism spectrograph. (Photo courtesy Bausch & Lomb Optical Co., Rochester, N.Y.)

range. Glass prisms can also be designed for use at higher wave lengths at some sacrifice of shorter wave lengths. Prism instruments tend to be better than grating instruments in freedom from astigmatism and spurious lines. Prisms also give a higher percentage collection of the total emitted radiation.

18–40. A simple and inexpensive emission spectral instrument is offered in the Spectranal (Todd Scientific Co., Springfield, Pa.). Metals are excited in either solid or solution form and their lines are inspected visually in a Bausch & Lomb prism spectroscope.

REAGENTS AND SUPPLIES

18–41. Needed reagents and supplies include electrodes (Fig. 18–9),

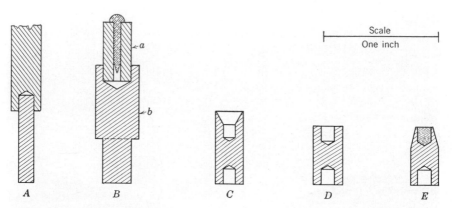

Fig. 18–9. Graphite electrodes for arc excitation of test elements in samples. *A*, upper, DC negative; *B*, lower, for iron spectra; *C*, sample crater, empty; *D*, crater for sulfide precipitates; *E*, sample crater filled, with excess graphite filed off. (From Vanselow and Liebig, *Spectrochemical Methods*, Berkeley, Calif.: University of California, 1948, p. 39.)

usually graphite rods of high purity to avoid or minimize the introduction of extraneous lines; spectrographic grade 35-mm photographic film or glass plates; and photographic processing chemicals. Cloth gauze is employed for sieving the sample to avoid contamination with metals.

PROCEDURE

18–42. The aim in the qualitative procedure is to detect as many elements as possible in the sample. Some difficulty is encountered in detecting a representative portion of both the more volatile elements in the first part of the exposure and the less volatile elements that tend to delay volatilization until the last part of the burn. Volatility of the sample is an especially important consideration in the qualitative analysis of soil or plant extracts. Spectrograph "buffers," which control the rate of volatilization, are generally added. Thus Na_2SO_4 or NaCl may be added to a slowly volatile silicate to speed up volatilization, or SiO_2 to the chloride or acetate extract of cations to slow down the rate of volatilization. Also, 3 or more separate spectrograms of the sample may be taken with different arcing time to represent elements of various volatilities in the sample. In one modification, a rotating disc of carbon or silver[23] continuously renews the sample for high temperature excitation much as spraying into the flame does for low temperature excitation (¶ 18–7).

18–43. Mounting the Sample. The soil sample, after having been dried and ground to pass a fine bolting cloth (ground with buffer salt in some cases), is placed in a high purity carbon electrode[24] which has been cratered to a sufficient depth (Fig. 18–9, C). A liquid sample is evaporated in a dish and powdered with a buffer, then mounted. Small amounts of solution may be evaporated in a crater directly. The crater containing the sample may be heated for 15 or 20 seconds in a small gas blowpipe flame at below red heat to remove moisture if its presence proves objectionable. Powdered samples of plant tissue, soil, rock, glass, paint, and minerals have been successfully analyzed qualitatively by direct placement in the carbon arc crater without buffer or other special arrangements.

18–44. Adjustment of Slit Width. The film background intensity must be controlled by adjustment of grating aperture, so as not to mask any of the lines of interest by over-exposure. With an ARL 1.5-m grating spectrograph, the slit width is adjusted at the start to a minimum (24 microns) and the grating apertures are set at an opening of 4 on a scale of 1 to 10. A narrow slit width is somewhat more desirable than wider ones (of over 60 microns) because with wider slit widths, prominent spectrum lines may at times overlap minor lines.

18–45. Arcing the Sample. A high current D.C. or A.C. arc is usually employed because it gives high sensitivity. Complete volatilization of the sample is easily achieved and all elements are thus represented in the spectrogram. The electrodes are spaced with the standard spacer (4 to 6 mm). First the iron spectrum is produced for reference purposes (iron sample, Fig. 18–9, B), by a 5-second spark. Then the grating aperture is opened to 10 and the first sample is energized by a 6-ampere A.C. arc for 10 to 30 seconds. Vanselow and Liebig[25] suggest a 10-second first exposure followed by a second spectrogram of the sample with the aperture grating at 5 for 40 seconds, and a third run with aperture grating set at 2 for 80 seconds. Additional spectrograms are run at narrower grating aperture

[23] Meloche and Shapiro, *Anal. Chem.*, 26:347 (1954).

[24] After preburning empty, for the same time as in the procedure. Commercial electrodes can be obtained sufficiently pure for most purposes. Electrodes may be purified by Soxlet extraction with 20 per cent HCl and the concentrated HNO_3 and finally with water according to the procedure of Vanselow and Liebig, *Spectrochemical Methods* (Berkeley: University of California, mimeo., 1948), p. 5.

[25] *Ibid.*, p. 11.

openings and longer exposure times if necessary to obtain complete volatilization of the sample. Lastly, an iron reference spectrum is again recorded.

18–46. For identification work with soil, paint, rock, glass, and minerals, ordinarily 1 arcing time can be selected as representative of a given material, thus permitting a satisfactory test with 1 spectrogram per sample. This is particularly an advantage when a large number of samples are to be checked qualitatively.

18–47. The film or plate is processed according to standard procedure, usually with a 3-minute development, 1-minute washing, and 2-minute fixing time, followed by washing in tap water, rinsing in distilled water, sponging off with fine textured synthetic sponges, and a 2-minute forced hot-air drying.

18–48. Interpretation of Results. The photographic film or plate bearing the spectrogram is mounted in a comparator (Fig. 18–10) and the spectral lines are projected in juxtaposition with those of a master spectrogram. After 1 or 2 lines for some known element in the sample have been located on the sample spectrogram (for example, the iron triplet at about 3100 A), it is orientated and locked with lines adjacent to the same lines on the master spectrogram. Unknown lines then can be identified.

18–49. The standard reference in which all known lines are listed is the MIT wave length tables[26] which give 100,000 lines from 2000 to 100,000 A. Most elements are readily identified by their persistent lines (*Raies Ultimes* or *letzten Linien*). These lines are observable if an element is present in any amount. If the persistent lines are absent for some element, the assumption can be made that the element is not present. If the presence of some element is in question, the problem is simply one of searching for the persistent lines. To identify each of various lines, the wave length is measured and referred to tables of elements arranged by wave lengths[27] for a list of possible elements represented. The more probable ones are then looked up in the second set of tables, which gives all emission wave lengths for each element. A series of lines in the spectrum corresponding to a given element serves to identify it positively. The identification of all of the significant lines present in the spectrogram is usually possible in this way.

18–50. If a grating spectrograph and Paschen mounting (Fig. 18–4) are employed, the spectrogram is easily projected with the test sample lines in juxtaposition to the standard spectrogram because the dispersion of the lines is always the same for a given wave length. If a prism instrument or Eagle-mounted grating instrument is employed, the dispersion must be

---

[26] Harrison, *MIT Wavelength Tables* (New York: John Wiley & Sons, Inc., 1950).
[27] Given in Harrison *et al., op. cit.;* Brode, *op. cit.;* and Ahrens, *Wavelength Tables of Sensitive Lines* (Cambridge, Mass.: Addison-Wesley Publishing Company, Inc., 1951).

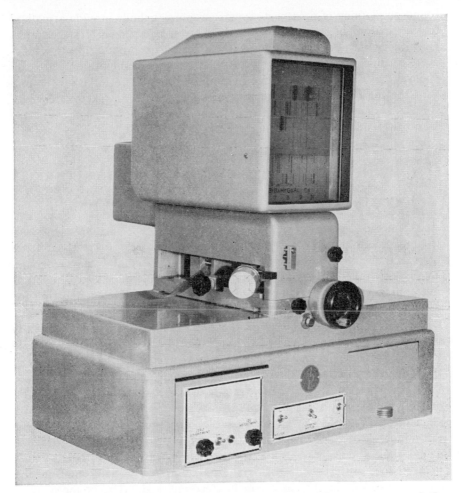

Fig. 18–10. ARL projection comparator-densitometer. The spectrogram of the test sample is set to track with a master spectrogram and the lines projected in juxtaposition for qualitative work. The densitometer can be used to measure light absorption of line and background for quantitative work. (Photo courtesy Applied Research Laboratories, Glendale, Calif.)

calculated or a standard spectrogram employed that has the same dispersion of the spectral lines as the test sample. Exact measurement of the position of the spectral lines with any type of photographic spectrogram may also be made by means of a mechanical traverse microscope, suitably calibrated.

18–51. Soil Analysis in Crime Detection. The detailed analysis of soil often becomes of interest in crime detection. The soil chemist is called upon for interpretation of possible identity of soil at the scene with that found on clothing of a suspect. Spectrographic methods provide a method for the analysis of as many as 70 elements on a few mgm of soil sample. General similarity of soil samples is not sufficient for proof of identity, however, because many soils are more or less alike in composition. The soil chemist can do service to justice in pointing out this relationship, to prevent the mistaken claim to identity of similar samples. The presence of similar amounts of the same elements in both samples presents evidence of probable identity; discrepancies between the two samples present evidence that identity is unlikely.

QUANTITATIVE ANALYSIS WITH THE ARC OR SPARK EMISSION SPECTROGRAPH

18–52. In devoting one complete issue of *Soil Science* to the arc and spark emission spectrograph, editor Bear[28] states ". . . the emission spectrograph merits much more consideration than it has yet received from biological scientists." Many soils laboratories now employ the technique. The objective here is to outline some of the broad principles of quantitative emission analysis. Because of the importance of routine application for gaining economy with the emission spectrochemical method, the use of cooperative facilities for the work of several departments and agencies is important. For organizations of size insufficient to develop such a laboratory, the use of commercial service laboratory[29] facilities helps.

18–53. Quantitative emission spectrochemical analysis has several advantages[30] over the wet chemical methods. The size of sample may be small, although this is usually a minor advantage. The identification of any element determined is absolutely positive, an important consideration for the minor elements. Furthermore, several minor elements can be determined simultaneously by fusion and extraction[31] or direct arcing of soil, plant tissue, or fertilizer.[32] The determination of Zr, important in the chemistry of soil development, can be accomplished.[33] Use of the method will undoubtedly lead to determination of elements not now considered in the analysis of soils and plants. Another advantage is that chemical isolation of a specific element is not required prior to analysis. It is necessary only to preconcentrate the element in question to the extent necessary for its determination. Sulfide and 8-hydroxyquinoline precipitations, which bring down whole suites of elements, are highly satisfactory for the preconcentration of many trace elements, even though large amounts of more

---

[28] Bear, *Soil Sci.*, 83:1 (1957).
[29] One example, Chicago Spectro Service Laboratory, Inc., 2454 W. 38th St., Chicago 32, Ill.
[30] Vanselow and Liebig, *op. cit.*, p. 28.
[31] Wark, *Anal. Chem.*, 26:203 (1954).
[32] O'Connor, *Ind. Eng. Chem., A.E.*, 13:597 (1941).
[33] Horton, *Anal. Chem.*, 25:1331 (1953).

common elements come down also. In fact, macro quantities of an element may be added to act as a carrier for recovery of some trace elements. The use of solid samples has the advantage over the solution system, such as is used with the flame photometer, that the entire ash or soil need not be brought into solution. Experience indicates that bringing of the entire ash of plants into solution, including all trace elements, is not as easily accomplished as is commonly thought. Quantitative spectrochemical analysis has been discussed at length.[34]

18–54. Accuracy. The accuracy of a spectrographic determination depends on: (a) instrument precision (capacity to give identical results under identical operating conditions); (b) uniformity between standard and test sample as to matrix composition, bonding of the elements present, and degree to which the spectroscopic buffer (¶ 18–42) is successful in its function; (c) amount of element available for analysis (the nearer to the optimum quantity of test element, the greater the accuracy); and (d) the particular element to be determined, since some elements inherently give a greater degree of accuracy than others. A report by Mathis[35] shows that an accuracy of 92 to 98 per cent is readily attained for a number of cations determined with spark excitation on solutions, but that accuracy with boron is only about 85 to 90 per cent with this method. With a D.C. arc, an accuracy of 85 to 96 per cent was obtained with plant ash and with solutions. The Quantometer (¶ 18–55), in eliminating the photographic problems, enhances precision by about one-third over the limits found with photographic methods. With the best available refinements of the procedure, including appropriate matrix for standards, spectroscopic buffers, preconcentration sufficient to bring the concentration to the optimum, using elements that lend themselves to greatest accuracy, and with mathematical treatment of the data, the error in the high temperature excitation methods is held to about 3 per cent. In practice, keeping the error within 10 per cent is considered satisfactory.

APPARATUS

18–55. Needed apparatus includes an arc or spark emission spectrograph of grating or prism type (¶ 18–37) with a recorder. Equipment for shaping the electrodes is needed unless preshaped electrodes are purchased. For photographic recorders, processing accessories and a comparator-densitometer (¶ 18–48) are needed. Automatic photocell and chart recorder equipment (Fig. 18–11) are highly efficient for routine work. Photomulti-

---

[34] Ahrens, *Spectrochemical Analysis* (Cambridge, Mass.: Addison-Wesley Publishing Company, Inc., 1950), pp. 76–120; Mitchell, Comm. Bur. Soil Sci. Tech. Com. 44, pp. 11–44 (1948); Harvey, *Spectrochemical Procedures* (Glendale, Calif.: Applied Research Laboratories, 1950), pp. 184–293.

[35] *J.A.O.A.C.,* 34:604 (1951).

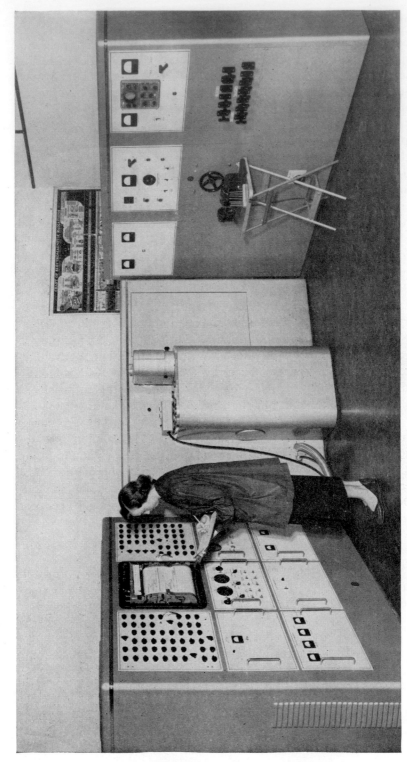

Fig. 18–11. ARL Quantometer. Excitation unit at right, grating spectrograph in center, and detector unit at left. Photocells are aligned for direct and simultaneous measurement and recording of intensity of critical spectral lines. (Photo courtesy Applied Research Laboratories, Glendale, Calif.)

plier cells are situated in adjustable positions, each placed to intercept the radiation at wave length maxima specific for an element to be determined. The intensities of spectral lines are graphed automatically. Such an instrument may be compared to a flame emission spectrophotometer (¶ 18–7) in mode of operation except that it employs the higher temperature of excitation of the conventional spectrograph. The usual photographic film exposure, its processing, and the densitometric measurement of intensity are thus supplanted.

REAGENTS AND SUPPLIES

18–56. Needed reagents and supplies include electrodes, usually graphite rods or discs; spectrographic grade 35-mm photographic film or glass plates, according to the design of the instrument; chemicals for internal standards; spectrographic buffers; and reagents for preconcentration of sample constituents. Copper, aluminum, and silver rods or discs are other possible electrode materials. The electrodes should be of highest purity to avoid or minimize the introduction of extraneous lines. A purification procedure was suggested in connection with qualitative emission spectrochemical analysis (¶ 18–43). One procedure (¶ 18–58) calls for coating the graphite electrode craters with DuPont methacrylate clear solution RC-901 diluted 5-fold with acetone, to prevent soaking-in of the sample solution.

PROCEDURE

18–57. The quantitative emission spectrochemical procedure involves the following steps: (a) qualitative exploration (¶ 18–42) for establishment of instrumental conditions suitable for the elements to be determined; (b) design of convenient and effective form of sample, buffer, matrix, crater shape or disc-wetting conditions; (c) preconcentration of elements, as necessary; (d) calibration of photographic emulsion response characteristic if a Quantometer is not available; (e) choice of internal standards; and (f) preparation of standard curves for the elements to be determined.

18–58. Form of Sample. The sample may be of ground soil or the whole-ash of plants, and thus be mounted in solid form. Plant tissue in pellet form has been employed. For the total elemental analysis of soil, Mitchell[36] air-dried the soil, ground it to pass 0.16 mm openings (100 meshes per inch), ignited it at 450°C to destroy the organic matter, and placed it in the electrode craters ready for arcing. Solutions resulting from extractions may be dried in an evaporating dish and mixed with the buffer (frequently Na_2SO_4) and internal standard by means of an agate pestle.[37] The plant

---

[36] Comm. Bur. Soil Sci., Tech. Com. 44 (1948).
[37] Vanselow and Liebig, *op. cit.*

ash solution has been evaporated in the crater filled with graphite powder[38] resulting from the crater drilling. The solution may be mixed with the buffer and internal standard in solution,[39] which gives thorough mixing, and then evaporated in the graphite electrode crater which has previously been sealed with methacrylate. For quantitative determination of cobalt, a 9-ampere D.C. arc with narrow electrodes and exposure until 1 to 2 seconds after the green color of iron internal standard spectrum disappears has been employed successfully. Alternatively, the solution may be used directly for excitation by means of a rotating graphite, copper, or silver disc (¶ 18–42), one side of which dips in the solution while simultaneously the other side is sparked with the upper electrode. In the latter procedure, a wetting agent is often added to facilitate uniform adherence of the solution to the electrode. Proper adjustment of the cycle must be made to avoid excessive evaporation of the solution by over-heating of the disc.

18–59. Preconcentration of the Test Element. Increasing the concentration of an element per unit weight of the matrix in which it is to be excited is termed *preconcentration* (¶ 18–53). One or more elements present in macro amounts are removed to increase the relative concentration of the test element. It is frequently necessary to preconcentrate some of the minor elements before spectrographic determination. A detailed procedure for preconcentration of soil cobalt with dithizone has been outlined by Carrigan and Erwin.[40] It illustrates in some detail the principles of preconcentration of a minor element. For total soil cobalt, 1 to 5 gm of soil sample, previously ignited for 5 to 6 hours at 450°C to destroy organic matter and ground to pass fine bolting cloth, is decomposed with 20 ml of 50 per cent HF and 4 ml of 72 per cent $HClO_4$ and the filtered acid insoluble residue is decomposed by a Na_2CO_3 fusion and HCl extraction. The resulting acid solutions each are extracted in the presence of 5 ml of 10 per cent sodium citrate buffer and 0.5 ml excess of 1 : 3 NH_4OH with 10 ml of 0.05 per cent dithizone in CCl_4 and then with three 5-ml portions of 0.01 per cent dithizone. To the combined dithizone extracts are added 2 ml of an Fe internal standard solution and the whole is evaporated to dryness in a 50-ml beaker. The residue is treated with 0.75 ml of concentrated H_2SO_4 and 6 drops of 72 per cent $HClO_4$, and the mixture is digested on a hot plate until the organic matter is destroyed. The H_2SO_4 is then fumed off by a flame playing across the beaker. The residue is dissolved, with heating, in 2 ml of 1 : 20 HNO_3 containing 2.5 mgm of Na_2SO_4 per ml. Then the solution is evaporated to 1 ml and transferred to a glass cone with a capillary tipped pipet (no washing is required because of the internal standard) for further evaporation to 0.2 ml, an aluminum heating block being em-

---

[38] Mathis, *Anal. Chem.*, 25:943 (1953).

[39] Carrigan and Erwin, *S.S.S.A. Proc.*, 15:145 (1951).

[40] *S.S.S.A. Proc.*, 15:145 (1951).

ployed. Finally, drops of this solution are transferred to the plastic-sealed electrode craters and evaporated to dryness. Cobalt extracts of soil with N and 6 N HCl, and with HOAc and NH$_4$OAc were similarly preconcentrated.

18–60. The dilute acid extractable trace elements Co, Ni, Mo, Cu, and Zn were preconcentrated by Mitchell[41] by 8-hydroxyquinoline. To 20 gm of soil is added 800 ml of 2.5 per cent HOAc (0.5 N, pH 2.5). The suspension is shaken over night and filtered. The cake is washed with distilled water and the combined filtrates are then evaporated to dryness. The residue is treated with H$_2$O$_2$ to remove organic matter, taken up in 50 ml of 4 N HCl and filtered through 9-cm Whatman No. 41 filter paper. Enough iron and aluminum in HCl solution are added to give the equivalent of 2 to 5 mgm of Fe$_2$O$_3$ and 30 mgm of Al$_2$O$_3$ total considering the amounts already present, and the solution is diluted to 150 ml. Then 15 ml of a 5 per cent solution of 8-hydroxyquinoline in 2 N HOAc is added, followed by 7 N NH$_4$OH dropwise until the color changes from yellow to emerald green at pH 1.8 to 1.9. Finally 50 ml of 2 N NH$_4$OH is added, and the solution is stirred and allowed to stand over night at room temperature. The precipitate is filtered on a 9-cm Whatman No. 540 filter paper and washed with cold water. After it is partially dried, the precipitate is ignited with the paper in a muffle furnace at 450°C. The precipitate is weighed, and ordinarily amounts to 30 to 50 mgm. If below 30 mgm, it is made up to 40 mgm by the addition of pure Al$_2$O$_3$ powder. The ash is thoroughly ground in a small agate mortar, and is then ready for emission spectrochemical analysis of the trace elements and the colorimetric determination of iron for application of the variable internal standard method.[42] Recovery of Pb, Sn, Cr, V, and Cd is incomplete by the 8-hydroxyquinoline procedure, but Mitchell and Scott[43] found that the addition of tannic acid and thionalide with the 8-hydroxyquinoline gave complete recovery of Co, Ni, Mo, Cr, V, Bi, Ge, Sn, Pb, Ti, Zn, Cd, and probably Ga, Th, and Ag. Addition of CdCl$_2$ was substituted for the addition of iron and thus the Zn determination made easier, since Fe interferes with the Zn determination. The Cd serves as an internal standard for Zn.

18–61. Calibration of Photographic Emulsion Response Curve. One of the greatest sources of error in the quantitative spectrochemical analysis arises from difficulties inherent in the photographic process. Use of the Quantometer (¶ 18–55) eliminates this source of error. In order to obtain reproducible photographic results, factors such as the age of the film, the age of the developer, the developing temperature, and the agitation during development must be rigidly controlled. Kodak spectrum analysis No. 1 film is usually used for quantitative analysis. The film is processed as fol-

---

[41] Comm. Bur. Soil Sci. Tech. Com. 44 (1948).
[42] Davidson and Mitchell, *J. Soc. Chem. Ind.,* 59:213 (1940).
[43] *J. Soc. Chem. Ind.,* 66:330 (1947).

lows: 3 minutes for development in D-19 (Eastman-Kodak), 10 seconds of acid wash, 1.5 minutes in fixer F-5 (Eastman), and 2 minutes of drying in an infrared dryer.

18–62. The photographic darkening in a spectral line is read with a densitometer. White light is suitable for measurement of the black emulsion darkening, which consists of metallic silver grains. Optical density, D, is related (¶ 17–13), to light transmission by:

$$D = \log_{10} \frac{1}{T} = \log_{10} \frac{100}{\% \text{ transmission}} \tag{18-4}$$

in which T is the ratio of transmitted to incident light intensity. The incident light intensity is, for convenience, taken as the intensity of light passing through the background or relatively clear portions of the film near the lines to be measured. The densitometer readings, D, are linearly related to concentration for low density lines (D below 1.25) and are related to the log of concentration for high density lines.

18–63. The first operation in quantitative work is the calibration of the photographic emulsion in the region of the spectrum used. A proper and accurate emulsion calibration is important. In the Churchill[44] 2-step filter method of calibration of photographic film, a quartz optical filter, one-half of which is clear and the other half aluminized to decrease the amount of light passing through it, is placed in front of the slit of the spectrograph. The light transmission percentage value of the aluminized portion relative to the clear portions is calibrated (the calibration is ordinarily furnished with the filter) as a function of wave length. To do this, an iron spectrogram is made, a portion of the light being passed through each portion of the 2-step filter. The 2 percentage transmissions for each pair of 30 iron lines in the desired spectral region (100 A band width) are measured by a densitometer and then plotted, one against the other, on linear graph paper. This is known as the preliminary emulsion calibration curve. The wave lengths of the analysis and the internal standard lines are usually chosen to fall within the linear portions of the emulsion response curve (2600 to 3300 A for spectrum analysis film No. 1). Churchill[45] gives directions for conversion of the preliminary to the final calibration curve and summarizes graphical calibration and interpretation of emission spectra.

18–64. Internal Standards. The use of internal standards in spectrographic analysis, pioneered by Gerlach,[46] has obviated many of the difficulties earlier experienced with attempts to compare directly the line densi-

---

[44] In Boltz, *Modern Instrumental Analysis* (Englewood Cliffs, N.J.: Prentice-Hall, Inc., 1952), p. 201. Further discussions of the calibration of photographic emulsion are given by Nachtrieb, *Spectrochemical Analysis* (New York: McGraw-Hill Book Company, Inc., 1950), pp. 102–141; and Sawyer, *Experimental Spectroscopy* (Englewood Cliffs, N.J.: Prentice-Hall, Inc., 1946), 192–214, 254–257.

[45] *Op. cit.*

[46] *Z. anorg. Chem.*, 142:383 (1925).

ties of standard and test spectrograms. Even though the conditions of excitation have been maintained as closely as possible alike, great differences in intensity occur for identical samples. The internal standard is used by placing a definite concentration of a selected element in with the test sample and exciting it simultaneously with the test elements. The intensity of 1 or more lines the standard emits is compared with the lines of the test element. Any variations in excitation conditions are then represented equally for both standard and test lines.

18–65. For the internal standard, an element is chosen that emits a spectral line with approximately the same excitation energy as the test element, and is located at a spectral position not too far distant from that of the test element. The internal standard line of course must not fall on or too near lines of other elements that may be present in the sample, and must be of an element that does not occur in appreciable or unpredictable amounts in the test sample. The internal standard line must not exhibit self absorption.

18–66. A good preliminary choice of an internal standard can usually be made in the basis of its similarity to the analysis element with respect to atomic weight, electron configuration and periodic group. Ideally, the members of the homologous pair, as the internal standard and the analysis element are often called, will excite similarly under differing environmental conditions. They are unaffected by enhancement (intensity increase of one member independent of the other) or degradation (loss of intensity of one member independent of the other) caused either by changes in the conditions of excitation or in the matrix composition. In practice, this situation is never completely attained. In the choice of an internal standard, it is first desirable to match the internal standard, and the analysis element as regards a similar rate of volatilization (Fig. 18–12).

18–67. Because of the minute quantities of internal standard required per sample for minor element work, the standard substances have been diluted[47] with Na_2SO_4 buffer salt in large enough quantities to permit weighing of each component, and the resultant powders are thoroughly mixed by grinding in an agate mortar, drying at 400°C, and regrinding. One part of the Na_2SO_4 mixture to 4 parts of solid sample has been employed. The internal standards and buffer may be added as solutions, when the sample is in solution, and all evaporated together.

18–68. The internal standard elements found to be appropriate for a number of plant constituents are listed in Table 18–3. As an internal standard, Mg from the $Mg(NO_3)_2$ used in plant tissue ashing or Ge in plants of high ash content has been employed[48] for the line width technique of spectrochemical analysis.

---

47 Vanselow and Liebig, *op. cit.*, p. 18.

48 O'Connor and Heinzelman, *Anal. Chem.*, 24:1667 (1952).

Fig. 18–12. Rate of vaporization of various elements during the arcing cycle, which provides a basis of selection of internal standard and test sample homologous pairs. (From Vanselow and Liebig, *Spectrochemical Methods,* Berkeley, Calif.: University of California, 1948, p. 41.)

18–69. Standard Curves of the Constituent to Be Determined. Because the amount of excitation of a constituent per unit concentration is strongly affected by the nature of the matrix or the bulk composition of the sample, the standards must be prepared with the same matrix as the test sample. As an added means of making the matrix uniform a spectrographic buffer is added as already explained.

18–70. A suitable range of concentrations of the test elements and in-

TABLE 18–3

Spectral lines employed for quantitative determination of a number of elements by arc emission, together with the appropriate internal standards*

Elements	Wave lengths (A.)			Internal standards
Ag	3208.7	3382.9		Ge
Al	3961.5	3082.2	2575.1	Be, Pd
As	2780.2	2456.5		Tl
Au	2676.0	3122.8		Ge, Pd
B	2497.7	2496.8		Pd, Ge
Ba	4554.0			Pd
Bi	3067.7	2898.0		Tl
Cb	4058.9	3094.2		Be
Cd	3261.1	3466.2		Tl
Co	3453.5	3405.1		Pd
Cr	4254.3	4274.8	2986.5	Pd
Cs	4555.4	4593.2		Tl
Cu	3247.5	3274.0		Ge, Pd
Fe	3020.6	3440.6	3021.1	Pd
Ga	2943.6	2874.2	2944.2	Ge
Hg	2536.5			Tl
In	4511.3	3256.1	2932.6	Ge
La	4086.7	4123.2		Pd
Li	3232.6	2741.3		Ge, Tl
Mn	4030.8	4034.5	2576.1	Pd
Mo	3132.6	3170.3	3208.8	Ge, Pd
Ni	3414.8	3458.5	3101.6	Pd
Pb	3683.5	2833.1	2614.2	Tl
Pt	3064.7	2998.0		Pd
Rb	4201.9			Tl
Sb	2598.1			Ge
Sn	3175.0	3262.3	3034.1	Ge
Sr	4607.3			Ge
Ta	3311.2	3318.8		Be
Ti	3653.5	3234.5		Pd, Be
V	4379.2	4384.7	4390.0	Pd
Zn	3345.0	3282.3		Tl
Zr	3392.0	3438.2	3273.1	Be

* From Vanselow and Liebig, *Spectrochemical Methods*, (Berkeley: University of California, mimeo., 1948), p. 35.

ternal standards is made up with chemically pure substances which, in aggregate, approximate the bulk composition of the test samples. If more than 3 elements are to be determined, it is sometimes advantageous to make a separate series of standards for each set of 3 elements. Selection of the elements to be grouped together in 1 standard preparation is made to provide a clear separation of the spectral lines to be measured (diagnostic lines are given in Table 18–3), both of test elements and of the internal standard. The spectrographic buffer is included in the formulation. Solid or liquid standards are then arced or sparked and the concentrations are further adjusted as necessary to give the proper range of spectral radiation intensity. The line densities are then converted to radiation intensities and the intensity ratio of internal standard to test element is then plotted against the concentration to obtain the working curve.

18–71. Interpretation of Results. The photographic spectrogram is placed in the comparator-densitometer (Fig. 18–10), and the characteristic lines (Table 18–3) of the elements to be determined are located as in qualitative analysis (¶ 18–57) by reference to the master spectrogram or reference spectrogram (frequently iron) recorded with that of the sample. Each worker usually accumulates a set of standard[49] spectrograms for the different elements and marks a series of index lines for comparisons with test samples. The Applied Research Laboratories supplies a library of standard film spectrograms for use with their grating spectrographs.

18–72. Then each spectral line density is measured as percentage transmission or as optical density (¶ 18–62) with the densitometer. In the densitometer, light passes from a very narrow slit through the spectral analysis line on the emulsion to a photocell and amplifier system. This scanning device is incorporated into the light projection system (Fig. 18–10) so that the density measurement can be observed as the deflection on a sensitive galvanometer. The percentage transmission of each line is referred to the photographic calibration curve (¶ 18–63) and the relative spectral line intensities are obtained. The ratio of intensity of the specific analytical line for each element to be determined to that of the internal standard or reference line is calculated. Then the quantity of the constituent may be calculated by proportion:

$$\text{Quantity, test element} = \frac{\text{Intensity ratio, test}}{\text{Intensity ratio, standard}} \times \text{Quantity, standard}$$

$$(18\text{–}5)$$

In practice, the intensity ratios for a series of standard samples of the test element are plotted against the quantities of the standard taken, and the quantities in the test samples are then read from the curve. Graphic calculators have been described.[50]

18–73. In the line-width method[51] of interpretation of the spectrogram, the width of the standard line on the microphotometer tracing is measured at the intensity (peak height) of the element the concentration of which is to be determined.

---

[49] For wave lengths of specific elements, the following references are recommended: Harrison, *op. cit.;* Ahrens, *Wavelength Tables of Sensitive Lines* (Cambridge, Mass.: Addison-Wesley Publishing Company, Inc., 1951) and *Spectrochemical Analysis* (Cambridge, Mass.: Addison-Wesley Publishing Company, Inc., 1950); Brode, *op. cit.,* pp. 400–658; Dingle, *Practical Applications of Spectrum Analysis* (London: Chapman & Hall, Ltd., 1950), pp. 86–122.

[50] Vanselow and Liebig, *J. Opt. Soc. Am.,* 34:219 (1944); Oplinger, *Anal. Chem.* 24:807 (1952); Frederickson, *Anal. Chem.,* 24:2019 (1952).

[51] O'Connor and Heinzelman, *Anal. Chem.,* 24:1667 (1952).

QUESTIONS

1. Explain how emission spectra originate, particularly with reference to the atomic mechanism.

2. Distinguish the fundamental principle of emission spectrophotometry from that of absorption spectrophotometry.

3. Compare emission and absorption spectrophotometry as to the common features involved in both their principles and procedures.

4. Distinguish the flame from arc and spark methods of excitation, particularly as to applicability to soil chemical analysis.

5. Draw a sketch of the general optical relations in emission spectrophotometry.

6. List several elements that are readily determined by flame excitation. Why are they more readily determined than other elements?

7. Contrast prisms and gratings as to the properties of the spectral array produced.

8. What types of information can be obtained in qualitative emission spectrochemical analysis?

9. List the advantages of quantitative emission spectrochemical analysis over other types of chemical analysis.

10. Explain the procedure by which an internal standard is generally used in quantitative emission spectrophotometry.

11. What is the purpose of spectroscopic buffers?

12. What should be the composition of the matrix of the standards?

13. Explain how preconcentration of a minor element for emission spectrochemical analysis may be easier than its chemical separation and determination by conventional wet chemical methods.

14. What order of accuracy can be achieved by emission spectrophotometric analysis of Na? Of K? Of Ca? Of Mg? State the methods of excitation and observation considered.

INDEX

Index

C

N	0	1	2	3	4	5	6	7	8	9	P.P. 1	2	3	4	5
10	0000	0043	0086	0128	0170	0212	0253	0294	0334	0374	4	8	12	17	21
11	0414	0453	0492	0531	0569	0607	0645	0682	0719	0755	4	8	11	15	19
12	0792	0828	0864	0899	0934	0969	1004	1038	1072	1106	3	7	10	14	17
13	1139	1173	1206	1239	1271	1303	1335	1367	1399	1430	3	6	10	13	16
14	1461	1492	1523	1553	1584	1614	1644	1673	1703	1732	3	6	9	12	15
15	1761	1790	1818	1847	1875	1903	1931	1959	1987	2014	3	6	8	11	14
16	2041	2068	2095	2122	2148	2175	2201	2227	2253	2279	3	5	8	11	13
17	2304	2330	2355	2380	2405	2430	2455	2480	2504	2529	2	5	7	10	12
18	2553	2577	2601	2625	2648	2672	2695	2718	2742	2765	2	5	7	9	12
19	2788	2810	2833	2856	2878	2900	2923	2945	2967	2989	2	4	7	9	11
20	3010	3032	3054	3075	3096	3118	3139	3160	3181	3201	2	4	6	8	11
21	3222	3243	3263	3284	3304	3324	3345	3365	3385	3404	2	4	6	8	10
22	3424	3444	3464	3483	3502	3522	3541	3560	3579	3598	2	4	6	8	10
23	3617	3636	3655	3674	3692	3711	3729	3747	3766	3784	2	4	5	7	9
24	3802	3820	3838	3856	3874	3892	3909	3927	3945	3962	2	4	5	7	9
25	3979	3997	4014	4031	4048	4065	4082	4099	4116	4133	2	3	5	7	9
26	4150	4166	4183	4200	4216	4232	4249	4265	4281	4298	2	3	5	7	8
27	4314	4330	4346	4362	4378	4393	4409	4425	4440	4456	2	3	5	6	8
28	4472	4487	4502	4518	4533	4548	4564	4579	4594	4609	2	3	5	6	8
29	4624	4639	4654	4669	4683	4698	4713	4728	4742	4757	1	3	4	6	7
30	4771	4786	4800	4814	4829	4843	4857	4871	4886	4900	1	3	4	6	7
31	4914	4928	4942	4955	4969	4983	4997	5011	5024	5038	1	3	4	6	7
32	5051	5065	5079	5092	5105	5119	5132	5145	5159	5172	1	3	4	5	7
33	5185	5198	5211	5224	5237	5250	5263	5276	5289	5302	1	3	4	5	6
34	5315	5328	5340	5353	5366	5378	5391	5403	5416	5428	1	3	4	5	6
35	5441	5453	5465	5478	5490	5502	5514	5527	5539	5551	1	2	4	5	6
36	5563	5575	5587	5599	5611	5623	5635	5647	5658	5670	1	2	4	5	6
37	5682	5694	5705	5717	5729	5740	5752	5763	5775	5786	1	2	3	5	6
38	5798	5809	5821	5832	5843	5855	5866	5877	5888	5899	1	2	3	5	6
39	5911	5922	5933	5944	5955	5966	5977	5988	5999	6010	1	2	3	4	6
40	6021	6031	6042	6053	6064	6075	6085	6096	6107	6117	1	2	3	4	5
41	6128	6138	6149	6160	6170	6180	6191	6201	6212	6222	1	2	3	4	5
42	6232	6243	6253	6263	6274	6284	6294	6304	6314	6325	1	2	3	4	5
43	6335	6345	6355	6365	6375	6385	6395	6405	6415	6425	1	2	3	4	5
44	6435	6444	6454	6464	6474	6484	6493	6503	6513	6522	1	2	3	4	5
45	6532	6542	6551	6561	6571	6580	6590	6599	6609	6618	1	2	3	4	5
46	6628	6637	6646	6656	6665	6675	6684	6693	6702	6712	1	2	3	4	5
47	6721	6730	6739	6749	6758	6767	6776	6785	6794	6803	1	2	3	4	5
48	6812	6821	6830	6839	6848	6857	6866	6875	6884	6893	1	2	3	4	4
49	6902	6911	6920	6928	6937	6946	6955	6964	6972	6981	1	2	3	4	4
50	6990	6998	7007	7016	7024	7033	7042	7050	7059	7067	1	2	3	3	4
51	7076	7084	7093	7101	7110	7118	7126	7135	7143	7152	1	2	3	3	4
52	7160	7168	7177	7185	7193	7202	7210	7218	7226	7235	1	2	2	3	4
53	7243	7251	7259	7267	7275	7284	7292	7300	7308	7316	1	2	2	3	4
54	7324	7332	7340	7348	7356	7364	7372	7380	7388	7396	1	2	2	3	4